I CAN Learn®
E D U C A T I O N   S Y S T E M S

JRL Enterprises, Inc.
New Orleans, Louisiana

Protected by U.S. Patents No. 5267865, 5441415, 5788508, 6064856, 6758674 and Des. 385431 and European Patent No. 0656139.

Algebra Textbook 11th Edition; Volume 2

ISBN-13: 978-0-9836370-3-5

JRL Enterprises, Inc.

912 Constantinople Street

New Orleans, LA 70115

www.icanlearn.com

Printed in the United States of America.

1 2   12 11

Table of Contents

HA1-200: Combined Inequalities

There are a number of ways to express the combination of inequalities, and different ways of combining inequalities are represented differently on the number line. When the word "and" appears between two inequalities, the mathematical sentence is called a **conjunction**.

Conjunction	A mathematical sentence that consists of two sentences connected by the word "and." A conjunction is true only if *both* sentences are true.

To find the solution of a conjunction, graph both inequalities. Consider the following: $x < 3$ and $x > -1$.

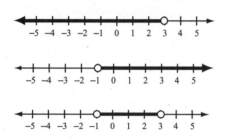

Graph $x < 3$. Place an open circle on 3 and shade all numbers to the left.

Graph $x > -1$. Place an open circle on -1 and shade all numbers to the right.

The solution is where the two graphs overlap.

This overlapping is called the **intersection**—the points that the two graphs share or have in common.

Intersection	The points that the two graphs share or have in common

This intersection is the solution of the conjunction. The actual solution can be written as $x > -1$ and $x < 3$, or in compact form, $-1 < x < 3$ (read "x is greater than -1 and less than 3").

The solution set is {all real numbers greater than -1 and less than 3}.

Any number between -1 and 3 makes both inequalities true. Remember that -1 and 3 are not included as part of the solution, because x is not equal to -1 or 3.

When the word "or" appears between two inequalities, the inequality is called a **disjunction**.

Disjunction	A mathematical sentence that consists of two sentences connected by the word "or." A disjunction is true if either or both sentences are true.

When finding the solution of a disjunction, you graph both inequalities. View the following: $x > 1$ or $x \leq -2$.

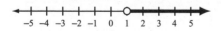

Graph $x > 1$. Place an open circle on 1 and shade all numbers to the right.

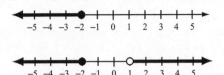

Graph $x \le -2$. Since x may be equal to -2, place a closed circle on -2 and shade all numbers to the left.

The solution is all points on both graphs.

When you combine the two graphs you have a **union**—all points on both graphs.

Union	All points on both graphs

The union is the solution of the disjunction. Thus, the solution to $x \le -2$ or $x > 1$ is {all real numbers less than or equal to -2 or greater than 1}.

When a conjunction or disjunction uses certain symbols, it is called a **combined inequality.**

Combined Inequality	A conjunction or disjunction expressed using $<$, $>$, $\ge$, and/or $\le$

Graph and state the solutions to the following examples.

Example 1   Graph and state the solution to $x < 0$ or $x \ge 1$.

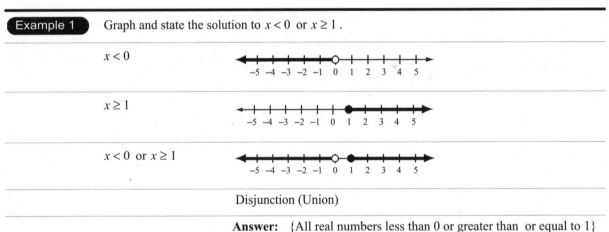

$x < 0$

$x \ge 1$

$x < 0$ or $x \ge 1$

Disjunction (Union)

Answer: {All real numbers less than 0 or greater than or equal to 1}

Example 2   Graph and state the solution to $x > -2$ and $x < 3$.

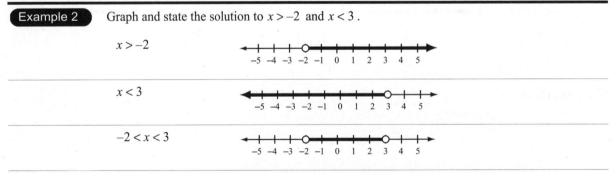

$x > -2$

$x < 3$

$-2 < x < 3$

Answer: {All real numbers between -2 and 3}

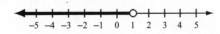

Example 3 Graph and state the solution to $x < 1$ and $x > 2$.

$x < 1$

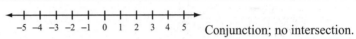

$x > 2$

$x < 1$ and $x > 2$

Conjunction; no intersection.

Answer: $\varnothing$ Null set; in this example, there is no solution because the two graphs do not intersect.

Problem Set

Graph the following:

1. $n > 4$ or $n < 3$ **2.** $x > 3$ or $x < -4$ **3.** $x > 2$ or $x < -2$ **4.** $n \leq 3$ and $n \geq 2$

5. $n < 3$ and $n < -1$ **6.** $n \leq -3$ or $n \geq 1$ **7.** $n \leq -4$ or $n \geq 1$ **8.** $x \geq 2$ and $x \leq 4$

9. $n < 4$ or $n > -4$ **10.** $n > 4$ and $n < 0$

11. Select the inequality that describes the graph below:

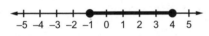

$x \geq 1$ or $x \leq 4$ $1 < x < 4$

$x > 1$ or $x < 4$ $-1 \leq x \leq 4$

12. Select the inequality that describes the graph below:

$-3 < x < 1$ $x \geq -3$ or $x \leq 1$

$x > -3$ or $x < 1$ $-3 \leq x \leq 1$

13. Select the inequality that describes the graph below:

$-2 < x < 1$ $x \geq -2$ or $x \leq 1$

$x > -2$ or $x < 1$ $-2 \leq x \leq 1$

14. Select the inequality that describes the graph below:

$x < -1$ or $x > 3$ $-1 \leq x \leq 3$

$x \leq -1$ or $x \geq 3$ $-1 < x < 3$

15. Select the inequality that describes the graph below:

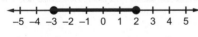

$-3 \leq x \leq 2$ $-3 < x < 2$

$x \geq -3$ or $x \leq 2$ $x > -3$ or $x < 2$

16. Select the inequality that describes the graph below:

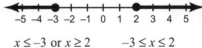

$x \leq -3$ or $x \geq 2$ $-3 \leq x \leq 2$

$x < -3$ or $x > 2$ $-3 < x < 2$

17. Select the inequality that describes the graph below:

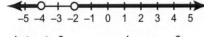

$-4 \leq x \leq -2$ $x < -4$ or $x > -2$

$-4 < x < -2$ $x \leq -4$ or $x \geq -2$

18. Graph: $4 \geq x \geq 1$

19. Graph: $-4 < x < -1$ **20.** Graph: $0 > x > -3$

HA1-205: Solving Combined Inequalities

This lesson requires you to do a bit of mixing and combining as you continue working with inequalities. In this lesson, you will identify graphed inequalities, solve inequalities using the four properties of real numbers, and graph the inequalities.

Before you actually begin solving and graphing inequalities, make sure you can identify graphed inequalities as conjunctions or disjunctions. Look at the examples below.

Example 1 $x < -2$ or $x \geq 1$

Answer: Disjunction

Example 2 $x \geq -4$ and $x \leq 2$ or written in compacted form $-4 \leq x \leq 2$

Answer: Conjunction

Example 3 $x < 21$ or $x > 28$

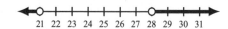

Answer: Disjunction

Example 4 $x > 102$ and $x \leq 104$ or $102 < x \leq 104$

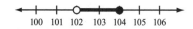

Answer: Conjunction

Now look at examples in which you need to solve the inequalities first.

Example 5   Solve and graph: $x + 4 > 8$ or $x + 3 \leq 4$

$$x + 4 > 8 \qquad\qquad x + 3 \leq 4$$
$$x + 4 - 4 > 8 - 4 \quad x + 3 - 3 \leq 4 - 3$$
$$x > 4 \qquad\qquad\quad x \leq 1$$

Step 1: Solve each inequality separately using the properties of real numbers.

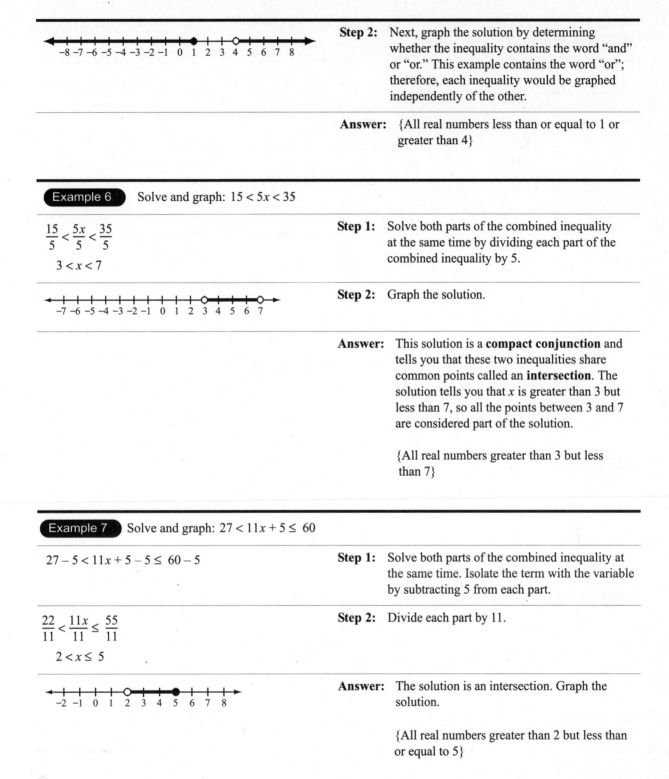

Step 2: Next, graph the solution by determining whether the inequality contains the word "and" or "or." This example contains the word "or"; therefore, each inequality would be graphed independently of the other.

Answer: {All real numbers less than or equal to 1 or greater than 4}

Example 6   Solve and graph: $15 < 5x < 35$

$\dfrac{15}{5} < \dfrac{5x}{5} < \dfrac{35}{5}$

$3 < x < 7$

Step 1: Solve both parts of the combined inequality at the same time by dividing each part of the combined inequality by 5.

Step 2: Graph the solution.

Answer: This solution is a **compact conjunction** and tells you that these two inequalities share common points called an **intersection**. The solution tells you that x is greater than 3 but less than 7, so all the points between 3 and 7 are considered part of the solution.

{All real numbers greater than 3 but less than 7}

Example 7   Solve and graph: $27 < 11x + 5 \leq 60$

$27 - 5 < 11x + 5 - 5 \leq 60 - 5$

Step 1: Solve both parts of the combined inequality at the same time. Isolate the term with the variable by subtracting 5 from each part.

$\dfrac{22}{11} < \dfrac{11x}{11} \leq \dfrac{55}{11}$

$2 < x \leq 5$

Step 2: Divide each part by 11.

Answer: The solution is an intersection. Graph the solution.

{All real numbers greater than 2 but less than or equal to 5}

Example 8 Solve and graph: $\frac{x}{2} > 6$ or $-3x > 12$

$\frac{x}{2} > 6$	$-3x > 12$	**Step 1:**	Solve each inequality separately. Use the properties of real numbers to isolate the variable in each inequality.
$2 \cdot \frac{x}{2} > 6 \cdot 2$	$\frac{-3x}{-3} > \frac{12}{-3}$		
$x > 12$	$x < -4$	**Step 2:**	Remember to reverse the inequality sign in the second inequality because you divided by a negative number.

Answer: This is a disjunction. Graph the union of both inequalities.

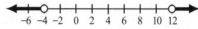

{All real numbers less than –4 or greater than 12}

Problem Set

Solve the following compound inequalities:

1. $2 - x < -2$ or $2 > 2x$

2. $6x \geq -6$ and $x - 5 \leq -3$

3. $-4x > -8$ or $x - 7 > -4$

4. $x + 8 > 11$ or $-2x > 12$

5. $63 > -7x > -14$

6. $8 < 11 + x < 13$

7. $2x > 8$ or $-3 + x < 7$

8. $2x > 16$ or $-5 + x < 4$

9. $-8 \leq x - 5 \leq -4$

10. $-7 < 7x < 42$

11. Solve and graph the compound inequality:
    $x < 10$ or $x > 5$

12. Solve and graph the compound inequality:
    $-3 + x > 8$ or $-x > -2$

13. Solve and graph the compound inequality:
    $-4 + x > -10$ or $-x > 1$

14. Solve the compound inequality:
    $-3x + 1 < 4$ and $-2x - 7 < 17$

15. Solve the compound inequality:
    $-3x + 4 < 10$ and $-4x - 7 < 17$

16. Solve the compound inequality:
    $-6x - 15 > -15$ and $-4x - 8 > 12$

17. Solve the compound inequality:
    $-2x + 8 > 10$ and $-6x + 8 > 50$

18. Solve the compound inequality:
    $17 < -3x + 11 < 23$

19. Solve and graph the compound inequality:
    $7 < 7x + 14 < 56$

20. Solve and graph the compound inequality:
    $-3x + 4 < 10$ and $-4x - 7 < 17$

In this lesson, you will solve absolute value equations. Absolute value equations are equations in which the variable is contained within absolute value symbols. In a previous lesson, you learned that the absolute value of a number is the distance a number is from zero on the number line.

Recall that distance is always represented by a positive number; therefore, the absolute value of a number is always positive. Look at the examples below.

$$|17| = 17 \qquad |-36| = 36 \qquad -|-15| = -15$$

Notice that in the third example, the final answer is negative. The original problem asked for the opposite of the absolute value of -15. The absolute value of -15 is $+15$ and the opposite of $+15$ is -15.

Before solving absolute value equations, study these examples that demonstrate evaluating expressions that contain absolute values.

Example 1
$$-|4| + |2|$$
$$= -4 + 2$$
$$= -2$$

Example 2
$$-|-3 + (-7)|$$
$$= -|-3 - 7|$$
$$= -|-10|$$
$$= -(10)$$
$$= -10$$

To understand the steps needed to solve absolute value equations, recall that the absolute value of $+6$ is 6 and the absolute value of -6 is 6. Therefore, in the equation $|x| = 6$, x could represent 6 or -6. Thus, all absolute value equations must be rewritten as disjunctions ("or" statements) to find all possible answers. You must assume that the quantity within the absolute value symbols is either equal to the constant on the other side of the equation, or equal to the opposite of the constant.

Example 3 Solve: $|x| = 7$

$|x| = 7$	$|7| = 7$	$|-7| = 7$
$x = 7$ or $x = -7$	$7 = 7$	$7 = 7$

Answer: $\{7, -7\}$

Steps for Solving Absolute Value Equations	<ul><li>Isolate the absolute value expression on one side of the equation.</li><li>Rewrite the equation as a disjunction. One equation will state the quantity within the absolute value symbol is equal to the constant and the other equation will state it is equal to the opposite of the constant.</li><li>Use the rules for solving equations to isolate the variable.</li><li>Check both answers.</li></ul>

Example 4   Solve: $|x - 4| = 8$

$x - 4 = 8$	or	$x - 4 = -8$
$x - 4 + 4 = 8 + 4$		$x + 4 - 4 = -8 + 4$
$x = 12$		$x = -4$

Step 1: Rewrite the equation as a disjunction and solve.

Check: $x = 12$	Check: $x = -4$
$|x - 4| = 8$	$|x - 4| = 8$
$|(12) - 4| = 8$	$|(-4) - 4| = 8$
$|8| = 8$	$|-8| = 8$
$8 = 8$ True	$8 = 8$ True

Step 2: Now, verify that both solutions are part of the solution set.

Answer: Since both solutions make the equation true, both are part of the solution set, $\{12, -4\}$.

Example 5   Solve: $|x| + 4 = 12$

$|x| + 4 = 12$

$|x| + 4 - 4 = 12 - 4$

$|x| = 8$

Step 1: Isolate the absolute value expression on one side of the equation. Because 4 is not part of the absolute value, subtract it from both sides.

$x = 8$ or $x = -8$

Step 2: Write as a disjunction and solve.

Check: $x = 8$	Check: $x = -8$
$|x| + 4 = 12$	$|x| + 4 = 12$
$|8| + 4 = 12$	$|-8| + 4 = 12$
$8 + 4 = 12$	$8 + 4 = 12$
$12 = 12$ True	$12 = 12$ True

Step 3: Now check both solutions.

Answer: Both solutions are part of the solution set $\{8, -8\}$.

Example 6   Solve: $|k| + 4 = 2$

$|k| + 4 = 2$

$|k| + 4 - 4 = 2 - 4$

$|k| = -2$

Step 1: Use the Subtraction Property to isolate the absolute value expression.

Step 2: This equation does not have a solution because the absolute value of a number can never be negative.

Answer: The solution is the null set, represented by $\varnothing$ or the empty set $\{\}$.

Example 7   Solve: $|m + 4| + 2 = 12$

$|m + 4| + 2 = 12$ $|m + 4| + 2 - 2 = 12 - 2$ $|m + 4| = 10$	**Step 1:** Simplify the equation by isolating the absolute value expression.

$m + 4 = 10$ or $(m + 4) = -10$ $m + 4 - 4 = 10 - 4$ $m + 4 = -10$ $m = 6$ $m + 4 - 4 = -10 - 4$ $m = -14$	**Step 2:** Rewrite the equation as a disjunction and solve.

Check: $m = 6$ Check: $m = -14$ $|m + 4| + 2 = 12$ $|m + 4| + 2 = 12$ $|(6) + 4| + 2 = 12$ $|(-14) + 4| + 2 = 12$ $|10| + 2 = 12$ $|-10| + 2 = 12$ $10 + 2 = 12$ $10 + 2 = 12$ $12 = 12$ True $12 = 12$ True	**Step 3:** Now check both solutions.

Answer: Both solutions are part of the solution set $\{-14, 6\}$.

Problem Set

Solve the following:

1. $|x| = 2$

2. $|y| = 3$

3. $|b| + 9 = 3$

4. $|x + 5| = 15$

5. $|4 + x| = 16$

6. $|x - 3| = 12$

7. $|x - 8| = 16$

8. $|x| + 12 = 21$

9. $|x| + 13 = 28$

10. $|x| + 2 = 10$

11. $|2x + 3| = 37$

12. $|2x + 4| = 38$

13. $|3x + 11| = 44$

14. $|4x + 2| = 6$

15. $|4x + 4| = 0$

16. $|4x + 7| = 9$

17. $|4x + 8| = 20$

18. $|3x + 6| - 4 = 8$

19. $|3x + 8| - 3 = 14$

20. $|x| + 10 = 26 - 8$

HA1-215: Solving Absolute Value Inequalities

You have learned the mathematical terms "disjunction" and "conjunction" and how to graph these combined inequalities. Remember that a **disjunction** contains the word "or", and the graph of its solution is both graphs—disjoined—or the union of both graphs. An example of a disjunction graph is shown below.

$$x > 1 \text{ or } x \le -1$$

A **conjunction** contains the word "and," and its graph is only the common part or the intersection of the two graphs. Look at the sample conjunction graph below.

$$x > -3 \text{ and } x < 4 \text{ or written in compact form, } -3 < x < 4$$

In this lesson, you will solve and graph absolute value inequalities. Recall from the previous lesson that solving an absolute value equation requires separating the equation into a disjunction.

$$|x| = 1$$
$$x = 1 \text{ or } x = -1$$

Solving absolute value inequalities is a similar process. If the absolute value expression is greater than the constant, the inequality will be rewritten as a disjunction. One inequality will show the quantity within the absolute value symbols as greater than the constant. The second inequality will show the quantity within the absolute value symbols as less than the opposite of the constant. You must reverse the inequality sign and take the opposite of the constant.

$$|x| > 1$$
$$x < -1 \text{ or } x > 1$$

The solution set is $\{x : x > 1 \text{ or } x < -1\}$. This is read the set of all x such that $x > 1$ or $x < -1$.

If the absolute value expression is less than the constant, the inequality will be rewritten as a conjunction. One inequality will show the quantity within the absolute value symbols as less than the constant. The second inequality will show the quantity within the absolute value symbols as greater than the opposite of the constant. You must reverse the inequality sign and take the opposite of the constant.

$$|x| < 1$$
$$x < 1 \text{ and } x > -1$$
$$-1 < x < 1$$

The solution set is $\{x : x < 1 \text{ and } x > -1\}$ or $\{x : -1 < x < 1\}$. This is read the set of all x such that $-1 < x < 1$.

Steps for Solving Absolute Value Inequalities	• Isolate the absolute value expression on one side of the inequality. • If the absolute value expression is greater than the constant, rewrite it as a disjunction. If the absolute value expression is less than the constant, rewrite it as a conjunction. Remember to reverse the inequality sign and use the opposite of the constant in the second inequality. • Use the rules for solving combined Inequalities. • Graph the solution set. Remember the graph of a conjunction is the intersection of the graphs and the graph of a disjunction is the union of the graphs.

Look at the following examples.

Example 1   Solve and graph: $|x| < 2$

$x < 2$ and $x > -2$ or

$-2 < x < 2$ written in compact form

Step 1: The absolute value expression is less than the constant. Rewrite it as a conjunction.

Step 2: Graph the solution set.

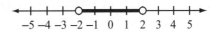

Answer: $\{x: -2 < x < 2\}$

Example 2   Solve and graph: $|x| \geq 4$

$x \geq 4$ or $x \leq -4$

Step 1: The absolute value expression is greater than the constant. Rewrite it as a disjunction.

Step 2: Graph the solution set.

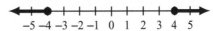

Answer: $\{x: x \leq -4 \text{ or } x \geq 4\}$

You can solve more complicated absolute value inequalities by following the same steps. Look closely at the following examples.

Example 3 Solve and graph: $|x - 2| < 4$

$x - 2 < 4$ and $x - 2 > -4$	**Step 1:** Because the absolute value expression is less than the constant, rewrite it as a conjunction. Set up two inequalities, one as it is and another with a negative answer and reversed inequality sign.

$$\begin{array}{cc} x - 2 < 4 & x - 2 > -4 \\ x - 2 + 2 < 4 + 2 & \text{and} \quad x - 2 + 2 > -4 + 2 \\ x < 6 & x > -2 \\ \multicolumn{2}{c}{-2 < x < 6} \end{array}$$

Step 2: Solve each inequality using inverse operations.

Step 3: Graph the resulting conjunction.

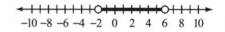

$$-10\ -8\ -6\ -4\ -2\ \ 0\ \ 2\ \ 4\ \ 6\ \ 8\ \ 10$$

Answer: $\{x: -2 < x < 6\}$

Example 4 Solve and graph: $|x - 4| > 1$

$$\begin{array}{cc} x - 4 > 1 & x - 4 < -1 \\ x - 4 + 4 > 1 + 4 & \text{or} \quad x - 4 + 4 < -1 + 4 \\ x > 5 & x < 3 \end{array}$$

Step 1: Write two inequalities, one just as it is and another with a negative answer and reversed sign.

Step 2: Solve each inequality using inverse operations. The result is a disjunction.

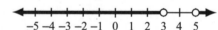

$$-5\ -4\ -3\ -2\ -1\ \ 0\ \ 1\ \ 2\ \ 3\ \ 4\ \ 5$$

Answer: $\{x: x < -3 \text{ or } x > 5\}$

Example 5 Solve and graph: $|4x + 6| + 2 > 16$

$|4x + 6| + 2 - 2 > 16 - 2$ $|4x + 6| > 14$	**Step 1:** Isolate the absolute value expression by subtracting 2 from both sides.
$4x + 6 > 14$ or $4x + 6 < -14$	**Step 2:** Because the absolute value expression is greater than the constant, rewrite as a disjunction.
$4x + 6 - 6 > 14 - 6$ or $4x + 6 - 6 < -14 - 6$	**Step 3:** Use inverse operations to isolate the variable term.

$\dfrac{4x}{4} > \dfrac{8}{4}$	or $\dfrac{4x}{4} < \dfrac{-20}{4}$	**Step 4:** Divide both sides by 4 to isolate the variable.
$x > 2$	$x < -5$	

Step 5: Graph the solution.

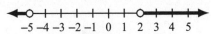

Answer: $\{x : x < -5 \text{ or } x > 2\}$

Problem Set

Graph the following:

1. $|a| \leq 5$

2. $|x| < 7$

Solve the absolute value inequalities:

3. $|-2 + x| > 6$

4. $|5x| > 10$

5. $|10 + x| < 13$

6. $|7x| < -21$

7. $|x + 3| > -5$

8. $|4x| > 16$

9. $|3x| > -9$

10. $|-4x| > 40$

11. $|2n - 7| \leq 15$

12. $|2c + 12| > 8$

13. $|2x + 1| < 13$

14. $|2x + 8| < 10$

15. $|3x + 1| < 4$

16. $|3x - 9| > 18$

17. $|6x - 15| > -15$

18. $|x + 4| + 18 > 24$

19. $|2x + 5| - 8 \leq 3$

20. $8 + |m - 4| > 19$

HA1-276: Factoring Sums and Differences of Cubes

Previously, we have learned how to factor the difference of two squares $(a^2 - b^2)$.

Difference of Squares	$a^2 - b^2 = (a+b)(a-b)$

Now we will learn two more factorization formulas: the **sum of cubes** $(a^3 + b^3)$ and the **difference of cubes** $(a^3 - b^3)$.

Sum of Cubes	$a^3 + b^3 = (a+b)(a^2 - ab + b^2)$

Difference of Cubes	$a^3 - b^3 = (a-b)(a^2 + ab + b^2)$

Example 1   Factor the binomial $x^3 + y^3$.

$a^3 + b^3 = (a+b)(a^2 - ab + b^2)$

$\qquad = (x+y)(x^2 - xy + y^2)$

Step 1:   Use the formula for the sum of cubes with $a = x$ and $b = y$.

Answer: $x^3 + y^3 = (x+y)(x^2 - xy + y^2)$

Example 2   Factor the binomial $c^3 - 7^3$.

$a^3 - b^3 = (a-b)(a^2 + ab + b^2)$

$\qquad = (c-7)(c^2 + c \cdot 7 + 7^2)$

Step 1:   Use the formula for the difference of cubes with $a = c$ and $b = 7$.

$\qquad = (c-7)(c^2 + 7c + 49)$

Step 2:   Simplify.

Answer: $c^3 - 7^3 = (c-7)(c^2 + 7c + 49)$

Example 3 Factor the binomial $x^3 + 27$.

$x^3 + 27 = x^3 + 3^3$	**Step 1:** Notice that $27 = 3^3$.
$a^3 + b^3 = (a+b)(a^2 - ab + b^2)$ $= (x+3)(x^2 - x \cdot 3 + 3^2)$	**Step 2:** Use the formula for the sum of cubes with $a = x$ and $b = 3$.
$= (x+3)(x^2 - 3x + 9)$	**Step 3:** Simplify.
	Answer: $x^3 + 27 = (x+3)(x^2 - 3x + 9)$

Example 4 Factor the binomial $64 - 125z^3$.

$64 - 125z^3 = 4^3 - 5^3 z^3$	**Step 1:** Notice that $64 = 4^3$ and $125 = 5^3$.
$4^3 - (5z)^3 =$	**Step 2:** Group the 5 and the z terms, since they have the same power.
$a^3 - b^3 = (a-b)(a^2 + ab + b^2)$ $= (4 - 5z)(4^2 + 4(5z) + (5z)^2)$	**Step 3:** Use the formula for the difference of cubes with $a = 4$ and $b = 5z$.
$= (4 - 5z)(16 + 20z + 25z^2)$	**Step 4:** Simplify.
	Answer: $64 - 125z^3 = (4 - 5z)(16 + 20z + 25z^2)$

Example 5 Factor the binomial $x^6 - (4y)^6$.

Step 1: Notice that $x^6 = x^3 \cdot x^3$ and $(4y)^6 = (4y)^3 \cdot (4y)^3$.

$x^6 - (4y)^6 = x^3 \cdot x^3 - (4y)^3 \cdot (4y)^3$

Step 2: Combining terms we get $x^6 = x^3 \cdot x^3 = (x^3)^2$ and $(4y)^6 = (4y)^3 \cdot (4y)^3 = [(4y)^3]^2$. Now we can use the sum of cubes and difference of squares with $a = x^3$ and $b = (4y)^3$.

$(x^3)^2 - [(4y)^3]^2 = (x^3 + (4y)^3)(x^3 - (4y)^3)$

Step 3: Apply the sum of cubes formula for $(x^3 + (4y)^3)$ and the difference of cubes formula for $(x^3 - (4y)^3)$ with $a = x$ and $b = 4y$.

$$x^3 + (4y)^3 = (x + 4y)(x^2 - x(4y) + (4y)^2)$$
$$x^3 - (4y)^3 = (x - 4y)(x^2 + x(4y) + (4y)^2)$$

Step 4: Multiply both expressions together and simplify.

$$(x^3 + (4y)^3)(x^3 - (4y)^3) = (x + 4y)(x^2 - x(4y) + (4y)^2)(x - 4y)(x^2 + x(4y) + (4y)^2)$$
$$= (x + 4y)(x^2 - 4xy + 16y^2)(x - 4y)(x^2 + 4xy + 16y^2)$$

Step 5: Regroup the factors so the binomial factors are written first.

$$(x + 4y)(x - 4y)(x^2 - 4xy + 16y^2)(x^2 + 4xy + 16y^2)$$

Answer: $x^6 - (4y)^6 = (x + 4y)(x - 4y)(x^2 - 4xy + 16y^2)(x^2 + 4xy + 16y^2)$

Problem Set

Factor completely:

1. $y^3 - z^3$

2. $d^3 - e^3$

3. $m^3 + p^3$

4. $g^3 + h^3$

5. $k^3 - m^3$

6. $q^3 - r^3$

7. $s^3 + v^3$

8. $w^3 + z^3$

9. $c^3 + 11^3$

10. $f^3 + 4^3$

11. $5^3 + n^3$

12. $7^3 + s^3$

13. $w^3 - 1^3$

14. $6^3 - k^3$

15. $r^3 - 13^3$

16. $c^3 + 216$

17. $e^3 + 343$

18. $f^3 + 27$

19. $h^3 + 512$

20. $m^3 - 8$

21. $n^3 - 1,000$

22. $x^3 - 729$

23. $s^3 - 1,728$

24. $216y^3 + 1,000$

25. $729 - 8x^3$

26. $343c^3 + 27$

27. $1,331x^3 + 512$

28. $729x^3 + 343$

29. $27f^3 - 1,000$

30. $64c^3 - 3,375$

31. $d^6 - 64e^6$

32. $y^6 - 729$

33. $b^6 - (4m)^6$

34. $c^6 - (5g)^6$

35. $d^6 - (7h)^6$

36. $(5k)^6 - (3n)^6$

37. $(4y)^6 - (9x)^6$

38. $(12a)^6 - (5b)^6$

39. $(10s)^6 - (8r)^6$

40. $(11m)^6 - (3n)^6$

In previous lessons, you factored polynomials in the form $x^2 + bx + c$, with the c term being greater than or less than zero. Essentially, you had to find the two factors that, when multiplied, equal the value of the c term, and when added, equal the coefficient of the b term. This lesson will add steps to the process you used to determine the binomial factors of trinomials.

You will notice that a trinomial has an additional variable in the term—an a. The variable a indicates that a coefficient is part of the first term. This means that you must give more attention to finding the first terms of the binomial factors. Then, follow the same steps you used in previous lessons to find the b and c terms of the trinomial. After factoring, use the FOIL method to check the two resulting binomials to ensure that they equal the original trinomial. Let's begin by factoring a trinomial that has a coefficient in the first term.

Example 1   Determine the binomial factors of the trinomial $3x^2 - 20x - 7$.

$1x \cdot 3x$	**Step 1:** Find the factors of the first term. Next, think about two factors that equal the coefficient 3. Since 3 is a prime number, it has only two possible factors: 1 and 3. Thus, you have the first factors of the binomials.
$-1 \cdot 7$ $-7 \cdot 1$	**Step 2:** Find the factors of the last term.
	Step 3: Try a combination of factors of the first and last terms of the binomials until you find the middle term of the trinomial. Since the first terms of the binomials now have coefficients, the order in which you write the second terms is very important. *Note: Remember that the factors will probably be binomials, so try to put the answer in binomial form.*
$(3x - 1)(x + 7)$	**Step 4:** Let's try using -1 as the second term in the first binomial, and 7 as the second term in the second binomial.
$\begin{aligned} 3x \cdot 7 &= 21x \\ -1 \cdot (x) &= -x \end{aligned} \Big\} \rightarrow \begin{array}{r} 21x \\ -1x \\ \hline 20x \end{array}$	**Step 5:** Using the second and third steps of FOIL, multiply to see if you get the same middle term as the trinomial.
$\begin{aligned} (3x + 1)(x - 7) &= -21x \\ 1 \cdot (x) &= x \end{aligned}$ $\begin{aligned} 3x \cdot (-7) &= -21x \\ 1 \cdot (x) &= x \end{aligned} \Big\} \rightarrow \begin{array}{r} -21x \\ +1x \\ \hline -20x \end{array}$	**Step 6:** The middle term you need is $-20x$ rather than $20x$. Since the binomial factor pair you tested did not equal the middle term of the trinomial, test another set of factors. In this case, the only other factor pair is 1 and -7. Since 20 is the correct coefficient, do not change the order of the second term; simply change the sign.

Answer: $3x^2 - 20x - 7 = (3x + 1)(x - 7)$

Example 2   Find the binomial factors of the trinomial $9x^2 + 20x + 4$.

$9x \cdot x$	**Step 1:** Find the factors of the first term.
$3x \cdot 3x$	

$1 \cdot 4$	**Step 2:** Find the factors of the last term.
$-1 \cdot -4$	
$2 \cdot 2$	
$-2 \cdot -2$	

$(9x + 2)(x + 2)$	**Step 3:** Try a combination of the factors of the first and last terms of the binomials until you find the middle term of the trinomial.

Answer: $9x^2 + 20x + 4 = (9x + 2)\,(x + 2)$

Example 3   Find the binomial factors of the trinomial $4x^2 - 8xy - 21y^2$.

$4x \cdot x$	**Step 1:** Find the factors of the first term.
$2x \cdot 2x$	

$-1y \cdot 21y$	**Step 2:** Find the factors of the last term.
$1y \cdot -21y$	
$3y \cdot -7y$	
$-3y \cdot 7y$	

$(2x - 7y)(2x + 3y)$	**Step 3:** Try a combination of the factors of the first and last terms of the binomials until you find the middle term of the trinomial.

Answer: $4x^2 - 8xy - 21y^2 = (2x - 7y)\,(2x + 3y)$

Problem Set

For each problem, determine which of the choices is a factor of the given trinomial:

1. $12x^2 + 7x + 1$

$4x + 3$	$3x + 4$
$4x + 4$	$3x + 1$

2. $2x^2 + 13x + 15$

$x + 3$	$2x - 3$
$2x + 5$	$x + 5$

3. $8x^2 - 14x + 3$

$4x - 3$	$2x + 3$
$4x + 1$	$2x - 3$

4. $6y^2 - 41y - 7$

$y + 7 \qquad y + 1$

$y - 7 \qquad 6y + 7$

5. $3x^2 - 11x + 6$

$x - 2 \qquad 3x - 3$

$3x - 2 \qquad 2x - 3$

6. $12y^2 + 31y + 20$

$5y + 2 \qquad 4y - 3$

$3y + 4 \qquad 4y + 3$

7. $8y^2 + 14y + 3$

$4y + 1 \qquad 2y + 1$

$2y - 3 \qquad 4y + 3$

8. $15x^2 - x - 2$

$3x - 1 \qquad x + 2$

$5x + 2 \qquad 3x + 1$

Factor each of the following trinomials:

9. $2x^2 + 7x + 5$

10. $7x^2 + 9x + 2$

11. $9x^2 + 3x - 2$

12. $15x^2 - x - 2$

13. $2x^2 - 9x + 4$

14. $21x^2 + 5x - 6$

15. $6x^2 + 5x - 4$

16. $9x^2 + 6x - 8$

17. $8x^2 - 2xy - y^2$

18. $6x^2 + 25xy + 14y^2$

19. $15x^2 + 34xy + 15y^2$

20. $15x^2 - 13xy + 2y^2$

HA1-295: Factoring by Removing a Common Factor and Grouping

Think of properties and concepts that you have used in algebra to help you solve equations or simplify expressions. One method that you have used is the Distributive Property. Recall that this property converts one term into two or more terms. Consider the expression $7(a + 2)$. Using the Distributive Property, $7(a + 2)$ becomes $7a + 14$. Although the number of terms increases, the Distributive Property simplifies the expression, making it easier to manipulate.

Now, consider grouping terms. Remember that if you are given an expression such as $2x + 4y - x + 5y$, it can be grouped by like terms to form a new expression, $x + 9y$. Note that the original expression has four different terms, but once it is simplified, it has only two terms.

As you continue to study the factoring process, you will be able to simplify expressions even faster once you remove common factors and group like terms. You already have learned these concepts in previous lessons; you are now going to combine these steps to ensure that each expression is in its simplest terms.

Look carefully at the expression $2x(5x + 9) + 7(5x + 9)$. The binomial $(5x + 9)$ appears in two places: once being multiplied by $2x$, and again being multiplied by 7. Because $(5x + 9)$ is a factor of both terms, it is referred to as the **common factor**. To simplify, you *remove* the common binomial factor $(5x + 9)$ by writing it as a stand-alone term inside a set of parentheses. Then, you regroup the other terms, making sure you follow the rules regarding placement of positive and negative signs. Therefore, $2x(5x + 9) + 7(5x + 9) = (5x + 9)(2x + 7)$.

Try to select the common binomial factor in the examples below.

Example 1   Factor: $3x(5x + 9) - 13(5x + 9)$

$5x + 9$	**Step 1:** Find the common binomial factor.
$(5x + 9)(3x - 13)$	**Step 2:** Group the remaining terms and put in parentheses.
	Answer: $(5x + 9)(3x - 13)$

Example 2   Factor: $3(a + 7) + c(7 + a) - f(a + 7)$

$(a + 7)$	**Step 1:** Find the common binomial factor.
$(a + 7)(3 + c - f)$	**Step 2:** Group the remaining terms and put in parentheses. *Note: Although $(7 + a)$ in the second term is not written in the same order as $(a + 7)$, they are still common terms according to the Commutative Property.*
	Answer: $(a + 7)(3 + c - f)$

Now consider four-term polynomials in which the common factor is not obvious.

Example 3   Factor: $25xy + 30x + 15y + 18$

$\mathbf{25xy + 30x} + 15y + 18$	**Step 1:** Determine whether or not the first two terms contain a common factor.
$5x(5y + 6) + \mathbf{15y + 18}$	**Step 2:** Check the last two terms to see if there is another common factor.

$5x(5y+6)+3(5y+6)$	**Step 3:** Place the common factors in one set of parentheses.
$(5y+6)(5x+3)$	**Step 4:** Place the remaining terms in separate parentheses.
	Answer: $(5y+6)(5x+3)$

Example 4   Factor: $63xy+21x+45y+15$

$63xy+21x+45y+15$	**Step 1:** Determine whether or not the first two terms contain a common factor.
$21x(3y+1)+45y+15$	**Step 2:** Check the last two terms to see if there is another common factor.
$21x(3y+1)+15(3y+1)$	**Step 3:** Place the common factors in one set of parentheses.
$(21x+15)(3y+1)$	**Step 4:** Place the remaining terms in separate parentheses.
	Answer: $(21x+15)(3y+1)$

Problem Set

Factor the following:

1. $2x(y+2)+4(y+2)$ **2.** $3a(b-1)+2(b-1)$ **3.** $4y(x+2)-3(x+2)$

4. $x(3y+2)+5(3y+2)$ **5.** $5a(b+5)-(b+5)$ **6.** $4c(d-2)+3(2-d)$

7. $3x(y-4)-2(4-y)$ **8.** $5a(2b-5)+4(5-2b)$ **9.** $4xy-y+12x-3$

10. $2ab+b+12a+6$ **11.** $5xy-10y+7x-14$ **12.** $6cd+3d+10c+5$

Solve:

13. Which of the following is a factor of the polynomial below?

$$3x^2+9x+2xy+6y$$

$3x+2y$	$x+2$
$2x+3y$	$y+3$

14. Which of the following is a factor of the polynomial below?

$$2x^2+6x+xy+3y$$

$y+3$	$2x+y$
$2x+3$	$3x+y$

15. Which of the following is a factor of the polynomial below?

$$3x^2-15x+2xy-10y$$

$x-5$	$3x+2$
$2y-5$	$x+2y$

16. Which of the following is a factor of the polynomial below?

$$4a^2+3a+4ab+3b$$

$a+b$	$b+3$
$a+3$	$4a+b$

17. Which of the following is a factor of the polynomial below?

$$3ay-15bx+5ax-9by$$

$a-3b$	$3y-5$
$a+3b$	$3y-5x$

18. Which of the following is a factor of the polynomial below?

$$4ay+10bx+5ax+8by$$

$a-2b$	$5y+4x$
$4y+5$	$a+2b$

19. Factor: $x^2-6x+9-4y^2$ **20.** Factor: $x^2+10x+25-64y^2$

HA1-300: Factoring a Polynomial Completely

In the past, you mastered many tasks that seemed difficult at the time—tying your shoestrings, riding a bike, driving a car. Each of these tasks required learning a series of steps, one by one, and finally combining all of them to perform the tasks competently. In algebra, you must also master many skills and then combine those skills to solve complex problems.

Factoring is an important skill in algebra. You have learned the techniques for factoring polynomials that have been presented and developed in previous lessons. Now, it is important to use all that you have learned about factoring in order to factor polynomials completely. "Completely" is the key word here. A polynomial is *factored completely* when it is written as a prime polynomial—one that initially cannot be simplified or factored, or one that is written in its simplest form.

When factoring polynomials, you have learned:

Factoring Process	Example
Factor out a common factor.	$4x + 6 = 2(2x + 3)$
Factor the difference of squares.	$a^2 - b^2 = (a + b)(a - b)$
Factor a trinomial using FOIL.	$x^2 + 7x + 12 = (x + 3)(x + 4)$
Factor polynomials by grouping.	$3x^2 + 3xy + 2x + 2y = 3x(x + y) + 2(x + y)$ $= (x + y)(3x + 2)$

Let's factor some polynomials completely.

Example 1   Factor: $6y^2 - 96$

$= 6(y^2 - 16)$	**Step 1:** Factor out the common factor 6.
$= 6(y + 4)(y - 4)$	**Step 2:** Factor $y^2 - 16$, the difference of squares. The polynomial cannot be simplified further.
	Answer: $6y^2 - 96 = 6 (y + 4) (y - 4)$

Example 2   Factor: $8x^4 - 128$

$= 8(x^4 - 16)$	**Step 1:** Factor out the common factor.
$= 8(x^2 + 4)(x^2 - 4)$	**Step 2:** Factor the difference of squares.
$= 8(x^2 + 4)(x + 2)(x - 2)$	**Step 3:** Factor the difference of squares. The polynomial cannot be simplified further.
	Answer: $8x^4 - 128 = 8 (x^2 + 4) (x + 2) (x - 2)$

Example 3 Factor: $3y^2 + 30y - 72$

$= 3(y^2 + 10y - 24)$	**Step 1:** Factor out the common factor.
$= 3(y - 2)(y + 12)$	**Step 2:** Factor using FOIL. The polynomial cannot be simplified further.
	Answer: $3y^2 + 30y - 72 = 3(y - 2)(y + 12)$

Example 4 Factor: $3xy^2 - 12x + ay^2 - 4a$

$= 3x(y^2 - 4) + ay^2 - 4a$	**Step 1:** Factor out the common factor in the first two terms.
$= 3x(y^2 - 4) + a(y^2 - 4)$	**Step 2:** Factor out the common factor from the last terms.
$= 3x(y - 2)(y + 2) + a(y - 2)(y + 2)$	**Step 3:** Factor the difference of squares.
$= (3x + a)(y - 2)(y + 2)$	**Step 4:** Group like terms. The terms outside the parentheses can be grouped together first. Next, write the terms $(y - 2)$ and $(y + 2)$ only once because when the $3x$ and a are distributed, you get the expanded factored form again.
	Answer: $3xy^2 - 12x + ay^2 - 4a = (3x + a)(y - 2)(y + 2)$

Problem Set

Factor completely:

1. $5x^2 - 10x + 5$

2. $3x^2 - 30x + 75$

3. $a + 6a^2b - ab$

4. $32x^2 + 24b^2 - 40z^2$

5. $5x^2 + 20x - 60$

6. $2m^2 + 4m + 2$

7. $9x^2 + 45x$

8. $2x^2 - 98$

9. $8ab - 64a$

10. $x^3 - 4x$

11. $b^4 - 9b^2$

12. $-x^3 + 4x^2 + 12x$

13. $-4x^3 - 32x^2 - 64x$

14. $-3x^5 - 12x^4 - 9x^3$

15. $7ax^2 - 28a + ax^2 - 4a$

16. $x^3 - xy^2$

17. $x^3 - x^2 - 5x + 5$

18. $10x^4 - 34x^3 + 12x^2$

19. $27x^3 - 18x^2 - 45x$

20. $-8x^2 - 28x - 12$

An algebraic equation is a mathematical sentence that uses an equal sign (=) to relate one expression to another. Mastering algebraic equations will help you solve polynomial equations. There are two types of polynomial equations: **linear equations** and **quadratic equations**.

Linear Equation	An equation in the form $ax + b = 0$

Quadratic Equation	An equation in the form $ax^2 + bx + c = 0, \ a \neq 0$

Though you must still solve for an unknown variable when solving polynomial equations, you will find that factoring makes solving the equation easier. You also can use any of the properties discussed in earlier lessons to solve polynomial equations.

A polynomial equation can usually be solved by factoring, and then applying the **zero-product property**.

Zero-Product Property	If a and b are real numbers and $ab = 0$, then $a = 0$ or $b = 0$ or both a and $b = 0$.

This property states that if the product of two factors equals zero, then one or both factors must equal zero. This means that you must test each factor of a polynomial equation to see which factor equals zero.

Let's use the zero-product property to solve a quadratic equation.

Example 1   Solve: $x^2 - 16 = 0$

$(x + 4)(x - 4) = 0$

Step 1: Recall that you should try factoring the polynomial equation first. You should recognize immediately that the equation is the difference of two squares. The factored binomials are at left.

$$x + 4 = 0 \qquad x - 4 = 0$$
$$x + 4 - 4 = 0 - 4 \quad x - 4 + 4 = 0 + 4$$
$$x = -4 \qquad\quad x = 4$$

Step 2: Now, apply the zero-product property. Do this by setting each factor equal to 0, one at a time. Keep in mind that the answers you find are not the actual solutions to the equation: they are part of the replacement set. The **replacement set** is the set of numbers that may be substituted for a variable. The replacement set for the equation above is $\{-4, 4\}$.

Check: $x = -4$ Check: $x = 4$

$x^2 - 16 = 0$ $x^2 - 16 = 0$

$(-4)^2 - 16 = 0$ $(4)^2 - 16 = 0$

$16 - 16 = 0$ true $16 - 16 = 0$ true

Step 3: Next, you always should check each member of the replacement set by substituting it into the equation in the form $ax^2 + bx + c = 0$. If the equation is true, then the substituted number is a member of the solution set. The **solution set** is the set of all numbers from the replacement set that make the equation true. Let's test the replacement set $\{4, -4\}$.

Answer: Substituting either 4 or –4 makes the equation true; therefore, the solution set is $\{-4, 4\}$.

If an equation is not in the $ax^2 + bx + c = 0$ form, you must still simplify the equation before you can factor, as in the following example. Before you can factor, you must use the additive inverse to get all terms on one side; whether you add or subtract the number depends on its sign.

Example 2 Solve: $x^2 - 5x = -6$

$x^2 - 5x + 6 = -6 + 6$	**Step 1:** Use the additive inverse to move the –6 to the left member of the equation.
$x^2 - 5x + 6 = 0$	**Step 2:** Set the equation equal to 0.
$(x - 2)(x - 3) = 0$	**Step 3:** Factor the trinomial.
$x - 2 = 0 \quad x - 3 = 0$ $\qquad\quad$ or $x = 2 \qquad\quad x = 3$	**Step 4:** Set each factor equal to 0 and solve for x. The replacement set is $\{2, 3\}$.
Check: $x = 2$ $\qquad$ Check: $x = 3$ $x^2 - 5x + 6 = 0 \qquad x^2 - 5x + 6 = 0$ $(2)^2 - 5(2) + 6 = 0 \qquad (3)^2 - 5(3) + 6 = 0$ $4 - 10 + 6 = 0 \qquad 9 - 15 + 6 = 0$ $-6 + 6 = 0 \qquad -6 + 6 = 0$ $0 = 0$ True $\qquad 0 = 0$ True	**Step 5:** Substitute members of the replacement set into the equation to determine whether or not they are actual solutions to the equation. If the equation is true after the substitution has been made, then that solution is a member of the solution set.
	Answer: The substitution of 2 or 3 makes the equation true; therefore, the solution set is $\{2, 3\}$.

Let's use factoring to solve several different polynomials. Note that solutions are not always whole numbers: they may also be fractions or decimals.

Example 3 Solve: $x^2 + 9x = 0$

$x(x + 9) = 0$	**Step 1:** Factor out the common factor, which is x.
$x + 9 = 0 \qquad$ or $x = 0$ $x = -9$	**Step 2:** Set each factor equal to 0 and solve for x. The replacement set is $\{-9, 0\}$.
Check: $x = -9$ $\qquad$ Check: $x = 0$ $x^2 + 9x = 0 \qquad x^2 + 9x = 0$ $(-9)^2 + 9(-9) = 0 \qquad 0^2 + 9(0) = 0$ $81 - 81 = 0 \qquad 0 + 0 = 0$ $0 = 0$ True $\qquad 0 = 0$ True	**Step 3:** Substitute members of the replacement set into the equation to determine whether or not they are actual solutions to the equation.
	Answer: The substitution of –9 or 0 makes the equation true; therefore, the solution set is $\{-9, 0\}$.

Example 4 Solve: $8x^2 - 4x = 24$

$8x^2 - 4x - 24 = 24 - 24$	**Step 1:** Subtract 24 from both sides of the equation.
$8x^2 - 4x - 24 = 0$	**Step 2:** Set the equation equal to 0.
$(2x + 3)(4x - 8) = 0$	**Step 3:** Factor the trinomial.

Step 4: Set each factor equal to 0 and solve for x.

$$2x + 3 = 0 \qquad\qquad 4x - 8 = 0$$
$$2x + 3 - 3 = 0 - 3 \qquad 4x - 8 + 8 = 0 + 8$$
$$2x = -3 \qquad\qquad 4x = 8$$
$$\frac{2x}{2} = -\frac{3}{2} \qquad\qquad \frac{4x}{4} = \frac{8}{4}$$
$$x = -\frac{3}{2} \qquad\qquad x = 2$$

The replacement set is $\left\{ -\frac{3}{2}, 2 \right\}$.

Step 5: Substitute members of the replacement set into the equation to determine whether or not they are actual solutions of the equation.

Check: $x = -\frac{3}{2}$

$$8\left(-\frac{3}{2}\right)^2 - 4\left(-\frac{3}{2}\right) = 24$$
$$8\left(\frac{9}{4}\right) - 4\left(-\frac{3}{2}\right) = 24$$
$$18 - (-6) = 24$$
$$24 = 24 \text{ True}$$

Check: $x = 2$

$$8(2)^2 - 4(2) = 24$$
$$8(4) - 8 = 24$$
$$32 - 8 = 24$$
$$24 = 24 \text{ True}$$

Answer: The substitution of $-\frac{3}{2}$ or 2 makes the equation true; thus, the solution set is $\left\{ -\frac{3}{2}, 2 \right\}$.

Problem Set

Solve:

1. $w^2 - 9 = 0$

2. $x^2 + 5x + 6 = 0$

3. $x^2 - 169 = 0$

4. $x^2 + 7x + 12 = 0$

5. $x^2 + 12x + 27 = 0$

6. $x^2 - 2x - 35 = 0$

7. $x^2 + 3x - 54 = 0$

8. $x^2 - 5x - 6 = 0$

9. $5x(x + 2) = 0$

10. $3x(x - 6) = 0$

11. $a^2 + 64 = -16a$

12. $x^2 + x = 72$

13. $x^2 = 24 - 10x$

14. $2x^2 = 14x$

15. $2x^2 = 72$

16. $4x^2 - 24x + 20 = 0$

17. $20 + 6x = 2x^2$

18. $x^3 + x^2 - (4x + 4) = 0$

19. $x^3 + x^2 + (x + 1) = 0$

20. $30x^2 - x = 20$

HA1-310: The Practical Use of Polynomial Equations

Some students find word problems—sometimes called story problems—difficult to solve. You must approach these problems with logic, as well as skill. You need to use common sense, knowing that if you logically break down the problem into workable parts, you can find the solution. Often, key words in the problem let you know whether you must add, subtract, multiply, or divide. Finally, add the math skills you have already learned to help solve these types of problems. Let's consider how to use polynomial equations to solve word problems.

Example 1   Three consecutive integers have the sum of 33. What are the integers?

$x = $ 1st integer $(x + 1) = $ 2nd integer $(x + 2) = $ 3rd integer	**Step 1:** Choose a variable to represent the unknown quantity.
$x + (x + 1) + (x + 2) = 33$	**Step 2:** Set up the equation.
$3x + 3 = 33$	**Step 3:** Combine like terms.
$3x + 3 - 3 = 33 - 3$ $3x = 30$ $x = 10$	**Step 4:** Solve for x.
$x + 1 = 11$	**Step 5:** Solve for the second integer.
$x + 2 = 12$	**Step 6:** Solve for the third integer.
	Answer: The three consecutive integers are 10, 11, and 12.

Example 2   A rectangle has an area of 135 square inches. What is the rectangle's length and width if one side is 6 inches longer than the other side?

$x = $ width $(x + 6) = $ length	**Step 1:** Choose a variable to represent the unknown quantity. Use the formula $A = lw$.
$lw = A$	**Step 2:** Set up the equation.
$(x + 6)x = 135$ $x^2 + 6x = 135$	**Step 3:** Distribute x to terms in the parentheses.
$x^2 + 6x - 135 = 0$	**Step 4:** Put equation into $ax^2 + bx + c = 0$ format.
$(x + 15)(x - 9) = 0$	**Step 5:** Factor the trinomial.
$x + 15 = 0$ or $x - 9 = 0$ $x = -15$ $x = 9$	**Step 6:** Set each factor equal to 0 then solve for x.

width = x = 9 inches
length = $x + 6 = 9 + 6$
         = 15 inches

Step 7: Substitute the answers into the given measures. However, you do not need to substitute –15, because measurements cannot be negative. Thus, substituting 9 for x in both measurements, you get a width of 9 inches and length of 15 inches. You can check your answers by substituting both numbers into the original equation. When this is done, the equation is true; therefore, the answer is correct.

Answer: The length is 15 inches and the width is 9 inches.

Example 3   A square has an area of 81 square inches. What is the square's perimeter?

$A = s \cdot s$ or $A = s^2$
$s = \pm\sqrt{81} = \pm 9$
Therefore, $s = 9$

Step 1: Before you can determine the perimeter of the square, you must find the length of one side. Use the formula for the area of a square to determine the length of one of the sides. Since the area is 81 in.^{2}, take the square root of 81 to find the length of one side. We know that 81 has two square roots: 9 and –9. However, in practical problems like this, we can see that 9 is the only viable solution because a square cannot have a side whose length is less than or equal to zero.

$P = 4s$
$P = 4(9)$
$P = 36$ in.

Step 2: Substitute the value of s into the perimeter formula to determine the perimeter of the square, which is 36 in. *Note: The units for perimeter are not squared.*

When solving word problems, remember to be very precise when you write down information. Next, set up your equation and solve for x. Always go back and reread the question. Then use the first information that you wrote and the solution for x to completely answer the word problem.

Example 4   Four consecutive multiples of 4 have a sum of 88. What are the four integers?

x = first number
$(x + 4)$ = second number
$(x + 8)$ = third number
$(x + 12)$ = fourth number

Step 1: Choose a variable to represent the unknown quantity. Recall that the numbers will increase by four each time.

$x + (x + 4) + (x + 8) + (x + 12) = 88$

Step 2: Set up the equation.

$4x + 24 = 88$

Step 3: Simplify by combining like terms.

$4x + 24 - 24 = 88 - 24$
$4x = 64$

Step 4: Isolate the variable term by subtracting 24 from both sides.

$\dfrac{4x}{4} = \dfrac{64}{4}$
$x = 16$

Step 5: To solve for x, divide both sides by 4.

$x = 16$

$x + 4 = 16 + 4 = 20$

$x + 8 = 16 + 8 = 24$

$x + 12 = 16 + 12 = 28$

Step 6: Substitute x with 16 to find the first, second, third and fourth numbers.

$16 + 20 + 24 + 28 = 88$

Step 7: Verify that the sum of the integers is 88.

Answer: The four multiples are 16, 20, 24, and 28.

Problem Set

1. Find two consecutive positive integers whose product is 6. Separate the integers with a comma.

2. Find two consecutive negative integers whose product is 182. Separate the integers with a comma.

3. Find two consecutive positive integers whose product is 132. Separate the integers with a comma.

4. Find two consecutive negative integers whose product is 306. Separate the integers with a comma.

5. Find two consecutive positive even integers whose product is 288. Separate the integers with a comma.

6. Find two consecutive negative odd integers whose product is 399. Separate the integers with a comma.

7. Find two consecutive positive even integers whose product is 168. Separate the integers with a comma.

8. Find two consecutive negative odd integers whose product is 323. Separate the integers with a comma.

9. The formula $D = \dfrac{n(n-3)}{2}$ is used to find the number of diagonals, D, of a polygon with n sides. Find the number of sides of a polygon with 2 diagonals.

10. The formula $D = \dfrac{n(n-3)}{2}$ is used to find the number of diagonals, D, of a polygon with n sides. Find the number of sides of a polygon with 14 diagonals.

11. The area of a rectangular garden is 63 square feet. If the length is 2 feet more than the width, find the width of the garden.

12. The area of a rectangular garden is 45 square feet. If the length is 4 feet more than the width, find the length of the garden.

13. The area of a rectangular garden is 36 square feet. If the length is 5 feet more than the width, find the width of the garden.

14. The area of a rectangular garden is 120 square feet. If the length is 2 feet more than the width, find the length of the garden.

15. The area of a rectangular garden is 54 square feet. If the length is 3 feet more than the width, find the width of the garden.

16. The area of a rectangular garden is 96 square feet. If the length is 4 feet more than the width, find the length of the garden.

17. The area of a rectangular garden is 44 square feet. If the length is 7 feet more than the width, find the width of the garden.

18. The altitude of a triangle is two meters less than the base. If the area of the triangle is 40 square meters, find the length of the altitude.

19. The sum of the squares of two positive consecutive integers is 61. Find the integers. Separate the integers with a comma.

20. The sum of the squares of two positive consecutive integers is 313. Find the integers. Separate the integers with a comma.

HA1-315: Defining Rational Expressions and Determining the Restricted Values

In mathematics, "rational" and "irrational" have slightly different meanings than they do in English, but you can use what you know about the English definition of "rational" to remember the characteristics of rational expressions. Remember that "rational" means "with reason" or "logical and sensible." A rational expression must make sense and follow the rules and definitions of operations.

Rational Expression	An expression that can be written in the form $\frac{p}{q}$, where p and q are both polynomials, and $q \neq 0$

You know that $\frac{a}{b} = c$ shows the operation of division where a is divided by b, and the quotient is c. To check a

division problem, you know that if $\frac{a}{b} = c$, then $a = b \cdot c$. This is true in all cases, except when $b = 0$. Why?

Any number multiplied by zero equals zero, so zero for a divisor makes this expression false, because there is not

a defined way to check your answer; any answer multiplied by zero would be zero and never the dividend a.

$$\frac{6}{2} = 3 \text{ because } 6 = 3 \cdot 2 \text{ is true.} \qquad \frac{6}{0} \neq 0 \text{ because } 6 = 0 \cdot 0 \text{ is not true.}$$

In rational expressions, a variable is usually in the denominator. Remember that you never want a number to replace a variable that would make the entire denominator zero. If such were the case, the solution would be undefined for that specific value. Any number that makes a denominator zero is called a **restricted value**. Therefore, to determine whether or not a number is restricted, you only need to find the solutions that would make the denominator or divisor equal zero.

Example 1   Determine any restricted values for $\dfrac{3x + 16}{(x - 2)(x + 11)}$.

$x - 2 = 0$ or $x + 11 = 0$	**Step 1:** Look at the divisor $(x - 2)(x + 11)$. Set each factor equal to zero.
$x = 2$ $x = -11$	**Step 2:** Solve each equation for x.
	Answer: If x is 2 or –11, then the divisor would be zero; therefore, the solution set $\{2, -11\}$ makes this expression undefined.

Example 2   Determine any restricted values for $\dfrac{2x^3 + 7}{x^2 - 9x + 20}$.

$x^2 - 9x + 20 = 0$	**Step 1:** You cannot have zero as a divisor, so let the denominator equal zero and solve for x.
$(x - 5)(x - 4) = 0$	**Step 2:** Factor $x^2 - 9x + 20$.

$x - 5 = 0$ or $x - 4 = 0$	**Step 3:**	Set each factor equal to 0.
$x = 5$ $x = 4$	**Step 4:**	Solve each equation for x.
	Answer:	If x is 5 or 4, then the divisor would be zero. The solution set $\{4, 5\}$ makes this expression undefined.

Example 3 Determine any restricted values for $\dfrac{x + 45}{x^2 - 3x - 70}$.

$x^2 - 3x - 70 = 0$	**Step 1:**	Set the denominator equal to zero to find the restricted values.
$(x + 7)(x - 10) = 0$	**Step 2:**	Factor $x^2 - 3x - 70$
$x + 7 = 0$ or $x - 10 = 0$ $x = -7$ $x = 10$	**Step 3:**	Set each factor equal to zero and solve for x.
	Answer:	The values in the solution set $\{-7, 10\}$ make the expression undefined.

Problem Set

Find the value(s) of the variable for which the rational expression is undefined:

1. $\dfrac{3x + 1}{2 - x}$

2. $\dfrac{x - 4}{x - 13}$

3. $\dfrac{x^2 + 1}{x + 7}$

4. $\dfrac{x(x + 11)}{5 + x}$

5. $\dfrac{3x}{21 + x}$

6. $\dfrac{4(x - 6)}{x + 6}$

7. $\dfrac{x^2 + 2x - 4}{x}$

8. $\dfrac{x - 6}{3x}$

9. $\dfrac{5}{x + 4}$

10. $\dfrac{4}{x + 5}$

11. $\dfrac{x - 4}{3x + 6}$

12. $\dfrac{3}{(x + 2)(x - 3)}$

13. $\dfrac{x - 1}{6x + 3}$

14. $\dfrac{5x - 4}{x^2 + x - 12}$

15. $\dfrac{4x - 3}{x^2 + 2x - 15}$

16. $\dfrac{a^2 - 9a + 3}{a^2 - 100}$

17. $\dfrac{m(m^2 + 3)}{m^2 - 64}$

18. $\dfrac{-8}{4d^2 - 15d - 4}$

19. $\dfrac{2x(x - 6)}{9x^2 - 32x - 16}$

20. $\dfrac{-7(s - 8)}{s^2 - 36s - 6,400}$

A simplified rational expression is one in which the numerator and denominator have no common factors, other than one. Before you can simplify an expression, you must completely factor the numerator and denominator. To do this, remove any common factors in both the numerator and the denominator. Then cancel any like factors, if possible. We'll look at some examples, but first review how to simplify rational numbers.

Example 1   Simplify: $\dfrac{90}{135}$

$= \dfrac{45 \cdot 2}{45 \cdot 3}$

Step 1: Simplify the expression by removing the common factor from the numerator and denominator.

$= \dfrac{\cancel{45} \cdot 2}{\cancel{45} \cdot 3}$

$= \dfrac{2}{3}$

Step 2: Cancel any like factors that appear in both the numerator and denominator. There are no more common factors in either the numerator or denominator.

Answer: $\dfrac{90}{135} = \dfrac{2}{3}$

Example 2   Simplify: $\dfrac{y^2}{y^{12}}$

$= \dfrac{1}{y^{12-2}}$

Step 1: Subtract the smaller exponent from the larger exponent, and place the result in the denominator, since it has the larger exponent.

$= \dfrac{1}{y^{10}}$

Answer: $\dfrac{y^2}{y^{12}} = \dfrac{1}{y^{10}}$

Whenever you simplify rational expressions, you must state any restrictions on the variable. Restrictions simply mean that you are stating the numbers which cannot replace the variable in the denominator, because those numbers would make the denominator equal to zero. Remember that in rational expressions the denominator cannot be zero because an expression with zero in the denominator is undefined. For example, in the expression $\dfrac{1}{y^{10}}$, y cannot equal zero.

Example 3   Simplify $\dfrac{15x}{3x^2 + 9x}$ and state any restrictions on the variable.

$= \dfrac{3 \cdot 5 \cdot x}{3x(x+3)}$

Step 1: Simplify the expression by removing the common factor from the numerator and denominator.

$$= \frac{\cancel{3} \cdot 5 \cdot \cancel{x}}{3\cancel{x}(x+3)}$$

Step 2: Cancel any like factors that appear in both the numerator and denominator until there are no more common factors.

$$= \frac{5}{x+3}$$

Step 3: Rewrite the remaining factors as the solution.

$$3x^2 + 9x = 0$$
$$3x(x+3) = 0$$
$$3x = 0 \text{ or } x + 3 = 0$$
$$x = 0 \text{ or } x = -3$$

Step 4: Determine values of x that would make the denominator equal to zero. Set the denominator equal to zero and solve for x. These are the restricted values of x.

Answer: $\dfrac{5}{x+3}; \; x \neq -3, 0$

Example 4 Simplify $\dfrac{x^2 + 5x + 6}{x+2}$ and state any restrictions on the variable.

$$= \frac{(x+2)(x+3)}{(x+2)}$$

Step 1: Simplify the expression by factoring the numerator and removing the common factor from the numerator and denominator.

$$= \frac{\cancel{(x+2)}(x+3)}{\cancel{(x+2)}}$$

Step 2: Cancel any like factors that appear in both the numerator and denominator until there are no more common factors.

$$= x + 3$$

Step 3: Rewrite the remaining factor as the solution.

$$x + 2 = 0$$
$$x = -2$$

Step 4: Determine values of x that make the denominator equal to zero. Set the denominator equal to zero and solve for x. These are the restricted values of x.

Answer: $x + 3; \; x \neq -2$

Problem Set

Simplify:

1. $\dfrac{30m^5 n}{15mn}$

2. $\dfrac{100a^5}{30a^2}$

3. $\dfrac{22x^5 y}{24xy^4}$

4. $\dfrac{-2(a+b)}{10(a+b)}$

5. $\dfrac{32y}{18x}$

6. $\dfrac{a(b+3)}{a(b+3)}$

7. $\dfrac{8x-12}{12}$

8. $\dfrac{6x+10}{30}$

9. $\dfrac{x+5}{x^2-25}$

10. $\dfrac{x-7}{x^2-49}$

11. $\dfrac{5p+10}{6p+12}$

12. $\dfrac{13x+13}{13x-13}$

13. $\dfrac{a^2+8a}{8a+64}$

14. $\dfrac{4r-16}{4-r}$

15. $\dfrac{7-x}{2x-14}$

16. $\dfrac{10x-2x^2}{x^2-5x}$

17. $\dfrac{12a^2 b + 60ab}{a+5}$

18. $\dfrac{-a^2-2a+15}{12-4a}$

19. $\dfrac{b^2-25}{b^2-7b+10}$

20. $\dfrac{a^2-7a+12}{2a-8}$

HA1-325: Multiplying Rational Expressions

Recall that rational expressions appear in fractional form, such as

$$\frac{p}{q}$$

which means they have a numerator and a denominator. Fractions are, in essence, rational expressions, and are simplified just like the basic rational numbers you simplified in previous lessons. For instance, when multiplying fractions, you learned that in a problem like

$$\frac{4}{7} \cdot \frac{1}{2}$$

you checked to see if you could perform any simplification. Next, you multiplied the numerators, then you multiplied the denominators. Then you made sure that the final answer was in simplest terms.

Multiplying Rational Expressions	If $\frac{P}{Q}$ and $\frac{R}{S}$ are rational expressions, then $\frac{P}{Q} \cdot \frac{R}{S} = \frac{PR}{QS}$.

The main difference in the types of rational expressions in this lesson is that the numerator and the denominator contain polynomials. When you multiply rational expressions, you will use the same steps that you used to multiply fractions. The example below reviews how to factor and cancel exponents, which will help you when multiplying rational expressions.

As you review the following examples, use caution when you are canceling. Only use cancellation in the following situations:

- if a number in the numerator and denominator both share a common factor, such as in $\frac{5(x+3)}{10(x+2)} = \frac{(x+3)}{2(x+2)}$, where 5 is the greatest common factor (GCF) of 5 and 10;

- if identical factors appear in the numerator and the denominator, such as in $\frac{2(x+1)}{11(x+1)} = \frac{2}{11}$, where $(x+1)$ is the identical factor.

Note: Even if all factors are cancelled, a factor of 1 still remains.

Example 1   Multiply: $\frac{3x+9}{25x+5} \cdot \frac{15x+3}{2x+6}$

$= \frac{3(x+3)}{5(5x+1)} \cdot \frac{3(5x+1)}{2(x+3)}$ **Step 1:** Factor if possible.

$= \frac{3\cancel{(x+3)}}{5\cancel{(5x+1)}} \cdot \frac{3\cancel{(5x+1)}}{2\cancel{(x+3)}}$ **Step 2:** Cancel any identical factors or those numbers that share common factors.

$= \frac{3 \cdot 3}{5 \cdot 2}$ **Step 3:** Multiply the remaining factors and ensure the answer is in simplest terms.

$= \frac{9}{10}$

Answer: $\frac{9}{10}$

Example 2 Multiply: $\dfrac{x^2 + 7x + 12}{x^2 + 8x + 15} \cdot \dfrac{x + 3}{x + 4}$

$= \dfrac{(x + 3)(x + 4)}{(x + 3)(x + 5)} \cdot \dfrac{x + 3}{x + 4}$	**Step 1:** Factor if possible.
$= \dfrac{\cancel{(x + 3)}\cancel{(x + 4)}}{\cancel{(x + 3)}(x + 5)} \cdot \dfrac{x + 3}{\cancel{x + 4}}$	**Step 2:** Cancel any identical factors or numbers that share common factors.
$= \dfrac{x + 3}{x + 5}$	**Step 3:** Simplify.
Answer: $\dfrac{x + 3}{x + 5}$	

Example 3 Multiply: $\dfrac{3x^{10}y^6}{5x^2y^7} \cdot \dfrac{2x^3y^2}{4x^5y^8}$

$= \dfrac{6x^{13}y^8}{20x^7y^{15}}$	**Step 1:** Multiply constants and like variables in the numerators first by adding the exponents. Do the same for the denominators.
$= \dfrac{3x^6}{10y^7}$	**Step 2:** Divide the expression. Subtract the smaller exponent from the larger one; place the resulting exponent where the larger one was. Ensure the answer is in simplest terms.
Answer: $\dfrac{3x^6}{10y^7}$	

Problem Set

Multiply:

1. $\dfrac{15}{20} \cdot \dfrac{16}{45}$

2. $\dfrac{18}{15} \cdot \dfrac{6}{45}$

3. $\dfrac{x^4}{y^6} \cdot \dfrac{y^2}{x^8}$

4. $\dfrac{2x^2}{y} \cdot \dfrac{7yz}{8x}$

5. $\dfrac{5y^5z^3}{6} \cdot \dfrac{12}{5y^7z}$

6. $\dfrac{(x + 4)}{6} \cdot \dfrac{22}{(x + 4)}$

7. $\dfrac{6(a - 8)}{18(a + 5)} \cdot \dfrac{(a + 5)}{a - 4}$

8. $\dfrac{(x + 3)(x + 1)}{(x + 4)(x - 3)} \cdot \dfrac{12(x + 4)}{3(x + 3)}$

9. $\dfrac{ab^2}{5} \cdot \dfrac{6}{ab}$

10. $\dfrac{6x^3y}{5x^2} \cdot \dfrac{15y}{3x^2}$

11. $\dfrac{x^2 - 100}{3x - 9} \cdot \dfrac{6x - 18}{x + 10}$

12. $\dfrac{15a - 5}{2a} \cdot \dfrac{4a^3}{9a - 3}$

13. $\dfrac{y^2 - 25}{9} \cdot \dfrac{18}{y + 5}$

14. $\dfrac{(m + n)^2}{60} \cdot \dfrac{20}{m^2 - n^2}$

15. $\dfrac{3y^2 - y}{9y^2 - 1} \cdot \dfrac{6y + 2}{5y}$

16. $\dfrac{8a + 16}{10a - 5} \cdot \dfrac{12a - 6}{4a + 8}$

17. $\dfrac{x^2 - 16}{4x - 12} \cdot \dfrac{x - 3}{x - 4}$

18. $\dfrac{x^2 - 2x - 15}{x - 6} \cdot \dfrac{3x - 18}{x^2 + 10x + 21}$

19. $\dfrac{b^2 - b - 20}{b^2 - 49} \cdot \dfrac{2b + 14}{2b + 8}$

20. $\dfrac{m^2 - m - 6}{m^2 + 6m + 8} \cdot \dfrac{m + 4}{3m - 9}$

In previous lessons, you simplified and multiplied rational expressions. To add to your mastery of rational numbers, you will now learn how to divide rational expressions. Remember that dividing one number by another is the same as multiplying a number by a number's inverse.

Dividing Rational Expressions	If $\dfrac{P}{Q}$ and $\dfrac{R}{S}$ are rational expressions and $R \neq 0,$ then $$\frac{P}{Q} \div \frac{R}{S} = \frac{P}{Q} \cdot \frac{S}{R} = \frac{P \cdot S}{Q \cdot R}$$

To divide rational numbers, multiply the first expression by the reciprocal, or inverse, of the second expression. Here is an example:

$$\frac{2}{3} \div \frac{3}{4}$$

$$= \frac{2}{3} \cdot \frac{4}{3}$$

$$= \frac{2 \cdot 4}{3 \cdot 3}$$

$$= \frac{8}{9}$$

You will use the same procedure for a problem that consists of variables and exponents.

$$\frac{x}{4} \div \frac{5}{3x^3}$$

$$= \frac{x}{4} \cdot \frac{3x^3}{5}$$

$$= \frac{x \cdot 3x^3}{4 \cdot 5}$$

$$= \frac{3x^4}{20}$$

Use the procedure below to solve division problems:

Step 1: Rewrite the problem. Change the division problem to a multiplication problem using the reciprocal of the second expression.

Step 2: Simplify if possible.

Step 3: Multiply the numerators first, then multiply the denominators.

Consider the following examples.

Example 1   Divide: $\dfrac{x^2}{y} \div \dfrac{y^3}{x^2}$

$= \dfrac{x^2}{y} \cdot \dfrac{x^2}{y^3}$

Step 1: Rewrite the problem. Change the division sign to a multiplication sign and take the reciprocal of the second fraction.

$= \dfrac{x^4}{y^4}$

Step 2: Multiply the numerators of the two fractions; then, multiply the denominators.

Answer: $\dfrac{x^4}{y^4}$

Example 2   Divide: $\dfrac{6x^3}{5y^2} \div \dfrac{3xy}{4}$

$= \dfrac{6x^3}{5y^2} \cdot \dfrac{4}{3xy}$

Step 1: Rewrite the problem, taking the reciprocal of the second fraction. Be sure to convert the division symbol to a multiplication symbol.

$= \dfrac{6x^3 \cdot 4}{5 \cdot 3xy^3}$

Step 2: Multiply the numerators of the two fractions; then, multiply the denominators. Cancel if possible.

$= \dfrac{24x^3}{15xy^3}$

$= \dfrac{\cancel{3} \cdot 8 \cdot \cancel{x^3}^{x^2}}{\cancel{3} \cdot 5 \cdot \cancel{x} \cdot y^3}$

$= \dfrac{8x^2}{5y^3}$

Answer: $\dfrac{8x^2}{5y^3}$

Consider an example that also requires factoring and cancellation.

Example 3   Divide: $\dfrac{x^2 + 20x + 100}{x^2 + 17x + 70} \div \dfrac{(x+12)}{(x+7)}$

$= \dfrac{(x+10)(x+10)}{(x+10)(x+7)} \cdot \dfrac{(x+7)}{(x+12)}$

Step 1: From the polynomials, rewrite the problem, taking the reciprocal of the second fraction. Be sure to convert the division symbol to a multiplication symbol.

$= \dfrac{\cancel{(x+10)}(x+10)}{\cancel{(x+10)}\cancel{(x+7)}} \cdot \dfrac{\cancel{(x+7)}}{(x+12)}$

Step 2: Factor and cancel common factors.

$$= \frac{x + 10}{x + 12}$$

Step 3: Multiply the numerators of the two fractions, then multiply the denominators.

Answer: $\frac{x + 10}{x + 12}$

Problem Set

Divide:

1. $\frac{8}{7} \div \frac{4}{3}$

2. $\frac{16}{14} \div \frac{2}{7}$

3. $\frac{x + 2}{x} \div \frac{x + 2}{20}$

4. $\frac{x^2}{y^3} \div \frac{y}{x^2}$

5. $\frac{14x^2}{9} \div \frac{28x^2}{18}$

6. $\frac{16}{5x^2} \div 20$

7. $\frac{12x^3}{15} \div \frac{50x}{9}$

8. $\frac{81}{4x^2} \div \frac{27}{16x}$

9. $\frac{x - 7}{1} \div \frac{x - 7}{14}$

10. $\frac{x + 5}{1} \div \frac{x + 5}{20}$

11. $\frac{3x + 18}{10x - 40} \div \frac{30x + 180}{15}$

12. $\frac{4x - 20}{28x + 56} \div \frac{24x - 120}{30x + 60}$

13. $\frac{7x + 28}{12x + 36} \div \frac{14x + 56}{36x + 108}$

14. $\frac{5x + 40}{4x - 8} \div \frac{20x + 160}{36x - 72}$

15. $\frac{27x + 135}{7x - 28} \div \frac{9x + 45}{14x - 56}$

16. $\frac{6ab^2}{4b} \div 2b$

17. $\frac{x + 4}{x - 4} \div \frac{2x + 8}{x^2 - 8x + 16}$

18. $\frac{x^2 - 4x}{x + 1} \div \frac{x^2 - 16}{x^2 - 1}$

19. $\frac{x^2 - 4}{x + 3} \div \frac{x^2 - 4x + 4}{x^2 - 9}$

20. $\frac{3x^2 + 9x}{2x^2 + 14x + 20} \div \frac{x}{x + 2}$

HA1-335: Finding the LCD of Rational Expressions and Changing Fractions to Equivalent Fractions

Imagine that you have been given an intricate jigsaw puzzle. You are amazed at the number of small pieces used to complete the puzzle, so you take it apart to count the individual pieces. Just as the puzzle can be reduced to its smallest piece, finding the least common denominator (LCD) also requires you to separate expressions into smaller expressions or numbers. The LCD is the smallest possible common denominator that all denominators can be divided into without a remainder. Sometimes the LCD of an expression is obvious. If it is not, using prime factorization allows you to generate a list of factors that can be multiplied to find the LCD. Here is a summary of the procedure for finding the least common denominator:

Step 1: Factor each denominator into *prime factors* (factors that cannot be broken down further).

Step 2: Write each different denominator factor the greatest number of times it appears in any denominator. Use exponents.

Step 3: Multiply these denominator factors to get the least common denominator.

This same procedure can be used to find the LCD for rational expressions. You will have to work more with polynomials while continuing to use factoring, canceling, and simplifying exponents.

The following example will review how to find the LCD of rational numbers.

Find the LCD of $\frac{1}{6}$ and $\frac{3}{8}$.

$$6: \quad 2 \cdot 3$$

$$8: \quad 2 \cdot 2 \cdot 2 = 2^3$$

$$\text{LCD:} \quad 2^3 \cdot 3 = 8 \cdot 3 = 24$$

Although the number 2 appears in both lists, it occurs the greatest number of times in the list of factors of 8. The number 3 appears as a factor only once, and is automatically used to find the LCD.

Example 1   Find the LCD of $\dfrac{2}{24x^3y^2}$ and $\dfrac{3}{16xy^4}$.

$\dfrac{2}{24x^3y^2}$

$= 2 \cdot 2 \cdot 2 \cdot 3 \cdot x \cdot x \cdot x \cdot y \cdot y$

$= 2^3 \cdot 3 \cdot x^3 \cdot y^2$

$\dfrac{3}{16xy^4}$

$= 2 \cdot 2 \cdot 2 \cdot 2 \cdot x \cdot y \cdot y \cdot y \cdot y$

$= 2^4 \cdot x \cdot y^4$

Step 1: Write each denominator in factored form, then convert to exponential form.

$2^4 \cdot 3 \cdot x^3 \cdot y^4$

Step 2: Write each number and variable the greatest number of times it appears as a product.

$48x^3y^4$

Step 3: Simplify.

Answer: The LCD is $48x^3y^4$.

Example 2　Find the LCD of $\dfrac{2x}{x^2 + 7x + 12}$ and $\dfrac{3y}{2x^2 + 10x + 12}$.

$x^2 + 7x + 12$ $= (x+4)(x+3)$	$2x^2 + 10x + 12$ $= (2x+6)(x+2)$ $= 2(x+3)(x+2)$	**Step 1:** Factor each denominator into prime factors. *Note: Since (2x+6) is not a prime factor, simplify it to 2(x+3).*
LCD $= 2(x+4)(x+3)(x+2)$		**Step 2:** Write the LCD by multiplying all factors of both denominators. For common factors, multiply them by the greatest number of times they appear in any denominator.
		Answer: The LCD is $2(x+4)(x+3)(x+2)$.

Another concept that should be familiar to you is forming equivalent fractions. Recall adding or subtracting fractions with unlike denominators. Before you can perform any computations, you must find the LCD.

Example 3　Find the numerator for the rational equation $\dfrac{4x}{5xy^2} = \dfrac{?}{35x^3y^4}$.

$5 \cdot \boxed{7} = 35$ $x \cdot \boxed{x^2} = x^3$ $y^2 \cdot \boxed{y^2} = y^4$	**Step 1:** Determine the factors by which $5xy^2$ should be multiplied by to get a product of $35x^3y^4$.
$4x \cdot 7x^2y^2 = 28x^3y^2$	**Step 2:** As you can see, $5xy^2$ was multiplied by $7x^2y^2$ to get $35x^3y^4$. Now, to find the missing numerator, multiply the numerator, $4x$, by $7x^2y^2$ to find the unknown numerator.
	Answer: $28x^3y^2$

Example 4　Find the numerator that will complete the equivalence $\dfrac{3y}{x-5} = \dfrac{?}{x^2 - 3x - 10}$.

$\dfrac{3y}{x-5} = \dfrac{?}{(x-5)(x+2)}$	**Step 1:** Factor $x^2 - 3x - 10$.
LCD $= (x-5)(x+2)$	**Step 2:** Find the LCD.
$\dfrac{3y}{x-5} = \dfrac{3y(x+2)}{(x-5)(x+2)}$	**Step 3:** Since you multiplied the denominator by $(x+2)$, you must also multiply the numerator by $(x+2)$.
	Answer: The numerator that will complete the equivalence is $3y(x+2)$.

Problem Set

1. What is the LCD of $\dfrac{6c}{10a}$ and $\dfrac{4b}{15ac}$?

2. What is the LCD of $\dfrac{3c}{10b}$ and $\dfrac{3}{4bc}$?

3. What is the LCD of $\dfrac{13a}{20bc}$ and $\dfrac{13a}{16b}$?

4. What is the LCD of $\dfrac{4}{7abc}$ and $\dfrac{1}{2a}$?

5. What is the LCD of $\dfrac{4}{5abc}$ and $\dfrac{bc}{2a}$?

6. Find the numerator of $\dfrac{5a}{9bc}$ if it is written as an equivalent fraction with denominator $27bc$.

7. Find the numerator of $\dfrac{1}{12ac}$ if it is written as an equivalent fraction with denominator $48abc$.

8. Find the numerator of $\dfrac{3}{16bc}$ if it is written as an equivalent fraction with denominator $32abc$.

9. Find the numerator of $\dfrac{c}{15ab}$ if it is written as an equivalent fraction with denominator $60ab$.

10. Find the numerator of $\dfrac{b}{6ac}$ if it is written as an equivalent fraction with denominator $60ac$.

11. What is the LCD of $\dfrac{5a}{6b^2c}$ and $\dfrac{4a}{15bc^2}$?

12. What is the LCD of $\dfrac{2c}{9a^2b^2}$ and $\dfrac{8}{15ab}$?

13. What is the LCD of $\dfrac{4a}{9bc}$ and $\dfrac{8}{21b^3c^3}$?

14. What is the LCD of $\dfrac{5b^2}{6a^2c^2}$ and $\dfrac{3a}{14b^2c^2}$?

15. Write $\dfrac{3a}{8c^2}$ as an equivalent fraction with a denominator of $16abc^2$.

16. Write $\dfrac{ab}{20c^3}$ as an equivalent fraction with a denominator of $20a^2bc^3$.

17. Write $\dfrac{7b}{9a^3}$ as an equivalent fraction with a denominator of $27a^3b$.

18. Find the LCD of $\dfrac{8y}{5y+30}$ and $\dfrac{4y}{y^2-36}$.

19. Find the LCD of $\dfrac{3b}{b^2+9b+8}$ and $\dfrac{7b}{b^2+16b+64}$.

20. Find the numerator which will produce equivalent fractions:
$$\dfrac{3b}{b^2+3b+2}=\dfrac{?}{(b+1)(b+2)^2}$$

Remember that rational expressions are fractions that contain numbers, variables, and exponents combined to form polynomials. In a previous lesson, you reviewed some concepts used when adding and subtracting rational expressions. Because rational expressions, like fractions, have a numerator and denominator, they must also have like denominators in order to be added or subtracted. Moreover, since you have to find the least common denominator (LCD) for expressions with unlike denominators, you will form equivalent fractions before you add or subtract the expressions. For example,

$$\frac{3}{4x} + \frac{5}{12x^2}$$

The first step is to find the LCD of both denominators. Use the steps you learned in previous lessons to do this.

$$\textbf{4x:} \quad 2 \cdot 2 \cdot x = 2^2 \cdot x$$

$$\textbf{12x}^2\textbf{:} \quad 2 \cdot 2 \cdot 3 \cdot x \cdot x = 2^2 \cdot 3 \cdot x^2$$

$$\textbf{LCD:} \quad 2^2 \cdot 3 \cdot x^2 = 12x^2$$

The LCD is $12x^2$. Once you find the LCD for both expressions, rewrite each rational expression as an equivalent fraction with the LCD as the denominator. In this example, the denominator of the first expression, $4x$, must be multiplied by $3x$ to get $12x^2$. Next, multiply the numerator, 3, by $3x$. Notice that the net effect is to multiply the first term by $\frac{3x}{3x}$, or 1.

$$\left(\frac{3}{4x} \cdot \frac{3x}{3x} \right) + \frac{5}{12x^2}$$

The second expression already has the denominator of $12x^2$; therefore, it remains the same.

$$= \frac{9x}{12x^2} + \frac{5}{12x^2}$$

$$= \frac{9x + 5}{12x^2}$$

Example 1 Simplify: $\dfrac{4}{6x} + \dfrac{5}{12x^2}$

$6x = 2 \cdot 3 \cdot x$ **Step 1:** Find the LCD.

$12x^2 = 2 \cdot 2 \cdot 3 \cdot x \cdot x = 2^2 \cdot 3 \cdot x^2$

$LCD = 2^2 \cdot 3 \cdot x^2 = 12x^2$

$$= \left(\frac{4}{6x} \cdot \frac{2x}{2x} \right) + \frac{5}{12x^2}$$

Step 2: Find equivalent fractions. Multiply $\frac{4}{6x}$ by $\frac{2x}{2x}$ to convert it to an equivalent fraction. The other fraction, $\frac{5}{12x^2}$, already has the LCD and does not need to be converted.

$$= \frac{8x}{12x^2} + \frac{5}{12x^2}$$

$$= \frac{8x + 5}{12x^2}$$

Step 3: Add the fractions, since they now have common denominators. *Note: You cannot combine 8x and 5, because they are not like terms. Write them as separate terms in the numerator.*

Answer: $\dfrac{8x + 5}{12x^2}$

Example 2   Simplify: $\dfrac{3}{x^2 - 16} + \dfrac{3}{x - 4}$

$$\frac{3}{(x+4)(x-4)} + \frac{3}{x-4}$$

Step 1: Factor $x^2 - 16$ since it is not prime.

$$(x+4)(x-4) = (x+4)(x-4)$$
$$x - 4 = x - 4$$
$$\text{LCD: } (x+4)(x-4)$$

Step 2: Find the LCD.

$$= \frac{3}{(x+4)(x-4)} + \left(\frac{3}{x-4} \cdot \frac{x+4}{x+4} \right)$$

$$= \frac{3}{(x+4)(x-4)} + \frac{3x + 12}{(x+4)(x-4)}$$

Step 3: Find equivalent fractions.

$$= \frac{3 + 3x + 12}{(x+4)(x-4)}$$

$$= \frac{3x + 15}{(x+4)(x-4)}$$

Step 4: Add the fractions. *Note: $3x + 15$ factors as $3(x + 5)$, but does not lead to any cancellations.*

Answer: $\dfrac{3x + 15}{(x+4)(x-4)}$

When you subtract fractions, they must also have common denominators. Therefore, use the same process to subtract fractions that you use to add fractions. If any denominator is not a prime factor, you must factor it before you find the LCD. Then, form equivalent fractions so you can subtract. Make sure to use the correct sign when subtracting numbers.

Example 3   Simplify: $\dfrac{6}{3x + 7} - \dfrac{2}{9x + 21}$

$$\frac{6}{3x + 7} - \frac{2}{3(3x + 7)}$$

Step 1: Factor the denominators if they are not already prime.

$$3x + 7 = 3x + 7$$
$$3(3x + 7) = (3x + 7) \cdot 3$$
$$\text{LCD} = 3(3x + 7)$$

Step 2: Find the LCD.

$$= \left(\frac{6}{(3x+7)} \cdot \frac{3}{3} \right) - \frac{2}{3(3x+7)}$$

$$= \frac{18}{3(3x+7)} - \frac{2}{3(3x+7)}$$

Step 3: Find equivalent fractions.

$$= \frac{18 - 2}{3(3x+7)}$$

$$= \frac{16}{3(3x+7)}$$

Step 4: Subtract the fractions.

Answer: $\dfrac{16}{3(3x+7)}$

Problem Set

Simplify:

1. $\dfrac{7d}{8} - \dfrac{3d+5}{8}$

2. $\dfrac{9}{5n} - \dfrac{3}{10n}$

3. $\dfrac{6}{y-1} + \dfrac{4}{y-1}$

4. $\dfrac{3}{x} + \dfrac{5}{x}$

5. $\dfrac{x+2}{2x} + \dfrac{x+4}{2x}$

6. $\dfrac{3x+2}{x-4} - \dfrac{x-1}{x-4}$

7. $\dfrac{3x}{x+2} - \dfrac{x-4}{x+2}$

8. $\dfrac{6x+3}{3x+4} + \dfrac{3x-5}{3x+4}$

9. $\dfrac{6x^2}{x+4} + \dfrac{2x^2}{x+4}$

10. $\dfrac{3}{4z} + \dfrac{-7}{4z}$

11. $\dfrac{3}{2n} + \dfrac{2}{n^2} - \dfrac{2}{8n}$

12. $\dfrac{4}{3n} - \dfrac{5}{6n^2} + \dfrac{7}{12n}$

13. $\dfrac{4}{3n-18} - \dfrac{2}{3n+12}$

14. $\dfrac{5}{4x} + \dfrac{1}{x} - \dfrac{7}{6x^2}$

15. $\dfrac{x}{3x-6} - \dfrac{7}{3x+15}$

16. $\dfrac{x}{2x+2} - \dfrac{3}{2x+6}$

17. $\dfrac{9}{5c-10} - \dfrac{6}{5c+20}$

18. $\dfrac{12}{x^2+4x+4} + \dfrac{1}{x^2-4}$

19. $\dfrac{-11}{x^2-9} - \dfrac{7}{x^2-3x}$

20. $\dfrac{2}{x^2-1} + \dfrac{4}{x^2-3x+2}$

HA1-345: Adding and Subtracting Polynomials and Rational Expressions

You have probably heard the expression, "That's like comparing apples and oranges." The saying reminds us that it doesn't work to compare two things that have no features in common. You learned the mathematical equivalent of this when you learned about operations with fractions. That is, you can only add fractions that have like, or common, denominators. To add or subtract polynomials and rational expressions, you must also have common denominators. You then multiply the numerators by whatever factor was required to achieve the common denominator. In this process, you must factor, use the FOIL method of multiplying binomials, and combine positive and negative expressions.

Review how to find the least common denominator (LCD) and how to add simple fractions.

Example 1   Simplify: $\dfrac{5}{x} + \dfrac{2}{3}$

$LCD = 3x$	**Step 1:** Find the LCD. Factor each denominator, then multiply all factors. Use each factor the greatest number of times it occurs in either factored denominator.
$= \left(\dfrac{5 \cdot 3}{x \cdot 3}\right) + \left(\dfrac{2 \cdot x}{3 \cdot x}\right)$	**Step 2:** Give each fraction the LCD, then adjust the numerators by multiplying each numerator by the same factor that its denominator was multiplied by to reach the LCD. The first fraction has the x in the denominator, but needs the factor 3 to form the LCD, $3x$, so multiply both numerator and denominator by 3. The second denominator has the 3, but needs the factor x to form $3x$, so multiply both numerator and denominator by x.
$= \dfrac{15}{3x} + \dfrac{2x}{3x}$	**Step 3:** Simplify, combine like terms, and add.

Answer: $\dfrac{15 + 2x}{3x}$

Example 2   Simplify: $\dfrac{7}{x} - 12$

$LCD = x$	**Step 1:** Find the LCD. Remember that any whole number is assumed to have a denominator of one.
$= \dfrac{7}{x} - \left(\dfrac{12}{1} \cdot \dfrac{x}{x}\right)$	**Step 2:** Give each fraction the LCD. Then adjust the numerators: multiply each numerator by the same factor by which you multiplied its denominator to get the LCD.
$= \dfrac{7}{x} - \dfrac{12x}{x}$	**Step 3:** Simplify, combine like terms and add.

Answer: $\dfrac{7 - 12x}{x}$

It is very important to understand how to get a common denominator for these problems. Consider all the factors represented by the denominators and use each factor the greatest number of times it is used in any denominator. Each denominator must already have the LCD or you must be able to multiply the denominator by some factor(s) to form the LCD.

Now try a few examples with polynomials and rational expressions.

Example 3   Simplify: $\dfrac{2}{3a} + \dfrac{1}{6a^2} + \dfrac{4}{a}$

$3a = 3 \cdot a$ $6a^2 = 2 \cdot 3 \cdot a^2$ $a = a$	**Step 1:** Factor each denominator.
$2 \cdot 3 \cdot a^2 = 6a^2$ $LCD = 6a^2$	**Step 2:** Multiply all factors, using each factor the greatest number of times it occurs in the factored denominators. Each denominator must be $6a^2$ before you can add.
$\left(\dfrac{2}{3a} \cdot \dfrac{2a}{2a}\right) + \dfrac{1}{6a^2} + \left(\dfrac{4}{a} \cdot \dfrac{6a}{6a}\right)$	**Step 3:** Make equivalent fractions. Adjust the first and third fractions to have denominators of $6a^2$. The second fraction already has this denominator.
$= \dfrac{4a}{6a^2} + \dfrac{1}{6a^2} + \dfrac{24a}{6a^2}$ $= \dfrac{4a + 1 + 24a}{6a^2}$ $= \dfrac{1 + 28a}{6a^2}$	**Step 4:** Combine and simplify.

Answer: $\dfrac{1 + 28a}{6a^2}$

Example 4   Simplify: $\dfrac{3}{x^2 - 9} - \dfrac{7}{x + 3}$

$x^2 - 9 = (x + 3)(x - 3)$ $x + 3 = (x + 3)$ $LCD = (x + 3)(x - 3)$	**Step 1:** Factor each denominator and determine the LCD.
$\dfrac{3}{(x + 3)(x - 3)} - \left(\dfrac{7}{x + 3} \cdot \dfrac{x - 3}{x - 3}\right)$	**Step 2:** The first fraction already has the LCD, so adjust the second fraction by multiplying the numerator and denominator by $(x - 3)$ to reach the LCD.
$\dfrac{3}{(x + 3)(x - 3)} - \dfrac{7x - 21}{(x + 3)(x - 3)}$ $= \dfrac{3 - (7x - 21)}{(x + 3)(x - 3)}$ $= \dfrac{-7x + 24}{(x + 3)(x - 3)}$	**Step 3:** Combine and simplify.

Answer: $\dfrac{-7x + 24}{(x + 3)(x - 3)}$

Example 5   Simplify: $\dfrac{3x}{x+5}+x-7$ (Remember: $\dfrac{3x}{x+5}+x-7=\dfrac{3x}{x+5}+\dfrac{x-7}{1}$)

$LCD = x+5$	**Step 1:** You only have to consider $x+5$ for the LCD.

$\dfrac{3x}{x+5}+\left(\dfrac{x-7}{1}\cdot\dfrac{x+5}{x+5}\right)$

Step 2: The first fraction already has the LCD. Multiply the numerator and denominator of the second fraction by $(x+5)$ to reach the LCD.

Remember $x-7=\dfrac{x-7}{1}$.

$=\dfrac{3x}{x+5}+\dfrac{(x-7)(x+5)}{x+5}$

Step 3: Use FOIL to multiply $(x-7)$ and $(x+5)$.

$=\dfrac{3x+(x^2-2x-35)}{x+5}$

$=\dfrac{x^2+x-35}{x+5}$

Step 4: Simplify the numerator.

Answer: $\dfrac{x^2+x-35}{x+5}$

Problem Set

Simplify:

1. $\dfrac{y-5}{8}+8$ **2.** $3+\dfrac{7}{n}$ **3.** $\dfrac{5}{x}+4$

4. $\dfrac{2}{c}+12$ **5.** $10-\dfrac{4}{m}$ **6.** $6-\dfrac{3}{a}$

7. $\dfrac{3}{5y}+5$ **8.** $7-\dfrac{1}{t}$ **9.** $\dfrac{3}{7y}-4$

10. $\dfrac{3x-4}{5}+2$ **11.** $\dfrac{5n}{n-2}+n-7$ **12.** $4w-\dfrac{w+6}{w}$

13. $8a-\dfrac{a+4}{5}$ **14.** $4x-\dfrac{x-1}{3}$ **15.** $d+2-\dfrac{8d}{5}$

16. $\dfrac{t+4}{7}-10t$ **17.** $\dfrac{2b+2}{3}-4b$ **18.** $\dfrac{3x}{x+4}+x-2$

19. $\dfrac{5c}{2c-8}-(4c+4)$ **20.** $2m-3-\dfrac{4m}{6m+5}$

In algebra, some rational expressions have fractions in the numerator, denominator, or both. This is called a **complex fraction**.

Complex Fraction	A rational expression with fractions in the numerator, denominator, or both

If you remember the laws of simple fractions, solving complex fractions will seem quite natural. Recall that the quotient of two mixed numbers, such as $4\frac{1}{2} \div 2\frac{1}{4}$, can be written as a fraction: $\dfrac{4\frac{1}{2}}{2\frac{1}{4}}$

Look at the steps that are required to solve complex fractions. When you divide fractions, you actually multiply the first fraction by the *reciprocal* of the second fraction. Before you perform the multiplication, try to cancel any common factors. If you cannot find any common factors, multiply the numerators, then multiply the denominators. Expressions sometimes become very complex when they contain exponents; use the law of exponents to multiply the terms. You can also use the law of exponents to simplify the results of the complex fractions.

Review the following examples.

Example 1　Simplify: $\dfrac{x^2 y}{10} \div \dfrac{x^4}{15y}$

$= \dfrac{x^2 y}{10} \cdot \dfrac{15y}{x^4}$

Step 1: Take the reciprocal of the second fraction and then multiply.
Note: When dividing, use the reciprocal of the divisor.

$= \dfrac{x^2 \cdot y \cdot 15 \cdot y}{10 \cdot x^4}$

Step 2: Simplify using the laws of exponents and common factors. Simplify $\dfrac{15}{10}$ to $\dfrac{3}{2}$.

$= \dfrac{\overset{1}{\cancel{x^2}} \cdot y \cdot \overset{3}{\cancel{15}} \cdot y}{\underset{2}{\cancel{10}} \cdot \underset{x^2}{\cancel{x^4}}}$

Then simplify $\dfrac{x^2}{x^4}$ to $\dfrac{1}{x^2}$.

$= \dfrac{3y^2}{2x^2}$

Step 3: Multiply the remaining numerators and then the denominators.

Answer: $\dfrac{3y^2}{2x^2}$

Example 2   Simplify: $\dfrac{\frac{4x}{9}}{\frac{2x^2}{3}}$

$= \dfrac{4x}{9} \div \dfrac{2x^2}{3}$

Step 1: Rewrite the fraction, taking the reciprocal of the second fraction. Be sure to change the division symbol to a multiplication symbol.

$= \dfrac{4x}{9} \cdot \dfrac{3}{2x^2}$

$= \dfrac{4 \cdot x \cdot 3}{9 \cdot 2 \cdot x^2}$

Step 2: Simplify both fractions. Use the laws of exponents to simplify the variables.

$= \dfrac{\overset{2}{\cancel{4}} \cdot \overset{1}{\cancel{x}} \cdot \overset{1}{\cancel{3}}}{\underset{3}{\cancel{9}} \cdot \underset{1}{\cancel{2}} \cdot \underset{x}{\cancel{x^2}}}$

$= \dfrac{2}{3x}$

Step 3: Multiply the remaining numerators and then the denominators.

Answer: $\dfrac{2}{3x}$

Example 3   Simplify: $\dfrac{20a}{\frac{5a^2}{4}}$

$= \dfrac{20a}{1} \div \dfrac{5a^2}{4}$

Step 1: Rewrite the fraction, taking the reciprocal of the second fraction. Remember to make the division sign a multiplication sign. Because $20a$ does not have a denominator, place it over 1.

$= \dfrac{20a}{1} \cdot \dfrac{4}{5a^2}$

$= \dfrac{20 \cdot a \cdot 4}{1 \cdot 5 \cdot a^2}$

Step 2: Simplify both fractions. Use the laws of exponents to simplify the variables.

$= \dfrac{\overset{4}{\cancel{20}} \cdot \overset{1}{\cancel{a}} \cdot 4}{1 \cdot \underset{1}{\cancel{5}} \cdot \underset{a}{\cancel{a^2}}}$

$= \dfrac{16}{a}$

Step 3: Multiply the remaining numerators and then the denominators.

Answer: $\dfrac{16}{a}$

In the previous examples you simplified the complex fraction by rewriting it in the form $\dfrac{a}{b} \div \dfrac{c}{d}$, taking the reciprocal of the second fraction, and then multiplying them. When a complex fraction either contains a fraction in both the numerator and denominator or contains several terms, you can simplify the expression by multiplying every term in the numerator and denominator by the LCD.

Try the example below.

Example 4 Simplify: $\dfrac{\dfrac{3}{y}-\dfrac{2y}{x}}{\dfrac{y}{1}}$

$=\dfrac{\dfrac{3}{y}-\dfrac{2y}{x}}{\dfrac{y}{1}}$

Step 1: Rewrite the denominator of the complex fraction as a fraction.

LCD $= xy$

Step 2: Find the LCD of the complex fraction.

$=\dfrac{\dfrac{3}{y}\cdot xy-\dfrac{2y}{x}\cdot xy}{\dfrac{y}{1}\cdot xy}$

Step 3: Multiply the numerator and denominator of the complex fraction by the LCD.

$=\dfrac{\dfrac{3}{\cancel{y}}\cdot \cancel{x}y-\dfrac{2y}{\cancel{x}}\cdot x\cancel{y}}{\dfrac{y}{1}\cdot xy}$

$=\dfrac{3x-2y^2}{xy^2}$

Step 4: Simplify the remaining complex fraction.

Answer: $\dfrac{3x-2y^2}{xy^2}$

Problem Set

Simplify:

1. $\dfrac{\dfrac{7}{10}}{\dfrac{2}{5}}$

2. $\dfrac{\dfrac{6}{7}}{\dfrac{8}{9}}$

3. $\dfrac{\dfrac{r^3}{8}}{\dfrac{r}{6}}$

4. $\dfrac{\dfrac{7n^2}{6}}{3n}$

5. $\dfrac{\dfrac{7}{18}}{\dfrac{2}{9}}$

6. $\dfrac{\dfrac{10}{c^2}}{\dfrac{15}{c}}$

7. $\dfrac{\dfrac{3n}{2}}{\dfrac{9}{2n}}$

8. $\dfrac{\dfrac{x}{5}}{\dfrac{x}{15}}$

9. $\dfrac{\dfrac{3a^2b}{5a}}{\dfrac{9ab^2}{10}}$

10. $\dfrac{\dfrac{3xy}{4}}{\dfrac{x^2y^2}{9}}$

11. $\dfrac{\dfrac{4}{m}+\dfrac{3}{m^2}}{m}$

12. $\dfrac{\dfrac{4}{y}-\dfrac{1}{x}}{x}$

13. $\dfrac{\dfrac{a}{b}+\dfrac{a}{3b}}{b}$

14. $\dfrac{\dfrac{2x}{y}-\dfrac{y}{x}}{xy}$

15. $\dfrac{\dfrac{3x}{x+3}}{x-1}$

16. $\dfrac{\dfrac{x}{4}+\dfrac{y}{x}}{2x}$

17. $\dfrac{\dfrac{1}{t}-\dfrac{st}{2}}{t}$

18. $\dfrac{\dfrac{2x}{3}+\dfrac{y}{x}}{\dfrac{2}{x}+\dfrac{y}{x}}$

19. $\dfrac{\dfrac{3}{y}+\dfrac{1}{2y}}{y+\dfrac{y}{2}}$

20. $\dfrac{\dfrac{1}{x}-\dfrac{1}{y}}{\dfrac{x}{y}+\dfrac{y}{x}}$

HA1-365: Solving Rational Equations

Like building blocks, mathematical concepts can be combined to form more complex structures. Combining your knowledge of adding and subtracting rational expressions and solving simple equations, you can solve complex rational equations. Remember that to add or subtract rational expressions, you must have a common denominator in each term. To solve rational equations, you must isolate the variable by performing the same operations on both sides of the equal sign.

Practice finding the least common denominators (LCD) to solve these simple equations. This also eliminates fractions from the equation before solving for x.

Example 1   Solve for x: $\dfrac{3}{x} + \dfrac{7}{4} = \dfrac{26}{4x}$

$\dfrac{3}{x}(4x) + \dfrac{7}{4}(4x) = \dfrac{26}{4x}(4x)$	**Step 1:** Identify the denominators: x, 4, and $4x$. The LCD is $4x$.
$\dfrac{3}{x}(4x) + \dfrac{7}{4}(4x) = \dfrac{26}{4x}(4x)$	**Step 2:** Multiply each term by $4x$ and simplify.
$12 + 7x = 26$	**Step 3:** The equation is cleared of fractions and can now be solved.
$12 + 7x - 12 = 26 - 12$	**Step 4:** Isolate $7x$ by subtracting 12 from each side of the equation.
$\dfrac{7x}{x} = \dfrac{14}{7}$ $x = 2$	**Step 5:** Divide both sides by 7.
$\dfrac{3}{x} + \dfrac{7}{4} = \dfrac{26}{4x}$ $\dfrac{3}{2} + \dfrac{7}{4} = \dfrac{26}{8}$ $\dfrac{12}{8} + \dfrac{14}{8} = \dfrac{26}{8}$ $\dfrac{26}{8} = \dfrac{26}{8}$	**Step 6:** Check.

Answer: $x = 2$

Example 2   Solve for x: $\dfrac{3}{8} - \dfrac{2}{6x} = \dfrac{5}{12x}$

$\dfrac{3}{8}(24x) - \dfrac{2}{6x}(24x) = \dfrac{5}{12x}(24x)$	**Step 1:** The denominators are 8, $6x$, and $12x$. The LCD is $24x$.
$\dfrac{3}{8}(24x) - \dfrac{2}{6x}(24x) = \dfrac{5}{12x}(24x)$	**Step 2:** Multiply each term by $24x$ and simplify.
$9x - 8 = 10$	**Step 3:** The equation is cleared of fractions and can be solved for x.
$9x - 8 + 8 = 10 + 8$	**Step 4:** Isolate $9x$ by adding 8 to each side of the equation.

$$\frac{9x}{9} = \frac{18}{9}$$

$$x = 2$$

Step 5: Divide both sides by 9.

$$\frac{3}{8} - \frac{2}{6x} = \frac{5}{12x}$$

$$\frac{3}{8} - \frac{2}{12} = \frac{5}{24}$$

$$\frac{9}{24} - \frac{4}{24} = \frac{5}{24}$$

$$\frac{5}{24} = \frac{5}{24}$$

Step 6: Check.

Answer: $x = 2$

You will use the same steps, even when you are solving more complicated rational equations.

Example 3 Solve for x: $\dfrac{5}{x-5} + \dfrac{2}{3} = \dfrac{9}{3x-15}$.

$x - 5$

3

$3x - 15 = 3(x - 5)$

Step 1: Look at the denominators and factor when possible. The LCD is $3(x - 5)$.

$$\frac{5}{x-5}[3(x-5)] + \frac{2}{3}[3(x-5)] = \frac{9}{3(x-5)}[3(x-5)]$$

Step 2: Multiply each term by $3(x - 5)$. After cancellation, multiply what is left.

$$\frac{5}{\cancel{x-5}}[3\cancel{(x-5)}] + \frac{2}{\cancel{3}}[\cancel{3}(x-5)] = \frac{9}{\cancel{3(x-5)}}[\cancel{3(x-5)}]$$

$$(5 \cdot 3) + [2(x-5)] = 9$$

$$15 + 2x - 10 = 9$$

$$5 + 2x = 9$$

$$2x + 5 - 5 = 9 - 5$$

$$2x = 4$$

$$\frac{2x}{2} = \frac{4}{2}$$

$$x = 2$$

Step 3: Solve the equation by isolating x using inverse operations.

$$\frac{5}{x-5} + \frac{2}{3} = \frac{9}{3x-15}$$

Step 4: Check.

$$\frac{5}{2-5} + \frac{2}{3} = \frac{9}{3(2)-15}$$

$$\frac{5}{-3} + \frac{2}{3} = \frac{9}{-9}$$

$$-\frac{5}{3} + \frac{2}{3} = -\frac{9}{9}$$

$$-\frac{3}{3} = -\frac{9}{9}$$

$$-1 = -1$$

Answer: $x = 2$

Work through two more examples, finding the LCD, clearing the fractions, and solving for x.

Example 4 Solve for x: $\dfrac{3}{x-4} + \dfrac{17}{x^2-7x+12} = \dfrac{5}{x-3}$

Step 1: Determine the LCD from the denominators. The LCD is $(x-3)(x-4)$.

$x-4$

$x-3$

$x^2 - 7x + 12 = (x-3)(x-4)$

Step 2: Simplify the equation. After cancellation, multiply what is left. In this case you will need to use the Distributive Property.

$$\frac{3}{x-4}[(x-3)(x-4)] + \frac{17}{(x-3)(x-4)}[(x-3)(x-4)] = \frac{5}{x-3}[(x-3)(x-4)]$$

$$\frac{3}{x-4}[(x-3)(x-4)] + \frac{17}{(x-3)(x-4)}[(x-3)(x-4)] = \frac{5}{x-3}[(x-3)(x-4)]$$

$$3(x-3) + 17 = 5(x-4)$$

$$3x - 9 + 17 = 5x - 20$$

Step 3: Solve for x using inverse operations.

$$3x - 9 + 17 = 5x - 20$$

$$3x + 8 = 5x - 20$$

$$3x + 8 - 3x = 5x - 20 - 3x$$

$$8 = 2x - 20$$

$$8 + 20 = 2x - 20 + 20$$

$$28 = 2x$$

$$\frac{28}{2} = \frac{2x}{2}$$

$$14 = x$$

Step 4: Check.

$$\frac{3}{x-4} + \frac{17}{x^2 - 7x + 12} = \frac{5}{x-3}$$

$$\frac{3}{14-4} + \frac{17}{(14)^2 - 7(14) + 12} = \frac{5}{14-3}$$

$$\frac{3}{10} + \frac{17}{196 - 98 + 12} = \frac{5}{11}$$

$$\frac{3}{10} + \frac{17}{110} = \frac{5}{11}$$

$$\frac{33}{110} + \frac{17}{110} = \frac{5}{11}$$

$$\frac{50}{110} = \frac{5}{11}$$

$$\frac{5}{11} = \frac{5}{11}$$

Answer: $x = 14$

Example 5   Solve for x: $\dfrac{5}{x+1} - \dfrac{3}{7x} = \dfrac{4}{x}$

$x + 1 = x + 1$

$7x = 7 \cdot x$

$\quad x = x$

Step 1: Determine the LCD, which is $7x(x+1)$.

$$\frac{5}{x+1}[7x(x+1)] - \frac{3}{7x}[7x(x+1)] = \frac{4}{x}[7x(x+1)]$$

$$\frac{5}{\cancel{x+1}}[7x(\cancel{x+1})] - \frac{3}{\cancel{7x}}[\cancel{7x}(x+1)] = \frac{4}{\cancel{x}}[7\cancel{x}(x+1)]$$

$$35x - 3x - 3 = 4(7x + 7)$$

$$35x - 3x - 3 = 28x + 28$$

Step 2: Multiply each term by the LCD.

$$35x - 3x - 3 = 28x + 28$$

$$32x - 3 = 28x + 28$$

$$32x - 3 - 28x = 28x + 28 - 28x$$

$$4x - 3 = 28$$

$$4x - 3 + 3 = 28 + 3$$

$$4x = 31$$

$$x = \frac{31}{4}$$

Step 3: Solve for x.

Answer: $x = \dfrac{31}{4}$

For each of the previous examples, you have been able to obtain a result that is a solution to each equation. You have assumed that each answer is a solution. However, since you are solving equations that involve rational expressions, there are restrictions on the possible value of the variable. Some values will make the denominator of the expression become zero, making the expression undefined. For this reason, it is necessary to check all results. It is possible to get an answer that is NOT a solution.

The next example illustrates this case.

Example 6   Solve for x: $\dfrac{5}{x-1} - \dfrac{6}{(x+2)(x-1)} = \dfrac{2x+7}{(x+2)(x-1)}$

Step 1:   Determine the LCD, which is $(x+2)(x-1)$.

Step 2:   Multiply each term by the LCD.

$$\frac{5}{x-1}[(x+2)(x-1)] - \frac{6}{(x+2)(x-1)}[(x+2)(x-1)] = \frac{2x+7}{(x+2)(x-1)}[(x+2)(x-1)]$$

$$\frac{5}{\cancel{x-1}}[(x+2)\cancel{(x-1)}] - \frac{6}{\cancel{(x+2)(x-1)}}[\cancel{(x+2)(x-1)}] = \frac{2x+7}{\cancel{(x+2)(x-1)}}[\cancel{(x+2)(x-1)}]$$

Step 3:   Solve for x.

$$5(x+2) - 6 = 2x+7$$
$$5x + 10 - 6 = 2x+7$$
$$5x + 4 = 2x+7$$
$$5x + 4 - 4 = 2x+7-4$$
$$5x = 2x+3$$
$$5x - 2x = 2x-2x+3$$
$$3x = 3$$
$$\frac{3x}{3} = \frac{3}{3}$$
$$x = 1$$

But if $x = 1$, then each denominator becomes zero and the expressions will be undefined.

Therefore, this equation has no solution.

It is important to verify that each result obtained is, in fact, a solution.

Answer: $\varnothing$

Problem Set

Solve the following for the given variable:

1. $\dfrac{a}{4} + \dfrac{a}{5} = 9$ **2.** $\dfrac{m}{6} + \dfrac{m}{4} = 5$ **3.** $\dfrac{a}{2} - \dfrac{a}{5} = 3$ **4.** $\dfrac{m}{5} - \dfrac{m}{3} = 2$ **5.** $\dfrac{2}{3x} + \dfrac{1}{4} = \dfrac{17}{12x}$

6. $\dfrac{1}{6a} + \dfrac{3}{8} = \dfrac{5}{3a}$ **7.** $\dfrac{2}{3x} - \dfrac{1}{6} = \dfrac{7}{9x}$ **8.** $\dfrac{5}{2a} - \dfrac{1}{4} = \dfrac{15}{6a}$ **9.** $\dfrac{3}{5}y - \dfrac{1}{2}y = 2$ **10.** $\dfrac{2}{3}x - \dfrac{3}{8}x = \dfrac{1}{2}$

11. $\dfrac{a-1}{a} - \dfrac{5}{3a} = \dfrac{1}{4}$ **12.** $\dfrac{2r-7}{5} = \dfrac{r}{6} - \dfrac{2r}{5}$ **13.** $\dfrac{2x-1}{5} = \dfrac{x+1}{2}$ **14.** $\dfrac{x}{x-2} = \dfrac{2}{x-2} + 3$

15. $\dfrac{2n}{3} - \dfrac{n+4}{2} = \dfrac{3n-1}{4}$ **16.** $\dfrac{2r-5}{r+2} - 3 = \dfrac{3}{r+2}$ **17.** $\dfrac{m}{m+5} = 3 - \dfrac{5}{m+5}$ **18.** $\dfrac{3x-4}{x-1} = 2 + \dfrac{x+4}{x+1}$

19. $\dfrac{3}{x-1} + \dfrac{1}{x(x-1)} = \dfrac{2}{x}$ **20.** $\dfrac{1}{x+3} + \dfrac{x}{(x+3)(x+1)} = \dfrac{1}{x+1}$

Graphs are common in many areas of our lives. In mathematics, we represent a number of different things with graphs, like equations, solutions to equations, or solutions to systems of equations. It is important to know how to read them. In this lesson, you will learn some basic concepts that will help you read graphs. A graph begins with something called a **coordinate system**. A coordinate system is made up of two number lines that intersect at zero, and are arranged so that they make a right angle. To understand how the coordinate system is set up, let's look at a regular, horizontal number line.

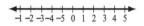

Notice how the zero is between the negative numbers and the positive numbers. The zero is called the **origin**, and the negative numbers go to the left, while the positive numbers go to the right. Now let's look at a vertical number line.

The zero is still between the positive and negative numbers, but this time the positive numbers go up, and the negative numbers go down. If you connect these two number lines at their origins, you get a coordinate system, like the one to the right.

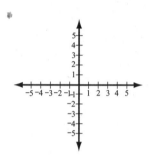

The point where the two number lines meet is called the **origin** of the coordinate system, and it is where both number lines are equal to zero. The horizontal number line is called the *x*-axis, and the vertical number line is called the *y*-axis.

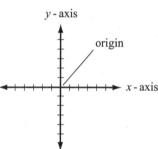

The coordinate system can be divided into four sections, called quadrants. The quadrants are named: Quadrant I (or QI for short), Quadrant II (QII), Quadrant III (QIII), and Quadrant IV (QIV). The top right quadrant is QI, and the others are numbered in a counter-clockwise fashion.

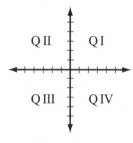

Every point in a coordinate system has a unique location, and a unique name based on that location. The name of a point is called an **ordered pair**, and it is written as (x, y). The x is the number that corresponds to the location of the point relative to the *x*-axis, and it is called the *x*-coordinate of the point. The y is the number that corresponds to the location of the point relative to the *y*-axis, and it is called the *y*-coordinate of the point. It is important to always write the *x*-coordinate first, followed by the *y*-coordinate.

Example 1   Graph the ordered pair (3,–2) and identify the quadrant where it is located.

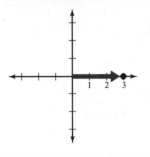

Step 1:   Starting at the origin, move three units to the right.

Step 2:   Move down two units and place your point.

Answer: The ordered pair (3,–2) is in the 4th quadrant.

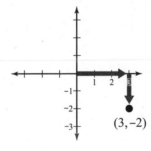

(3,–2)

Example 2   Graph the ordered pair (–2, 3).

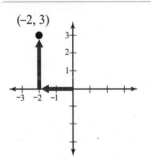

(–2, 3)

Step 1:   Start at the origin; move two units to the left.
Step 2:   Move three units up and place the point.

Answer: The ordered pair (–2, 3) is in Quadrant II.

There are two more important things to note. First, if you choose a point on the *x*-axis or on the *y*-axis, then that point is not considered to be in any of the four quadrants; it is on an axis. Second, the coordinates of the origin itself are (0, 0).

Example 3   Find the coordinates of the ordered pairs for each letter on the graph below.

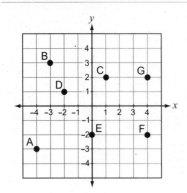

Answer: See the following table for answers.

For extra practice, look at the ordered pairs in the table below. Cover up the last column to see if you can determine the quadrant for each ordered pair.

Point	Coordinate	Quadrant
A	(−4,−3)	QIII
B	(−3, 3)	QII
C	(1, 2)	QI
D	(−2, 1)	QII
E	(0,−2)	Quadrantal Point (a point that lies on an axis)
F	(4,−2)	QIV
G	(4, 2)	QI

Problem Set

Identify the Quadrant (I, II, III, or IV), On the x-axis, On the y-axis, or On the origin for each of the following:

1. Identify the location of the point (3, 0) in the coordinate plane.

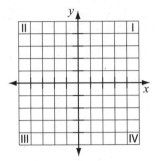

2. Identify the location of the point (0, –3) in the coordinate plane.

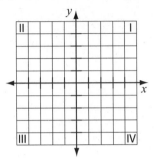

3. Identify the location of the point (3, –2) in the coordinate plane.

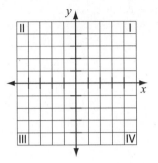

4. Identify the location of the point (–4, 2) in the coordinate plane.

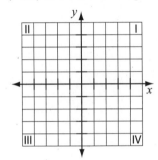

5. Identify the location of the point (–2, –3) in the coordinate plane.

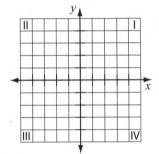

6. Identify the location of the point (0, 0) in the coordinate plane.

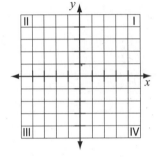

7. Identify the location of a point in the coordinate plane with a positive x-coordinate and a negative y-coordinate.

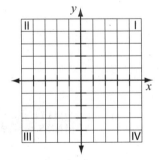

8. Identify the location of a point in the coordinate plane with a negative x-coordinate and a negative y-coordinate.

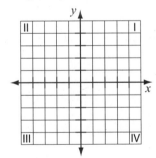

Solve:

9. Which graph shows the ordered pair (–2, 4)?

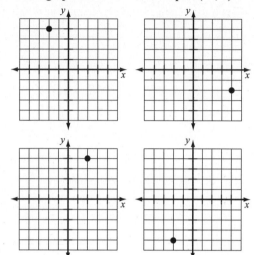

10. Which graph shows the ordered pair (–2, –4)?

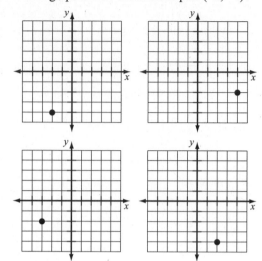

11. Which graph shows the ordered pair (–4, 1)?

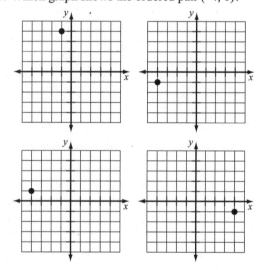

12. Which graph shows the ordered pair (3, –4)?

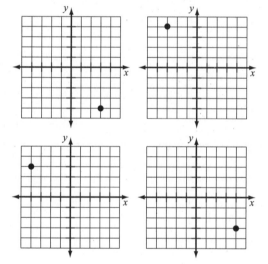

13. Name the point that is the graph of (–2, 0).

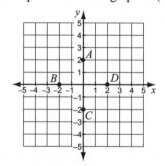

14. Name the point that is the graph of (1,–2).

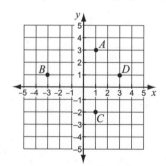

15. Name the point that is the graph of (0,–2).

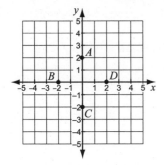

16. Name the point that is the graph of (3, 1).

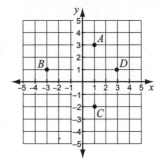

17. What is the ordered pair for point *L*?

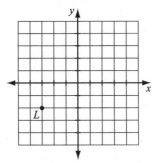

18. What is the ordered pair for point *R*?

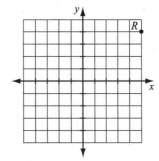

19. What is the ordered pair for point *K*?

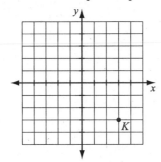

20. What is the ordered pair for point *M*?

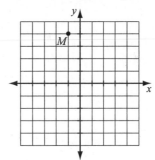

HA1-375: Identifying Solutions of Equations in Two Variables

Recall that an equation with only one variable has only one solution. For example, let's look at the equation $x + 5 = 8$. If you solve this equation, you get:

$$x + 5 = 8$$
$$x + 5 - 5 = 8 - 5$$
$$x = 3$$

and so you see that the solution to the equation $x + 5 = 8$ is 3. You don't stop there, though. You need to check this answer to make sure that it is correct. To check our answer, you go back to the original equation, and substitute our answer for the variable. In this case, you want to substitute 3 for x, which gives us:

$$3 + 5 = 8$$
$$8 = 8$$

Since it is true that 8 equals 8, we have verified that the answer is correct. In this lesson, you will move to the next step–finding solutions of equations with two variables. Here is an example of an equation with two variables, both to the first power: $x + y = 8$. The two variables are x and y. We say that they are both "to the first power" because they have no exponents. An equation like this one has many solutions. One possible solution is $x = 3$ and $y = 5$, because if you substitute 3 for x and 5 for y, you get $3 + 5 = 8$, which is true. When you have a pair of numbers for x and y like this, where both numbers must be used at the same time, you can write the numbers as an ordered pair. For example, you would write the pair $x = 3$ and $y = 5$ as the ordered pair (3, 5). Therefore, (3, 5) is a solution to the equation $x + y = 8$.

Remember that in ordered pairs, the x-value always comes first, and the y-value always comes second. Let's consider the ordered pair (1, 7) in relation to the equation $x + y = 8$. You want to determine if this ordered pair is a solution for this equation. To do this, you substitute 1 for x and 7 for y. This gives us $1 + 7 = 8$, which is true. Therefore, (1, 7) is also a solution for this equation. At this point, you should begin to see other possible solutions for this equation. As a matter of fact, the solutions for $x + y = 8$ are any pairs of numbers whose sum is 8. Can you think of other solutions?

Let's try some other examples. Remember that a solution to an equation with two variables is any ordered pair (x, y) that will make the equation true when the x-value is substituted for x in the equation, and the y-value is substituted for y.

Example 1   Determine whether or not the ordered pair (–3, 5) is a solution for $3x + y = -4$.

$3(-3) + (5) = -4$	**Step 1:** Substitute the ordered pair (–3, 5) for x and y.
$-9 + 5 = -4$	**Step 2:** Simplify the equation.
$-4 = -4$ true	
	Answer: The solution makes the equation true. Therefore, (–3, 5) is a solution.

Example 2   Determine whether or not the ordered pair (4, 0) is a solution for the equation $2x - 4y = 7$.

$2(4) - 4(0) = 7$	**Step 1:** Substitute the ordered pair (4, 0) for x and y.
$8 - 0 = 7$	**Step 2:** Simplify the equation.
$8 = 7$ false	
	Answer: Note that 8 does not equal 7. The statement is false. Therefore, (4, 0) is not a solution to this equation.

Example 3   Determine whether or not the ordered pair $(-5, 2)$ is a solution for the equation $8 - y = 6$.

$8 - (2) = 6$	**Step 1:** Substitute the ordered pair $(-5, 2)$ for x and y. Because there is no x in the equation, you can only substitute the y value.
$6 = 6$	**Step 2:** Simplify the equation.
	Answer: The equation is true; therefore, $y = 2$ is a solution. This is an equation with only one variable, so there is only one solution for the variable. Any ordered pair that has 2 for a y-value will be a solution to this equation.

Example 4   Determine whether the ordered pairs below are solutions for the equation $-x + 2y = 7$.
$$(-7, 0) \quad (5, 6) \quad (0, -7)$$

$-(-7) + 2(0) = 7$ $7 + 0 = 7$ $7 = 7$ true	**Step 1:** Substitute the ordered pair $(-7, 0)$, which gives $7 = 7$. Therefore, $(-7, 0)$ is a solution, since the equation is true.
$-(5) + 2(6) = 7$ $-5 + 12 = 7$ $7 = 7$ true	**Step 2:** Use the ordered pair $(5, 6)$, which gives $7 = 7$. The equation is true. This ordered pair is also a solution.
$-(0) + 2(-7) = 7$ $0 - 14 = 7$ $-14 = 7$ false	**Step 3:** Use the ordered pair $(0, -7)$. This gives $-14 = 7$, which is not true. This is not a solution to the equation.

Answer: The ordered pairs $(-7, 0)$ and $(5, 6)$ are solutions.

Note: This equation has two variables, so there are an infinite number of solutions.

Problem Set

1. Determine whether the ordered pair $(2, -3)$ is a solution to the given equation:
$$x + 3y = 11$$

    Not a solution   Solution

2. Determine whether the ordered pair $(6, 1)$ is a solution to the given equation:
$$2x - 3y = 9$$

    Not a solution   Solution

3. Determine whether the ordered pair $(1, -2)$ is a solution to the given equation:
$$x + 5y = -9$$

    Solution   Not a solution

4. Determine whether the ordered pair $(2, 4)$ is a solution to the given equation:
$$x - 4y = 0$$

    Not a solution   Solution

5. Determine whether the ordered pair $(2, -3)$ is a solution to the given equation:
$$2x + 3y = 13$$

    Solution   Not a solution

6. Determine whether the ordered pair $(-2, -8)$ is a solution to the given equation:
$$x + y = -10$$

    Not a solution   Solution

7. Determine whether the ordered pair $(5, -1)$ is a solution to the given equation:
$$5x + 4y = 21$$

    Not a solution   Solution

8. Determine whether the ordered pair $(2, 0)$ is a solution to the given equation:
$$6x + y = 12$$

    Solution   Not a solution

9. Determine whether the ordered pair $(-1, -3)$ is a solution to the given equation:
$$x - 5y = -14$$

    Solution   Not a solution

10. Determine whether the ordered pair $(-2, 3)$ is a solution to the given equation:
$$-2y - x = -1$$

    Solution   Not a solution

11. Which ordered pair is a solution for the equation?
$$3x + 2y = 2$$

    $(-4, 7)$ $(2, 2)$ $(7, -4)$

12. Which ordered pair is a solution for the equation?
$$2x - 3y = 6$$

    $(6, 2)$ $(-2, 0)$ $(0, 3)$

13. Which ordered pair is a solution for the equation?
$$5x - y = 17$$

    $(3, -2)$ $(0, -22)$ $(2, 2)$

14. Which ordered pair is a solution for the equation?
$$2x - 4y = -4$$

    $(-1, -4)$ $(1, 2)$ $(-4, -1)$

15. Which ordered pair is a solution for the equation?
$$x + 3y = 1$$

    $(0, 1)$ $(1, 0)$ $(2, 2)$

16. Which ordered pair is a solution for the equation?
$$2x - y = -14$$

    $(10, -2)$ $(-4, -6)$ $(-2, 10)$

17. Which ordered pair is a solution for the equation?
$$2x + 5y = 8$$

    $(1, 2)$ $(-1, 2)$ $(-6, 0)$

18. An airplane averaged 225 miles per hour on a trip. The equation $d = 225t$ can be used to calculate the distance, d, that the plane flies in t hours. On a trip to Mississippi, the plane flew for two hours and traveled 450 miles. Does this information satisfy the equation? Answer yes or no.

19. Harold averages 17 points per game in basketball. The equation $p = 17g$ can be used to calculate the total points, p, that he scores in g games. After 8 games, he scored a total of 135 points. Does this information satisfy the equation? Answer yes or no.

20. Heather averages 88 points per test in History. The equation $p = 88t$ can be used to calculate the points, p, that she totals in t tests. After 4 tests, she scored 352 points. Does this information satisfy the equation? Answer yes or no.

There are many ways to combine the various areas of mathematics, and the different combinations allow us to do different things. One useful combination is algebra and geometry. By pairing up these two areas of mathematics, you can display solutions to equations using the coordinate system. Graphing solutions of linear equations using this combination is the topic of this lesson. There are two ideas you should review before proceeding. First, remember how to verify solutions to two-variable equations. If you have an equation $5x + 2y = 9$, and you want to know if the ordered pair $(1, 2)$ is a solution, substitute the x-value, 1, for x in the equation, and the y-value, 2, for y. Then simplify the resulting equation. Doing this would give you the following:

$$5(1) + 2(2) = 9$$
$$5 + 4 = 9$$
$$9 = 9$$

Since it is true that $9 = 9$, the ordered pair $(1, 2)$ is indeed a solution to the equation $5x + 2y = 9$. Take this process one step further. Suppose that you want an x-value of 3 in your solution to this equation. To find the complete solution, you need to determine the y-value. To do so, substitute the x-value, 3, for x in the equation. This gives you $5(3) + 2y = 9$. This is an equation with one variable, which you can then solve:

$$5(3) + 2y = 9$$
$$15 + 2y = 9 \quad \text{simplify}$$
$$2y = -6 \quad \text{subtract 15 from both sides}$$
$$y = -3 \quad \text{divide both sides by 2}$$

Therefore, if you want x to be 3, then y must be -3. You have found a new solution to the equation, the ordered pair $(3, -3)$. You can also reverse this process: if you know what the y-value is, you can determine the x-value by substituting the value of y in the equation and solving for x.

The second idea to review is the concept of a coordinate system. Remember that a coordinate system is two number lines that intersect at their origins. The horizontal number line is the x-axis, and the vertical number line is the y-axis. Remember that the positive numbers on the x-axis go the right, while the negative numbers go the left. For the y-axis, the positive numbers go up, and the negative numbers go down. The point where the two number lines meet is called the origin. Here is a picture of a coordinate system.

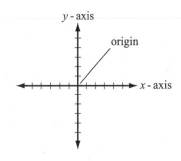

Also, remember that any point anywhere in a coordinate system has a name. The name of a point is called the coordinates of the point, and any pair of coordinates can be plotted. In this lesson we will focus on linear equations.

Linear Equation	A linear equation is an equation that can be written in the form $Ax + By = C$, where A, B, and C are real numbers and A and B are not both zero.

An example of a linear equation is the equation $5x + 2y = 9$. To understand the definition of a linear equation, think about the characteristics of a linear equation. One characteristic is that you must have at least one variable; either x or y, or both. This is why the definition says that A and B cannot both be zero; if both are zero, there are no variables. The other characteristic is that there are no visible exponents on the variables. This classifies the equation as linear.

You know that the solutions to linear equations are ordered pairs, and you also know that any linear equation has infinitely many ordered pairs as solutions. Since any given linear equation has an infinite number of solutions, there is no way to write down all the ordered pairs that are solutions. The graph of a linear equation is a way to represent all the ordered pairs that are solutions of the given linear equation, without actually listing every single ordered pair.

Example 1   Graph the line that contains the points (0, 3), (1, 0), (–1, 6), (2, –3).

Step 1:   Plot and label each ordered pair on the graph.   **Step 2:**   Draw the line that connects the points.

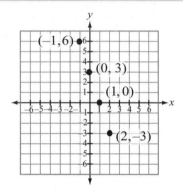 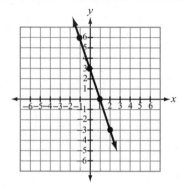

In this example, you were given a set of points, you plotted them and connected them with a line. Putting arrows on both ends of the line indicates that the line continues forever in both directions, meaning that the line is infinite. Any linear equation can be graphed in the same way. The graph of any linear equation is a line (notice the similarity between the words "linear" and "line"). To graph a linear equation, you need to draw a line. As you just saw in Example 1, to draw a line you need a collection of points. Then you can connect them and put arrows at the ends.

Recall the previous linear equation: $5x + 2y = 9$. You already know that the ordered pairs (1, 2) and (3, –3) are solutions for this equation, so you have two points on the line that will be the graph of this equation. To draw the graph, simply plot the two points and connect them with a line.

The result is the graph that you see here.

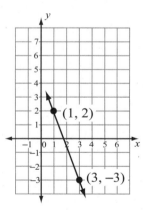

Once you have the graph of a linear equation, you can choose any point on that line, and the coordinates of that point will be a solution to the equation that is represented by the graph. For example, look at the new point shown on this graph, the point (–1, 7).

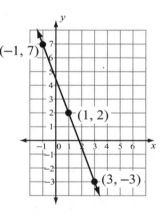

This coordinate pair should be a solution to the equation. To verify that it is a solution, substitute –1 for x and 7 for y, as follows.

$$5(-1) + 2(7) = 9$$
$$-5 + 14 = 9$$
$$9 = 9$$

Because $9 = 9$ is true, you have verified that the point (–1, 7) is a solution to the equation that you graphed. This will hold true for any point that you choose on the line.

Look at another example.

Example 2   Graph the equation $2x + 3y = 6$.

x	y
-3	
0	
3	

Step 1: You need to find solutions to this equation so that you will have ordered pairs that you can plot. To do this, create a table. In the left column, select some numbers to use as x-values. This example uses -3, 0, and 3, although any numbers will do. Now find the corresponding y-values.

$$2(-3) + 3y = 6 \qquad 2(0) + 3y = 6 \qquad 2(3) + 3y = 6$$
$$-6 + 3y = 6 \qquad 0 + 3y = 6 \qquad 6 + 3y = 6$$
$$-6 + 6 + 3y = 6 + 6 \qquad 3y = 6 \qquad 6 - 6 + 3y = 6 - 6$$
$$3y = 12 \qquad \frac{3y}{3} = \frac{6}{3} \qquad 3y = 0$$
$$\frac{3y}{3} = \frac{12}{3} \qquad y = 2 \qquad y = 0$$
$$y = 4$$

Step 2: To find the corresponding y-values for the table, take each x-value individually, substitute it for x in the equation, and solve for y. You will find that the y-values are 4, 2, and 0, respectively.

x	y	Ordered Pair
-3	4	$(-3, 4)$
0	2	$(0, 2)$
3	0	$(3, 0)$

Step 3: Fill in the y-values in the table, and write down the resulting ordered pairs.

Step 4: Plot the ordered pairs and connect them with a line, putting arrows on the ends of the line.

Answer:

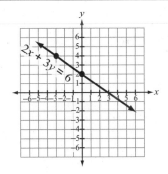

The x-intercept and the y-intercept are important points on any graph. They are the points, if any, at which the graph of an equation crosses, or intercepts, the x- and y-axes.

x-Intercept	The x-intercept is the point where the graph of an equation crosses the x-axis.

y-Intercept	The y-intercept is the point where the graph of an equation crosses the y-axis.

Look at the line in Example 2. The line crosses the x-axis at the point $(3, 0)$, so the x-intercept is 3. The graph crosses the y-axis at the point $(0, 2)$, so the y-intercept is 2. If you think about x-intercepts in general, you know that they will always be points that lie on the x-axis. Because they lie on the x-axis, their y-coordinates will always be zero. Likewise, y-intercepts will always be points that lie on the y-axis, and will therefore always have x-coordinates of zero. Look at the intercepts that you just found, $(3,0)$ and $(0,2)$, and notice where the zeroes are in these points.

One of the reasons that x- and y-intercepts are important is that they can be used to easily graph linear equations, as you will see in the next example.

Example 3   Graph the equation $x + 2y = 4$ by finding the x-intercept and the y-intercept.

x	y
0	
	0

Step 1: You are being asked to graph the equation by finding the x- and y-intercepts. So, instead of just filling in some random x-values in the T table, fill in 0 for x, which will give you the y-intercept, and fill in 0 for y, which will give you the x-intercept.

$$(0) + 2y = 4 \qquad x + 2(0) = 4$$
$$2y = 4 \qquad\qquad x + 0 = 4$$
$$y = 2 \qquad\qquad\quad x = 4$$

Step 2: Find the missing values for the table. First substitute 0 for x and find the missing y-value, then substitute 0 for y to find the missing x-value.

x	y	Ordered Pair
0	2	$(0, 2)$
4	0	$(4, 0)$

Step 3: Fill in the table and find the ordered pairs. You will find that the y-intercept is $(0, 2)$, and the x-intercept is $(4, 0)$.

Step 4: Plot the points and draw a line.

Answer:

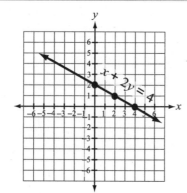

It is recommended that you always find three ordered pair solutions. If you make an error during calculations, the points will not line up. You must then check your work.

Let $x = 2$, then
$$2 + 2y = 4$$
$$2y = 2$$
$$y = 1$$

The third point is $(2, 1)$. Notice it is on our graphed solution.

The next example shows a special type of linear equation that has no y-intercept.

Example 4   Graph the equation $x = -2$.

x	y
-2	
-2	
-2	

Step 1: Create a table. As you look at this equation, though, you will see that the only x-value that is ever valid is -2. You cannot substitute any other value for x in this equation and have the equation hold true; therefore, you can only put -2 in the x column of the table.

x	y	Ordered Pair
-2	-3	$(-2,-3)$
-2	0	$(-2,0)$

Step 2: Fill in the y-values. Since there is no y in the equation at all, substituting the x-values for x won't tell you anything. Since there is no y in the equation, the y-values can be anything. You can just fill in some random numbers for y-values, and determine the resulting ordered pairs

Step 3: Plot the points and draw the line.

Answer:

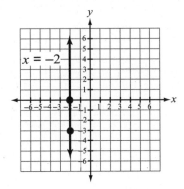

Notice in the above equation ($x = -2$) there was no y-variable, which means no y-intercept. No y-intercept means the graphed solution does not cross the y-axis, making the graph a vertical line. Similarly, a horizontal line would not cross the x-axis, so its equation would not have an x-variable.

Problem Set

Solve:

1. Which of the following graphs has an x-intercept of -4?

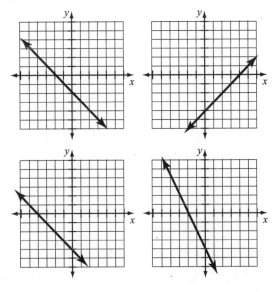

2. Which of the following graphs has a y-intercept of -2?

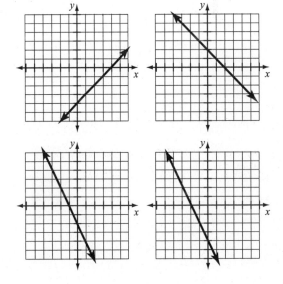

3. Which of the following graphs has an *x*-intercept of 1?

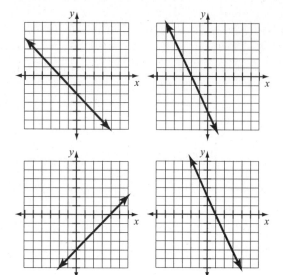

4. Which of the following graphs has a y-intercept of 4?

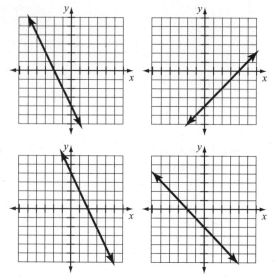

5. Find the *x*-intercept and *y*-intercept for the equation:

$$2x + y = -6$$

6. Find the *x*-intercept and *y*-intercept for the equation:

$$4x - y = 4$$

7. Find the *x*-intercept and *y*-intercept for the equation:

$$2x + y = -8$$

8. Find the *x*-intercept and *y*-intercept for the equation:

$$2x - 3y = -6$$

Graph the following equations:

9. $x - 5 = 0$

10. $y + 3 = 0$

11. $2x - 6 = 2$

12. $3y + 18 = 0$

13. $2x + y = -4$

14. $x + y = 7$

15. $x - y = -2$

16. $x - y = 3$

17. $4x - 3y = 12$

18. $2x + 4y = -16$

19. $3x - 5y = -15$

20. $4x + 3y = 12$

HA1-382: Solving Linear Equations Using the Graphing Calculator

Linear equations can be solved using the TI-83 Plus™ graphing calculator. To do this, we separate the equations and find the x-coordinate of the point where the graphs intersect. The calculator allows us to find this intersection point easily.

Our process has five steps:
- Step 0: (Settings) Initialize the calculator to a standard set of values so that we have a common starting point.
- Step 1: (Enter the expressions) Enter the symbolic form of the two sides of the equation to be analyzed.
- Step 2: (Graph) Obtain the graphs of the form $y =$ left-hand side and $y =$ right-hand side.
- Step 3: (Identify Intersection Point) Use other Intersect feature of the graphing calculator to verify the x-coordinate of the point where the graphs intersect.
- Step 4: (Solve) Use information about the x-coordinate of the intersection point to solve the original equation.

Note: Before doing any of these examples you should check your calculator's settings to be sure that it will function as described above.

Press the MODE key and be sure that your settings appear as shown below.

Next press the 2nd ZOOM keys and be sure that your settings appear as shown below.

Next press the ZOOM key then the 6 key to select the standard window setting.

Press the WINDOW key to get the following screen.

```
WINDOW
 Xmin=-10
 Xmax=10
 Xscl=1
 Ymin=-10
 Ymax=10
 Yscl=1
 Xres=1
```

Example 1   Use the graphing calculator to solve the equation $5x + 3 = 7$.

Step 0: (Settings) Make sure you have the default settings described above.

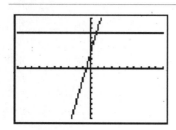

Step 1: (Enter the expression) Press the $\boxed{Y=}$ key and enter the expression $5x + 3 = 7$ into the Y_1 slot and 7 into the Y_2 slot.

Step 2: (Graph) Press the $\boxed{GRAPH}$ key. From the graph, we see that the two graphs intersect at a point in the first quadrant.

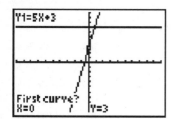

Step 3: (Identify Intersection Point) Next, we will find where the graphs of Y_1 and Y_2 intersect (the x-coordinate of this point is the solution to our original equation). This is done by pressing $\boxed{2nd}\boxed{TRACE}$ followed by $\boxed{5}$.

You will be prompted for the first curve with a screen like the one to the left. Press $\boxed{ENTER}$.

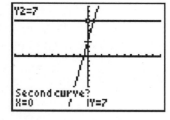

Now you will be prompted for the second curve with a screen like the one to the left. Press $\boxed{ENTER}$ again.

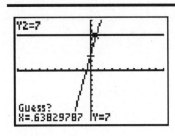

You will be prompted for a guess with a screen like the one to the left. Use the ◄ and ► keys to move the highlighted point as close as possible to the intercept you are trying to verify and press ENTER.

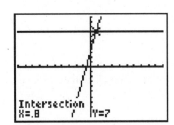

You should get a screen like the one to the left.

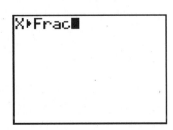

This gives an intersection point whose x-coordinate is 0.8. Convert this to fraction form by pressing the keys 2nd MODE to return to the home screen. Press the keys X,T,Θ,n MATH 1 to get the screen to the left.

Finally, press ENTER and you will see a screen like the one to the left.

So, our solution as a fraction is $x = \frac{4}{5}$.

Step 4: (Solve) The equation $5x + 3 = 7$ is satisfied by the value $x = 0.8 = \frac{4}{5}$.

Answer: The solution of $5x + 3 = 7$ is $x = 0.8 = \frac{4}{5}$.

Example 2 Use the graphing calculator to solve the equation $0.5(x - 2.4) = 4(0.2 - 0.5x) + 0.3$.

Step 0: (Settings) Make sure you have the default settings as described in the beginning of the lesson.

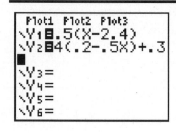

Step 1: (Enter the expression) Press the $\boxed{Y=}$ key and enter the expression $0.5(x-2.4)$ into the Y_1 slot and $4(0.2-0.5x)+0.3$ into the Y_2 slot.

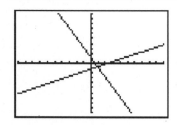

Step 2: (Graph) Press the $\boxed{\text{GRAPH}}$ key. We see that the two graphs intersect at a point in the fourth quadrant.

Step 3: (Identify Intersection Point) Next, find the place where the graph of Y_1 and Y_2 intersect (the x-coordinate of this point is the solution to our original equation). This is done by pressing $\boxed{\text{2nd}}\boxed{\text{TRACE}}$ followed by $\boxed{5}$.

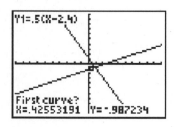

You will be prompted for the first curve with a screen like the one to the left. Press $\boxed{\text{ENTER}}$.

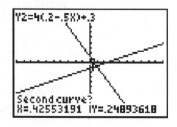

Now you will be prompted for the second curve with a screen like the one to the left. Press $\boxed{\text{ENTER}}$ again.

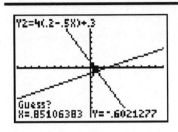

You will be prompted for a guess with a screen like the one to the left. Use the ◄ and ► keys to move the highlighted point as close as possible to the intercept you are trying to verify and press ENTER.

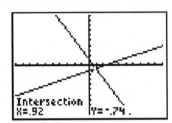

The calculator should display a screen like the one to the left.

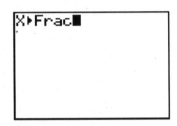

This gives us an intersection point with an x-coordinate of 0.92. Convert this to fraction form by pressing the keys 2nd MODE to return to the home screen. Next, press the keys X,T,Θ,*n* MATH 1 to get a screen like the one shown to the left.

Finally, press ENTER and you will get a screen like the one to the left.

So our solution expressed as a fraction is $x = 0.92 = \dfrac{23}{25}$.

Step 4: (Solve) The equation $0.5(x - 2.4) = 4(0.2 - 0.5x) + 0.3$ is satisfied by the value $x = 0.92 = \dfrac{23}{25}$.

Answer: The solution of $0.5(x - 2.4) = 4(0.2 - 0.5x) + 0.3$ is

$$x = 0.92 = \dfrac{23}{25}.$$

Example 3   Use the graphing calculator to solve the equation $5x - 23 = 40 - 2x$.

Step 0: (Settings) Make sure you have the default settings as described in the beginning of the lesson.

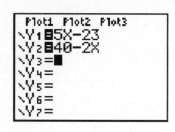

Step 1: (Enter the expression) Press the $\boxed{Y=}$ key and enter the expression $5x - 23$ into the Y_1 slot and $40 - 2x$ into the Y_2 slot.

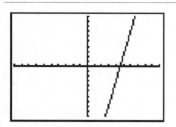

Step 2: (Graph) Press the $\boxed{\text{GRAPH}}$ key. Since we can only see one graph, the other graph (and the intersection point) must not be visible in this window.

Resize the window using the $\boxed{\text{ZOOM}}\boxed{3}$ keys and then pressing $\boxed{\text{ENTER}}$ again.

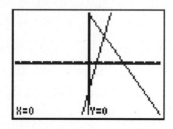

You should see the other graph appear as in the screen shown to the left.

Step 3: (Identify Intersection Point) Next, find the place where the graphs of Y_1 and Y_2 intersect (the x-coordinate of this point is the solution to our original equation). This is done by pressing $\boxed{\text{2nd}}\boxed{\text{TRACE}}$ followed by $\boxed{5}$.

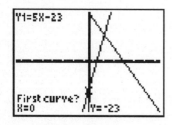

You will be prompted for the first curve with a screen like the one to the left. Press $\boxed{\text{ENTER}}$.

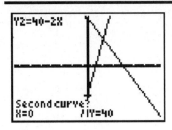

Now you will be prompted for the second curve with a screen like the one to the left. Press ENTER again.

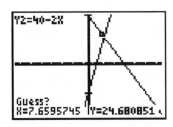

You will be prompted for a guess with a screen like the one to the left. Use the ◄ and ► keys to move the highlighted point as close as possible to the intercept you are trying to verify and press ENTER.

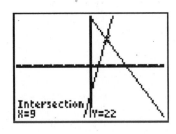

The calculator should display a screen like the one to the left.

This gives us an intersection point whose x-coordinate is 9. Therefore, our solution is $x = 9$.

Step 4: (Solve) The equation $5x - 23 = 40 - 2x$ is satisfied by the value $x = 9$.

Answer: The solution of $5x - 23 = 40 - 2x$ is $x = 9$.

Problem Set

1. Solve using the graphing calculator:
$$5x = 2x + 6$$

2. Solve using the graphing calculator:
$$27 = 6x - 3$$

3. Solve using the graphing calculator:
$$9(x - 8) - 4(x - 13) = 3x + 2$$

4. Solve using the graphing calculator:
$$-4x - 8 + x = 3 - 5x - 5 + 4x$$

5. Solve using the graphing calculator:
$$\frac{1}{3}x - 14 = 24$$

6. Solve using the graphing calculator:
$$\frac{x + 6}{4} - \frac{3x - 4}{2} = \frac{-1 - 2x}{6}$$

7. Solve using the graphing calculator:
$$5b + \frac{4}{3} = \frac{2}{9}$$

8. Solve using the graphing calculator:
$$2.4x - 11.01 = 7.23$$

9. Solve using the graphing calculator:
$$\frac{x + 1}{6} + \frac{3x + 1}{5} = 3 - \frac{7x + 1}{2}$$

10. Solve using the graphing calculator:
$$2.43x + 3.1 = 1.73(2x - 16) - 0.03(5x - 146)$$

HA1-385: Finding the Slope of a Line from Its Graph or from the Coordinates of Two Points

Think about the word "slope." What comes to mind? There are many images that can be associated with this word. One of them might be a tall, pointy roof on a house, or a snow-covered ski slope, or a tall, steep bridge or road. All these things have a common characteristic: a slanted surface. In each case, it is possible to talk about how steep that slanted surface is. This lesson discusses the idea of slope mathematically, that is, the measure of how steep a line is.

In previous lessons, you learned about different types of lines. Some lines slanted upward from left to right, while others slanted downward from left to right. Some lines were vertical, while others were horizontal. The slant of a line is referred to as its **slope**.

<table>
<tr>
<td>**Slope of a Line**</td>
<td>Slope of a line is the ratio of the change in the y-coordinates to the corresponding change in the x-coordinates. For any two points (x_1, y_1) and (x_2, y_2) on a line, the slope is found as
$$m = \frac{(y_2 - y_1)}{(x_2 - x_1)}$$</td>
</tr>
</table>

Example 1   Find the slope of the line that contains the points (1, 0) and (0, 2).

$m = \dfrac{y_2 - y_1}{x_2 - x_1}$

$m = \dfrac{2 - 0}{0 - 1}$

Step 1:   Substitute the given coordinates into the formula.

$m = \dfrac{2}{-1}$

$m = -2$

Step 2:   Simplify the expression.

Answer: The slope of the line with the ordered pairs (1, 0) and (0, 2) is –2.

Now that you have seen a concrete example of how to calculate slope, let's go back to the general idea. Another common way to think about slope is $\dfrac{\text{rise}}{\text{run}}$. The "rise" refers to the vertical change, which is the change in the y-coordinates. It is called "rise" because it indicates how many spaces up (or down) you have to count to get from one point on the line to another point. The "run" refers to the horizontal change, or the change in the x-coordinates. It is called "run" because it indicates how many spaces to the right (or left) you have to count to get from one point to another point.

Consider the line that you have drawn here, through the points $(-2, -3)$ and $(1, 4)$.

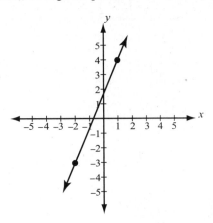

Using these points in the slope formula you see that the slope of this line is $\frac{7}{3}$. Suppose that you use these two points, and the portion of the line between these points, to draw a right triangle. Beginning with the point that is further to the left, $(-2, -3)$, you draw one leg of the triangle going straight up, until you are even with the other point. Then you draw the other leg of the triangle going to the right to touch the second point, $(1, 4)$. The result is what you see in the next graph.

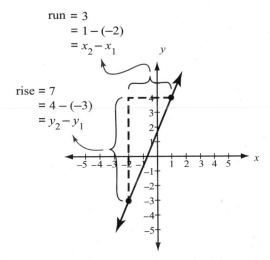

The vertical leg of the triangle is the rise. Looking at the graph, you can see that the length of this leg is 7 spaces. That is because you have to count up 7 spaces to get from the point $(-2, -3)$ to the point $(1, 4)$. Notice that this length is equal to the difference in the y-coordinates of the two points: $4 - (-3) = 7$. The horizontal leg of the triangle is the run. Looking at the graph, you see that the length of this leg is 3 spaces, because you have to count 3 spaces to the right to get from the vertical leg to the point $(1, 4)$. Notice how this length is equal to the difference in the x-coordinates: $1 - (-2) = 3$. You can use this $\frac{\text{rise}}{\text{run}}$ to find the slope of a line that has already been graphed.

The next example illustrates how to use this rise/run method.

Example 2   Find the slope of the line graphed below.

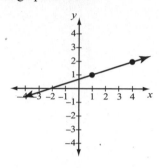

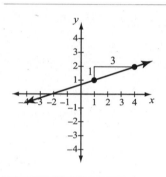

Step 1: Make the triangle as discussed above by drawing a vertical line up from the first point until it is even with the second point. Then draw a horizontal line from there to the second point.

$$\frac{\text{rise}}{\text{run}} = \frac{1}{3}$$

Step 2: Write the slope by putting the number of rise units, 1, over the number of run units, 3, to form the fraction $\frac{1}{3}$.

Answer: The slope is $\frac{1}{3}$.

Note that in Example 2 that, although the ordered pairs are not explicitly given, you could use the slope formula to find the slope of the line. In Example 2, instead of being given two points, you have a graph of a line. Once you choose two points on the line and determine their coordinates, you can use the coordinates in the slope formula. This is what you see in Example 3.

Example 3   Find the slope of the line graphed below.

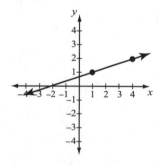

(1, 1) and (4, 2)

Step 1: Determine the coordinates of the indicated points.

$$m = \frac{2-1}{4-1} = \frac{1}{3}$$

Step 2: Use these coordinates in the slope formula.

Answer: The slope is $\frac{1}{3}$.

One thing to remember about the rise/run method is that the direction in which you count is very important. In Example 2, you counted up 1, and so you rose 1. If you had counted down instead, you would still have called it a rise, but you would have made it negative. For example, if you had to count down 3, you would say that the rise is –3, and you would put –3 in the numerator when you form the fraction in Step 2. Likewise, in Example 2, you counted to the right 3, and so you ran 3. If you had counted to the left instead, you would have had a negative run. For example, if you had to count to the left 5, you would say that the run is –5, and you would put –5 in the denominator when you form the fraction.

Why is the slope of a line important? The numerical value of the slope of the line tells you about the slant, or tilt, of the line, and how steep the line is. Notice that in Example 1, the slope that you found was negative, and, in Example 2, the slope was positive. Compare the graphs of the two lines from those examples. Looking at the two lines, you see that the first line has a negative slope, and the line is drawn down from left to right. The second graph has a positive slope, and the line is drawn up from left to right. Also, looking at the actual numerical values of the slopes, you see that $|-2|$ is greater than $\left|\frac{1}{3}\right|$, and the line with slope –2 is steeper. These observations follow the general rules. A line with negative slope goes down from left to right. A graph with positive slope goes up from left to right. The larger the absolute value of the slope of a line, the steeper the line. Let's consider two special cases: a vertical line and a horizontal line. Here is the graph of a vertical line, with the points (–2, 3) and (–2, 1) labeled.

Example 4   Find the slope of the line graphed below.

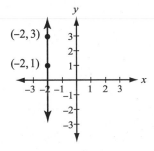

$$m = \frac{1-3}{-2-(-2)} = \frac{-2}{0}$$

Step 1: Calculate the slope using the slope formula.

Step 2: By calculating the slope of this line, you see that a zero results in the denominator of the fraction, which makes the fraction undefined. This will always happen with vertical lines, since the x-coordinates of all points on any vertical line are always the same. Therefore, vertical lines have undefined slope.

Answer: The slope is undefined.

Example 5 Find the slope of the line graphed below.

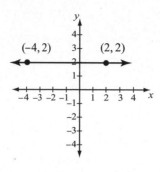

$$m = \frac{2-2}{2-(-4)} = \frac{0}{6} = 0$$

Step 1: Calculate the slope using the slope formula.

Step 2: By calculating the slope of this line, you see that a zero results in the numerator of the fraction, which makes the fraction itself equal to 0. This will always happen with horizontal lines, since the y-coordinates of all points on any horizontal line are always the same. Therefore, horizontal lines have a slope of 0.

Answer: The slope is 0.

Previously, you have chosen which point to use as (x_1, y_1) and which point to use as (x_2, y_2). It actually doesn't matter which set of coordinates you use as (x_1, y_1) and (x_2, y_2), as long as you don't change your mind halfway through the problem.

Example 6 Find the slope of the line graphed below, using the rise/run method:

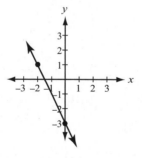

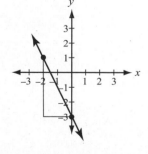

Step 1: Draw a vertical line down from the first point until it is even with the second point. Then draw a horizontal line from there to the second point.

Step 2: Find the rise by determining the number of units it takes to move downward from the first point to be even with the second point. The rise will be negative, because you are moving downward.

Step 3: Find the run by determining the number of units it takes to move right to the second point. The run will be positive, because you are moving to the right.

$$m = \frac{\text{rise}}{\text{run}} = \frac{-4}{2} = -2$$

Step 4: Put the number for the rise over the number for the run to form the fraction $\frac{-4}{2}$. Simplify the fraction. The slope is –2.

$$m = \frac{y_2 - y_1}{x_2 - x_1}$$

$$m = \frac{-3 - 1}{0 - (-2)}$$

$$m = \frac{-4}{2}$$

$$m = -2$$

Step 5: Using the coordinates: Substitute the coordinates of the points plotted on the graph into the slope formula. The coordinates are (–2, 1) and (0, –3).

Answer: The slope is –2.

Problem Set

1. Find the slope of the line containing the given points: (0, 0) and (2, 2)

2. Find the slope of the line containing the given points: (2, 3) and (3, 6)

3. Find the slope of the line containing the given points: (2, 1) and (6, 9)

4. Find the slope of the line containing the given points: (3, 9) and (4, 16)

5. Find the slope of the line containing the given points: (1, 6) and (3, 16)

6. Find the slope of the line containing the given points: (1, 2) and (3, 4)

7. Find the slope of the line containing the given points: (0, 3) and (5, 3)

8. Find the slope of the line containing the given points: (3, 2) and (5, 8)

9. Find the slope of the line containing the given points: (3, 0) and (4, 6)

10. Find the slope of the line containing the given points: (4, 4) and (6, 6)

11. Find the slope of the line containing the given points: (–10, 0) and (8,–6)

12. Find the slope of the line containing the given points: (–4, 2) and (–4,3)

13. Find the slope of the line containing the given points: (–6, 3) and (4, 1)

14. Find the slope of the line containing the given points: (1, 0) and (0,–4)

15. Find the slope of the line containing the given points: (0, 1) and (3,−2)

16. Find the slope of the line containing the given points: (−6,−7) and (−2,−8)

17. Find the slope of the line containing the given points: (−4,−2) and (−1, 0)

18. Find the slope of the line from its graph:

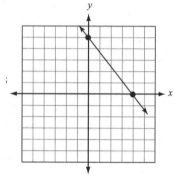

19. Find the slope of the line from its graph:

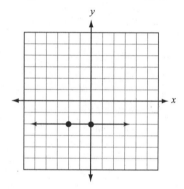

20. Find the slope of the line from its graph:

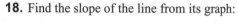

Linear equations, like $3x + y = 5$, have graphs in the coordinate plane that are represented by lines. If the linear equation is written in a different form, we can determine the slope and the y-intercept of the line. For example, the linear equation $3x + y = 5$ can be rewritten as $y = -3x + 5$. In this form, we can determine that the slope of the line is -3 (falls 3 units for each unit moved to the right) and the y-coordinate of the y-intercept is 5 [intersects the y-axis at the point (0,5)].

Notice that this information can be read directly from the form of the equation when it is written in the specific form $y = mx + b$, where $m = 3$ and $b = 5$. This form of an equation of a line is called the **Slope-Intercept Form**. The original form of the equation of the line $3x + y = 5$, is called the **Standard Form** ($Ax + By = C$, where $A = 3$, $B = 1$, and $C = 5$).

Note: The procedure for changing a line from standard form to slope-intercept form is to solve the equation for y and then to write the other part of the equation in the form $mx + b$.

Standard Form of a Linear Equation	$Ax + By = C$, where A, B, and C are real numbers (written in integer form when possible). $A \geq 0$, A and B are not both zero.

Slope-Intercept Form of a Linear Equation	$y = mx + b$, where m is the slope and b is the y-coordinate of the y-intercept $(0, b)$.

Example 1 Change the equation $4x + 5y = 10$ into slope-intercept form.

$4x - 4x + 5y = 10 - 4x$ **Step 1:** Subtract $4x$ from both sides of the equation.
$\quad\quad 5y = 10 - 4x$

$\dfrac{5y}{5} = \dfrac{10}{5} - \dfrac{4x}{5}$ **Step 2:** Divide both sides of the equation by 5.

$y = 2 - \dfrac{4}{5}x$

$y = -\dfrac{4}{5}x + 2$ **Step 3:** Write in the form $y = mx + b$.

Answer: $y = -\dfrac{4}{5}x + 2$

Note: In general, when changing a line given in slope-intercept form into standard form, we move all the terms with the variables x and y to one side of the equation, and the constant to the other side of the equation.

Example 2 Write the equation $y = 4x - 3$ in standard form.

$$-4x + y = 4x - 4x - 3$$
$$-4x + y = -3$$

Step 1: Subtract $4x$ from both sides of the equation.

$$-1(-4x + y) = (-1)(-3)$$
$$4x - y = 3$$

Step 2: Multiply both sides of the equation by -1 to make the coefficient of x positive.

Answer: $4x - y = 3$

Example 3 Write the equation of the line $3x - 5y = 4$ in slope-intercept form. Then use this form to find the slope and y–intercept of the line.

$$3x - 3x - 5y = -3x + 4$$
$$-5y = -3x + 4$$

Step 1: Subtract $3x$ from both sides of the equation.

$$\frac{-5y}{-5} = \frac{-3x}{-5} + \frac{4}{-5}$$
$$y = \frac{3}{5}x - \frac{4}{5}$$

Step 2: Divide both sides of the equation by -5.

$$m = \frac{3}{5}$$

y-intercept: $\left(0, -\frac{4}{5}\right)$

Step 3: Determine the slope and y-intercept using $y = mx + b$.

Answer: The line $3x - 5y = 4$ written in slope-intercept form is $y = \frac{3}{5}x - \frac{4}{5}$.

The line has slope $m = \frac{3}{5}$ and the y-intercept is $\left(0, -\frac{4}{5}\right)$.

Example 4 Write the equation $y = -\frac{1}{2}x - 1$ in standard form.

$$\frac{1}{2}x + y = -\frac{1}{2}x + \frac{1}{2}x - 1$$
$$\frac{1}{2}x + y = -1$$

Step 1: Add $\frac{1}{2}x$ to both sides of the equation.

$$2\left(\frac{1}{2}x + y\right) = 2(-1)$$
$$x + 2y = -2$$

Step 2: Multiply both sides by 2 since A, the coefficient of x, must be written in integer form when possible.

Answer: $x + 2y = -2$

Example 5   Write the equation $y = \dfrac{1}{4}x + \dfrac{5}{6}$ in standard form.

$-\dfrac{1}{4}x + y = \dfrac{1}{4}x - \dfrac{1}{4}x + \dfrac{5}{6}$ **Step 1:**   Subtract $\dfrac{1}{4}x$ from both sides of the equation.

$-\dfrac{1}{4}x + y = \dfrac{5}{6}$

$12\left(-\dfrac{1}{4}x + y\right) = 12\left(\dfrac{5}{6}\right)$ **Step 2:**   Since the coefficients of x and y (A and B) must be written in integer

$-3x + 12y = 10$ form when possible, multiply both sides by 12, the LCD of $\dfrac{1}{4}$ and $\dfrac{5}{6}$.

$-1(-3x + 12y) = (-1)(10)$ **Step 3:**   Multiply both sides by -1 since A, the coefficient of x, must be positive.

                         Answer: $3x - 12y = -10$

Problem Set

Write the following equations in slope-intercept form:

1. $6x + 3y = 7$ 2. $14x - 7y = -4$ 3. $12x + 3y = 24$ 4. $16x + 4y = -20$

5. $30x + 6y = 42$ 6. $18x + 3y = 5$ 7. $15x - 5y = 40$

Write the following equations in standard form:

8. $y = -8x + 4$ 9. $y = -12x + 7$ 10. $y = -11x - 32$ 11. $y = -7x - 8$

12. $y = 2x + 5$ 13. $y = 10x - 8$ 14. $y = 6x + 12$ 15. $y = 9x - 1$

Write the following equations in slope-intercept form:

16. $2x - 4y = 8$ 17. $7x - 3y = 12$ 18. $4x - 7y = 21$ 19. $10x + 8y = 32$

20. $11x - 9y = 27$ 21. $3x + 4y = 16$ 22. $12x + 5y = 25$

Write the following equations in standard form:

23. $y = -\dfrac{3}{5}x - 8$ 24. $y = -\dfrac{3}{4}x + 9$ 25. $y = -\dfrac{5}{6}x - 4$ 26. $y = -\dfrac{7}{9}x + 8$

27. $y = -\dfrac{8}{3}x + 16$ 28. $y = -\dfrac{5}{8}x - 7$ 29. $y = -\dfrac{4}{7}x + 9$ 30. $y = -\dfrac{9}{2}x - 13$

31. $y = \dfrac{1}{3}x + \dfrac{1}{5}$ 32. $y = \dfrac{3}{4}x - \dfrac{2}{5}$ 33. $y = \dfrac{2}{9}x + \dfrac{1}{3}$ 34. $y = \dfrac{5}{6}x - \dfrac{3}{4}$

35. $y = \dfrac{3}{8}x + \dfrac{1}{6}$ 36. $y = \dfrac{3}{7}x - \dfrac{2}{3}$ 37. $y = \dfrac{8}{5}x + \dfrac{4}{9}$ 38. $y = \dfrac{21}{4}x - \dfrac{1}{2}$

39. $y = \dfrac{2}{3}x + \dfrac{1}{6}$ 40. $y = \dfrac{3}{4}x + \dfrac{1}{7}$

HA1-395: Finding the Equation of a Line Parallel or Perpendicular to a Given Line

In previous lessons, you learned how to find the slope of a line given two points or a line on a graph. You also learned the different forms for the equation of a line. First, let's review the different forms for the equation of a line.

Standard Form for the Equation of a Line	$Ax + By = C$, where A, B, and C are real numbers, $A \geq 0$, and A and B are not both zero.

Slope-intercept Form for the Equation of a Line	$y = mx + b$, where m is the slope of the line and $(0, b)$ is the y-intercept.

Recall that the importance of writing an equation in slope-intercept form is that you can determine the slope and y-intercept from the equation of the line.

This is useful in determining whether two lines are parallel or perpendicular. Equations of lines that are parallel or perpendicular to a given line can be written using the relationship between their slopes.

Parallel Lines	Lines that lie in the same plane that do not intersect

For example, lines j and k are parallel lines.

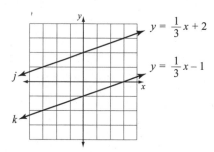

The equation of line j is $y = \frac{1}{3}x + 2$, and the equation of line k is $y = \frac{1}{3}x - 1$. Both of these equations are written in

the form $y = mx + b$, where m is the slope and $(0, b)$ is the y-intercept. Notice that both lines have a slope of $\frac{1}{3}$ and

their y-intercepts are different. Parallel lines have the same slope and different y-intercepts. **If m_1 and m_2 are slopes of parallel lines, then $m_1 = m_2$.**

Equations of lines that are perpendicular to a given line can be written using the relationship between their slopes.

Perpendicular Lines	Lines that intersect to form right angles, or 90-degree angles

For example, lines *l* and *n* are perpendicular lines.

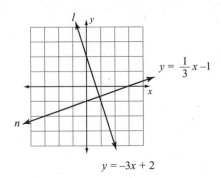

The equation of line *l* is $y = -3x + 2$, and the equation of line *n* is $y = \frac{1}{3}x - 1$. Both of these equations are written

in the form $y = mx + b$, where *m* is the slope and $(0, b)$ is the *y*-intercept. The slope of line *l* is –3 and the slope of

line *n* is $\frac{1}{3}$. The numbers –3 and $\frac{1}{3}$ are opposite reciprocals of each other. This means that their signs are opposites

and their absolute values are reciprocals. Perpendicular lines have slopes that are opposite reciprocals of each other.

If m_1 and m_2 are slopes of perpendicular lines, then m_2 is the opposite reciprocal of m_1.

Example 1   Write an equation of a line that is parallel to $y = 2x - 4$.

$y = mx + b$ $y = 2x - 4$ $m_1 = 2$	**Step 1:** Find the slope of the given line using the slope-intercept form of the equation of a line.
$m_2 = 2$	**Step 2:** Find the slope of the parallel line using the fact that parallel lines have the same slope.
$y = mx + b$ $y = 2x + b$	**Step 3:** Substitute into the slope-intercept form of the equation of a line and use any value for *b*, except for the value in the given equation.

Note that *b* can be any value except –4.   **Answer:** $y = 2x + 1$

Example 2   Find the slope of a line that is perpendicular to the line whose graph is shown.

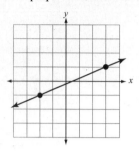

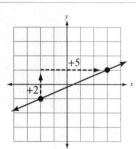

Step 1: Find the slope of the given line using $m = \dfrac{\text{rise}}{\text{run}}$.

The rise is 2 and the run is 5.

$$m_1 = \frac{2}{5}$$

The opposite reciprocal of $\dfrac{2}{5}$ is $-\dfrac{5}{2}$.

Step 2: Find the opposite reciprocal of m_1.

$$m_2 = -\frac{5}{2}$$

Step 3: m_2 is the opposite reciprocal of m_1.

Answer: $-\dfrac{5}{2}$

Example 3 Determine if the lines of the given equations are parallel, perpendicular, or neither.

$$x - 2y = 6$$
$$y = 2x + 3$$

$x - 2y = 6$ $-x + x - 2y = -x + 6$ $-2y = -x + 6$ $\dfrac{-2y}{-2} = \dfrac{-x}{-2} + \dfrac{6}{-2}$ $y = \dfrac{1}{2}x - 3$ $y = mx + b$ $m_1 = \dfrac{1}{2}$	**Step 1:** Find the slope of the first line by putting the equation in slope-intercept form.

$y = 2x + 3$ $y = mx + b$ $m_2 = 2$	**Step 2:** Find the slope of the second line. *Note: The equation is in slope-intercept form*

The lines are not parallel because the slopes are not equal. The opposite reciprocal of 2 is $-\dfrac{1}{2}$. Therefore, the lines are not perpendicular because the opposite reciprocal of m_2 is not equal to m_1.	**Step 3:** Compare the slopes.

Answer: Neither

Example 4 Write an equation in slope-intercept form for a line that is parallel to $5x + 2y = -8$ and passes through the point $(-4, 3)$.

$5x + 2y = -8$ $-5x + 5x + 2y = -5x - 8$ $2y = -5x - 8$ $\dfrac{2y}{2} = \dfrac{-5x}{2} - \dfrac{8}{2}$ $y = -\dfrac{5}{2}x - 4$ $y = mx + b$ $m_1 = -\dfrac{5}{2}$	**Step 1:** Find the slope of the given line by putting the equation in slope-intercept form.

$m_2 = -\dfrac{5}{2}$	**Step 2:** If m_1 and m_2 are slopes of parallel lines, then $m_1 = m_2$.

$$y = mx + b$$

$$3 = -\frac{5}{2}(-4) + b$$

$$3 = 10 + b$$

$$3 - 10 = 10 - 10 + b$$

$$-7 = b$$

Step 3: Since the parallel line passes through the point $(-4, 3)$, substitute $x = -4$, $y = 3$, and $m = -\frac{5}{2}$ into the slope-intercept form and solve for b.

$$y = mx + b$$

$$y = -\frac{5}{2}x - 7$$

Step 4: Now substitute the values for m and b into the slope-intercept form.

Answer: $y = -\frac{5}{2}x - 7$

Example 5   A city planner is drawing the roads for a development on a coordinate plane. One of the roads passes through the points $(1, 9)$ and $(5, 2)$. Find the equation in slope-intercept form of a second road that is perpendicular to the given road and passes through the point $(7, 4)$.

$$m_1 = \frac{y_2 - y_1}{x_2 - x_1}$$

$$m_1 = \frac{2 - 9}{5 - 1}$$

$$m_1 = -\frac{7}{4}$$

Step 1: Find the slope of the line for the first road using the formula for finding the slope of a line given two points on the line.

The opposite reciprocal of $-\frac{7}{4}$ is $\frac{4}{7}$.

Step 2: Find the opposite reciprocal of m_1.

$$m_2 = \frac{4}{7}$$

Step 3: m_2 is the opposite reciprocal of m_1.

$$y = mx + b$$

$$4 = \frac{4}{7}(7) + b$$

$$4 = 4 + b$$

$$4 - 4 = 4 - 4 + b$$

$$0 = b$$

Step 4: Since the perpendicular line passes through the point $(7, 4)$, substitute $x = 7$, $y = 4$, and $m = \frac{4}{7}$ into the slope-intercept form and solve for b.

$$y = mx + b$$

$$y = \frac{4}{7}x + 0$$

$$y = \frac{4}{7}x$$

Step 5: Now substitute the values for m and b into the slope-intercept form.

Answer: The equation of the second road is $y = \frac{4}{7}x$.

Problem Set

Solve:

1. Which equation of a line is parallel to the graph of $y = 8x - 3$?

$$y = -8x + 5 \qquad y = 8x + 5$$
$$y = -\frac{1}{8}x + 5 \qquad y = \frac{1}{8}x + 5$$

2. Which equation of a line is perpendicular to the graph of $y = 5x + 1$?

$$y = \frac{1}{5}x + 2 \qquad y = -\frac{1}{5}x + 2$$
$$y = -5x + 2 \qquad y = 5x + 2$$

3. Which equation of a line is parallel to the graph of $y = \frac{1}{2}x - 12$?

$$y = \frac{1}{2}x - 10 \qquad y = -\frac{1}{2}x - 10$$
$$y = 2x - 10 \qquad y = -2x - 10$$

4. Which equation of a line is parallel to the graph of $y = -4x + 2$?

$$y = 4x + 9 \qquad y = -4x + 9$$
$$y = \frac{1}{4}x + 9 \qquad y = -\frac{1}{4}x + 9$$

5. Which equation of a line is parallel to the graph of $y = -\frac{3}{7}x$?

$$y = -\frac{7}{3}x - 9 \qquad y = \frac{3}{7}x - 9$$
$$y = -\frac{3}{7}x - 9 \qquad y = \frac{7}{3}x - 9$$

6. Which equation of a line is perpendicular to the graph of $y = -3x + 6$?

$$y = -3x - 2 \qquad y = 3x - 2$$
$$y = \frac{1}{3}x - 2 \qquad y = -\frac{1}{3}x - 2$$

7. Which equation of a line is perpendicular to the graph of $y = \frac{2}{9}x$?

$$y = \frac{2}{9}x + 2 \qquad y = -\frac{9}{2}x + 2$$
$$y = \frac{9}{2}x + 2 \qquad y = -\frac{2}{9}x + 2$$

8. Which equation of a line is perpendicular to the graph of $y = -\frac{1}{2}x - 7$?

$$y = -2x - 4 \qquad y = 2x - 4$$
$$y = -\frac{1}{2}x - 4 \qquad y = \frac{1}{2}x - 4$$

9. Find the slope of a line that is parallel to the line whose graph is shown.

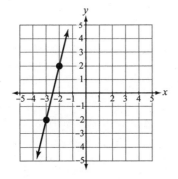

10. Find the slope of a line that is parallel to the line whose graph is shown.

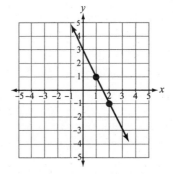

11. Find the slope of a line that is parallel to the line whose graph is shown.

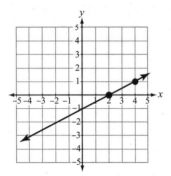

12. Find the slope of a line that is perpendicular to the line whose graph is shown.

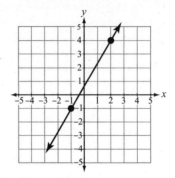

13. Find the slope of a line that is perpendicular to the line whose graph is shown.

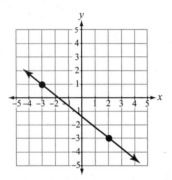

14. Find the slope of a line that is perpendicular to the line whose graph is shown.

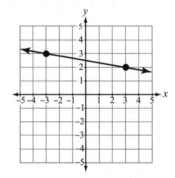

15. Find the slope of a line that is parallel to the line whose graph is shown.

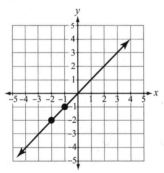

16. Determine if the lines of the given equations are parallel, perpendicular, or neither.

$$y = \frac{1}{2}x - 4$$

$$2y = x - 12$$

17. Determine if the lines of the given equations are parallel, perpendicular, or neither.

$$y = 3x + 2$$

$$2x - 6y = 9$$

18. Determine if the lines of the given equations are parallel, perpendicular, or neither.

$$5x + y = -1$$

$$x - 5y = 10$$

19. Determine if the lines of the given equations are parallel, perpendicular, or neither.

$$-3x + 2y = -8$$
$$y = \frac{3}{2}x$$

20. Determine if the lines of the given equations are parallel, perpendicular, or neither.

$$10x + 6y = 25$$
$$5x - 3y = 10$$

21. Determine if the lines of the given equations are parallel, perpendicular, or neither.

$$-3x - 6y = 19$$
$$y = 2x + 1$$

22. Determine if the lines of the given equations are parallel, perpendicular, or neither.

$$y = \frac{9}{2}x - 14$$
$$2y = 20x + 9$$

23. Determine if the lines of the given equations are parallel, perpendicular, or neither.

$$7x - 4y = -2$$
$$-14x + 8y = 5$$

24. Write an equation in slope-intercept form for a line that is parallel to $y = -3x - 1$ and passes through the point $(1, 4)$.

25. Write an equation in slope-intercept form for a line that is parallel to $y = \frac{3}{4}x + 9$ and passes through the point $(-8, 1)$.

26. Write an equation in slope-intercept form for a line that is parallel to $x + y = -3$ and passes through the point $(-7, 0)$.

27. Write an equation in slope-intercept form for a line that is perpendicular to $y = 4x + 5$ and passes through the point $(-4, -2)$.

28. Write an equation in slope-intercept form for a line that is perpendicular to $y = x - 7$ and passes through the point $(4, 1)$.

29. Write an equation in slope-intercept form for a line that is perpendicular to $x + 2y = 4$ and passes through the point $(-6, 8)$.

30. Write an equation in slope-intercept form for a line that is perpendicular to $-5x - 2y = 10$ and passes through the point $(5, 4)$.

31. The sides of a railroad track lie in parallel lines. When placed on a coordinate plane, one of the parallel sides lies on the line $x + 3y = 12$ and the other parallel side passes through the point $(3, 6)$. Find an equation of the other parallel side.

32. Two airplanes are observed on a screen that is on a coordinate plane. The first airplane is traveling at a constant speed so that its path lies on the line $6x + 5y = 10$. The second airplane is flying on a linear path that contains the point $(6, 12)$ and is perpendicular to the path of the first plane. Find an equation of the path of the second airplane.

33. The streets of a neighborhood are drawn on a coordinate plane. A man walked in the neighborhood along a street containing the points (5, 2) and (9, –2). A woman walked along a parallel street in the same neighborhood that contains the point (0, 3). Find an equation of the line containing the street on which the woman walked.

34. A piece of tile with perpendicular sides is placed on a coordinate plane as shown. Point A is at (–3, –1) and point B is at (1, –4). Find an equation of the line that contains points A and D.

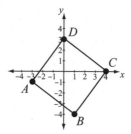

35. The equation of the line that models the population growth of deer in forest A is $y = 5x + 20$. The line that models the population growth of deer in forest B contains the point (2, 50) and is parallel to the line modeling population growth of deer in forest A. Find an equation of the line that models the population growth of deer in forest B.

36. Supply and demand equations are studied in economics classes. The supply equation for a certain product is $y = \frac{1}{5}x + 10$. The demand equation for this product describes a line perpendicular to the graph of the supply equation and it contains the point (5, 799). Find the demand equation for this product.

37. A plumber is laying two pipes that are perpendicular to each other. Pipe P contains the points (1, 1) and (4, 3). Pipe Q lies on a line perpendicular to pipe P and it contains the point (4, 8). Find the equation of the line containing pipe Q.

38. The lines on a highway lie in parallel lines. When placed on a coordinate plane, the equation describing the line on the left side is $x + 3y = 9$. The line on the right contains the point (3, 8) and is parallel to the line on the left. Find an equation of the line on the right.

39. Two trains are traveling on parallel railroad tracks. When placed on a coordinate plane, the first train passes through the points (–1, 2) and (3, 4). The second train passes through the point (6, –4). Find an equation of the line containing the path of the second train.

40. Mariah used a coordinate plane to draw perpendicular lines for an art project. The equation of the first line she drew was $x + y = 8$. The second line contained the point (4, 7) and was perpendicular to the first line. Find an equation of the second line.

HA1-398: Graphing Linear Equations Using Slope and *y*-intercept or Slope and a Point

In order to sketch the graph of a line, $y = mx + b$, we need to find two distinct points that lie on the line.

If we are given one point and the slope of the line, we can find a second point on the line using the slope.
- First, locate and plot the point that is given.
- Next, use the slope $m = \dfrac{\text{rise}}{\text{run}}$ to find the second point.
- Finally, draw a line through the two points to sketch the graph.

Using these steps, you can find a second point on a graph if you know one point.

Example 1   Sketch the graph of the line that passes through the point $(-2, 4)$ with slope, $m = -3$.

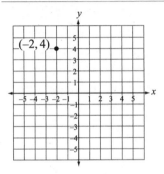

Step 1: Plot the given point, $(-2, 4)$.

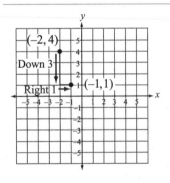

Step 2: Use the slope to find the second point. Since the slope, *m*, is equal to -3 or $-\dfrac{3}{1}$, move from the point $(-2, 4)$ down 3 units and to the right 1 unit to locate the second point, $(-1, 1)$.

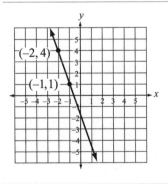

Step 3: Draw a line through the two points.

Answer: See graph in Step 3.

Example 2   Sketch the graph of the line $y = \frac{3}{2}x - 5$ using a point and the slope.

$m = \frac{3}{2}$

Step 1: Determine the slope of the line. Since the equation of the line is in slope-intercept form $y = mx + b$, we can see that the slope is $\frac{3}{2}$.

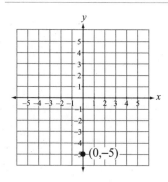

Step 2: Find a point on the line. Since the line is in slope-intercept form $y = mx + b$, we can see that the y-coordinate of the y-intercept is -5. Therefore, the point on the line is the y-intercept $(0, -5)$

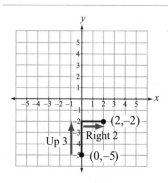

Step 3: Use the slope to find the second point. Since the slope, m, is equal to $\frac{3}{2}$, we move from the point $(0, -5)$ up 3 units and to the right 2 units to locate the second point, $(2, -2)$.

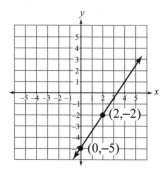

Step 4: Draw a line through the two points.

Answer: See graph in Step 4.

Example 3   Sketch the graph of the line that passes through $(-3, -5)$ with slope $\dfrac{7}{4}$.

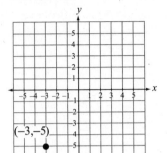

Step 1:   Plot the given point, $(-3, -5)$.

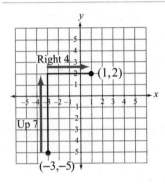

Step 2:   Use the slope to find the second point. Since the slope, m, is $\dfrac{7}{4}$, we move from the point $(-3, -5)$ up 7 units and to the right 4 units to locate the second point, $(1, 2)$.

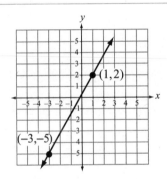

Step 3:   Draw a line through the two points.

Answer: See graph in Step 3.

Example 4   Sketch the graph of the line that passes through $(-3, 1)$ with slope $-\dfrac{4}{5}$.

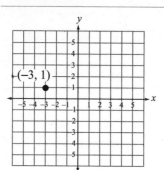

Step 1: Plot the given point $(-3, 1)$.

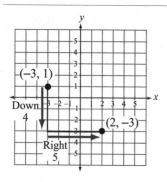

Step 2: Use the slope to find the second point. Since the slope, m, is equal to $-\dfrac{4}{5}$, we move from the point $(-3, 1)$ down 4 units and to the right 5 units to locate the second point, $(2, -3)$.

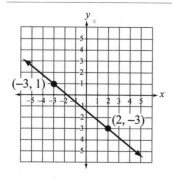

Step 3: Draw a line through the two points.

Answer: See graph in Step 3.

Example 5   Angela bought a condominium in 2003 for $120,000. The condominium increased in value by $5,000 every two years for the first seven years. Find the graph that represents the value of the condominium from the year 2003 to the year 2008.

$m = \dfrac{5,000}{2}$

Step 1: Determine the slope from the information given. The problem states that the condominium increases in value by $5,000 every 2 years. Therefore, the slope, m, is $\dfrac{5,000}{2}$.

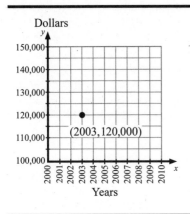

Step 2: Establish a point from the information given. Since the condominium was bought in the year 2003 for $120,000, the point on the line is (2003, 120,000).

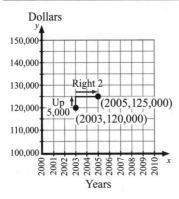

Step 3: Use the slope and point to find the second point. Since the slope is $\frac{5,000}{2}$, move up 5,000 units and to the right 2 units to locate the second point, (2005, 125,000).

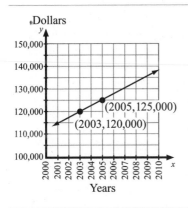

Step 4: Draw a line through the 2 points.

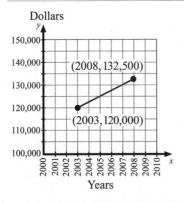

Step 5: Delete the sections to the left of 2003 and to the right of 2008.

Answer: See graph in Step 5.

Problem Set

1. Graph the line that passes through the point (3, 1) and has a slope of 2.

2. Graph the line that passes through the point (−1, 4) and has a slope of 2.

3. Graph the line that passes through the point (−3, −2) and has a slope of 3.

4. Graph the line that passes through the point (5, −4) and has a slope of 1.

5. Graph the line that passes through the point (−4, 0) and has a slope of 1.

6. Graph the line that passes through the point (−5, −6) and has a slope of 2.

7. Graph the line that passes through the point (−4, −7) and has a slope of 8.

8. Graph the line that passes through the point (10, −3) and has a slope of 4.

9. Graph the equation using the slope and y-intercept: $y = 2x - 4$.

10. Graph the equation using the slope and y-intercept: $y = 3x + 1$.

11. Graph the equation using the slope and y-intercept: $y = 4x - 5$.

12. Graph the equation using the slope and y-intercept: $y = 2x + 5$.

13. Graph the equation using the slope and y-intercept: $y = 6x - 1$.

14. Graph the equation using the slope and y-intercept: $y = 5x - 5$.

15. Graph the equation using the slope and y-intercept: $y = 7x - 3$.

16. Graph the line that passes through the point (3, −2) and has a slope of $\frac{4}{3}$.

17. Graph the line that passes through the point (−4, −6) and has a slope of $\frac{1}{3}$.

18. Graph the line that passes through the point (−7, 2) and has a slope of $\frac{3}{4}$.

19. Graph the line that passes through the point (−10, −1) and has a slope of $\frac{5}{6}$.

20. Graph the line that passes through the point (−2, 4) and has a slope of $\frac{2}{5}$.

21. Graph the line that passes through the point (3, 0) and has a slope of $\frac{2}{3}$.

22. Graph the line that passes through the point (2, 5) and has a slope of $\frac{1}{2}$.

23. Graph the line that passes through the point (4, −3) and has a slope of $\frac{4}{5}$.

24. Graph the equation using the slope and y-intercept: $y = -\frac{2}{3}x + 1$.

25. Graph the equation using the slope and y-intercept: $y = -\frac{1}{2}x - 4$.

26. Graph the equation using the slope and y-intercept: $y = -\frac{3}{5}x + 4$.

27. Graph the equation using the slope and y-intercept: $y = -\frac{1}{4}x - 5$.

28. Graph the equation using the slope and y-intercept: $y = -\frac{1}{3}x + 2$.

29. Graph the equation using the slope and y-intercept: $y = -\dfrac{1}{6}x - 3$.

30. Graph the equation using the slope and y-intercept: $y = -\dfrac{2}{5}x + 3$.

31. Sean bought a new motorcycle in 2000 for $11,500. The value of the motorcycle depreciates $2,000 per year for the first three years. Find the graph that represents the depreciation of the motorcycle from the year 2000 to the year 2003.

32. Carolina bought a new car in 2000 for $18,500. The value of the car depreciates $2,500 per year for the first three years. Find the graph that represents the depreciation of value of the car from the beginning of 2000 to the beginning of 2003.

33. Bryant bought a new sports car in 2002 for $45,000. The value of the car depreciates $2,500 per year for the first three years. Find the graph that represents the depreciation of the value of the sports car from the beginning of 2002 to the beginning of 2005.

34. The initial temperature of a cup of coffee is 200° F. The cup of coffee is left on a table to cool down. The temperature of the coffee cools down by 40° per hour for the first three hours. Find the graph that represents the temperature of the cup of coffee over the first three hours.

35. A particular stock is said to increase $50 each year, on average. Your initial investment in this stock is $500. Find the graph that represents the value of your stock over the next ten years.

36. A particular stock is said to increase $50 each year, on average. Your initial investment in this stock is $600. Find the graph that represents the value of your stock over the next six years.

37. Sharon is saving her babysitting money for college. She currently has $50 saved at home in her piggy bank. She plans to babysit this summer, charging $5 per hour. Find the graph that represents the amount she has earned after babysitting 10 hours during the summer.

38. Marissa is saving her babysitting money for college. She currently has $40 saved at home in her piggy bank. She plans to babysit this summer, charging $5 per hour. Find the graph that represents the amount she has after babysitting 10 hours during the summer.

39. An organization is raising money throughout the school year. Their beginning balance is $350. They anticipate earnings of $125 for each fundraiser. Find the graph that represents the balance amount that they anticipate having after three fundraisers.

40. Over the past 5 years the total amount of rainfall in a certain region has been decreasing at the rate of $\dfrac{1}{3}$ inch per year. At the beginning of the 5-year period, the amount of rainfall per year was 6 inches. Find the graph of the rainfall amounts in this region over the 5-year period.

HA1-401: How Variations of "*m*" and "*b*" Affect the Graph of $y = mx + b$

Linear equations written in slope-intercept form, $(y = mx + b)$, have graphs with slope m and y-intercept (0, b). The slope is written in the form $m = \dfrac{\text{rise}}{\text{run}}$. The "rise" refers to the vertical change in the y-coordinates. The "run" refers to the horizontal change in the x-coordinates. For example, the line $y = 3x + 2$ has slope $m = 3$ and y-intercept (0, 2).

The slope determines the direction of the line. In other words, the slope measures how fast the line rises or falls as it moves from left to right on the graph. Lines with positive slopes rise from left to right. Lines with negative slopes fall from left to right.

The slope also determines the inclination of the line. If the slope, m, is equal to 1, the line forms a 45° angle with respect to the x-axis. If the slope is greater than 1, the inclination of the line increases and the line rises toward the y-axis. If the slope is less than 1, the inclination of the line decreases and the line falls toward the x-axis. The slope of a horizontal line is neither positive nor negative and it neither falls nor rises. The slope of the vertical line is always undefined.

The y-coordinate, b, of the linear equation $y = mx + b$ determines the y-intercept of the line. If b is positive, the line is shifted b units up on the y-axis. If b is negative, the line is shifted b units down on the y-axis.

Example 1   Determine the direction of the equation $y = -5x$.

$m = -5$	**Step 1:** Determine the slope of the line.
	Step 2: Since the slope is negative, the line falls downward from left to right.
	Answer: The line falls downward from left to right.

Example 2   Sketch the graphs of the three lines $y = 3x + 2$, $y = x + 2$, and $y = -4x + 2$, and observe the effect of changing the slope of the line.

y-intercepts: (0, 2)	**Step 1:** Notice that these linear equations are all in slope-intercept form and have the same y-intercept.
$m_1 = 3$ $m_2 = 1$ $m_3 = -4$	**Step 2:** Notice the slope of each line. The first line, $y = 3x + 2$, has slope 3. The second line, $y = x + 2$, has slope 1 and the last line, $y = -4x + 2$, has slope -4.

Line 1: $y = 3x + 2$

First point: $(0, 2)$

Second point: $(1, 5)$

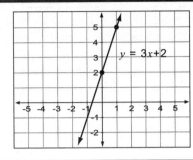

Step 3: To graph the first line, $y = 3x + 2$, start at the y-intercept, $(0, 2)$, and move up 3 units and to the right 1 unit (since the slope is $m = 3 = \frac{3}{1}$) to locate the second point, $(1, 5)$. Then, draw a line through the points.

Line 2: $y = x + 2$

First point: $(0, 2)$

Second point: $(1, 3)$

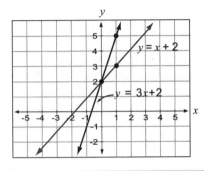

Step 4: To graph the next line, $y = x + 2$, start at the y-intercept $(0, 2)$ and move up 1 unit and to the right 1 unit (since the slope of the second line is $m = 1 = \frac{1}{1}$) to locate the second point $(1, 3)$. Then, draw a line through the points.

Line 3: $y = -4x + 2$

First point: $(0, 2)$

Second point: $(1, -2)$

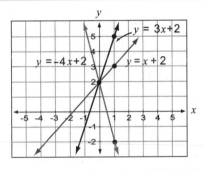

Step 5: To graph the last line, $y = -4x + 2$, start at the point $(0, 2)$ and move down 4 units and to the right 1 unit (since the slope of the second line is $m = -4 = -\frac{4}{1}$) to locate the second point $(1, -2)$. Then, draw a line through the points.

Answer: As the absolute value of the slope gets larger, the line is closer to becoming a vertical line.

If the slope is held constant, then variations in b correspond to parallel shifts of the line that pass through their new y-intercept. Consider the following example.

Example 3 Sketch the lines $y = 3x + 2$, $y = 3x$, and $y = 3x - 4$ on the same coordinate system and observe the effect of changing the y-intercept.

$$\text{Slope} = m = 3 = \frac{3}{1}$$

Step 1: Notice that each of these lines is given in slope-intercept form and that each line has the same slope.

$b_1 = 2$

$b_2 = 0$

$b_3 = -4$

Step 2: Determine the y-coordinates of the y-intercepts for the three lines.

y_1 – intercept (0, 2)

y_2 – intercept (0, 0)

y_3 – intercept (0, -4)

Step 3: Determine the y-intercepts of the three lines. The first line has the y-intercept (0, 2) since $b_1 = 2$. The second line has the y-intercept (0, 0) since $b_2 = 0$. The last line has the y-intercept (0, −4) since $b_3 = -4$.

Line 1: $y = 3x + 2$

First point: (0, 2)

Second point: (1, 5)

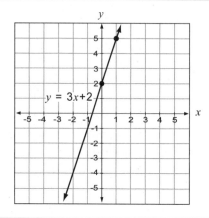

Step 4: To graph the first line, $y = 3x + 2$, start by plotting the point (0, 2) and move up 3 units and to the right 1 unit to the point (1, 5).

Line 2: $y = 3x$

First point: (0, 0)

Second point: (1, 3)

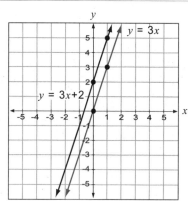

Step 5: To graph the second line, $y = 3x$, start by plotting the point (0, 0) and move up 3 units and to the right 1 unit to the point (1, 3).

Line 3: $y = 3x - 4$

First point: (0, −4)

Second point: (1, −1)

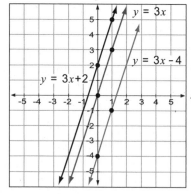

Step 6: To graph the last line, $y = 3x - 4$, start by plotting the point (0, −4) and move up 3 units and to the right 1 unit to the point (1, −1).

Answer: Note that the lines are parallel. The effect of changing the y-intercept causes the graphs to shift up or down.

Example 4   For the given equation of a line, $y = -\frac{2}{7}x + 5$, use the slope to estimate the measure of the angle formed with respect to the x-axis.

$m = -\frac{2}{7}$	**Step 1:** Determine the slope of the line.
$\left|-\frac{2}{7}\right| < 1$	**Step 2:** Take the absolute value of the slope and see if it is less than, greater than, or equal to 1.
	Step 3: Since the absolute value of the slope is less than one, the angle is less than $45°$.
	Answer: The measure of the angle formed with respect to the x-axis is less than $45°$.

Example 5   Compare the slopes and y-intercepts of the lines shown in the given graph.

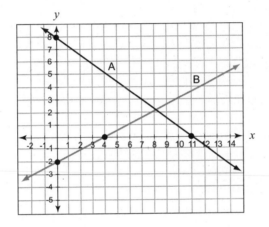

$m_A < 0$ $m_B > 0$ $m_A < 0 < m_B$	**Step 1:** The slope of line A is negative since it falls from left to right; the slope of line B is positive since it rises from left to right. Combining the statements, we see that the slope of line B is greater than zero, which is greater than the slope of line A.
$b_B < b_A$	**Step 2:** The value of b is the y-coordinate of the y-intercept. The y-intercept for line A is $(0, 8)$ and the y-intercept for line B is $(0, -2)$. Therefore, $b_A = 8$ and $b_B = -2$. This means that b_B is smaller than b_A.
$m_A < 0$ $m_B > 0$ $m_A < 0 < m_B$ $b_B < b_A$	**Answer:** The slope of line B is greater than the slope of line A, and the y-coordinate of line B is smaller than the y-coordinate of line A.

Problem Set

Evaluate.

1. Which of the following equations describes a line that rises upward from left to right and has positive direction?

$$y = 0x \qquad y = -10x$$

$$y = 10 \qquad y = 10x$$

2. Which equation matches the line graphed below?

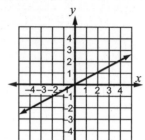

$$y = -2x$$

$$y = \frac{1}{2}x$$

$$y = 0$$

$$y = -\frac{1}{2}x$$

3. Which of the following equations describes a line that falls downward from left to right and has negative direction?

$$y = -8 \qquad y = 8x,$$

$$y = \frac{3}{8}x \qquad y = -8x$$

4. Which equation matches the line graphed below?

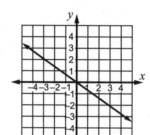

$$y = 2x$$

$$y = -\frac{2}{3}x$$

$$y = -2$$

$$y = \frac{3}{2}x$$

5. Which of the following equations describes a line that rises upward from left to right and has positive direction?

$$y = -\frac{2}{7}x \qquad y = 0$$

$$y = -\frac{1}{7}x \qquad y = \frac{3}{7}x$$

6. Which equation matches the line graphed below?

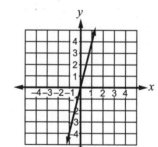

$$y = -4x$$

$$y = 4x$$

$$y = -\frac{1}{4}x$$

$$y = 0$$

7. Which of the following equations describes a line that falls downward from left to right and has negative direction?

$$y = \frac{1}{7}x \qquad y = -7x$$

$$y = 7x \qquad y = -7$$

8. Which equation matches the line graphed below?

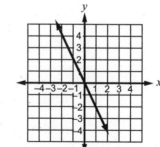

$$y = 2x$$

$$y = -2$$

$$y = -2x$$

$$y = \frac{1}{2}x$$

9. Which of the following equations describes a line that rises upward from left to right and has positive direction?

$$y = -x \qquad y = x$$

$$y = -2x \qquad y = 1$$

10. Which equation matches the line graphed below?

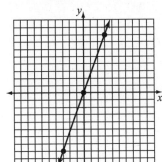

$$y = \frac{8}{3}x$$

$$y = -2x$$

$$y = -\frac{5}{2}x$$

$$y = 0$$

11. Which of the following equations describes a line that falls downward from left to right and has negative direction?

$$y = -\frac{2}{7} \qquad y = -\frac{2}{7}x$$

$$y = \frac{7}{2}x \qquad y = \frac{2}{7}x$$

12. Which equation matches the line graphed below?

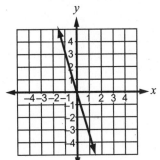

$$y = -\frac{10}{3}$$

$$y = -\frac{10}{3}x$$

$$y = \frac{10}{3}x$$

$$y = 3x$$

13. Which of the following equations describes a line that rises upward from left to right and has positive direction?

$$y = -\frac{1}{9}x \qquad y = -9x$$

$$y = 9x \qquad y = 9$$

14. Which equation matches the line graphed below?

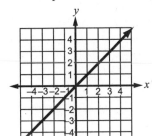

$$y = x$$

$$y = -x$$

$$y = 0x$$

$$y = 1$$

15. Which of the following equations describes a line that neither falls nor rises from left to right?

$$y = 10x \qquad x = 0$$

$$y = 0 \qquad y = -\frac{1}{10}x$$

16. Use the given graph of the line $y = -\frac{1}{4}x$ as a point of reference to describe how we may obtain the graph of the line $y = -\frac{1}{4}x - 5$.

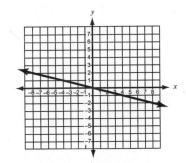

17. For the given equation of a line, $y = -\frac{1}{4}x$, use the slope to estimate the measure of the angle formed with respect to the x-axis.

       The angle is equal to $0°$.

       The angle is less than $45°$.

       The angle is greater than $45°$.

       The angle is equal to $45°$.

18. Use the given graph of the line $y = 2x$ as a point of reference to describe how we may obtain the graph of the line $y = 2x + 6$.

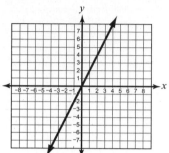

19. For the given equation of a line, $y = x - 10$, use the slope to estimate the measure of the angle formed with respect to the x-axis.

       The angle is less than $45°$.

       The angle is equal to $0°$.

       The angle is greater than $45°$.

       The angle is equal to $45°$.

20. Use the given graph of the line $y = -\frac{1}{2}x$ as a point of reference to describe how we may obtain the graph of the line $y = -\frac{1}{2}x - 4$.

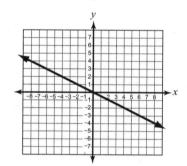

21. For the given equation of a line, $y = -2x + 3$, use the slope to estimate the measure of the angle formed with respect to the x-axis.

       The angle is equal to $45°$.

       The angle is equal to $0°$.

       The angle is greater than $45°$.

       The angle is less than $45°$.

22. Use the given graph of the line $y = -x$ as a point of reference to describe how we may obtain the graph of the line $y = -x + 3$.

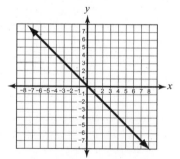

23. For the given equation of a line, $y = \frac{7}{5}x$, use the slope to estimate the measure of the angle formed with respect to the x-axis.

    The angle is greater than $45°$.

    The angle is equal to $45°$.

    The angle is less than $45°$.

    The angle is equal to $0°$.

24. Use the given graph of the line $y = x$ as a point of reference to describe how we may obtain the graph of the line $y = x - 6$.

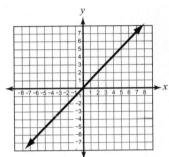

25. For the given equation of a line, $y = -x - 4$, use the slope to estimate the measure of the angle formed with respect to the x-axis.

    The angle is less than $45°$.

    The angle is greater than $45°$.

    The angle is equal to $45°$.

    The angle is equal to $0°$.

26. Use the given graph of the line $y = \frac{1}{2}x$ as a point of reference to describe how we may obtain the graph of the line $y = \frac{1}{2}x + \frac{8}{3}$.

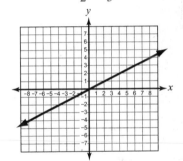

27. For the given equation of a line, $y = \frac{1}{8}x$, use the slope to estimate the measure of the angle formed with respect to the x-axis.

    The angle is equal to $45°$.

    The angle is greater than $45°$.

    The angle is equal to $0°$.

    The angle is less than $45°$.

28. Use the given graph of the line $y = -\frac{1}{5}x$ as a point of reference to describe how we may obtain the graph of the line $y = -\frac{1}{5}x - \frac{10}{3}$.

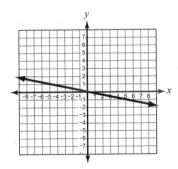

29. For the given equation of a line, $y = -3x - 12$, use the slope to estimate the measure of the angle formed with respect to the x-axis.

The angle is equal to $45°$.

The angle is greater than $45°$.

The angle is equal to $0°$.

The angle is less than $45°$.

30. Use the given graph of the line $y = 3x$ as a point of reference to describe how we may obtain the graph of the line $y = 3x + 3$.

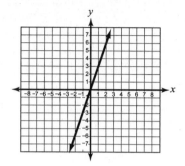

For problems 31-40, choose from the four answer sets given.

31. Compare the slopes and y-intercepts of the given graph.

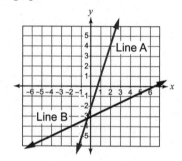

$m_A > m_B > 0$
$b_A > b_B$

$|m_A| > |m_B|$ $b_A > b_B$
$m_A > 0 > m_B$

$m_B > m_A > 0$
$b_B < b_A$

$|m_A| < |m_B|$ $0 > m_B$
$0 > m_A$ $b_A > b_B$

32. Compare the slopes and y-intercepts of the given graph.

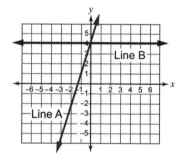

$|m_A| < |m_B|$ $0 = m_B$
$0 < m_A$ $b_A = b_B = 4$

$m_B > m_A$
$b_B = b_A = 4$

$m_A > 0$ $|m_A| > |m_B|$
$m_B = 0$ $b_A > b_B$

$m_A > 0$ $m_A > m_B$
$m_B = 0$ $b_A = b_B = 4$

33. Compare the slopes and y-intercepts of the given graph.

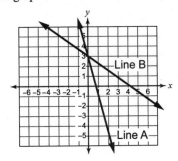

$m_A > m_B > 0$
$b_A = b_B = 3$
$\|m_A\| > \|m_B\| \qquad m_B < 0$
$m_A < 0 \qquad b_A = b_B = 3$
$m_B > m_A > 0$
$b_B > b_A$
$m_A < 0 \qquad \|m_B\| > \|m_A\|$
$m_B < 0 \qquad b_A = b_B = 3$

34. Compare the slopes and y-intercepts of the given graph.

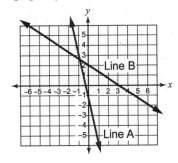

$\|m_A\| > \|m_B\| \qquad m_B < 0$
$m_A < 0 \qquad b_B > b_A$
$m_B > m_A > 0$
$b_B > b_A$
$m_A > m_B > 0$
$b_A < b_B$
$\|m_A\| > \|m_B\| \qquad b_A < b_B$
$m_A > 0 > m_B$

35. Compare the slopes and y-intercepts of the given graph.

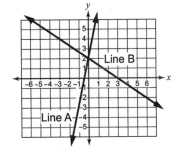

$\|m_A\| < \|m_B\| \qquad 0 > m_B$
$0 > m_A \qquad b_A < b_B$
$m_A > 0 > m_B \qquad b_A = b_B = 2$
$\|m_A\| > \|m_B\|$
$m_B > 0 > m_A$
$b_A = b_B = 2$
$\|m_A\| < \|m_B\| \qquad b_B = b_A = 2$
$m_B > 0 > m_A$

36. Compare the slopes and y-intercepts of the given graph.

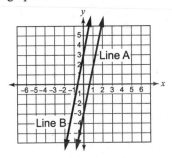

$m_A = m_B \qquad m_B < 0$
$m_A < 0 \qquad b_B > b_A$
$m_A > 0 \qquad m_A = m_B$
$m_B > 0 \qquad b_B > b_A$
$m_A > m_B > 0$
$b_A > b_B$
$m_B > m_A > 0$
$b_B > b_A$

37. Compare the slopes and y-intercepts of the given graph.

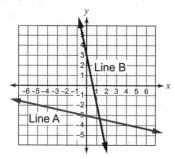

_____

$$m_A < m_B < 0$$
$$b_A < b_B$$

_____

$$|m_B| > |m_A| \qquad m_B < 0$$
$$m_A < 0 \qquad b_B > b_A$$

_____

$$|m_A| < |m_B| \qquad b_A < b_B$$
$$m_A > 0 > m_B$$

_____

$$m_B > m_A > 0$$
$$b_B > b_A$$

_____

38. Compare the slopes and y-intercepts of the given graph.

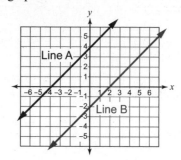

_____

$$m_A > 0 \qquad m_A = m_B$$
$$m_B > 0 \qquad b_A > b_B$$

_____

$$m_A = m_B \qquad m_B > 0$$
$$m_A > 0 \qquad b_B > b_A$$

_____

$$m_B > m_A > 0$$
$$b_B > b_A$$

_____

$$m_A > m_B > 0$$
$$b_A < b_B$$

_____

39. Compare the slopes and y-intercepts of the given graph.

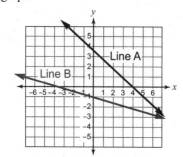

_____

$$|m_A| < |m_B| \qquad 0 > m_B$$
$$0 > m_A \qquad b_A > b_B$$

_____

$$m_B > m_A > 0$$
$$b_B > b_A$$

_____

$$m_A < 0 \qquad |m_A| > |m_B|$$
$$m_B < 0 \qquad b_A > b_B$$

_____

$$m_A > m_B > 0$$
$$b_A > b_B$$

_____

40. Compare the slopes and y-intercepts of the given graph.

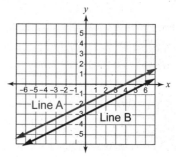

_____

$$m_A > 0 \qquad m_A = m_B$$
$$m_B < 0 \qquad b_B > b_A$$

_____

$$m_A > 0 \qquad m_A = m_B$$
$$m_B > 0 \qquad b_A > b_B$$

_____

$$m_B > m_A > 0$$
$$b_B < b_A$$

_____

$$m_A = m_B \qquad m_B < 0$$
$$m_A < 0 \qquad b_B < b_A$$

_____

In this lesson, we will learn how to translate a given **representation of a function** into another representation. We will use four different representations: **verbal description**, **table**, **graphs**, and **equations**.

A **function** is a relation in which each element of the **domain** is paired with exactly one element of the **range**. The **input** is an element taken from the domain of the function, and the **output** is the element of the range produced by the input.

The **independent variable** is the variable that takes values from the domain of the function, and the **dependent variable** is the variable that has its value computed from the value of the independent variable, using the function rule, and has its value in the range of the function.

A given representation of a function can be translated into any of the other representations. In order to translate from one representation to another, the independent variable and the dependent variable need to be identified first.

Function	A relation in which each element of the domain is paired with exactly one element of the range
Input	An element from the domain of the function
Output	An element from the range of the function produced by the input
Independent Variable	A variable whose values are taken from the domain of the function
Dependent Variable	A variable whose values are taken from the range of the function, and are determined by the values of the independent variable
Representation of a Function	One of the four ways to describe a function: • verbal description • table • graph • equation

In the first example, we will translate a given table representation into a graph.

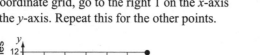

Example 1	Kristen began catching and collecting butterflies every week. The table shows the number of butterflies in her collection. Draw the graph that represents the table.

Week	Number of butterflies
1	2
2	4
3	6
4	8
5	10
6	12

x = number of weeks (independent variable)
y = number of butterflies (dependent variable)

Step 1: Identify the independent and dependent variables.

Since Kristen caught 2 butterflies in the first week, the first point is $(1, 2)$. On the coordinate grid, go to the right 1 on the x-axis and then up 2 on the y-axis. Repeat this for the other points.

Step 2: Plot the points on a graph.

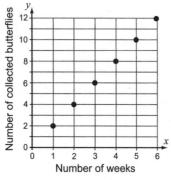

Step 3: Draw a straight line through the points.

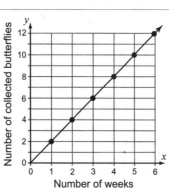

Answer:

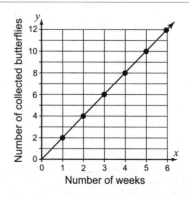

Example 2   Emily is reading a book. It takes her 6 days to read 40 pages. The graph below shows the number of pages Emily reads as a function of the number of days. Find an equation in slope-intercept form that represents the graph.

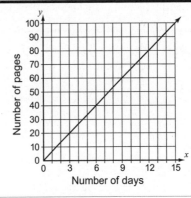

x = the number of days y = the number of pages	**Step 1:** Identify the independent and dependent variables.
Emily reads 40 pages every 6 days, so the number of pages per day that she reads is $\frac{40}{6} = \frac{20}{3}$. This is the slope of the function.	**Step 2:** Find the rate of change, or slope.
We see from the graph that the y-intercept is $(0, 0)$.	**Step 3:** Find the y-intercept.
The slope-intercept form of a straight line is $y = mx + b$, where m is the slope and $(0, b)$ is the y-intercept. Since $m = \frac{20}{3}$ and $b = 0$, the equation of the line is $y = \frac{20}{3}x + 0$ or $y = \frac{20}{3}x$.	**Step 4:** Use the slope-intercept form to find the equation for the function.
	Answer: The equation that represents this graph is $y = \frac{20}{3}x$.

Example 3   Given the equation $y = 3x + 2$, find a verbal description of the function.

The equation in slope-intercept form is $y = mx + b$. slope = m = 3 y-intercept = $(0, b) = (0, 2)$	**Step 1:** Identify the slope and y-intercept from the given equation.
Johnny saves \$3 per day. So, y = amount of money saved by Johnny (in dollars), and x = number of days since he started saving.	**Step 2:** Think of a situation where a quantity, y, increases at a rate of 3 units per each unit of another quantity, x.
When he started saving, Johnny already had \$2.00.	**Step 3:** Since the quantity, y, is 2 at the beginning, add this to the previous information.
	Answer: Johnny saves \$3 per day. When he started saving, he already had \$2.

Of course, the description we have given is only one of many possible ways, because different situations can be described by the same equation.

The next example gives a verbal description, and we are asked to find a graph that represents it.

Example 4   Mark started keeping a chart of his height at age 10, when he was 145 cm tall. He grew 4 cm every year. Draw a graph that represents this function.

x = number of years since he started keeping the growth chart y = his height (in cm)	**Step 1:** Identify the independent and dependent variables.
Since he grew at the rate of 4 cm per year, the slope is $m = 4$. Since he began when he was 145 cm tall, the y-intercept is $(0, b) = (0, 145)$.	**Step 2:** Find the slope and y-intercept.
The slope-intercept form is $y = mx + b$ where m = slope, $(0, b) = y$-intercept. Therefore, the equation is $y = 4x + 145$.	**Step 3:** Use the slope-intercept form to find the equation for the function.

Make a table:

Input	Process	Output
0	4(0) + 145	145
5	4(5) + 145	165
8	4(8) + 145	177

Step 4: Use the equation $y = 4x + 145$ to plot a few points, then draw a straight line through the points.

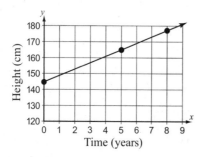

Answer:

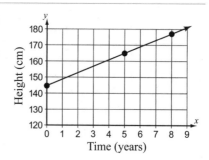

Note that we have started the y-axis at $y = 120$ because the table data range is from $y = 145$ to $y = 177$. There is no need to always start the x- or y-axes at zero, especially if we can get a graph that is simpler and easier to read by starting at different values.

The last example translates a table representation into a verbal description.

Example 5 Kalisha's mother is throwing a birthday party for her daughter. She is using the table to calculate how many pizzas she needs to order for her family and additional guests.

Give a verbal description that represents the table.

Number of guests (other than her family)	Number of pizzas for the party
4	3
8	4
12	5
16	6

---

x = number of guests (other than her family)
y = number of pizzas

Step 1: Identify the independent and dependent variables.

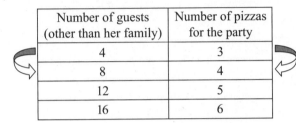

Number of guests (other than her family)	Number of pizzas for the party
4	3
8	4
12	5
16	6

Step 2: Calculate the change in number of pizzas from the first to the second pair of entries, and the corresponding change in number of guests.

$4 - 3 = 1$ is the change in the number of pizzas

$8 - 4 = 4$ is the change in number of guests

$$m = \frac{\text{change in number of pizzas}}{\text{change in number of guests}} = \frac{1}{4}$$

Step 3: Calculate the corresponding rate of change, or slope.

From Step 2, we need $\frac{1}{4}$ of a pizza per guest.

Step 4: Calculate the y-intercept $(0, b)$.

If we multiply $\frac{1}{4}$ by 4 we get 1, but the table entry

for 4 people is 3. This means that we need

$3 - 1 = 2$ pizzas if no guests are present.

So, $b = 2$.

Answer: Kalisha's mother needs to order 1 pizza for every 4 guests, plus 2 pizzas for her family.

Problem Set

Solve:

1. Which of the following best represents the graph?

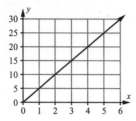

x	y
0	0
1	5
2	10
3	15
4	20
5	25

x	y
5	1
15	3
20	4
25	5

The x-values of the graph increase faster than the y-values.

$y = 5 + x$

2. The cost to enter a local water park is $13 per person.

Number of people	Price
1	$13
2	$26
3	$39
4	$52
5	$65
6	$78

Which of the following best depicts the information in the table?

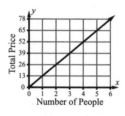

You will get a discount if you have 3 or more people

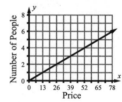

$y = 13 + x$

3. Kameryn has three Disney® movies. She will receive one each month from her grandparents through a movie club.

Months	Kameryn
0	3
1	4
2	5
3	6
4	7

Which of the following best shows the information from the table?

$y = 3x$

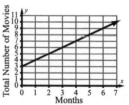

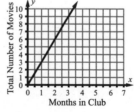

Kameryn will have 20 movies by the end of the year.

4. Noah rides his bike the same number of miles every day except Sunday. Every day he adds the number of miles he rides to his total. The table below shows his total for one week.

Days	Miles
1	3
2	6
3	9
4	12
5	15
6	18

Which is a valid representation of the table?

$y = 3 + x$

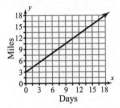

Noah rides 3 miles every day.

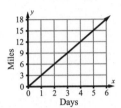

5. Katie makes her blackberry dumplings with 2 cups of sugar for every 5 cups of blackberries. The graph below shows the correct ratio of cups of sugar to cups of blackberries.

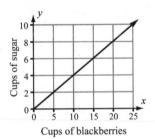

Which of the following is a valid representation of the graph?

Blackberries (cups)	Sugar (cups)
5	2
10	4
15	6

You will need 6 cups of sugar for 3 cups of blackberries.

Blackberries (cups)	Sugar (cups)
2	5
4	15
6	20

You will need 5 cups of sugar if you have 7 cups of blackberries.

6. Justin kept a graph of the number of hits he had this baseball season. The graph shows the total number of hits after each game.

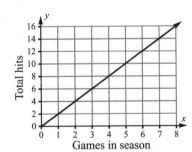

Which of the following best describes the information on the graph?

Justin did not strike out.

Justin had six hits in game 3.

Games	Total Hits
1	2
2	2
3	2
4	2

Games	Total Hits
1	2
2	4
3	6
4	8
5	10

7. Sally likes to make her own summer drink. For every two cups of Sally's special juice mixture, she needs three cups of water to get the perfect summer drink. The table shows the ratio of juice and water.

Juice (cups)	Water (cups)
2	3
4	6
6	9
8	12

Which of the following best represents the information in the table?

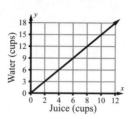

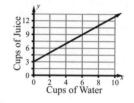

She will need 10 cups of water for 7 cups of juice.

She can make 7 cups of soft drink with 3 cups of juice.

8. A young boy collects stamps. He adds 4 stamps to his collection every week.

Weeks	Stamps
1	4
2	8
3	12
4	16

Which of the following is a valid representation of the table?

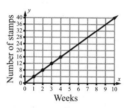

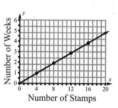

$y = 4$

He bought 8 stamps the third week.

9. The price for admittance for one person to the theater for a matinee is $5.50. The table below shows the total price based on the number of people.

Number of People	Total price
1	$5.50
2	$11.00
3	$16.50
4	$22.00
5	$27.50

Which of the following best represents the information in the table?

The fifth person will get in for a cheaper price.

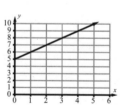

$y = x + 5.5$

$y = 5.5x$

10. Colin collects baseball cards. He already has 14 cards and will buy 1 each month with his allowance. The graph below depicts how Colin's baseball card collection will grow in the next months.

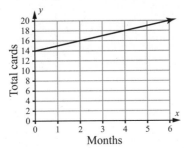

Which is a valid representation of the graph?

Months	Cards
1	14
2	28
3	42

$y = x + 14$

Colin will have 16 cards by the end of the first month.

$y = 14x$

11. Mary likes to collect tea cups. She now has six in her collection. She would like to buy one per month for the next year.

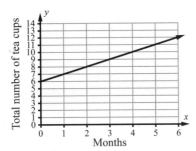

Which of the following is the best representation of the graph?

Months	Tea Cups
1	1
2	2
3	3

Mary's collection will double in three months.

$y = x + 6$

$y = 6x$

12. Joey's mom would like to find a way to get him to do his homework. Each day that he completes his homework, he will get a star. He will get a reward when he gets twenty stars. What is the best representation of the following graph?

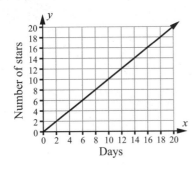

$y = x$

$y = -x$

Days	Number of Stars
1	1
2	2
3	6

Joey will get extra stars when he completes the chart.

13. Kelly and Lauren are making ice cream. For every 5 cups of mixture put into the machine, 4 cups of ice cream are formed.

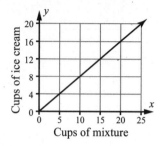

Which of the following is a valid representation of the graph?

Mixture (cups)	Ice Cream (cups)
4	5
8	10
12	15

You will have 10 cups of ice cream from 8 cups of mixture.

$$y = \frac{4}{5}x$$

$$y = \frac{5}{4}x$$

14. Kaleb has $7 in his bank. He will get $3 each day for helping with his younger brother. The table below shows how his money will increase daily.

Days	Total money
0	7
1	10
2	13
3	16
4	19

Which of the following is another representation of the information?

$$y = 3x$$

$$y = 3x + 7$$

Kaleb has twice as much money on the second day.

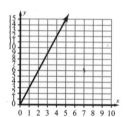

15. Nelly and Shelly are picking oranges for a local grower. He will let them keep 1 basket, which they may sell on their own, out of every four baskets they pick.

The chart below shows the number of baskets they collected and the number they kept for themselves.

Collected	Kept
4	1
8	2
12	3
16	4

Which of the following best represents the information in the table?

If they collect 6 baskets they will be able to keep 3 baskets for themselves.

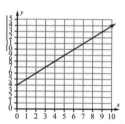

$$y = \frac{1}{4}x$$

$$y = 4 + x$$

16. Given the equation $y = 300 - x$, which of the following is a valid representation of the equation?

Bob has 300 trees on his lot and he sells one tree per day.

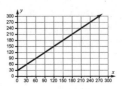

Days	Trees Sold
1	300
2	301
3	302

Bob has 300 trees on his lot. He plants one tree every day for each tree he sells.

17. Johnny and the other workers put in 5 hours of work on a project last weekend. Due to his other duties at the company, he will only be able to put in $\frac{4}{5}$ of the time the other workers can for the remainder of the project. Which of the following is the best representation of the information?

$$y = \frac{4}{5}x + 5 \qquad y = \frac{5}{4}x + 5$$

x	y
0	$\frac{4}{5}$
1	$\frac{8}{5}$
2	$\frac{16}{5}$

x	y
0	5
1	$\frac{25}{4}$
2	$\frac{15}{2}$

18. Given the equation $y = 5x - 3$, which of the following is a valid representation of the equation?

Tanya and Lane make jewelry boxes and can sell them for $5 each. They had to buy $3 in materials to start their project.

Janice makes homemade dolls. She can charge $5 per doll but has to pay $3 in material for each one.

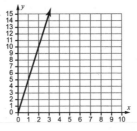

19. Given the equation, $y = \frac{2}{3}x + 11$, which of the following is a valid representation of the equation?

x	y
0	$\frac{2}{3}$
1	$\frac{4}{3}$
2	$\frac{8}{3}$

Angie saves $2 out of every $3 she is given for doing extra housework. She had $11 from her birthday money.

After having 11 baseball cards, Joe sold 2 for every three more he collected.

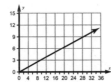

20. Which is a valid representation of the equation $y = 4x + 27$?

Tom has $4 in the bank and he saves $2 a week to buy a new bike.

x	y
1	4
2	8
3	12
4	13

Cleo has $2 in his bank. He plans on saving $4 every week from his allowance.

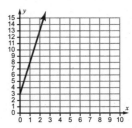

21. Sheila has 4 orange trees. She would like to slowly build an orchard by adding two orange trees each year. Which is a valid representation of the information?

$y = 2x + 4$ $\qquad$ $y = 2x$

Years	Trees
1	2
2	4
3	6

Years	Trees
1	4
2	8
3	16

22. Which of the following is the best representation of the equation $y = \frac{1}{2}x + 4$?

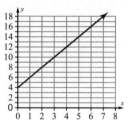

x	y
1	6
2	10
3	14
4	18

Linus and Lucy are both planning to bring spending money on vacation. Each begins with $4, but Lucy saves twice as much as Linus every week.

Linus and Lucy are both planning to bring spending money on the family vacation. They each begin with $4. Linus saves half as much as Lucy does each week.

23. Cain keeps a record of the number of fish he has caught while fishing with his dad. He has caught 10 so far this summer. He hopes to catch 3 fish every time they go fishing. Which of the following is the best representation of the information?

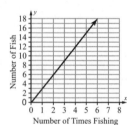

$y = 3x + 10$

Number of Times Fishing	Number of Fish
1	3
2	6
3	6
4	12

$y = 3x$

24. Colin has $1000 in the bank. He plans on saving $75 each month from his job for a down payment on a car. Which of the following is a valid representation of this information?

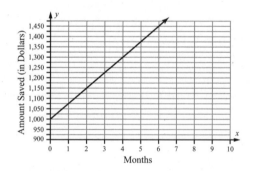

Months	Amount Saved (dollars)
1	1,000
2	75
3	150

Colin will have $300 in the bank after 4 months.

25. When Sara Grace was born, her parents were given 7 books to put on her shelf. She will be getting 2 books for every birthday until she is 18 years old. Which of the following is the best representation of the information?

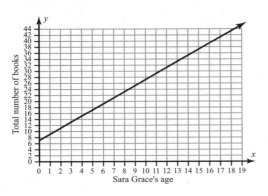

$y = 5 + 2x$ $y = 2x$

Sara Grace will have 10 books on her 8th birthday.

26. A local car rental company charges a $100 deposit plus $25 per day to rent one of its cars. Which of the following best depicts this information?

Days Rented	Total Charge
1	$125
2	$150
3	$175
4	$200

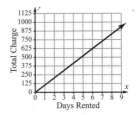

Days Rented	Total Charge
1	$25
2	$50
3	$75

27. Adam likes to play with small racing cars. He was given 5 for his birthday and he hopes to receive 5 more for every birthday. Which of the following is the best representation of the information?

$y = 5 + 2x$ $y = 2x$

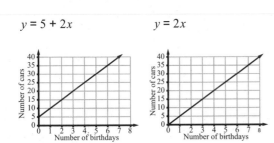

28. Mike had 200 tadpoles in his pond. He sells them only in pairs. Which of the following depicts the information?

Sales	Number of tadpoles in pond
0	200
1	198
2	196
3	194
4	192

Sales	Number of tadpoles in pond
0	200
1	202
2	204
3	206
4	208

$y = 2x + 200$ $y = 2x$

29. Jamie works with a company that makes water fountains and sculptures out of copper. He is paid $400 per week plus $50 for each sculpture he sells. Which of the following best depicts Jamie's wages with respect to the number of sculptures he sells per week?

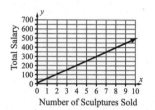

Sculptures Sold	Total Salary
1	400
2	50
3	100
4	150

$y = 50x$

30. Violet has six recipe cards in her file box. She wants to add three every month when she reads her magazines. Which of the following depicts this information correctly?

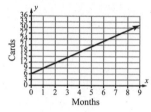

Months	Cards
1	3
2	6
3	9
4	12

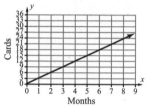

$y = x + 6$

31. J.J. is collecting CDs to start a disc jockey business. He plans to buy the same amount of CDs every two weeks with the money from his summer job. The table below shows how his collection was growing at different times.

Weeks	Number of CDs
4	15
8	21
12	27

Which of the following is a valid representation of the table?

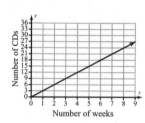

J.J. will double the number of CDs he has in 3 weeks.

J.J. started with 9 CDs and buys 3 every two weeks.

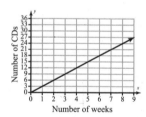

32. The height of a tree at various times is given in the following table.

Age (years)	Height (meters)
3	2
6	3.5

Which of the following is a valid representation of the table?

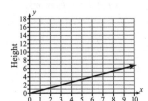

The tree was 5 m tall when it was 9 years old.

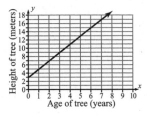

The tree doubles in height every three years.

33. A medical insurance company pays a set amount for a certain operation and an amount per day for a semi-private room. The table below shows the total cost over three days for the operation and the room.

Days	Total Cost
1	$1,625
2	$1,975
3	$2,325

Which of the following is a valid representation of the table?

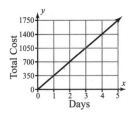

$y = 350x$

The operation costs $1,275 and the semi-private room costs $350 per day.

$y = 1,275 + x$

34. The chart indicates that the pressure, measured in atmospheres, increases as the depth of the water, in feet, increases.

Pressure	Depth of Fresh Water
1	0
2	34
3	68
4	102
5	136

Which is the best representation of the information in the chart?

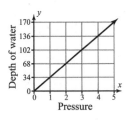

The pressure increases by 1 atmosphere for every 34 feet of water.

$y = 2x + 34$

The pressure of the water causes the depth of the water to increase.

35. Keri is planning a day in the city and will have to park in a downtown lot. She is using the graph to determine how much it will cost her to park in Lot A where her car is in a covered garage with valet parking.

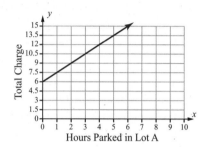

Hours Parked in Lot A

Which of the following is a valid representation of the graph?

$y = 6x$ Keri paid $6 to park in the lot and $1.50 for each hour.

$y = 1.50x$ Keri will have to pay a total of $15 for parking.

36. The following graph shows the cost of making long distance phone calls with a regional company. The company charges both a connection fee and an amount per minute.

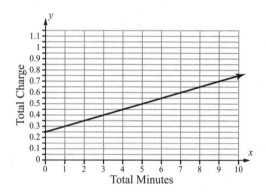

Total Minutes

Which of the following is a valid representation of the graph?

Shawn pays $0.05 per minute for her long distance phone calls.

Minutes	Total Cost of Calls
1	30
2	5
3	10

$y = 0.25x$ $y = 5x$

37. Devin is saving money to buy a computer. If he saves $220, his parents will pay the remaining portion. He will save the same amount every month. The graph shows how the money in his account is increasing.

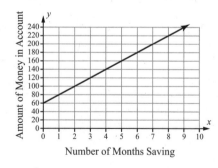

Number of Months Saving

Which of the following is a valid representation of the information on the graph?

Devin will have his money in 6 months. $y = 60x + 120$

Devin will have the $220 in 8 months if he saves $20 each month. $y = 60x$

38. John is driving from New Orleans to Houston. Which of the following is a valid representation of the information in the graph below?

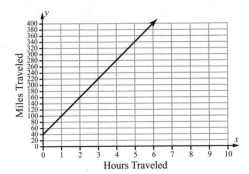

$y = 60x$

John will arrive in 4 hours..

Hours	Miles
1	40
2	100
3	160
4	220

John is already 40 miles from New Orleans and traveling at 60 miles per hour.

39. Bob uses his own car to travel on company business. He has a daily allowance for meals and lodging, and receives a certain amount per mile. He must turn in a daily log. He uses a graph for his records.

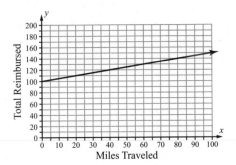

Which of the following is a valid representation of the graph?

Bob gets $100 per day for meals and lodging and $0.50 per mile traveled.

Bob gets paid the same for the mileage as he does for lodging and meals.

Miles	Lodging
10	110
25	120
60	130

$y = 100x + 0.50$

40. Which of the following is the best representation of the graph below?

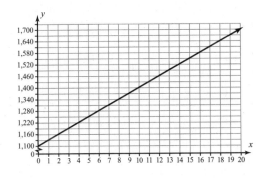

Gloria bought a used car for $1,100. It increases in value at the amount of $30 per month.

Todd makes $1,100 per month and has to pay $30 for insurance.

$y = 100x + 0.50$

Gerri has $1,100 and earns $30 per dress sold. Gerri will make $1,700 if she sells 20 dresses.

HA1-405: Determining an Equation of a Line Given the Slope and Coordinates of One Point

You have already learned about slope, and you know that there are two ways to calculate the slope of a line: using the slope formula, or counting spaces with the $\frac{\text{rise}}{\text{run}}$ method. You have also seen in previous lessons that, when you are solving problems concerning lines, you may be given an equation for the line, or two points that are on the line, or the graph of the line, or maybe even a combination. In cases where you are given a graph or a pair of points, you may find it helpful to see the equation. In this lesson, you will learn how to find the equation of a line if you know a point on the line and the slope.

Before you begin, let's review some information about lines. Remember that there are many forms for the equation of a line. The form that you will be using in this lesson is slope-intercept form. The following definition will help you remember what this form looks like.

Slope-Intercept Form	The slope-intercept form for the equation of a line is $y = mx + b$, where m is the slope of the line, and b is the y-intercept.

Recall that the y-intercept of a line is the point where the graph of the line crosses the y-axis. Now, suppose that you want to find an equation for the line that goes through the point (5, 3) and has slope $-\frac{3}{5}$. Begin with the slope-intercept form. You know that m represents the slope of the line, so you can substitute the slope, $-\frac{3}{5}$, for m. The x and the y represent the coordinates of points on the line; therefore, you can substitute the coordinates of the point for these variables. You can use 5 for x and 3 for y. Carrying out these substitutions gives you:

$$y = mx + b$$
$$3 = \left(-\frac{3}{5}\right)(5) + b$$

The only thing that you don't know is b, but you can solve this equation for b as follows:

$$3 = \left(-\frac{3}{5}\right)(5) + b$$
$$3 = -3 + b$$
$$6 = b$$

The y-intercept, b, for this line is 6. To finish the problem, you must write down the actual equation for the line.

You have all the information you need to do this. Simply go back to the slope-intercept form, and substitute only the slope and the y-intercept. Substituting $-\frac{3}{5}$ for m and 6 for b, and leaving x and y as they are, gives you the equation that you were looking for:

$$y = \left(-\frac{3}{5}\right)x + 6$$

This is the answer to the problem.

Look at the following examples.

Example 1   Find the equation for the line through the point (–6, 4) with slope $= \frac{1}{2}$.

$4 = \frac{1}{2}(-6) + b$	**Step 1:** Substitute the given information into the slope-intercept formula, $y = mx + b$.
$4 = \frac{(-6)}{2} + b$ $4 = -3 + b$ $4 + 3 = -3 + b + 3$ $7 = b$	**Step 2:** Solve for b.
$y = \frac{1}{2}x + 7$	**Step 3:** Rewrite the equation of the line, substituting only the slope and y-intercept.
	Answer: $y = \frac{1}{2}x + 7$

Example 2   Find the equation for the line through the point (10, –4) with slope = 2.

$-4 = 2(10) + b$	**Step 1:** Substitute the given information into the slope-intercept formula, $y = mx + b$, and simplify.
$-4 = 20 + b$ $-4 - 20 = 20 + b - 20$ $-24 = b$	**Step 2:** Solve for b.
$y = 2x - 24$	**Step 3:** Rewrite the equation of the line, substituting only the slope and y-intercept.
	Answer: $y = 2x - 24$

Before you finish this lesson, look at one more example.

Example 3   Write the equation of the line through point (6, 4) with slope $\frac{3}{2}$ in standard form.

$y = mx + b$	**Step 1:** Use the slope-intercept formula.
$4 = \frac{3}{2}(6) + b$	**Step 2:** Substitute $\frac{3}{2}$ for m, 4 for y, and 6 for x.
$4 = 9 + b$	**Step 3:** Simplify.
$4 - 9 = 9 + b - 9$ $-5 = b$	**Step 4:** Solve for b, the y-intercept.
$y = \frac{3}{2}x - 5$	**Step 5:** Substitute the slope and y-intercept into the slope-intercept form to write the equation of the line.

$$\frac{-3}{2}x + y = -5$$

Step 6: Rearrange the equation into standard form.

$$-2\left(\frac{-3}{2}x\right) + (-2)y = (-2)(-5)$$

$$3x - 2y = 10$$

Step 7: Multiply each side by –2 to make $A \geq 0$ and an integer.

Answer: $3x - 2y = 10$

Problem Set

1. Determine the equation of the line that has a slope of –2 and passes through the point (–3, 0). Write the equation in slope-intercept form.

2. Determine the equation of the line that has a slope of 1 and passes through the point (2, –6). Write the equation in slope-intercept form.

3. Determine the equation of the line that has a slope of 6 and passes through the point (4, –2). Write the equation in slope-intercept form.

4. Determine the equation of the line that has a slope of –3 and passes through the point (–3, 0). Write the equation in slope-intercept form.

5. Determine the equation of the line that has a slope of 2 and passes through the point (1, 4). Write the equation in slope-intercept form.

6. Determine the equation of the line that has a slope of 4 and passes through the point (2, 8). Write the equation in slope-intercept form.

7. Determine the equation of the line that has a slope of –3 and passes through the point (2, 7). Write the equation in slope—intercept form.

8. Determine the equation of the line that has a slope of 5 and passes through the point (1, 3). Write the equation in slope-intercept form.

9. Determine the equation of the line that has a slope of $-\frac{1}{4}$ and passes through the point (3, 1). Write the equation in slope-intercept form.

10. Determine the equation of the line that has a slope of $\frac{1}{2}$ and passes through the point (4, 2). Write the equation in slope-intercept form.

11. Determine the equation of the line that has a slope of 2 and passes through the point (5, 1). Write the equation in standard form.

12. Determine the equation of the line that has a slope of 3 and passes through the point (–2, –7). Write the equation in standard form.

13. Determine the equation of the line that has a slope of 3 and passes through the point (1, 2). Write the equation in standard form.

14. Determine the equation of the line that has a slope of 1 and passes through the point (–2, 1). Write the equation in standard form.

15. Determine the equation of the line that has a slope of –4 and passes through the point (0, 0). Write the equation in standard form.

16. Determine the equation of the line that has a slope of $\frac{4}{3}$ and passes through the point (0, –8). Write the equation in standard form.

17. Determine the equation of the line that has a slope of $-\frac{1}{2}$ and passes through the point (0, 4). Write the equation in standard form.

18. Raven charges a base price of $15.00 to baby-sit, as well as $3.00 per hour. Write an equation that will determine the total charge for Raven to baby-sit for x hours.

19. Taylor charges a base price of $10.00 to baby-sit, as well as $5.00 per hour. Write an equation that will determine the total charge for Taylor to baby-sit for x hours.

20. The population of the city of Mayfield is 55,000. If the population increases by 2,000 each year, what equation could be used to represent the population of the city in x years?

HA1-410: Determining an Equation of a Line Given the Coordinates of Two Points

By now, you know how to calculate slope, and how to find the equation of a line if you are given a point on the line and the slope. In this last lesson on slope and lines, you will learn how to put these two ideas together to find the equation of a line when you are given two points on the line. For this lesson, you need to remember two formulas: the slope formula and the slope-intercept form for the equation of a line. The following example demonstrates how to use the slope formula.

Example 1   Find the slope of the line through the points (3, 3) and (5, 6).

$$m = \frac{y_2 - y_1}{x_2 - x_1}$$

Step 1:   Write the slope formula.

$$m = \frac{6 - 3}{5 - 3}$$

Step 2:   Substitute the coordinates of the given points into the slope formula.

$$m = \frac{3}{2}$$

Step 3:   Simplify the fraction.

Answer: $\dfrac{3}{2}$

The second formula you need to remember is the slope-intercept form for the equation of a line: $y = mx + b$, where m is the slope and b is the y-intercept. This is the formula you use to get the equation for a line once you know the slope and a point on the line. Now, suppose that you want to find an equation for a line, but the only information you have is a pair of points on the line. You must first use those two points to find the slope of the line, then use that slope and one of the two original points together with slope-intercept form to get the equation. Look at the following example:

Example 2   Find the equation of the line that passes through the points (2, –2) and (5, 3).

$$m = \frac{y_2 - y_1}{x_2 - x_1}$$

$$m = \frac{3 - (-2)}{5 - 2}$$

$$m = \frac{5}{3}$$

Step 1:   Find the slope of the line.

$$y = mx + b$$

$$(-2) = \left(\frac{5}{3}\right)(2) + b$$

$$-2 = \frac{10}{3} + b$$

Step 2:   Substitute $\dfrac{5}{3}$ for the slope, 2 for x, and –2 for y. Once you know the slope, you can use the slope-intercept form to find the y-intercept. Do this by substituting the slope and one of the two original ordered pairs into the formula.

$$\frac{-10}{3} + (-2) = \left(\frac{10}{3}\right) + b - \frac{10}{3}$$

$$\frac{-10}{3} + \left(\frac{-2}{1}\right) = b$$

$$\frac{-10}{3} + \frac{-6}{3} = b$$

$$\frac{-16}{3} = -5\frac{1}{3} = b$$

Step 3: Solve for b.

$$y = \frac{5}{3}x + \left(-5\frac{1}{3}\right)$$

Step 4: Substitute the slope and y-intercept into slope-intercept form to write the equation of the line.

Answer: $y = \frac{5}{3}x + \left(-5\frac{1}{3}\right)$

Taking this process a step further, you can write the equation of the line in standard form. Remember that **standard form** is $ax + by = c$, where a, b and c are real numbers, $a \geq 0$, and a and b are not both zero. The next example demonstrates how to do this.

Example 3   Write the equation of the line through the points (3, 4) and (−3, −8) in standard form.

$$m = \frac{y_2 - y_1}{x_2 - x_1}$$

$$m = \frac{-8 - 4}{-3 - 3}$$

$$m = \frac{-12}{-6} = 2$$

Step 1: Find the slope of the line.

$$y = mx + b$$

$$4 = 2(3) + b$$

Step 2: Using slope-intercept form, substitute the values for slope and either ordered pair to find the y-intercept.

$$4 = 6 + b$$

$$4 - 6 = 6 + b - 6$$

$$-2 = b$$

Step 3: Solve for b.

$$y = 2x + (-2)$$

Step 4: Substitute the slope and y-intercept into the slope-intercept form.

$$y = 2x - 2$$

$$-2x + y = -2$$

$$-1(-2x + y) = (-1)(-2)$$

$$2x - y = 2$$

Step 5: Rearrange the equation into standard form.

Answer: $2x - y = 2$

Problem Set

Determine the equation of a line that contains the given points, and write the answer in slope-intercept form:

1. (–1, 1) and (1, 5)

2. (1, 0) and (2, 2)

3. (–2, 3) and (–1, 2)

4. (2, 3) and (3, 5)

5. (2, 2) and (1, 0)

6. (4, 3) and (2, 1)

7. (4, 2) and (6, 3)

8. (9, 3) and (4, 5)

9. (2, 3) and (8, 4)

10. (2, 3) and (1, 6)

Determine the equation of a line that contains the given points, and write the answer in standard form:

11. (–1, 5) and (2, 7)

12. (3, 1) and (1, –5)

13. (1, –3) and (5, 7)

14. (1, –1) and (3, 5)

15. (5, 1) and (3, 7)

16. (4, –3) and (–2, 3)

17. (3, –3) and (5, 3)

Solve:

18. A rental car company's rate (y) is a linear function of the number of days the car is rented (x). If the graph of the function includes the points (1, 75) and (6, 275), what is the equation of the line?

19. A blueprint of a wheelchair ramp shows two points: (0, 0) at the start of the ramp, and (60, 6) at the end of the ramp. What is the equation of the line between these two points?

20. Manuel wants to predict the cost of manufacturing tennis shoes (y). Two pairs cost $75 and ten pairs cost $303. If cost is expressed as a linear function of the number of pairs manufactured (x), what is the equation of the line?

HA1-415: Graphing Linear Inequalities with Two Variables

In this lesson, you will learn about graphing linear inequalities.

Linear Inequality	A linear statement that relates expressions to each other with inequality signs ($<$, $>$, $\leq$, or $\geq$)

A linear inequality looks very much like a linear equation, but there is an inequality symbol in place of the equal sign. For example, the equation $2x + y = 8$ is a linear equation, but $2x + y < 8$ is a linear inequality. Linear inequalities have many more solutions than linear equations. The reason is that inequality symbols relax the restrictions on what the variables can and cannot be. For example, $(0, 8)$ is a solution to the equation $2x + y = 8$. You can easily verify that this ordered pair is also a solution to the inequality $2x + y \leq 8$:

$$2(0) + 8 \leq 8$$
$$8 \leq 8$$

Because it is true that $8 \leq 8$, $(0,8)$ is a solution to the inequality. In fact, any solution to the linear equation $2x + y = 8$ will be a solution to the inequality $2x + y \leq 8$. Now consider the ordered pairs $(0, 0)$ and $(1, 2)$. Both of these ordered pairs are also solutions to the inequality $2x + y \leq 8$:

$$2(0) + 0 \leq 8 \qquad 2(1) + 2 \leq 8$$
$$0 + 0 \leq 8 \qquad 2 + 2 \leq 8$$
$$0 \leq 8 \qquad 4 \leq 8$$
$$\text{True} \qquad \text{True}$$

However, they are not solutions to the equation $2x + y = 8$:

$$2(0) + 0 = 8 \qquad 2(1) + 2 = 8$$
$$0 + 0 = 8 \qquad 2 + 2 = 8$$
$$0 = 8 \qquad 4 = 0$$
$$\text{False} \qquad \text{False}$$

The graph of a linear equation actually separates the coordinate plane into three sets of points: points on the line, points above the line, and points below the line. The line is called the boundary line and the regions on each side of the line are called half-planes.

Half-Plane	The regions formed when a boundary line divides the coordinate plane

The line that separates the two half-planes is called the **boundary line**, and it is the graph of the linear equation that would result if you changed the inequality symbol to an equal sign.

Boundary Line	The line that separates two half-planes

The graph of a linear inequality will include all points on one side of the boundary line and sometimes the line as well.

Shading is used to indicate which half-plane is indicated by the inequality.

Step 1: Identify the related linear equation.
Step 2: Substitute values for *x*, and solve for *y*.
Step 3: Find the ordered pairs of the equation.
Step 4: Plot the ordered pairs.
Step 5: Graph the boundary line. If the inequality symbol is
         < or >, use a dashed line for the boundary line. If the
         inequality symbol is greater than or equal to or less than or
         equal to, use a solid line, because then the line is part of
         the overall solution.
Step 6: Choose any point not on the boundary line. This point is
         called the **test point**. Substitute the coordinates of the
         test point into the inequality. If these numbers make the
         inequality true, then shade the half-plane that contains the
         test point. If these numbers make the inequality false, then
         shade the half-plane that does not contain the test point.
         The easiest test point to use is (0, 0) if it is not on the
         boundary line.

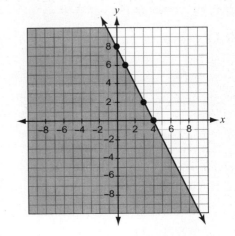

Example 1   Graph the inequality $3x + y \leq 10$.

---

x	y
1	7
2	4
3	1

Step 1: Identify the equation of the boundary line: $3x + y = 10$.
Step 2: Substitute values for *x* in the equation and solve for *y*.
Step 3: Find the ordered pairs: (1, 7), (2, 4) (3, 1).

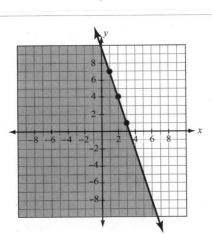

Step 4: Plot the ordered pairs: (1, 7), (2, 4) (3, 1).
Step 5: Graph the boundary line. Use a solid line because the
             inequality symbol is the less than or equal to symbol.
Step 6: Choose a test point (0, 0).

$$3x + y \leq 10$$
$$3(0) + 0 \leq 10$$
$$0 + 0 \leq 10$$
$$0 \leq 10$$

When you substitute the coordinates into the inequality,
you will see that the numbers make the inequality true, so
you will shade the side that contains the test point.

Example 2   Graph the inequality $y > 2x + 1$.

x	y
0	1
2	5
3	7

Step 1: Identify the equation of the boundary line: $y = 2x + 1$.
Step 2: Substitute values for x in the equation and solve for y.
Step 3: Find the ordered pairs: (0, 1); (2, 5); and (3, 7).

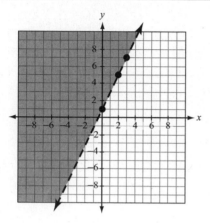

Step 4: Plot the ordered pairs.
Step 5: Graph the boundary line. Use a dashed line because the inequality symbol is the greater than symbol.
Step 6: Choose a test point: (0, 0). Substitute its coordinates into the inequality. $0 > 2(0) + 1$

$$0 > 1$$

Because these numbers make the inequality false, shade the side that does not contain the test point.

Example 3   Graph the inequality $x + y > 5$.

x	y
0	5
5	0
2	3

Step 1: Identify the equation of the boundary line: $x + y = 5$.
Step 2: Substitute values for x in the equation and solve for y.
Step 3: Find the ordered pairs: (0, 5), (5, 0), (2, 3).

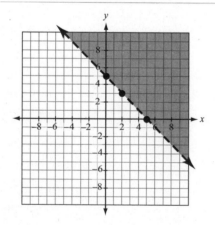

Step 4: Plot the ordered pairs.
Step 5: Graph the boundary line. Use a dashed line because the inequality symbol is the greater than symbol.
Step 6: Choose a test point (0, 0) and substitute it into the inequality. $0 + 0 > 5$

$$0 > 5$$

Because these numbers make the inequality false, shade the half of the side that does not contain the test point.

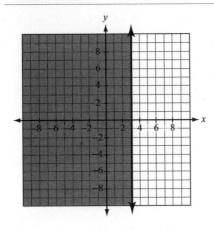

Example 4   Graph the inequality $x \le 3$.

Step 1: Identify the equation of the boundary line: $x = 3$.

Step 2: Because this inequality contains only an x and no y, the graph is a vertical line. Draw a vertical line through the point $(3, 0)$, since the equation is $x = 3$. Use a solid line because the inequality symbol is the less than or equal to symbol.

Step 3: Shade the half plane to the left of the line because the solution to the inequality includes all ordered pairs with x-values less than or equal to 3.

Problem Set

Graph the following linear inequalities:

1. $x \le -2$

2. $x > -2$

3. $x \le 3$

4. $y \ge 4$

5. $y < 4$

6. $x > -5$

7. $y < -1$

8. $y \le -3$

9. $y \le 3x$

10. $y \le -3x + 2$

11. $y < x - 2$

12. $y > 3x$

13. $y \ge 3x$

14. $y \ge 2x - 5$

15. $y \le \frac{1}{3}x$

16. $y > -\frac{1}{2}x + 2$

17. $2x - y \ge -2$

18. $2x - y \le -1$

19. $2x + 3y > 6$

20. $4x + 2y < 6$

HA1-416: Graphing Linear Inequalities with Two Variables Using the Graphing Calculator

In this lesson we will use the TI-83 Plus™ graphing calculator to describe the solutions of linear inequalities. The solutions to these inequalities are called half-planes. When we solve these inequalities, the linear equation defines a line or boundary that divides the coordinate plane into two half-planes. The coordinates that satisfy the inequality are the points on one of the half-planes.

If the line is included, the inequality symbols are $\geq$ or $\leq$ and the solution set is a closed half-plane. If the line is not included, the inequality symbols are $>$ or $<$ and the solution set is an open half-plane with the boundary represented by a dashed line.

The process has four steps:
- Step 0: (Settings) Initialize the calculator to a standard set of values so that we have a common starting point.
- Step 1: (Enter the expression) Enter the symbolic form of the inequality to be analyzed into the calculator.
- Step 2: (Graph) Obtain the graphs of the solution set from the symbolic form.
- Step 3: (Solve) Use information obtained graphically to describe the solution set or answer a specific question about the solutions of the inequality.

Before doing any of these examples you should check your calculator's settings to be sure that it will function as described above.

Press the MODE key and be sure that your settings appear as shown below.

Next press the 2nd ZOOM keys and be sure that your settings appear as shown below.

Press the ZOOM key then the 6 key to select the standard window setting.

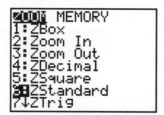

Press the WINDOW key to get the settings below.

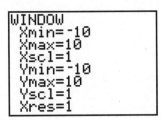

```
WINDOW
 Xmin=-10
 Xmax=10
 Xscl=1
 Ymin=-10
 Ymax=10
 Yscl=1
 Xres=1
```

Example 1   Is the point (2, 2) a solution to the linear inequality $y < 3x + 4$?

Step 0: (Settings) Make sure you have the default settings as described above.

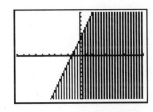

Step 1: (Enter the expression) Press the Y= key and enter the expression $3x + 4$ into the Y_1 slot.

Next, use the ◄ key to put the cursor as far to the left on the screen as possible.

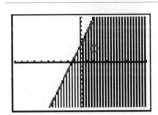

Note that the solid cursor becomes an underscore and it is blinking. Push ENTER ENTER ENTER to get the screen shown at left.

The symbol on the left tells the calculator to graph the solution to the "less than" or "less than or equal to" inequality type.

Step 2: (Graph) Press the GRAPH key.

Step 3: (Solve) Notice that all of the points "below" and to the "right" of the line are shaded. These points represent the points that satisfy the inequality. The points on the line are NOT part of the solution set. The point (2, 2) is clearly in the shaded region so it belongs to the solution set.

Answer: The point (2, 2) is a solution to the inequality $y < 3x + 4$.

Example 2   Which of the following set of ordered pairs is in the solution set of $4x - 3y \le 21$: $(1,-4)$, $(9, 8)$, $(6,-6)$, $(0,-7)$?

Step 0: (Settings) Make sure you have the default settings described at the beginning of the lesson.

Step 1: (Enter the expression) The inequality must be solved for y in order to use the graphing calculator.

Adding $3y$ to both sides gives us:
$$4x \le 3y + 21.$$
Subtracting 21 from both sides gives us:
$$4x - 21 \le 3y.$$
Finally, dividing both sides by 3 gives us:
$$\frac{4x - 21}{3} \le y \text{ or } y \ge \frac{4x - 21}{3}.$$

Press the $\boxed{Y=}$ key and enter the expression $\dfrac{4x - 21}{3}$ into the Y_1 slot.

Use the $\boxed{\triangleleft}$ key to put the cursor as far to the left on the screen as possible. Note that the solid cursor becomes an underscore and it is blinking. Press $\boxed{ENTER}$ $\boxed{ENTER}$ so that the screen looks like the one to the left.

The symbol on the left tells the calculator to graph the solution to the "greater than" or "greater than or equal to" inequality type.

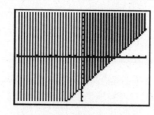

Step 2: (Graph) Press the $\boxed{GRAPH}$ key.

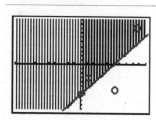

Step 3: (Solve) Notice that all of the points "above" and to the "left" of the line are shaded. These points represent the points that satisfy the inequality. The points on the line are part of the solution set. The points $(1,-4)$, and $(9, 8)$ are in the shaded region so they belong to the solution set. The point $(0,-7)$ is on the line and is also included in the solution set. The point $(6,-6)$ is not in the solution set.

Answer: The points $(1, -4)$, $(9, 8)$, and $(0, -7)$ belong to the solution set, but the point $(6, -6)$ does not.

Problem Set

1. Which of the following set of ordered pairs is in the solution set of $x - y \geq 2$?

   (6, 3)   (–1, –1)

   (–4, 0)   (–4, –2)

2. Which of the following set of ordered pairs is in the solution set of $3x - 6y > 15$?

   (2, 1)   (3.5, –2.5)

   (–5, 0)   (0, –2)

3. Which of the following set of ordered pairs is in the solution set of $-3x + 2y \geq 4$?

   (–1, –1)   (2, 1)

   (2, 5)   (0, 0)

4. Which of the following set of ordered pairs is in the solution set of $4x - 3y < 21$?

   (3, –4)   (0, –7)

   (6, –6)   (9, 8)

5. Sam bought x number of chocolate bars for $1.50 each and y number of candies for 50 cents each. He spent less than $10. Use the graphing calculator to graph the inequality $1.50x + 0.50y < 10$ and determine which of the following points represents a reasonable number of chocolate bars and candies bought.

   (3, –2)   (–1, 4)

   (4, 10)   (3, 7)

6. In her piggy bank, Keisha had x number of quarters and y number of nickels; together, the coins totaled more than $1.50. Use the graphing calculator to graph the inequality $0.25x + 0.05y > 1.50$ and determine which of the following points represents a reasonable number of quarters and nickels Keisha collected.

   (5, 3)   (9, –4)

   (–2, 4)   (5, 8)

7. Jim bought x CDs for $14 each and y DVDs for $21 each. He spent no more than $84. Use the graphing calculator to graph the inequality $14x + 21y \leq 84$ and determine which of the following points represents a reasonable possible total for the number of CDs and DVDs Sam bought.

   (–1, 4)   (5, –2)

   (3, 2)   (4, 3)

8. ABC school purchased new computer equipment for its computer labs. The school purchased x computers at $1,850 each and y printers at $545 each. The school spent no less than $29,500. Use the graphing calculator to graph the inequality $1850x + 545y \geq 29,500$ and determine which of the following points represents a reasonable number of computers and printers the school purchased.

   (–5, 36)   (18, 3)

   (10, 4)   (20, –2)

9. Draw the graph that represents the solution of the inequality $y > \frac{1}{4}x - 3$.

10. Draw the graph that represents the solution of the inequality $8x + 4y \leq 6$.

A **relation** is a set of ordered pairs like: {(1, 4), (2, 4), (3, 6), (5, 0), (2,–2), (–5, 8)}.

Relation	A set of ordered pairs

Each ordered pair has two coordinates: the x-coordinate, or first coordinate, and the y-coordinate, or second coordinate. For example, in the ordered pair (1, 4), 1 is the "x" coordinate and 4 is the "y" coordinate.

The set of first coordinates (x-coordinates) of the ordered pairs in the relation is called the **domain** of the relation. The set of second coordinates (y-coordinates) of the ordered pairs is called the **range** of the relation.

Domain of a Relation	The set of all x-coordinates (first coordinates) from the ordered pairs in the relation

Range of a Relation	The set of all y-coordinates (second coordinates) from the ordered pairs in the relation

Since relations consist of ordered pairs, we can create a graph of a relation by plotting points in a Cartesian Plane. Relations can also be given by equations.

Example 1   What is the domain of the relation {(1, 4), (2, 4), (3, 6), (5, 0), (2, –2), (–5, 8)}?

Step 1:   The x-coordinates of the ordered pairs in the relation are {1, 2, 3, 5, –5}, so this is the domain of the relation. Notice that although 2 appears in two of the ordered pairs, it only appears once in the domain.

Answer: The domain of the relation is {1, 2, 3, 5, –5}.

Example 2   Express the mapping as a set of ordered pairs and state the domain and range of the relation.

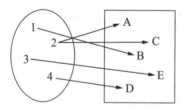

Ordered pairs:
{(1, B), (2, A), (2, C), (3, E), (4, D)}

Step 1:   Find the set of ordered pairs.

Domain: {1, 2, 3, 4}

Step 2:   Find the domain.
Note: Remember, the domain is the set of all x-values (first coordinates).

Range: {A, B, C, D, E}

Step 3: Find the range.

Note:Remember, the range is the set of all y-values (second coordinates).

Answer: Set of ordered pairs: {(1, B), (2, A), (2, C), (3, E), (4, D)}
Domain: {1, 2, 3, 4}
Range: {A, B, C, D, E}

Example 3   Graph the relation: {(1,4), (2,4), (3,6), (5,0), (2, −2), (−5,8)}

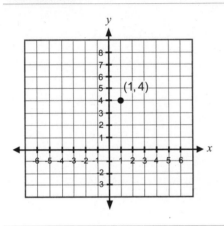

Step 1: To plot the point (1, 4), start at the origin and move 1 unit to the right, and then 4 units upward. This is the point (1, 4).

Step 2: Continue plotting the remaining points in the same manner.

Answer: The graph of the relation consists of the plotted points of all of the ordered pairs.

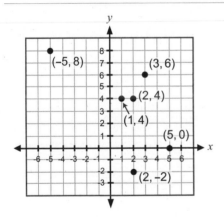

Relations can also be given by equations. For example, the set of all points (x, y) that satisfy the equation $4x + 3y = 11$ forms a relation.

Example 4   Check if the ordered pairs $(2, 1)$ and $(1, 2)$ satisfy the relation $4x + 3y = 11$.

$4x + 3y = 11$

$4(2) + 3(1) \stackrel{?}{=} 11$

$8 + 3 \stackrel{?}{=} 11$

$11 = 11$ True

Step 1:   First, check the point $(2, 1)$. Substitute 2 for x and 1 for y, and we get 11. Therefore, the point $(2, 1)$ satisfies the relation.

$4x + 3y = 11$

$4(1) + 3(2) \stackrel{?}{=} 11$

$4 + 6 \stackrel{?}{=} 11$

$10 \neq 11$ False

Step 2:   Next, check the point $(1, 2)$. Substitute 1 for x and 2 for y, and we get 10. Therefore, the point $(1, 2)$ does not satisfy the relation.

Answer: The point $(2, 1)$ satisfies the relation determined by the equation $4x + 3y = 11$ and the point $(1, 2)$ does not.

Example 5   In the following picture, a relation is represented as a graph made up of many ordered pairs. Find the domain and the range.

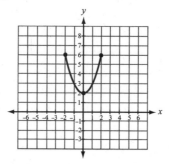

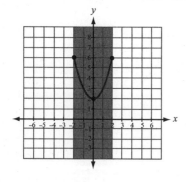

Step 1:   The domain consists of all x-values for points that are on the graph. From the picture you can see that x-values begin at -2 and end at 2. Therefore, the domain is the set of all x-values from -2 to 2.

This is written as $-2 \leq x \leq 2$.

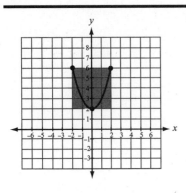

Step 2: The range consists of all *y*-values for points that are on the graph. From the picture you can see that the *y*-values begin at 2 and end at 6. Therefore, the range is the set of all *y*-values from 2 to 6. This is written as $2 \leq y \leq 6$.

Answer: The domain of the relation is $-2 \leq x \leq 2$ and the range of the relation is $2 \leq y \leq 6$.

Problem Set

1. Using the table below, state the domain and the range of the relation.

x	10	–1	–2	10
y	6	–2	3	3

2. What are the coordinates of point V?

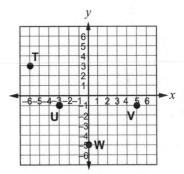

3. Use the mapping below to find the domain and the range of the relation.

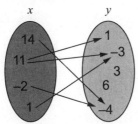

4. What are the coordinates of point W?

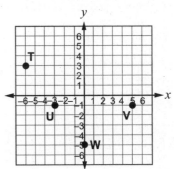

5. State the domain and range of the given relation:

$\{(0, 2), (-2, 0), (-4, -2), (-4, 0)\}$

6. What are the coordinates of point A?

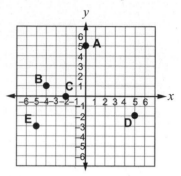

7. Given the following set of points in the plane, state the domain and the range.

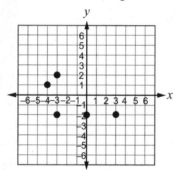

8. What are the coordinates of point B?

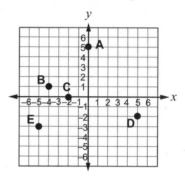

9. Given the following set of points in the plane, state the domain and the range.

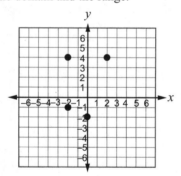

10. What are the coordinates of point C?

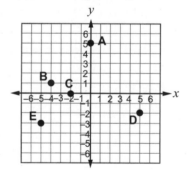

11. From the table below, state the domain and the range of the relation.

x	−1	3	4	7
y	0	0	0	0

12. What are the coordinates of point D?

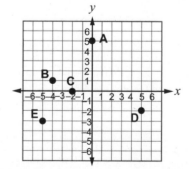

13. Use the mapping below to find the domain and the range of the relation.

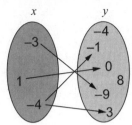

14. What are the coordinates of point E?

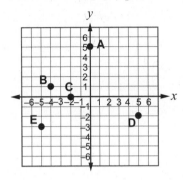

15. Given the following set of points in the plane, state the domain and the range.

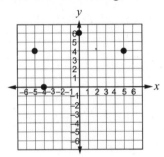

16. Use a compound inequality to describe the range of the given graph.

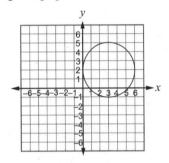

17. Do the ordered pairs (–3, 6) and (0, 4) satisfy the relation $2x + 3y = 12$?

Both points satisfy the relation.

Neither point satisfies the relation.

(0, 4) satisfies the relation.

(–3, 6) satisfies the relation, but (0, 4) does not.

18. Use a compound inequality to describe the domain of the given graph.

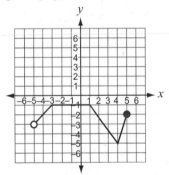

19. Do the ordered pairs (3, 2) and (0, 8) satisfy the relation $2x - y = 8$?

Both points satisfy the relation.

Neither point satisfies the relation.

(0, 8) satisfies the relation. but (3, 2) does not.

(3, 2) satisfies the relation, but (0, 8) does not.

20. Use a compound inequality to describe the range of the given graph.

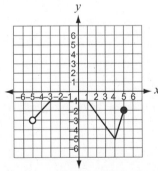

21. Do the ordered pairs (3, –2) and (–2, 1) satisfy the relation $4x + 9y = -6$?

    (3, –2) satisfies the relation, but (–2, 1) does not.

    Both points satisfy the relation.

    Neither point satisfies the relation.

    (3, –2) satisfies the relation, but (–2, 1) does not.

22. Use a compound inequality to describe the domain of the given graph.

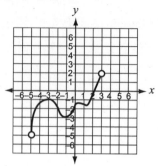

23. Do the ordered pairs (–2, 6) and (1, 9) satisfy the relation $5x - y = -4$?

    (1, 9) satisfies the relation, but (–2, 6) does not.

    (–2, 6) satisfies the relation, but (1, 9) does not.

    Both points satisfy the relation.

    Neither point satisfies the relation.

24. Use a compound inequality to describe the range of the given graph.

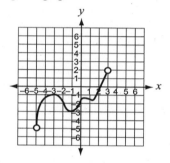

25. Do the ordered pairs (1, 3) and (–1, 1) satisfy the relation $-3x + 2y = 4$?

    Both points satisfy the relation.

    (1, 3) satisfies the relation, but (–1, 1) does not.

    Neither point satisfies the relation.

    (–1, 1) satisfies the relation, but (1, 3) does not.

26. Use a compound inequality to describe the domain of the given graph.

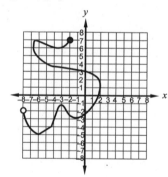

27. Do the ordered pairs (16, 5) and (–5, –2) satisfy the relation $-3y + x - 1 = 0$?

    Neither point satisfies the relation.

    Both points satisfy the relation.

    (16, 5) satisfies the relation, but (–5, –2) does not.

    (–5, –2) satisfies the relation, but (16, 5) does not.

28. Use a compound inequality to describe the range of the given graph.

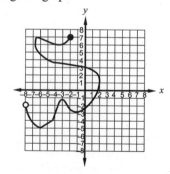

29. Do the ordered pairs $(-2, -9)$ and $(2, 5)$ satisfy the relation $x - y = 7$?

Both points satisfy the relation.

Neither point satisfies the relation.

$(-2, -9)$ satisfies the relation, but $(2, 5)$ does not.

$(2, 5)$ satisfies the relation, but $(-2, -9)$ does not.

30. Use a compound inequality to describe the domain of the given graph.

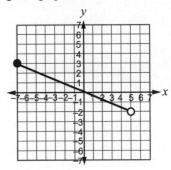

31. For the relation $3x - y = 6$, complete the table of values.

x	2		6
y		3	

32. For the relation $x + y = 5$, complete the table of values.

x		2	
y	-3		-5

33. For the relation $x + 2y = 10$, complete the table of values.

x	0	-2	
y			-5

34. For the relation $6x + 2y = 15$, complete the table of values.

x		0	
y	3		6

35. For the relation $7x + y = 14$, complete the table of values.

x	0		2
y		7	

36. For the relation $4x - 3y = 12$, complete the table of values.

x		-3	
y	2		-4

37. For the relation $x + 2y = 6$, complete the table of values.

x	0		4
y		-1	

38. For the relation $9x - 5y = 1$, complete the table of values.

x	0		-4
y		-2	

39. For the relation $-3x + 4y = 24$, complete the table of values.

x		-8	
y	-3		3

40. For the relation $x - y = 2$, complete the table of values.

x		-1	
y	-2		-1

A **relation** is a set of ordered pairs; these pairs can be specified in a number of ways:

- We can list the ordered pairs that make up the relation: $\{(1, 2), (2, 3), (4, 7)\}$

- We can write these in the form of a table:

x	1	2	4
y	2	3	7

- We can draw a relation like a map:

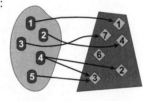

- We can plot points on a plane:

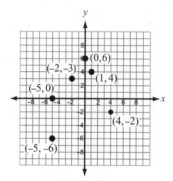

- We can create a graph of many ordered pairs:

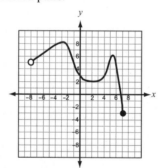

- Finally, we can specify a relation by an equation which the points in the relation must satisfy:

$$(x + y)(x - y) = 0$$

Functions are special types of relations. A **function** is a relation in which each element of the domain is paired with exactly one element of the range.

To determine whether or not a relation is a function, we must check that each element from the domain is paired with exactly one element from the range.

Note: **Two or more elements of the domain of a function might be paired with the same element of the range. However, one element of the domain can never be paired with more than one element of the range.**

Function	A relation in which each element of the domain is paired with exactly one element of the range

---

Example 1   Write the ordered pairs represented by this function.

x	-2	10	5	8
y	3	1	8	4

$\{(-2, 3), (10, 1), (5, 8), (8, 4)\}$ **Step 1:** Write each matched set of numbers as an ordered pair.

Answer: $\{(-2, 3), (10, 1), (5, 8), (8, 4)\}$

Example 2   Find the domain and range of the given function.

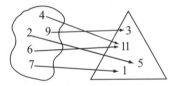

$\{(4, 11), (9, 3), (2, 5), (6, 11), (7, 1)\}$ **Step 1:** Find the set of ordered pairs that belongs to this function.

Domain: $\{4, 9, 2, 6, 7\}$ **Step 2:** Find the domain. (Remember, the domain is the set of all x-values.)

Range: $\{11, 3, 5, 1\}$ **Step 3:** Find the range. (Remember, the range is the set of all y-values.)

Answer: The domain is $\{4, 9, 2, 6, 7\}$ and the range is $\{11, 3, 5, 1\}$.

Example 3   Is the relation $\{(1, 5), (2, 6), (3, 7), (4, 1)\}$ a function?

Domain: $\{1, 2, 3, 4\}$ **Step 1:** Determine the domain of the set of ordered pairs.

Step 2: Determine whether or not each element of the domain is paired with exactly one element of the range.

Answer: This relation is a function, since each element of the domain is paired with exactly one element of the range.

Example 4 The relation is given as the set of points in the plane. Write the relation as a set of ordered pairs, find its domain, and determine whether or not it is a function.

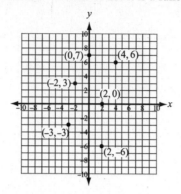

{(−3, −3), (−2,3), (0,7), (2,0), (2, −6), (4,6)}	**Step 1:**	Write the ordered pairs that make up the relation.
Domain: {−3, −2, 0, 2, 4}	**Step 2:**	Determine the domain of the set of ordered pairs.
	Step 3:	Determine if each element of the domain is paired with exactly one element of the range. The *x*-value 2 is paired with two different *y*-values, 0 and −6. Therefore, the relation is not a function.
	Answer:	The graph of the relation does not represent a function.

There is an easier method to determine whether or not the previous example is the graph of a function. This method is called the **vertical line test**. If there is a vertical line that intersects the graph at more than one point, the graph of the relation is NOT a function. If no vertical lines hit the graph more than once, the graph represents the graph of a function.

Vertical Line Test	If there is a vertical line that intersects the graph at more than one point, the graph of the relation is not a function. If no vertical lines hit the graph more than once, the graph represents the graph of a function.

For instance, in Example 4, if a vertical line is drawn at $x = 2$, the vertical line intersects two points in the relation. Therefore, the relation is not a function.

Example 5   Does the given graph represent the graph of a function?

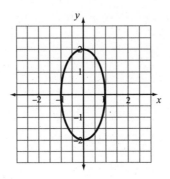

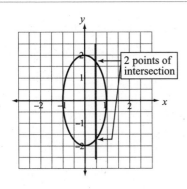

Step 1: We apply the vertical line test and see that there are vertical lines that intersect this graph more than once. Therefore, this relation is not a function.

Answer: The vertical line test shows that this graph is not the graph of a function.

Problem Set

Solve:

1. Write the ordered pairs represented by this function:

x	-2	0	-1	7
y	6	-2	3	3

2. Use the vertical line test to determine whether or not the given graph is the graph of a function. Write "yes" if it is a function and "no" if it is not a function.

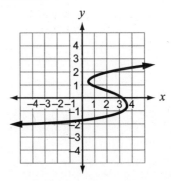

3. Write the ordered pairs represented by this function:

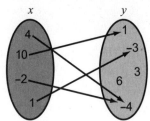

4. Use the vertical line test to determine whether or not the given graph is the graph of a function. Write "yes" if it is a function and "no" if it is not a function.

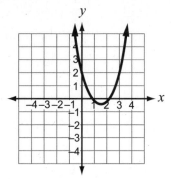

5. Write the ordered pairs represented by this function:

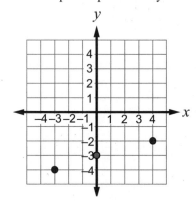

6. Use the vertical line test to determine whether or not the given graph is the graph of a function. Write "yes" if it is a function and "no" if it is not a function.

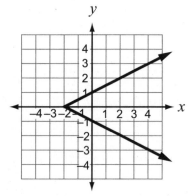

7. Write the ordered pairs represented by this function:

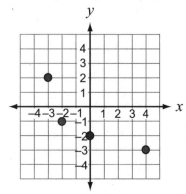

8. Use the vertical line test to determine whether or not the given graph is the graph of a function. Write "yes" if it is a function and "no" if it is not a function.

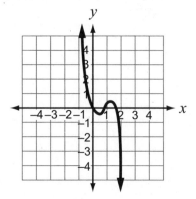

9. Write the ordered pairs represented by this function:

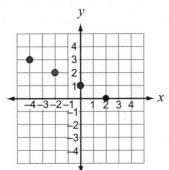

10. Use the vertical line test to determine whether or not the given graph is the graph of a function. Write "yes" if it is a function and "no" if it is not a function.

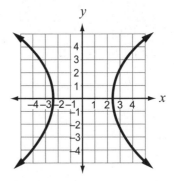

11. Write the ordered pairs represented by this function:

x	−1	1	3	5
y	0	0	0	0

12. Use the vertical line test to determine whether or not the given graph is the graph of a function. Write "yes" if it is a function and "no" if it is not a function.

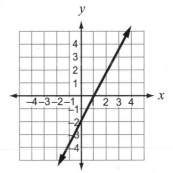

13. Write the ordered pairs represented by this function:

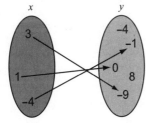

14. Use the vertical line test to determine whether or not the given graph is the graph of a function. Write "yes" if it is a function and "no" if it is not a function.

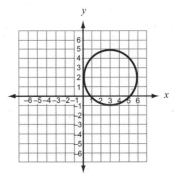

15. Write the ordered pairs represented by this function:

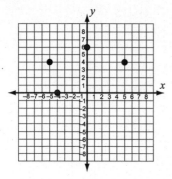

16. Find the range of the given function:

x	−2	1	−1	8
y	6	−2	4	4

17. Find the domain of the given function:

x	−2	1	−1	8
y	6	−2	4	4

18. Find the range of the given function:

{(2, 3), (−2, 4), (0, 4), (1, 7)}

19. Find the domain of the given function:

{(2, 3), (−2, 4), (0, 4), (1, 7)}

20. Find the range of the given function:

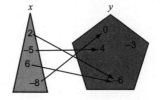

21. Find the domain of the given function:

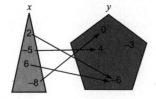

22. Find the range of the given function:

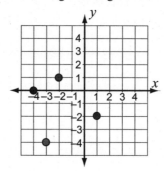

23. Find the domain of the given function:

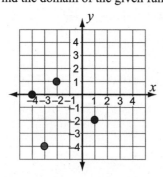

24. Find the range of the given function:

x	−1	5	−2	6
y	3	−1	−1	3

25. Find the domain of the given function:

x	−1	5	−2	6
y	3	−1	−1	3

26. Find the range of the given function:

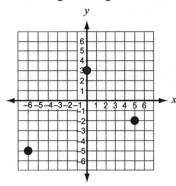

27. Find the domain of the given function:

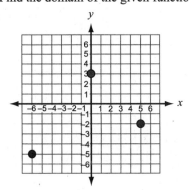

28. Find the range of the given function:

$\{(-5, 1), (2, -4), (0.5, 7.9)\}$

29. Find the domain of the given function:

$\{(-5, 1), (2, -4), (0.5, 7.9)\}$

30. Find the range of the given function:

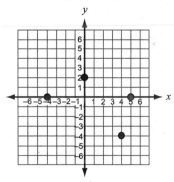

31. Is the following relation a function?
Answer yes or no.

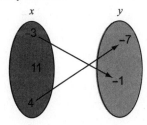

32. Is the following relation a function?
Answer yes or no.

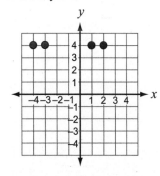

33. Is the following relation a function? Answer yes or no.

$$\{(-7, 2), (-5, 1), (-7, 0)\}$$

34. Is the following relation a function? Answer yes or no.

x	−1	0	−3	5
y	6	3	3	3

35. Is the following relation a function? Answer yes or no.

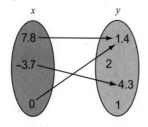

36. Is the following relation a function? Answer yes or no.

$$\{(0, 10), (5, 10), (10, 10)\}$$

37. Is the following relation a function? Answer yes or no.

x	0	3	4
y	−2	−1	−2

38. Is the following relation a function? Answer yes or no.

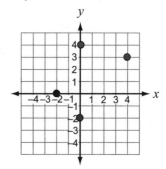

39. Which of the following relations represents a function?

$$\{(3, 2), (4, 2), (3, -5)\}$$
$$\{(7, -7), (4, 2), (7, 0)\}$$
$$\{(-1, 4), (2, 0), (-3, 4)\}$$
$$\{(0, 2), (4, 2), (4, -5)\}$$

40. Is the following relation a function? Answer yes or no.

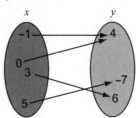

It is important to review what we have learned about relations and functions. A **relation** is a set of ordered pairs. The **domain** of a relation is the set of all first coordinates (x-coordinates) from the ordered pairs in the relation. The **range** of a relation is the set of all second coordinates (y-coordinates) from the ordered pairs in the relation.

A **function** is a relation in which <u>each</u> element of the domain is paired with <u>exactly one</u> element of the range. Recall that we can check to see whether or not the graph of a relation is a function by using the vertical line test. The **vertical line test** states that a graph is the graph of a function if any vertical line drawn on the graph crosses the graph at no more than one point.

To determine the domain of a function, we determine the x-coordinates of all points on the graph. To determine the range of a function, we determine the y-coordinates of all of the points on the graph.

Example 1	Suppose that a function is given by the equation $y = 5x - 6$ and the domain is given as $\{-2, -1, 0, 1, 2, 3\}$. What is the range of this function?

$y = 5(-2) - 6$
$= -10 - 6$
$= -16$

Step 1: Substitute $x = -2$ into the equation and solve.

$y = 5(-1) - 6$
$= -5 - 6$
$= -11$

Step 2: Substitute $x = -1$ into the equation and solve.

$y = 5(0) - 6$
$= 0 - 6$
$= -6$

Step 3: Substitute $x = 0$ into the equation and solve.

$y = 5(1) - 6$
$= 5 - 6$
$= -1$

Step 4: Substitute $x = 1$ into the equation and solve.

$y = 5(2) - 6$
$= 10 - 6$
$= 4$

Step 5: Substitute $x = 2$ into the equation and solve.

$y = 5(3) - 6$
$= 15 - 6$
$= 9$

Step 6: Substitute $x = 3$ into the equation and solve.

Answer: The range is $\{-16, -11, -6, -1, 4, 9\}$.

In general, the variable that takes values from the domain of the function is called an **independent variable**. The variable whose values are computed from the values of the independent variable and form the range of the function is called the **dependent variable**.

Independent Variable	The variable that takes its value from the domain

Dependent Variable	The variable whose values are computed from the values of the independent variable and form the range of the function

Note: Unless specified otherwise, when solving an equation for one of the variables, that variable becomes the dependent variable and the other variable becomes the independent variable.

Example 2   Given the equation $y = 4z - 10$, find the independent and dependent variables.

Dependent variable: y **Step 1:**   Since the equation is solved for y, y is the dependent variable and its values form the range.

Independent variable: z **Step 2:**   The remaining variable, z, is the independent variable, and its values form the domain.

     Answer: The dependent variable is y, and the independent variable is z.

Example 3   A function has a range of $\{-4, 0, 4\}$. Its independent variable, a, and its dependent variable, b, satisfy the equation $4a - 3b = 12$. Find the domain.

$$4a - 3(-4) = 12$$
$$4a + 12 = 12$$
$$4a = 0$$
$$a = 0$$

Step 1:   Substitute $b = -4$ into the equation and solve.

$$4a - 3(0) = 12$$
$$4a + 0 = 12$$
$$4a = 12$$
$$a = 3$$

Step 2:   Substitute $b = 0$ into the equation and solve.

$$4a - 3(4) = 12$$
$$4a - 12 = 12$$
$$4a = 24$$
$$a = 6$$

Step 3:   Substitute $b = 4$ into the equation and solve.

     Step 4:   All of the values from steps 1, 2, and 3 make up the domain.

     Answer: The domain is $\{0, 3, 6\}$.

Example 4   Determine whether or not the following equation $3x + 6y = 12$ is a function, given that x is the independent variable and y is the dependent variable.

$$6y = -3x + 12$$
$$y = -\frac{1}{2}x + 2$$

Step 1:   Solve the equation for y, since y is the dependent variable.

$x = 0$	$x = 2$
$y = -\frac{1}{2}(0) + 2$	$y = -\frac{1}{2}(2) + 2$
$y = 2$	$y = -1 + 2$
	$y = 1$

Step 2: For every real number x, determine if there is one and only one value for y.

Step 3: As we see in the examples in Step 2, if we choose any number for x, we will obtain one, and only one, value for y.

Answer: The equation $3x + 6y = 12$ is a function.

Example 5   Find the domain and range of the function from the graph.

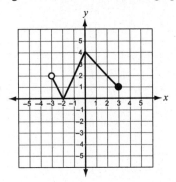

Step 1: Notice that the graph has an open circle at the point $(-3, 2)$. This means the point is not included in the function.

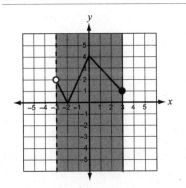

Step 2: Draw vertical lines through the endpoints on the left and right sides of the graph at $x = -3$ and $x = 3$. Since the point $(-3, 2)$ is not included in the function, use a dashed line at $x = -3$.

$-3 < x \le 3$

Step 3: Determine the domain, or x-coordinates, of all points. The x-values are between -3 and 3, with -3 not included.

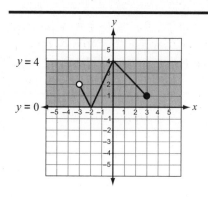

$y = 4$

$y = 0$

Step 4: Draw horizontal lines through the highest and lowest points on the graph at $y = 0$ and $y = 4$.

$0 \leq y \leq 4$

Step 5: Determine the range, or the y-coordinates of all points. The y-values are between 0 and 4, with both numbers included.

Answer: The domain is $-3 < x \leq 3$, and the range is $0 \leq y \leq 4$.

Problem Set

1. Find the range of $y = 3x^2 + 2$ when the domain is $\{-3, 0, 2\}$.

2. Find the range of $y = -3x + 2$ when the domain is $\{-4, -1, 3.5\}$.

3. Find the range of $y = 6 - 4x^2$ when the domain is $\{-1, 1, 2\}$.

4. Find the range of $y = 5 - 2x$ when the domain is $\{-4, -2, 3.5\}$.

5. Find the range of $y = -x^2 + 7$ when the domain is $\{-1, 0, 2\}$.

6. Find the range of $y = -6x - 1$ when the domain is $\{-3, -2, -1\}$.

7. Find the range of $y = -2x^2$ when the domain is $\{-1, 0, 2\}$.

8. Find the range of $y = 3x - 12$ when the domain is $\{-3, -1, 1\}$.

9. A function has a range of $\{0, 4, -4\}$. Its dependent variable, y, and its independent variable, x, satisfy the equation $4x - y = 8$. Find the domain of the function.

10. A function has a range of $\{-2, -1, 3\}$. Its dependent variable, v, and its independent variable, u, satisfy the equation $2u + 3v = 0$. Find the domain of the function.

11. A function has a range of $\{-6, 0, 3\}$. Its dependent variable, y, and its independent variable, x, satisfy the equation $3x + y = -12$. Find the domain of the function.

12. A function has a range of $\{-2, -1, 4\}$. Its dependent variable, v, and its independent variable, u, satisfy the equation $u - v = 10$. Find the domain of the function.

13. A function has a range of $\{2.5, -2, -4.5\}$. Its dependent variable, y, and its independent variable, x, satisfy the equation $x - 2y = 12$. Find the domain of the function.

14. A function has a range of $\{-5, 2, 9\}$. Its dependent variable, v, and its independent variable, u, satisfy the equation $7u + v = 9$. Find the domain of the function.

15. A function has a range of $\{8, 4, -4\}$. Its dependent variable, y, and its independent variable, x, satisfy the equation $y = 2x - 6$. Find the domain of the function.

16. Which of the following equations represents a function with dependent variable y?

$$x^2 - 2y^2 = 4 \qquad x^2 - 2y = 4$$
$$x^2 - 2y^2 = 4 - 2y \qquad x - 2y^2 = 4$$

17. Which of the following equations represents a function with independent variable x?

$$y^2 + 2x = 9 \qquad 6 - x = y^2$$
$$3x - 2y = 6 \qquad x^2 - 4 = 12$$

18. Which of the following equations represents a function with independent variable u?

$$u = -3 \qquad v + 3 = 2u - (2 - v)$$
$$4u^2 + v = 16 \qquad u + v^2 = -2$$

19. Which of the following equations represents a function with dependent variable v?

$$u + 2v = 6 \qquad u = 1$$
$$u + v^2 = 0 \qquad v^2 = 9 - u$$

20. Which of the following equations represents a function with dependent variable y?

$$3y + x = 3(2 + y) \qquad y = -4$$
$$x^2 + y^2 = 4 \qquad x = -2$$

21. Which of the following equations represents a function with independent variable x?

$$y = 9 - (x - y) \qquad x = 9 - 2y^2$$
$$y = 9 - 2x^2 \qquad x = 3$$

22. Which of the following equations represents a function with independent variable u?

$$u^2 = 2v \qquad u + v^2 = 2$$
$$u = 2 \qquad v^2 = 2$$

23. Which of the following equations represents a function with dependent variable v?

$$u = 4 \qquad v = 4 + 3(u^2 - 1)$$
$$u = 4 + 3v^2 \qquad u + v = 3 - (2 - v)$$

24. Which of the following is a function that has a dependent variable, v, given that u is the independent variable?

$$v = 4x^2 - 1 \qquad u = 4v^2 - 1$$
$$v = 4u^2 - 1 \qquad y = 4u^2 - 1$$

25. Which of the following is a function that has an independent variable, u, given that v is the dependent variable?

$$4x - v = 7 \qquad y = 4u - 7$$
$$4u - v = 7 \qquad 4u - v^2 = 7$$

26. Which of the following is a function that has a dependent variable, y, given that x is the independent variable?

$$x^2 + v = 4 \qquad x^2 + y = 4$$
$$x + y^2 = 4 \qquad u + x^2 = 4$$

27. Which of the following is a function that has an independent variable, x, given that y is the dependent variable?

$$3u - 2y = 10 \qquad 3x - 2v = 10$$
$$3x - 2y^2 = 10 \qquad 3x - 2y = 10$$

28. Which of the following is a function that has a dependent variable, v, given that u is the independent variable?

$$u^2 + 2y = 8 \qquad u^2 + 2v = 8$$
$$u + 2v^2 = 8 \qquad x + 2v^2 = 8$$

29. Which of the following is a function that has an independent variable, u, given that v is the dependent variable?

$$y = -4u + 3 \qquad u = -4v^2 + 3$$
$$v = -4x + 3 \qquad v = -4u + 3$$

30. Which of the following is a function that has a dependent variable, y, given that x is the independent variable?

$$y + x^2 = 0 \qquad y + u^2 = 0$$
$$y^2 + x = 0 \qquad v + x^2 = 0$$

31. Write the domain of the given function:

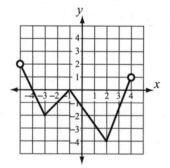

32. Write the range of the given function:

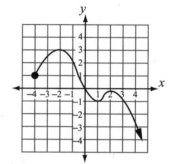

33. Write the domain of the given function:

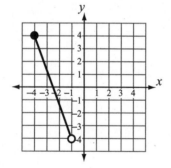

34. Write the range of the given function:

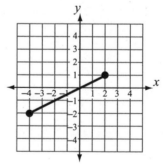

35. Write the domain of the given function:

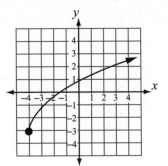

36. Write the range of the given function:

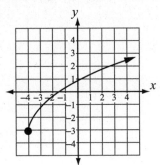

37. Write the domain of the given function:

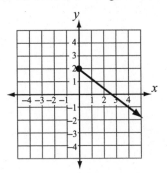

38. Write the range of the given function:

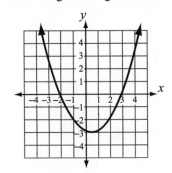

39. Write the range of the given function:

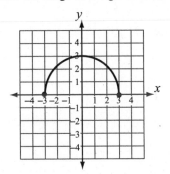

40. Write the domain of the given function:

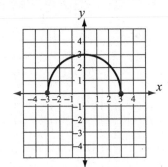

An equation in the form $y = mx + b$ has a graph that is a linear function. We treat the variable x as the independent variable (domain) and the variable y as the dependent variable (range). To emphasize the function-like properties of this equation, we replace y with another name, like f, g, or "cost." To show that the value of f depends on x, the equation $y = 4x + 5$ may be written as $f(x) = 4x + 5$. This is called **function notation**.

Note: This is not "f times x." It is a notation that shows that the function f has an independent variable x. It is read "f of x."

For a value of x in the domain (let's say $x = 3$), we can compute a value for the range. In the equation $y = 4x + 5$, the value for the range is $f(3) = 4(3) + 5 = 12 + 5 = 17$. Notice that we have replaced all of the x-values in the original equation with the number 3. A function is a rule that assigns exactly one output to each input.

Symbolically, this function can be represented by:

$$3 \text{ (input)} \rightarrow 17 \text{ (output)}$$

In general, we have:

$$x \text{ (input)} \rightarrow f(x) \text{ (output)}$$

Function Rule	A rule that assigns exactly one output to each input

---

Example 1   Let the function $k(x) = x^2 - 2x$. What is the independent variable? What is the value of the function when the independent variable has a value of 8?

The function k has the independent variable x.	**Step 1:** Identify the independent variable.
$k(8) = 8^2 - 2(8)$	**Step 2:** Substitute $x = 8$ into the function.
$= 64 - 16$ $= 48$	**Step 3:** Simplify.
	Answer: The independent variable is x and $k(8) = 48$.

Example 2   If $f(x) = x^2 + 3x - 2$, what is $f(-1)$, $f(0)$, and $f(5)$?

$f(-1) = (-1)^2 + 3(-1) - 2$ $= 1 - 3 - 2$ $= -2 - 2$ $= -4$	**Step 1:** To compute $f(-1)$ we replace each x with -1.

$$f(0) = (0)^2 + 3(0) - 2$$
$$= 0 + 0 - 2$$
$$= 0 - 2$$
$$= -2$$

Step 2: To compute $f(0)$ we replace each x with 0.

$$f(5) = (5)^2 + 3(5) - 2$$
$$= 25 + 15 - 2$$
$$= 40 - 2$$
$$= 38$$

Step 3: To compute $f(5)$ we replace each x with 5.

Answer: $f(-1) = -4, f(0) = -2, f(5) = 38.$

Example 3 Given the following table:

A) Find $g(1)$

B) Find a when $g(a) = 2$

a	4	1	-2	-6
$g(a)$	-6	3	2	1

Step 1: In $g(1)$, $a = 1$, so locate 1 in the first row of the table.

a	4	1	-2	-6
$g(a)$	-6	3	2	1

Step 2: Look in the second row of the table for the output value.

a	4	1	-2	-6
$g(a)$	-6	3	2	1

$$g(1) = 3$$

Step 3: To find a when $g(a) = 2$, locate 2 in the second row of the table.

a	4	1	-2	-6
$g(a)$	-6	3	2	1

Step 4: Look in the first row of the table for the input value.

a	4	1	-2	-6
$g(a)$	-6	3	2	1

$a = -2$ when $g(a) = 2$

Answer: A) $g(1) = 3$

B) $a = -2$ when $g(a) = 2$

Example 4   Consider the graph of the function shown below. Find $f(1)$ and $f(4)$.

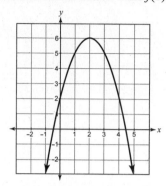

$f(1) = 5$

Step 1: $f(1)$ denotes an input of 1. An input of 1 means that $x = 1$. Looking at the vertical line $x = 1$, we see that the corresponding y-value is 5.

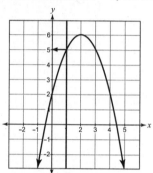

$f(4) = 2$

Step 2: $f(4)$ denotes an input of 4. An input of 4 means that $x = 4$. Looking at the vertical line $x = 4$, we see that the corresponding y-value is 2.

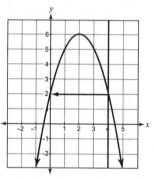

Answer: $f(1) = 5$ and $f(4) = 2$

Example 5 Consider the graph of the function shown.

A) Find x such that $f(x) = 7$.

B) Find x such that $f(x) = -1$.

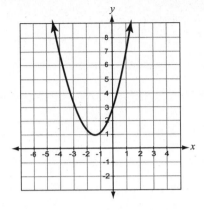

Step 1: To find the input value x when $f(x) = 7$, draw a horizontal line through 7 on the y-axis. We can see that x can either be -4 or 1.

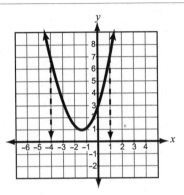

Step 2: Note that this does not contradict the idea of functions, because each value of the domain still determines only one value of the range.

Step 3: For the output of -1, we draw the horizontal through the line $y = -1$.

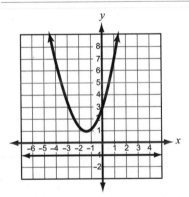

Step 4: Since this line does not intersect our graph we know that -1 is not in the range. Therefore, x is undefined at -1.

Answer: A) When $f(x) = 7$, $x = -4$ or $x = 1$

B) When $f(x) = -1$, x is undefined.

Problem Set

1. Let $f(x) = 4 - 2x$. Find $f(-2)$.

2. Let $g(x) = 5 - x^2$. Find $g(-3)$.

3. Let $g(u) = u^2 - 2u$. Find $g(-1)$.

4. Let $k(x) = 5 + 3x - x^2$. Find $k(1)$.

5. Let $r(x) = 5 - 3x + x^2$. Find $r(0)$.

6. Let $p(x) = 2x^2 - 7$. Find $p(-3)$.

7. Let $q(a) = a^2 - 6a + 2$. Find $q(2)$.

8. Let $g(x) = 6 - 9x$. Find $g(-1)$.

9. Use the table to find $f(2)$.

x	-4	-3	2	-1
$f(x)$	8	4	0	-2

10. Use the table to find $g(4)$.

t	0	5	4	-5
$g(t)$	4	3	2	1

11. Use the table to find $f(-6)$.

a	-6	-2	2	6
$f(a)$	2	4	8	-6

12. Use the table to find $r(-2)$.

u	9	5	-2	-5
$r(u)$	6	4	9	-2

13. Use the table to find $f(0)$.

c	0	1	2	3
$f(c)$	5	3	1	0

14. Use the table to find $f(-2)$.

x	0	1	-2	3
$f(x)$	6	-5	-2	-2

15. Use the table to find $g(-6)$.

a	4	1	-2	-6
$g(a)$	-6	3	2	1

16. Find all values of t, such that $f(t) = 15$.

t	3	6	11	15
$f(t)$	15	12	15	6

17. Find all values of x, such that $g(x) = 3$.

x	3	6	9	12
$g(x)$	3	3	3	3

18. Find all values of t, such that $f(t) = 0$.

t	0	1	2	3
$f(t)$	-2	-4	-6	-8

19. Find all values of u, such that $p(u) = -1$.

u	2	-1	4	5
$p(u)$	-1	3	3	-1

20. Find all values of a, such that $h(a) = -5$.

a	-5	-3	-1	1
$h(a)$	3	-1	-5	-9

21. Find all values of x, such that $q(x) = 0$.

x	3	6	0	12
q(x)	0	0	1	0

22. Find all values of t, such that $w(t) = 3$.

t	3	4	5	6
w(t)	2	3	2	1

23. Find all values of x, such that $f(x) = -2$.

x	3	0	-3	-2
f(x)	-2	2	-2	2

24. Find $h(3)$ from the graph of the function h as shown.

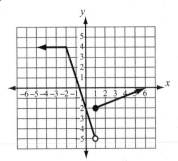

25. Find $h(1)$ from the graph of the function h as shown.

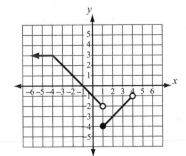

26. Use the graph of g shown below to find the value of $g(0)$.

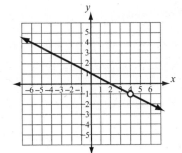

27. Use the graph of p shown below to find the value of $p(-4)$.

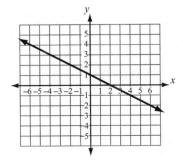

28. Use the graph of p shown below to find the value of $p(4)$.

29. Use the graph of q shown below to find the value of $q(2)$.

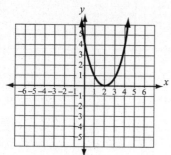

30. Use the graph of f shown below to find the value of $f(-2)$.

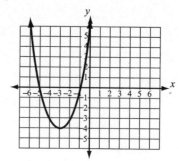

31. Find x such that $f(x) = -3$, using the graph of the function f as shown.

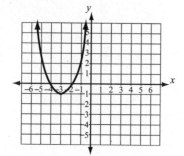

32. Find x such that $g(x) = 0$, using the graph of the function g as shown.

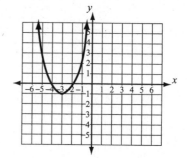

33. Find x such that $h(x) = -2$, using the graph of the function h as shown.

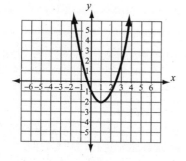

34. Find x such that $h(x) = -1$, using the graph of the function h as shown.

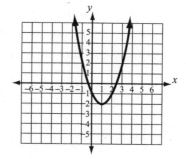

35. Find x such that $f(x) = -4$, using the graph of the function f as shown.

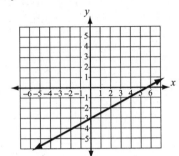

36. Find x such that $g(x) = -4$, using the graph of the function g as shown.

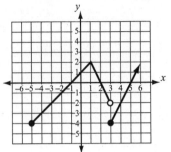

37. Find x such that $g(x) = 0$, using the graph of the function g as shown.

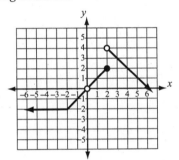

38. Find x such that $g(x) = 1$, using the graph of the function g as shown.

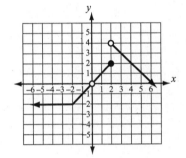

39. Find x such that $g(x) = 3$, using the graph of the function g as shown.

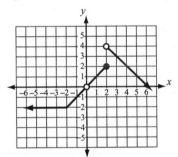

40. Find x such that $g(x) = 5$, using the graph of the function g as shown.

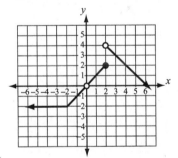

HA1-441: Applications of Functions and Relations Involving Distance, Rate, and Time

One common application of functions is to model the motion of a moving object. We often use graphs to show the relationship between distance, speed, and time.

This relationship is given by $d = rt$ where d is the distance traveled, r is the speed of travel, and t is the time traveled.

When the distance traveled and time traveled are both known, we can solve this equation for r to get the average speed.

.

Average Speed	For an object in motion:
	Average speed $= \dfrac{\text{Distance traveled}}{\text{Time traveled}}$
	$r = \dfrac{d}{t}$
	r – average speed
	d – distance traveled
	t – time traveled

Example 1   A bike rider took 2.5 hours to travel 37.5 miles. What was the rider's average speed on this trip?

$d = 37.5$ miles $t = 2.5$ hours $r = ?$	**Step 1:** Identify the values given in the problem that are needed to calculate the average speed.
$r = \dfrac{d}{t}$	**Step 2:** Determine the appropriate formula.
$r = \dfrac{37.5 \text{ miles}}{2.5 \text{ hours}}$	**Step 3:** Substitute the given values into the formula.
$r = 15$ mph (miles per hour)	**Step 4:** Simplify to find the average speed. Make sure to include the appropriate units.
	Answer: The rider's average speed on this trip was 15 mph.

Example 2 A salesman started on his travels at 6:00 a.m. The graph represents the distance he traveled as a function of time. On this graph, $t = 0$ corresponds to 6:00 a.m. What was the salesman's average speed during the first two hours of his trip?

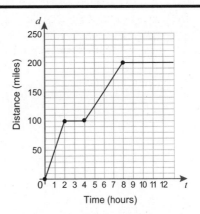

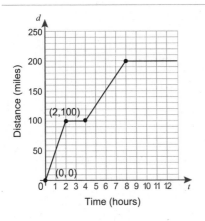

$d = 100 - 0 = 100$ miles

$t = 2 - 0 = 2$ hours

$r = ?$

Step 1: Read the graph to determine which of the values given in the problem are needed to calculate the average speed. The distance traveled is the difference between the number of miles traveled from the starting time and the ending time. The time traveled is the difference between the number of hours from the starting time and the ending time.

$r = \dfrac{d}{t}$

Step 2: Determine the appropriate formula.

$r = \dfrac{100 \text{ miles}}{2 \text{ hours}}$

Step 3: Substitute the given values into the formula.

$r = 50$ mph

Step 4: Simplify to find the average speed. Make sure to include the appropriate units.

Answer: During the first two hours of the trip, the salesman's average speed was 50 mph.

Example 3
A salesman started on his travels at 6:00 a.m. The graph represents the distance he traveled as a function of time. On this graph, $t = 0$ corresponds to 6:00 a.m. What time was his first stop, and how long did it last?

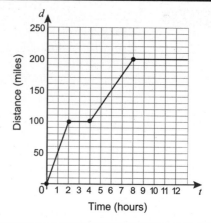

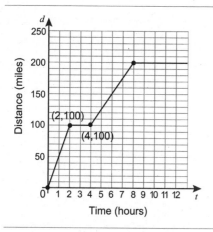

Step 1: Look for the first interval in which the distance is constant. This interval is represented by a horizontal line segment.

Since $t = 0$ corresponds to 6:00 a.m., $t = 2$ corresponds to 8:00 a.m. and $t = 4$ corresponds to 10:00 a.m.

Step 2: Find the values of t that correspond to the times of the day at the beginning and end of the interval.

$4 - 2 = 2$ hours

Step 3: Calculate the time traveled by subtracting beginning time from ending time.

Answer: The salesman first stopped at 8:00 a.m., and he remained for 2 hours.

Example 4

The graph represents the speed, r, given as a function of time, t, during the twelve hours of a trip. The time $t = 0$ corresponds to 7:00 a.m. How many miles were traveled from 1:00 p.m. to 5:00 p.m.?

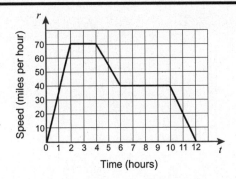

Step 1: Determine the time traveled and the rate for the times given in the problem.

Since $t = 0$ corresponds to 7:00 a.m., 1:00 p.m. corresponds to $t = 6$, and 5:00 p.m. corresponds to $t = 10$.

The time traveled is $t = 10 - 6 = 4$ hours.

In this interval of time, the graph gives the speed $r = 40$ mph.

$d = rt$

$d = (40 \text{ mph})(4 \text{ hours})$

Step 2: Using the relationship $d = rt$, substitute the appropriate values into the formula.

$d = 160$ miles

Step 3: Calculate the distance covered. Make sure to include the appropriate units.

Answer: From 1:00 p.m. to 5:00 p.m., 160 miles were traveled.

Example 5 The graph represents the speed, *r*, given as a function of time, *t*, during the twelve hours of a trip. The time $t = 0$ corresponds to 7:00 a.m. At what times during this trip was the vehicle's speed decreasing?

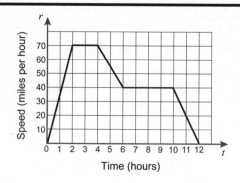

Step 1: Reading the graph from left to right, find the intervals during which the graph decreases.

The speed is decreasing from 70 to 40 mph in the interval from $t = 4$ to $t = 6$, and from 40 to 0 mph in the interval from $t = 10$ to $t = 12$.

Step 2: Find the times of day that correspond to the values of *t*.

The interval from $t = 4$ to $t = 6$ corresponds to the interval from 11:00 a.m. to 1:00 p.m., and the interval from $t = 10$ to $t = 12$ corresponds to the interval from 5:00 p.m. to 7:00 p.m.

Answer: The speed was decreasing from 11:00 a.m. to 1:00 p.m. and from 5:00 p.m. to 7:00 p.m.

Problem Set

1. Carlos rode his bicycle 54 miles in 3 hours. What was his average speed?

2. Janice drove 450 miles in 9 hours. What was the average speed for the trip?

3. An airplane trip of 1,800 miles took 5 hours. What was the average speed over the course of the trip?

4. Edith took a stroll through her neighborhood one evening. She covered a distance of 2.4 miles in 2 hours. What was her average speed?

5. Greg jogged a distance of 2 miles in 0.4 hour. What was his average speed?

6. William ran a 26-mile marathon in 5 hours. What was his average speed?

7. Janice rode a train a distance of 648 miles. The entire trip took 12 hours. What was the average speed of the train?

8. Kathy ran 2.8 miles in 20 minutes. What was her average speed?

9. Jorge left his house at 7:00 a.m. to go for a walk. The distance, d, he walked as a function of time, t, is shown below, where $t = 0$ corresponds to 7:00 a.m. What was Jorge's average speed from 9:00 a.m. to 10:00 a.m.?

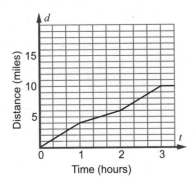

10. Janice took a long ride on her bicycle one day. She left at 7:00 a.m. Her distance traveled, d, as a function of time, t, is shown below, where $t = 0$ corresponds to 7:00 a.m. What was Janice's average speed from 10:00 a.m. to 4:00 p.m.?

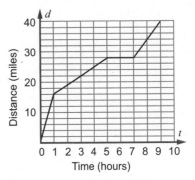

11. Calvin took a ride on his motorcycle one day to visit a friend. He left at 9:00 a.m. His distance traveled, d, as a function of time, t, is shown below, where $t = 0$ corresponds to 9:00 a.m. What was Calvin's average speed from 10:00 a.m. to 12:00 p.m.?

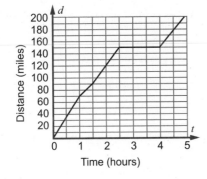

12. A family left at 6:00 a.m. for a trip in their car. The distance traveled, d, in their car as a function of time, t, is shown below, where $t = 0$ corresponds to 6:00 a.m. At what average speed did they travel from 8:00 a.m. to 1:00 p.m. that day?

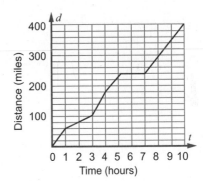

13. An airplane left an airport at 5:00 a.m. The distance traveled, d, as a function of time, t, is shown, where $t = 0$ corresponds to 5:00 a.m. What was plane's average speed from 7:00 a.m. to 1:00 p.m.?

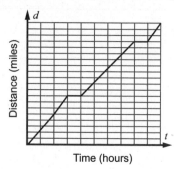

Distance (miles)

Time (hours)

14. A bus that left at 9:00 a.m. traveled between towns. The distance traveled, d, as a function of time, t, is shown, where $t = 0$ corresponds to 9:00 a.m. What was the average speed of the bus from 10:00 a.m. to 2:00 p.m.?

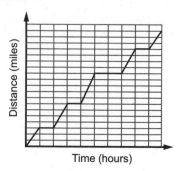

Distance (miles)

Time (hours)

15. A train left the station at 8:00 p.m. The distance traveled, d, as a function of time, t, is shown, where $t = 0$ corresponds to 8:00 p.m. What was the average speed of the train from 9:30 p.m. to 10:30 p.m.?

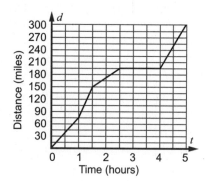

Distance (miles)

Time (hours)

16. Frank left his house at 8:00 a.m. to go for a walk. Along the way he met a friend and stopped for a while to talk. The distance, d, he walked as a function of time, t, is shown, where $t = 0$ corresponds to 8:00 a.m. What time did Frank stop to talk to his friend, and what time did he resume walking?

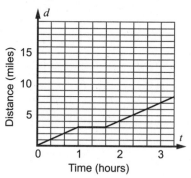

Distance (miles)

Time (hours)

17. Jonathan took a ride on his motorcycle one day to visit a friend. He left at 8:00 a.m. His distance traveled, d, as a function of time, t, is shown below, where $t = 0$ corresponds to 8:00 a.m. What time did he arrive at his friend's house, and what time did he leave?

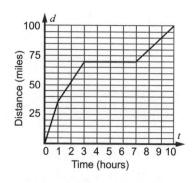

Distance (miles)

Time (hours)

18. Mary took a trip on an airplane. She left at 6:00 a.m. The distance traveled, d, as a function of time, t, is shown, where $t = 0$ corresponds to 6:00 a.m. There were two stops during her trip. What time did the second stop begin, and what time did it end?

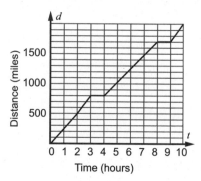

Distance (miles)

Time (hours)

19. Irene took a walk on the beach and stopped at various times to collect sea shells. She began her walk at 8:00 a.m. Her distance traveled, *d*, as a function of time, *t*, is shown below, where *t* = 0 corresponds to 8:00 a.m. When was the longest time that she stopped?

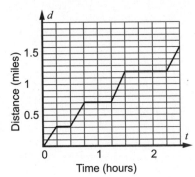

20. A family drove along a scenic route during their vacation and made many stops along the way. The distance traveled, *d*, as a function of time, *t*, is shown in the graph below, where *t* = 0 corresponds to 10:00 a.m. When did they stop for the longest length of time?

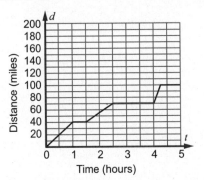

21. Don drove to visit a friend and encountered road construction along the way. The distance traveled, *d*, as a function of time, *t*, is shown below, where *t* = 0 corresponds to 7:00 a.m. When was the shortest length of time that Don was completely stopped on his trip?

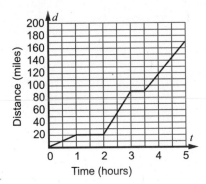

22. Jacques is training for a marathon. He went jogging one day, but he stopped twice to rest. His distance traveled, *d*, as a function of time, *t*, is shown below, where *t* = 0 corresponds to 6:00 a.m. What time did his first stop begin, and what time did it end?

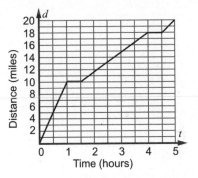

23. Jacques is training for a marathon. He went jogging one day, but he stopped twice to rest. His distance traveled, *d*, as a function of time, *t*, is shown below, where *t* = 0 corresponds to 6:00 a.m. What time did his second stop begin, and what time did it end?

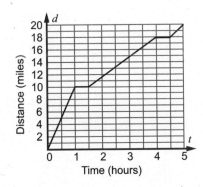

24. Manuel rode his bicycle between two cities. He left one city at 7:00 a.m. The graph represents the speed, *r*, as a function of time, *t*, where *t* = 0 corresponds to 7:00 a.m. How many miles did Manuel ride from 10:00 a.m. to 11:00 a.m.?

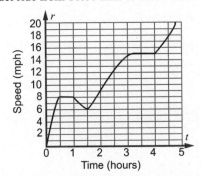

25. An airplane flew between from two cities but had a stop along the way. The graph represents the speed, *r*, as a function of the time, *t*, where *t* = 0 corresponds to 8:00 a.m. How many miles did the plane fly from 8:30 a.m. and 10:00 a.m.?

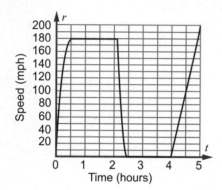

26. A family left home at 7:00 a.m. to take a trip in their car. The graph represents the speed, *r*, as a function of time, *t*, where *t* = 0 corresponds to 7:00 a.m. How many miles did the family go from 1:00 p.m. to 4:00 p.m.

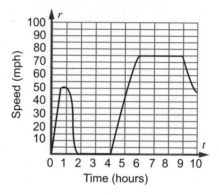

27. A tour bus left at 9:00 a.m. The graph below represents the speed, *r*, of the bus as a function of time *t*, where *t* = 0 corresponds to 9:00 a.m. How many miles did the bus travel from 11:00 a.m. to 1:00 p.m.?

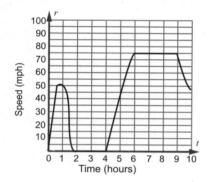

28. Jackie ran a race that started at 8:00 a.m. The graph represents the speed, *r*, as a function of time, *t*, where *t* = 0 corresponds to 8:00 a.m. How far did she run from 8:15 a.m. to 10:15 a.m.?

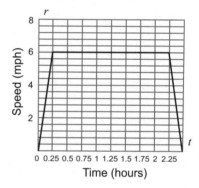

29. Jessica went horseback riding for a day. She left at 7:00 a.m. The graph represents the speed, r, of the horse as a function of time t, where $t = 0$ corresponds to 7:00 a.m. How many miles did the horse travel from 2:00 p.m. to 4:00 p.m.?

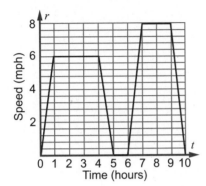

30. Maria took a five hour flight on an airplane that left at 10:00 a.m. The graph below represents the speed, r, of the airplane as a function of time, t, where $t = 0$ corresponds to 10:00 a.m. How many miles did the plane travel from 11:00 a.m. and 2:00 p.m.?

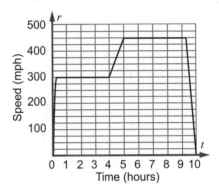

31. Nanette went for a long motorcycle ride one day. The graph shows the speed, r, that she traveled as a function of time, t. During what time interval did she stop for a while?

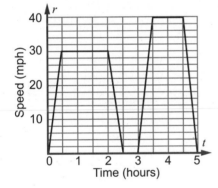

32. Nanette rode her motorcycle one day. The graph shows the speed, r, that she traveled as a function of time, t. What is her speed on the time interval $0.5 \leq t \leq 2$?

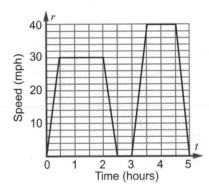

33. Janelle went for a long motorcycle ride one day. The graph shows the speed, r, that she traveled as a function of time, t. During what time interval did her speed sharply decrease from 40 miles per hour to 0 miles per hour?

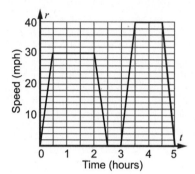

34. Benny took a ten-hour airplane flight from one city to another. The graph shows the speed, r, of the plane as a function of time, t. During what time interval did the plane's speed increase steadily from 300 mph to 450 mph?

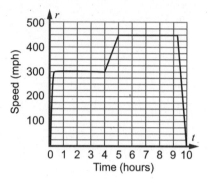

35. Marsha drove home from college during spring break on her way, she encountered some traffic. What was the fastest speed that she reached?

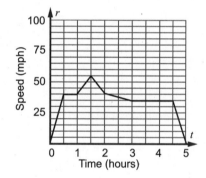

36. Marsha drove home from college during spring break. On her way, she encountered some traffic. Twice she had to maintain a constant speed for a period of time. What was the constant speed that she maintained for the shorter period of time?

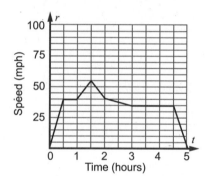

37. A family decided to travel by car to visit some relatives. The beginning part of their trip is shown by the graph below, where the car's speed, r, is a function of time, t. At one point on their trip, they were able to drive at a constant speed. For approximately how long were they able to drive at this constant speed?

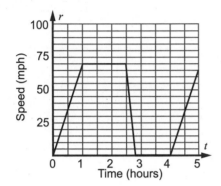

38. A family decided to travel by car to visit some relatives. The beginning part of their trip is shown by the graph below, where the car's speed, r, is a function of time, t. At one point on their trip, they were able to drive at a constant speed. Find this constant speed.

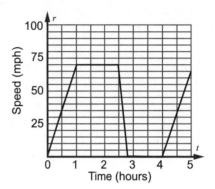

39. A bullet train was taking passengers on a tour. The graph below shows the first part of the tour. The speed, r, of the train is a function of the time, t. At one point on the tour, the train stopped. How long was it stopped?

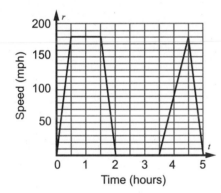

40. A bullet train took passengers on a tour. The graph below shows the first part of the tour. The speed, r, of the train is a function of the time, t. The speed of this train steadily increased twice from 0 mph to 180 mph. How long did it take for the speed to increase from 0 mph to 180 mph the second time?

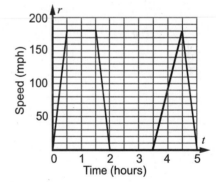

HA1-445: Evaluating Composite Functions

In algebra, you will sometimes need to evaluate composite functions. The process that you follow to do this can be compared to a miniature assembly line. A composite function contains two or more functions. To evaluate a composite function, start with the innermost function, and keep moving outward, simplifying the expression at each step, until the outermost function is complete. Each function along the way plays a part in producing the correct solution.

Before you start evaluating composite functions, let's review the process of evaluating functions.

Example 1   If $f(x) = 2x^2 - 3x + 9$, evaluate $f(-4)$.

$f(-4) = 2(-4)^2 - 3(-4) + 9$ **Step 1:**   Substitute -4 for every x in the definition of $f(x)$.

$\begin{aligned} f(-4) &= 2(-4)^2 - 3(-4) + 9 \\ &= 2(16) + 12 + 9 \\ &= 32 + 12 + 9 \\ &= 53 \end{aligned}$ **Step 2:**   Simplify the expression.

Answer: For $f(x) = 2x^2 - 3x + 9$, $f(-4)$ is 53.

A composite function can be written as $f(g(x))$, for two given functions $f(x)$ and $g(x)$. It is read as "f of g of x." Here are some examples that show you how to evaluate composite functions.

Example 2   Evaluate $g(f(2))$, given $f(x) = 2x^2 + 1$ and $g(x) = \sqrt{x} - 3$.

$\begin{aligned} f(x) &= 2x^2 + 1 \\ f(2) &= 2(2)^2 + 1 \\ &= 2(4) + 1 \\ &= 8 + 1 \\ &= 9 \end{aligned}$ **Step 1:**   Begin by evaluating the innermost function first. Substitute 2 for every x in the definition of $f(x)$ and simplify.

$\begin{aligned} g(x) &= \sqrt{x} - 3 \\ g(9) &= \sqrt{9} - 3 \\ &= 3 - 3 \\ &= 0 \end{aligned}$ **Step 2:**   Substitute the value you found for $f(2)$ into definition of $g(x)$. In this example, you evaluate $g(9)$.

Answer: $g(f(2)) = 0$

Example 3   Evaluate $h(f(10))$, for $h(x) = |2x - 1|$ and $f(x) = \sqrt{x - 1}$.

$\begin{aligned} f(10) &= \sqrt{10 - 1} \\ &= \sqrt{9} \\ &= 3 \end{aligned}$ **Step 1:**   Evaluate the innermost function, $f(10)$, by substituting 10 for each x in the definition of $f(x)$ and simplifying.

$h(x) = |2x - 1|$

$h(3) = |2(3) - 1|$

$\quad = |6 - 1|$

$\quad = |5|$

$\quad = 5$

Step 2: Evaluate the outer function by replacing each x in the definition of $h(x)$ with a 3 and simplifying.

Answer: $h(f(10)) = 5$

The order that the functions appear in the expression for the composite function is very important. You must always evaluate the innermost function first, then apply that solution to the outermost function. The next example uses the same two functions that were used in Example 3, but they are written in a different order in the expression for the composite function.

Example 4 Evaluate $f(h(3))$, given $h(x) = |2x - 1|$ and $f(x) = \sqrt{x - 1}$.

$h(3) = |2(3) - 1|$

$\quad = |6 - 1|$

$\quad = |5|$

$\quad = 5$

Step 1: Evaluate the innermost function, $h(3)$, by substituting 3 for each x in the definition of $h(x)$ and simplifying.

$f(5) = \sqrt{5 - 1}$

$\quad = \sqrt{4}$

$\quad = 2$

Step 2: Evaluate the outer function by replacing each x in the definition of $h(x)$ with 5 and simplifying.

Answer: $f(h(3)) = 2$

Problem Set

1. If $f(x) = 2x + 1$ and $g(x) = 5x$, find $f(g(0))$.

2. If $f(x) = x - 5$ and $g(x) = 2x$, find $g(f(3))$.

3. If $f(x) = 4x$ and $g(x) = x + 5$, find $f(g(3))$.

4. If $f(x) = 2x$ and $g(x) = 3x + 1$, find $f(g(-2))$.

5. If $f(x) = x + 1$ and $g(x) = 4x$, find $f(g(2))$.

6. If $f(x) = 5x$ and $g(x) = 1 + x^2$, find $f(g(-3))$.

7. If $g(x) = x^2 - 1$ and $h(x) = -4x$, find $h(g(-1))$.

8. If $f(x) = 3 - x^2$ and $g(x) = 3x + 5$, find $f(g(-3))$.

9. If $f(x) = 7 - x$ and $g(x) = x^2 + 3$, find $f(g(-2))$.

10. If $g(x) = x^2$ and $h(x) = 2 - 3x$, find $h(g(-4))$.

HA1-447: Identifying Number Patterns

In this lesson, we will identify number patterns. When numbers are arranged in a pattern, they form a sequence. A sequence is an ordered list of numbers.

Sequence	An ordered list of numbers

When identifying number patterns, we classify them as one of three types. These three types are arithmetic, geometric, and quadratic. Once the type of sequence is identified, we can use that information to help solve problems.

The first type of sequence is an arithmetic sequence. An arithmetic sequence is also called a linear sequence.

Arithmetic Sequence	A sequence of numbers in which the difference between any two consecutive terms is constant

If the sequence is arithmetic, the next term is obtained by adding a fixed number to the previous term. This fixed number is equal to the difference between any two consecutive terms. The formula below can be used.

Next term of an arithmetic sequence = previous term + difference

The next type of sequence is a geometric sequence. A geometric sequence is also called an exponential sequence.

Geometric Sequence	A sequence of numbers in which the ratio between any two consecutive terms is constant

If the sequence is geometric, the next term is obtained by multiplying a fixed number to the previous term. This fixed number is equal to the ratio between any two consecutive numbers. The formula below can be used.

Next term of a geometric sequence = previous term • ratio

The last type of sequence is a quadratic sequence.

Quadratic Sequence	A sequence of numbers in which the second difference of any two consecutive terms is a non-zero constant

Second Difference	The difference of two consecutive first differences

However, if the sequence is not arithmetic, geometric, or quadratic, we create two subsequences. One subsequence consists of the even-numbered terms; the other subsequence consists of the odd-numbered terms. We then check the differences, second differences, and ratios to determine whether the subsequences are arithmetic, geometric, or quadratic.

Example 1   Determine the pattern of the sequence of numbers: 1, 7, 17, 31, 49, ...

Sequence	1		7		17		31		49
Differences		6		10		14		18	

Step 1:   Create a table and determine the differences between two consecutive terms of the sequence.

Sequence	1		7		17		31		49
Differences		6		10		14		18	
2nd Differences			4		4		4		

Step 2:   Since the differences are not constant, determine the second differences.

2nd Difference: 4

Step 3:   Since the second differences are constant, the sequence is quadratic.

Answer: The sequence is quadratic.

Example 2   Find the next term in the sequence of numbers: 100, 80, 64, 51.2, _____.

Sequence	100		80		64		51.2		?
Differences		−20		−16		−12.8			

Step 1:   Create a table and determine the differences between two consecutive terms of the sequence.

Sequence	100		80		64		51.2		?
Differences		−20		−16		−12.8			
2nd Differences			4		3.2				

Step 2:   Since the differences are not constant, determine the second differences.

Ratios		$\frac{4}{5}$		$\frac{4}{5}$		$\frac{4}{5}$			
Sequence	100		80		64		51.2		?
Differences		−20		−16		−12.8			
2nd Differences			4		3.2				

Step 3:   Since the second differences are not constant, determine the ratios. The ratios are constant, so the sequence is geometric.

Next term = previous term · ratio

$$= 51.2\left(\frac{4}{5}\right)$$

$$= 40.96$$

Step 4:   To find the next term in the sequence, multiply the ratio by the previous term.

Answer: The next term in the sequence is 40.96.

Example 3 Which of the statements about the following diagram is false?

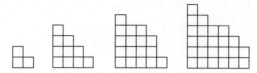

The pattern of the number of squares is arithmetic.

The difference between consecutive terms is 7.

The next term is obtained by adding the previous term and the difference.

The number of squares in the fifth term is 168.

Step #	1	2	3	4	5
Number of Squares	3	10	17	24	?

Step 1: Create a table.

Step #	1	2	3	4	5
Number of Squares	3	10	17	24	?
Differences		7	7	7	

Step 2: Determine if the sequence is arithmetic, geometric, or quadratic.

Step #	1	2	3	4	5
Number of Squares	3	10	17	24	31
Differences		7	7	7	7

Step 3: Calculate the fifth term of the sequence by using the formula for finding the next term of an arithmetic sequence.

Next term = previous term + difference

= 24 + 7

= 31

Since the pattern is arithmetic and has a constant difference of 7 between two consecutive terms, the first two statements are true.

Since the pattern is arithmetic, the next term is found by adding the previous term and the difference. Therefore, the third statement is also true.

Using the formula for finding the next term of an arithmetic sequence, the fifth term is equal to 31.

Since the fourth statement states that the fifth term is 168, the fourth statement is false.

Step 4: Analyze the four given statements to determine which one is false.

Answer: The statement "The number of squares in the fifth term is 168." is false.

Example 4 Louis is making bracelets with charms arranged in patterns. The first four patterns are below. If Louis continues following the pattern, how many charms will the fifth bracelet have?

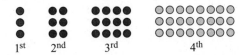

1st   2nd   3rd   4th

Step 1: Create a table and determine the differences between two consecutive terms in the pattern.

Steps	1	2	3	4	5
Number of Charms	3	6	12	24	?
Differences		3	6	12	

Step 2: Since the differences are not constant, the sequence is not arithmetic. Examine the ratios in the pattern.

Step #	1	2	3	4	5
Ratios		2	2	2	
Number of Charms	3	6	12	24	?
Differences		3	6	12	

Step 3: The ratios are constant, so the pattern is geometric.

Step #	1	2	3	4	5
Ratios		2	2	2	
Number of Charms	3	6	12	24	?
Differences		3	6	12	

Next term = previous term · ratio

        = 24 · 2

        = 48

Step 4: Calculate the next term. Recall that for a geometric sequence, the next term is equal to the product of the previous term and the ratio.

Step #	1	2	3	4	5
Ratios		2	2	2	2
Number of Charms	3	6	12	24	48
Differences		3	6	12	

Answer: The fifth bracelet will have 48 charms.

Example 5

Tracey is helping her little sister decorate eggs with dots. The number of dots on each egg is shown in the pattern below. If they continue to follow the pattern, how many dots will Tracey and her sister put on each of the next two eggs?

$$4, 6, 12, 10, 36, 14, \underline{\hspace{1cm}}, \underline{\hspace{1cm}}$$

Ratios		$\frac{3}{2}$	2	$\frac{5}{6}$	$\frac{18}{5}$	$\frac{7}{18}$		
Sequence	4	6	12	10	36	14	?	?
Differences		2	1	3	3	1		
2nd Differences			−1	2	0	−2		

Step 1: Create a table and determine the type of pattern by finding the differences, second differences, and ratios.

Ratios		3		3				
Subsequence (1st, 3rd, 5th, ... terms)	4		12		36			
Sequence	4	6	12	10	36	14	?	?
Subsequence (2nd, 4th, 6th, ... terms)		6		10		14		
Difference			4		4			

Step 2: Since none of the techniques produced constant results, the sequence is not arithmetic, quadratic, or geometric. Create two subsequences: one consisting of the odd-numbered terms and one consisting of the even-numbered terms. Examine each of the subsequences.

Ratios		3		3				
Subsequence (1st, 3rd, 5th, ... terms)	4		12		36			
Sequence	4	6	12	10	36	14	?	?
Subsequence (2nd, 4th, 6th, ... terms)		6		10		14		
Difference			4		4			

Step 3: The subsequence consisting of the 1st, 3rd, and 5th terms is geometric because its ratios are constant. The subsequence consisting of the 2nd, 4th, and 6th terms is arithmetic because its differences are constant.

Geometric Sequence:

$$\text{Next term} = \text{previous term} \cdot \text{ratio}$$
$$= 36 \cdot 3$$
$$= 108$$

Step 4: Calculate the next two terms. Recall that for a geometric sequence, the next term is equal to the previous term times the ratio, and for an arithmetic sequence, the next term is equal to the previous term plus the difference.

Ratios		3		3		3		
Subsequence (1st, 3rd, 5th, ... terms)	4		12		36		108	
Sequence	4	6	12	10	36	14	108	18
Subsequence (2nd, 4th, 6th, ... terms)		6		10		14		
Difference			4		4		4	

Arithmetic Sequence:

$$\text{Next term} = \text{previous term} + \text{difference}$$
$$= 14 + 4$$
$$= 18$$

Answer: The number of dots on each of the next two eggs will be 108 and 18, respectively.

Problem Set

1. Determine the pattern of the following sequence of numbers:
$$4, 8, 12, 16,...$$

2. Determine the pattern of the following sequence of numbers:
$$15, 12, 9, 6,...$$

3. Determine the pattern of the following sequence of numbers:
$$5, -1, -7, -13,...$$

4. Determine the pattern of the following sequence of numbers:
$$2, -6, 18, -54,...$$

5. Determine the pattern of the following sequence of numbers:
$$3, 6, 12, 24,...$$

6. Determine the pattern of the following sequence of numbers:
$$64, 16, 4, 1,...$$

7. Determine the pattern of the following sequence of numbers:
$$3, 5, 8, 12,...$$

8. Determine the pattern of the following sequence of numbers:
$$3, 4, 7, 12,...$$

9. Find the next term in the given sequence of numbers:
$$4, 13, 22, \_\_\_$$

10. Find the next term in the given sequence of numbers:
$$20, 12, 4, \_\_\_$$

11. Find the next term in the given sequence of numbers:
$$-9, -3, 3, \_\_\_$$

12. Find the next term in the given sequence of numbers:
$$5, 20, 80, \_\_\_$$

13. Find the next term in the given sequence of numbers:

$$80, -40, 20, \_\_\_$$

14. Find the next term in the given sequence of numbers:

$$3, -6, 12, \_\_\_ .$$

15. Find the next term in the given sequence of numbers:

$$-9, -17, -25, \_\_\_$$

16. Determine which of the statements about the following diagram is false.

1st Step   2nd Step   3rd Step   4th Step

The pattern of the number of squares is geometric.

The number of squares is two times the step number.

The next step is obtained by adding two squares to the previous step.

The number of squares in the 5th step is 10.

17. Determine which of the statements about the following diagram is false.

Stage 1   Stage 2   Stage 3   Stage 4

The number of triangles in stage 5 is 25.

The pattern of the number of triangles is quadratic.

The number of rows of triangles is equal to the stage number.

The number of triangles is two times the stage number.

18. Determine which of the statements about the following diagram is false.

1st step   2nd step   3rd step   4th step

The number of dots in the 5th step is 16.

The same number of dots is added to each step.

The pattern of the number of dots is geometric.

The number of dots in each step is two times the number of dots in the previous step.

19. Determine which of the statements about the following diagram is false.

1st Step   2nd Step   3rd Step   4th Step

The pattern of the number of dots is quadratic.

The number of dots is equal to the step number.

The number of dots in the 5th step is 5.

The next step is obtained by adding one additional triangle with one dot.

20. Determine which of the statements about the following diagram is false.

1st step   2nd step   3rd step   4th step

The same number of dots is added to each step.

The pattern of the number of dots is arithmetic.

The number of columns is one more than the step number.

The number of dots in step 5 is 14.

21. Determine which of the statements about the following diagram is false.

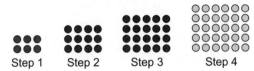

Step 1   Step 2   Step 3   Step 4

The number of columns is 2 more than the step number.

The next step is obtained by adding one more row and one more column of dots.

The same number of dots is added to each step.

The pattern of the number of dots is quadratic.

22. Determine which of the statements about the following diagram is false.

Step 1   Step 2   Step 3   Step 4

The pattern of the number of dots is arithmetic.

The number of dots in step 5 is 32.

Each step has twice as many dots as the previous step.

Each step has the same number of rows.

23. Determine which of the statements about the following diagram is false.

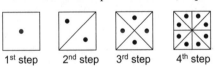

1ˢᵗ Step   2ⁿᵈ Step   3ʳᵈ Step   4ᵗʰ Step

The same number of squares is added to each step.

The number of squares in step 5 is 15.

The number of squares in each bottom row equals the step number.

The pattern of the number of squares is quadratic.

24. Frank is putting up fence sections in his yard. Each square in the diagram represents a section of fence. If the pattern continues, how many fence sections will be up in the yard on the 12th day?

1ˢᵗ Day   3ʳᵈ Day   4ᵗʰ Day   5ᵗʰ Day
     2ⁿᵈ Day

25. Jessica is making some square designs to use on a painting. She is making them according to the pattern shown. If the pattern continues, how many dots will be inside the square in the 7th step?

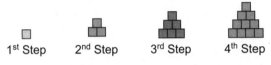

1ˢᵗ step   2ⁿᵈ step   3ʳᵈ step   4ᵗʰ step

26. Karl is arranging triangles as shown in the diagram. If he continues, how many shaded triangles will be in step 6?

Step 1   Step 2   Step 3   Step 4   Step 5

27. Juanita is making a design out of beads according to the given pattern. How many beads will she need for stage 10?

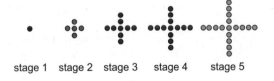

stage 1   stage 2   stage 3   stage 4   stage 5

28. How many small squares will there be in stage 10 if the pattern below continues?

stage 1   stage 2   stage 3   stage 4

29. Maria is saving pennies every day for as long as she can. She saves according to the pattern below. How many pennies will she have on day 10?

day 1 day 2 day 3   day 4   day 5

30. How many shaded squares will be in step 10 in the given diagram?

step 1   step 2   step 3   step 4

31. Carla planted some flowers, and each month she recorded the height in inches of a particular flower. The sequence below shows the heights in inches after each month. What is the height of the flower in the 7th and 8th months, respectively?

2, 3, 4, 6, 8, 12, _____, _____

32. Determine the next two terms in the sequence:
32, 35, 42, 46, 52, 57, ___, ___

33. Each week, Hamilton deposits some of his paycheck into an account. However, every other week he deposits less money into the account in order to pay bills. At this time, he may also withdraw money. His balances, in dollars, in his account after each payday are shown in the sequence below. How much money, in dollars, will he have after the 5th and 6th paychecks?

20, 35, 40, 45, 80, 55, ___, ___

34. Determine the next two terms in the sequence:
10, 13, 42, 39, 74, 117, ____, ____

35. The number of seats in each row from front to back in an auditorium is listed in a sequence. How many seats are in rows 7 and 8, respectively?

11, 15, 20, 26, 29, 37, ___, ___

36. Determine the next two terms in the sequence:
265, 112, 530, 448, 1,060, 1,792, _____, _____

37. As a skydiver is falling, her distances (in feet) from the ground are recorded after each second, and are shown in the sequence below. How far (in feet) from the ground will she be after the 7th and 8th seconds, respectively?

2,565, 1,620, 855, 540, 285, 180, ___, ___

38. The yearly population figures of a small town are given in the sequence below. What is the population during each of the next two years?
1,200 1,450, 2,200, 1,950, 3,200, 2,450, __, __

39. Martha has a garden of plants. Sometimes the plants reproduce, and sometimes they die. After each month, she counts the number of plants and records the number in the sequence below. If the sequence continues in this pattern, how many plants will be in the garden in each of the next two months?

2, 5, 6, 15, 18, 25, ____, ____

40. Determine the next two terms in the sequence:
7, 13, 14, 11, 28, 9, ____, ____

HA1-448: Finding the nth Term of a Pattern

Recall that a sequence of numbers where the difference between two consecutive terms is constant is called an arithmetic or linear sequence. The next term in an arithmetic sequence of numbers can be obtained by adding a fixed number to the previous term. This fixed number is equal to the difference between any two consecutive terms.

Also, recall that a geometric or exponential sequence is a sequence of numbers where the ratio between two consecutive terms is constant. The next term in a geometric sequence is obtained by multiplying the previous term by a fixed number. This fixed number is equal to the ratio between any two consecutive terms.

While both of these techniques are useful when we need to find the first few terms in a sequence, it can be very time-consuming to use this method to find terms that come later in the sequence. In these situations, we need a method for finding the nth term of a given sequence.

For an arithmetic sequence, the formula for finding the nth term is:.

Finding the nth Term of an Arithmetic Sequence	n^{th} term = (first term) + $(n-1)d$, where d is the difference between any two consecutive terms in the sequence.

For a geometric sequence, the formula for finding the nth term is:

Finding the nth Term of a Geometric Sequence	n^{th} term = (first term) $\cdot r^{n-1}$, where r is the ratio between any two consecutive terms in the sequence.

Example 1   Find the nth term in the following sequence: 4, 8, 16, 32,...

Sequence	4	8	16	32
Differences		4	8	16

Step 1: Find the differences between consecutive terms to determine if the sequence is arithmetic.

Since the differences between consecutive terms are not constant, the sequence is not arithmetic.

Ratios		2	2	2
Number of dots	4	8	16	32
Differences		4	8	16

Step 2: Find the ratios between consecutive terms to determine if the sequence is geometric.

Since the ratios are constant, the sequence is geometric.

n^{th} term = (first term) $\cdot r^{n-1}$, where r is the ratio between any two consecutive terms in the sequence

Step 3: Recall the formula for finding the nth term of a geometric sequence.

n^{th} term $= (4) \cdot 2^{n-1}$

Step 4: Substitute 4 for "first term" and 2 for r.

n^{th} term $= 4 \cdot 2^{n-1}$ **Step 5:** Simplify.

Answer: n^{th} term $= 4 \cdot 2^{n-1}$

Example 2   The first term in a sequence is 3, and the difference between consecutive terms is 3. Find the expression for the nth term.

Since the difference between consecutive terms, 3, is constant, the sequence is arithmetic.

Step 1: Identify the type of sequence.

n^{th} term $=$ first term $+ (n-1)d,$ where d is the difference between any two consecutive terms in the sequence

Step 2: Recall the formula for finding the nth term of an arithmetic sequence.

n^{th} term $= 3 + (n-1)3$

Step 3: Substitute 3 for "first term", and 3 for d.

n^{th} term $= 3 + 3n - 3$
n^{th} term $= 3n$

Step 4: Simplify.

Answer: The expression for the nth term of this sequence is $3n$.

Example 3   Which expression represents the number of dots in each step of the pattern of objects below?

1st   2nd   3rd   4th

$5 \cdot \left(\dfrac{8}{5}\right)^{n-1}$ $3n+2$

$n^2 + 4$ $n^3 + 4$

Step 1: Create a table to organize the information.

Step number	1	2	3	4
Number of dots				
$5 \cdot \left(\dfrac{8}{5}\right)^{n-1}$				
$n^2 + 4$				
$3n + 2$				
$n^3 + 4$				

Step number	1	2	3	4
Number of dots	5	8	13	20
$5 \cdot \left(\dfrac{8}{5}\right)^{n-1}$				
$n^2 + 4$				
$3n + 2$				
$n^3 + 4$				

Step 2: Count the number of dots in each step and record these numbers in the table.

Step number	1	2	3	4
Number of dots	5	8	13	20
$5 \cdot \left(\dfrac{8}{5}\right)^{n-1}$	5	8	12.8	
$n^2 + 4$	5	8	13	20
$3n + 2$	5	8	11	
$n^3 + 4$	5	12		

Step 3: Evaluate each expression by substituting the step number for n. Continue checking an expression until the result is an incorrect number of dots.

Answer: $n^2 + 4$ is the expression that represents the number of dots in each step of the pattern of objects.

Example 4   Which expression represents the number of squares in each step of the pattern of objects below?

1st   2nd   3rd   4th

$6n - 6$ 6^{n-1}

$n^2 - n$ $n^3 - n$

Step 1: Create a table to organize the information.

Step number	1	2	3	4
Number of squares				
$6n - 6$				
$n^2 - n$				
6^{n-1}				
$n^3 - n$				

Step number	1	2	3	4
Number of squares	0	6	24	60
$6n - 6$				
$n^2 - n$				
6^{n-1}				
$n^3 - n$				

Step 2: Count the number of squares in each step and record these numbers in the table.

Step number	1	2	3	4
Number of squares	0	6	24	60
$6n - 6$	0	6	12	
$n^2 - n$	0	2		
6^{n-1}	1			
$n^3 - n$	0	6	24	60

Step 3: Evaluate each expression by substituting the step number for n. Continue checking an expression until the result is an incorrect number of dots.

Answer: $n^3 - n$ is the expression that represents the number of squares in each step of the pattern of objects.

Example 5 The figures below represent the first four steps in a sequence. Find the number of dots in the 8th step.

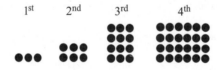

1st   2nd   3rd   4th

Step number	1	2	3	4
Number of dots	3	6	12	24

Step 1: Create a table and count the number of dots in each step.

Ratios		2	2	2	
Number of dots	3		6		12	24
Differences		3	6	12	

Step 2: Determine whether the sequence is arithmetic or geometric by calculating the differences and ratios between consecutive terms.

n^{th} term $= (\text{first term}) \cdot r^{n-1}$, where r is the ratio between any two consecutive terms in the sequence

Step 3: Recall the formula for finding the nth term of a geometric sequence.

n^{th} term $= (3) \cdot 2^{n-1}$ n^{th} term $= 3 \cdot 2^{n-1}$	**Step 4:** Substitute 3 for "first term" and 2 for r to obtain the expression for the nth term.
n^{th} term $= 3 \cdot 2^{8-1}$ n^{th} term $= 3 \cdot 2^{7}$ n^{th} term $= 3 \cdot 128$ n^{th} term $= 384$	**Step 5:** Evaluate the expression for $n = 8$.

Answer: There are 384 dots in the 8th step.

Problem Set

1. Find the nth term in the following sequence:
6, 10, 14, 18,...

2. Find the nth term in the following sequence:
19, 14, 9, 4,...

3. Find the nth term in the following sequence:
−12, −4, 4, 12,...

4. Find the nth term in the following sequence:
5, 2, −1, −4,...

5. Find the nth term in the following sequence:
$9, 3, 1, \frac{1}{3}, \dots$

6. Find the nth term in the following sequence:
2, −4, 8, −16, ...

7. Find the nth term in the following sequence:
3, 15, 75, 375,...

8. Find the nth term in the following sequence:
$-16, 4, -1, \frac{1}{4}, \dots$

9. The first term in a sequence is 12, and the difference between consecutive terms is 3. Find the expression for the nth term.

10. The first term in a sequence is −6, and the difference between consecutive terms is 5. Find the expression for the nth term.

11. The first term in a sequence is 21, and the difference between consecutive terms is −3. Find the expression for the nth term.

12. The first term in a sequence is −2, and the difference between consecutive terms is −4. Find the expression for the nth term.

13. The first term in a sequence is 4, and the difference between consecutive terms is 3. Find the expression for the nth term.

14. The first term in a sequence is 3, and the ratio between consecutive terms is −2. Find the expression for the nth term.

15. The first term in a sequence is –6, and the ratio between consecutive terms is $\frac{1}{2}$. Find the expression for the nth term.

16. Which expression represents the number of shaded triangles in each step?

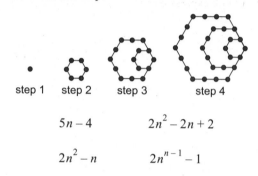

$$3 + 2(n - 2) \qquad n^2 + n - 1$$

$$\frac{n^2 + n}{2} \qquad \frac{(2n + 1)(n + 1)}{6}$$

17. Which expression represents the number of white squares in each stage?

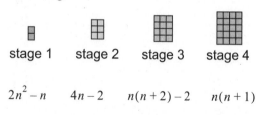

$$n^2 - 2n + 1 \qquad n^2 - 1$$

$$n^2 + 2n - 2 \qquad 2^{n-1}$$

18. Which expression represents the number of dots shown in each step?

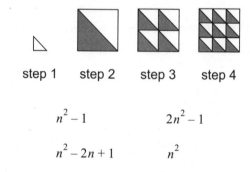

$$5n - 4 \qquad 2n^2 - 2n + 2$$

$$2n^2 - n \qquad 2n^{n-1} - 1$$

19. Which expression represents the number of dots in each stage?

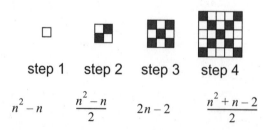

$$6^{n-1} \qquad \frac{5n^2 - 5n + 2}{2}$$

$$5n - 4 \qquad 2n^n - 2n + 2$$

20. Which expression represents the number of shaded triangles in each step?

step 1   step 2   step 3   step 4

$$n^2 - 1 \qquad 2n^2 - 1$$

$$n^2 - 2n + 1 \qquad n^2$$

21. Which expression represents the number of squares in each stage?

stage 1   stage 2   stage 3   stage 4

$$2n^2 - n \qquad 4n - 2 \qquad n(n + 2) - 2 \qquad n(n + 1)$$

22. Which expression represents the number of shaded squares in each step?

step 1   step 2   step 3   step 4

$$n^2 - n \qquad \frac{n^2 - n}{2} \qquad 2n - 2 \qquad \frac{n^2 + n - 2}{2}$$

23. The number of dots increases by one in each stage, and all possible line segments connecting the dots are drawn. Which expression represents the number of line segments connecting the dots in each stage?

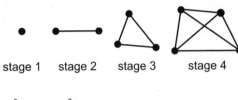

stage 1   stage 2   stage 3   stage 4

$$\dfrac{n^2 - n}{2} \qquad \dfrac{n^2 - 2n + 1}{2} \qquad n - 1 \qquad n^2 - n$$

24. Which expression represents the number of squares in each step?

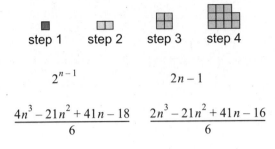

step 1   step 2   step 3   step 4

$$2^{n-1} \qquad\qquad 2n - 1$$

$$\dfrac{4n^3 - 21n^2 + 41n - 18}{6} \qquad \dfrac{2n^3 - 21n^2 + 41n - 16}{6}$$

25. Which expression represents the number of shaded squares in each stage?

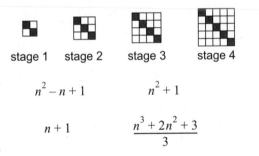

stage 1   stage 2   stage 3   stage 4

$$n^2 - n + 1 \qquad\qquad 2n - 1$$

$$2n^2 - 1 \qquad\qquad \dfrac{3n^3 - 2n^2 - n + 3}{3}$$

26. Which expression represents the number of dots in each step?

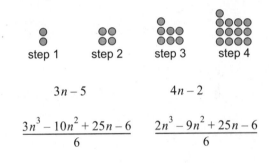

step 1   step 2   step 3   step 4

$$3n - 5 \qquad\qquad 4n - 2$$

$$\dfrac{3n^3 - 10n^2 + 25n - 6}{6} \qquad \dfrac{2n^3 - 9n^2 + 25n - 6}{6}$$

27. Which expression represents the number of shaded squares in each stage?

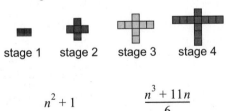

stage 1   stage 2   stage 3   stage 4

$$n^2 - n + 1 \qquad\qquad n^2 + 1$$

$$n + 1 \qquad\qquad \dfrac{n^3 + 2n^2 + 3}{3}$$

28. Which expression represents the number of dots in each step?

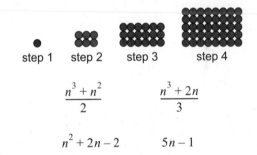

step 1   step 2   step 3   step 4

$$\dfrac{n^3 + n^2}{2} \qquad\qquad \dfrac{n^3 + 2n}{3}$$

$$n^2 + 2n - 2 \qquad\qquad 5n - 1$$

29. Which expression represents the number of squares in each stage?

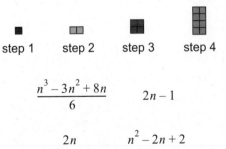

stage 1   stage 2   stage 3   stage 4

$$n^2 + 1 \qquad\qquad \dfrac{n^3 + 11n}{6}$$

$$3n - 1 \qquad\qquad 2n^2 + 3n - 3$$

30. Which expression represents the number of squares in each step?

step 1   step 2   step 3   step 4

$$\dfrac{n^3 - 3n^2 + 8n}{6} \qquad\qquad 2n - 1$$

$$2n \qquad\qquad n^2 - 2n + 2$$

31. If the pattern continues, how many dots would be in the 40th stage?|

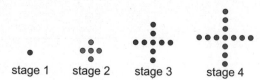

stage 1   stage 2   stage 3   stage 4

32. In each stage, one additional point is placed on the line separating it into parts. For example, in stage 3 there are 3 points which separate the line into 4 parts. Into how many parts would the line be separated in stage 90?

step 1   step 2

step 3   step 4

33. If the pattern continues, how many white triangles would be in the 14th stage?

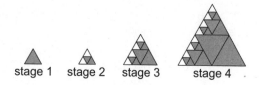

stage 1   stage 2   stage 3   stage 4

34. If the pattern continues, how many squares would be in the 20th step?

step 1   step 2   step 3   step 4

35. Find the 29th term of the sequence: $-10, -6, -2, 2, \ldots$

36. Find the 50th term of the sequence: $39, 36, 33, 30, \ldots$

37. Find the 45th term of the sequence: $2, 7, 12, 17, \ldots$

38. Find the 10th term of the sequence: $512, 256, 128, 64, \ldots$

39. Find the 12th term of the sequence: $5, 15, 45, 135, \ldots$

40. Find the 10th term of the sequence: $1, -3, 9, -27, \ldots$

Suppose you are a shoe salesperson and work on commission. For every pair of shoes you sell, you earn $5.00. If you sold 20 pairs of shoes on Monday, 15 pairs of shoes on Wednesday, and 25 pairs of shoes on Friday, how much commission did you earn?

Set up a chart in which x = number of pairs of shoes sold and y = the amount of commission.

x	y
20	$100
15	$ 75
25	$125

You might not realize it, but you have just completed a problem using **direct variation**. The word "variation" means that something varies or changes; in this lesson it will be x and y. Direct variation means that x and y change proportionally and in the same direction. Therefore, if x increases, y increases proportionally. Similarly, if x decreases, then y also decreases. Thus, in the above example, you can say that y varies directly with x; or the amount of commission varies directly with the number of pairs of shoes sold.

Direct Variation	A function in the form $y = kx$, where $k \neq 0$, and y is proportional to x This can also be stated as "y varies directly as x."

Looking at the chart, you can see that the relationship between the two quantities can be written in the form $y = 5x$, where 5 is called the **constant of variation** or the **constant of proportionality**. Notice that the direct variation is written as $y = 5x$. This implies that direct variation is a function in the form $y = kx$, where k is the constant of variation and k *cannot equal zero.*

Note: The concept of function will be developed in other lessons.

Constant of Variation	The constant k in a direct variation $y = kx$

Example 1   Find the constant of variation k if y varies directly with x: $y = 5x$.

Step 1:   This is in the form $y = kx$, so you can say that "y varies directly as x," or "y is directly proportional to x." The constant of variation, k, is 5.

Answer: 5

Example 2 Find the constant of variation k if y varies directly with x: $\dfrac{y}{x} = 6$.

$\dfrac{y}{x} = 6$

$y = 6x$

Step 1: Put it in the form $y = kx$ by multiplying both sides of the equation by x. The constant of variation is 6.

Answer: 6

There are two ways to approach problems involving direct variation: using the constant of variation and using proportions. You should know how to use both methods.

Example 3 y varies directly with x; if $y = 5$ when $x = 30$, find y when $x = 90$.

$y = kx$

$(5) = k(30)$

$5 = 30k$

Step 1: Because this is a direct variation pattern, you can use the form $y = kx$. In the first part of this problem, you are given values for x and y. Substitute these values into the equation.

$\dfrac{5}{30} = \dfrac{30k}{30}$

$\dfrac{1}{6} = k$

Step 2: The variation constant, or k, is the only unknown variable, so solve for k. Therefore, the constant of variation is $\dfrac{1}{6}$. The original problem, however, has not been solved. Recall that you must find y when $x = 90$.

$y = \dfrac{1}{6}x$

$y = \dfrac{1}{6}(90)$

$= \dfrac{90}{6}$

$= 15$

Step 3: Write the equation, substitute the known values, and solve for y.

Answer: If $y = 5$ when $x = 30$, then $y = 15$ when $x = 90$.

Example 4 M is directly proportional to N; if $M = 60$ when $N = 12$, find M when $N = 9$.

$M = kN$

Step 1: Write the equation.

$60 = k(12)$

Step 2: Substitute known values.

$\dfrac{60}{12} = \dfrac{12k}{12}$

$5 = k$

Step 3: Solve for k.

$M = kN$

$M = 5N$

Step 4: Find the value of M when $N = 9$ by substituting the value found for k into the constant variation formula. For all values of M and N, $M = 5N$.

$M = 5(9)$

$M = 45$

Step 5: Substitute 9 for N and simplify.

Answer: If $M = 60$ when $N = 12$, then $M = 45$ when $N = 9$.

Now look at an example using proportions.

Example 5   Suppose it takes 12 gallons of gas to go 264 miles. How many gallons will it take to travel 440 miles? Notice that you are dealing with gallons of gas and miles. Since the number of miles depends on the number of gallons, you can call miles y and gallons x. To set up a proportion, you need four values: x_1, x_2, y_1, y_2. In this case, $x_1 = 12$ gallons, $y_1 = 264$ miles, $x_2 =$ unknown gallons, and $y_2 = 440$ miles. Notice that x_1 and x_2 have the unit gallons and y_1 and y_2 have the unit miles.

$\dfrac{y_1}{x_1} = \dfrac{y_2}{x_2}$

Step 1: Set up the proportion with y values on top and x values on bottom.

$\dfrac{264}{12} = \dfrac{440}{x_2}$

Step 2: Substitute the known values.

$12(440) = 264 \cdot x_2$

Step 3: Cross multiply.

$\dfrac{5,280}{264} = \dfrac{264x_2}{264}$

20 gallons $= x_2$

Step 4: Divide both sides of the equation by 264.

Answer: Therefore, 20 gallons of gas will allow you to travel 440 miles.

Problem Set

1. Does y vary directly as x? $y = 7x$

      No   Yes

2. Does y vary directly as x? $y = \dfrac{2}{x}$

      Yes   No

3. Does y vary directly as x?

x	1	2	3	4	5
y	4	8	12	16	20

      Yes   No

4. Does y vary directly as x?

x	10	18	28	40
y	5	6	7	8

      No   Yes

5. Does y vary directly as x?

x (temp.)	y (amt. of water)
20	−4
25	−5
−30	6
35	7

Yes   No

6. Find the constant of variation, k, where y varies directly as x if $y = 30$ when $x = 5$.

7. Find the constant of variation, k, where y varies directly as x if $y = 8$ when $x = 8$.

8. Find the constant of variation, k, where y varies directly as x if $y = 7$ when $x = 13$.

9. Find the constant of variation, k, where y varies directly as x if $y = 0.8$ when $x = 0.2$.

10. Find the constant of variation, k, where y varies directly as x if $y = 18$ when $x = -3$.

11. Assume P is directly proportional to T. If $P = 5$ when $T = 2$, find T when $P = 9$. Answer should be in decimal form.

12. Assume y is directly proportional to x. If $y = 5$ when $x = 4$, find y when $x = 12$.

13. Assume y is directly proportional to x. If $y = 24$ when $x = -12$, find x when $y = -12$.

14. Assume y varies directly as x. If $y = -15$ when $x = 3$, find y when $x = -4$. (Find k first, and use k to find y.)

15. Assume y varies directly as x. If $y = 16$ when $x = 8$, find x when $y = 4$.

16. Assume M is directly proportional to X. If $M = 2$ when $X = 10$, find M when $X = 27$.

17. Assume y is directly proportional to x. If $y = -4$ when $x = 8.4$, find x when $y = 12$.

18. A worker's earnings vary directly for the amount of time worked. If the worker earns \$89 for 20 hours of work, what will the individual earn for working 15 hours?

19. On a blueprint, 3 centimeters represents 30 meters. How many meters will 7 centimeters represent?

20. If 36 candles cost \$28.00, how much would 8 candles cost? (Round answer to the nearest hundredth.)

HA1-453: Solving Problems Involving Inverse Variation

In a previous lesson, you learned about direct variation. Recall that direct variation involves two quantities that change in the same direction—one quantity increases as the other increases, and if one quantity decreases, the other one also decreases. You also learned that the relationship between the two quantities is in the form $y = kx$.

Similarly, inverse variation involves two quantities, but this time the two quantities vary inversely. This means that as one quantity increases, the other quantity decreases, and vice versa.

Inverse Variation	A function in the form $y = \dfrac{k}{x}$, where $x \neq 0$ and $k \neq 0$ This can also be stated as "y varies inversely with x," or "y is inversely proportional to x."

For example, suppose you are driving on an interstate; naturally, as your distance increases, the amount of gas in your tank decreases. This is an example of an inverse variation. The equation for inverse variation is similar to direct variation. Instead of multiplying the constant of variation, k, by each x value, you divide the constant of variation by x.

Recall that equations can be written differently, depending on the variable being solved. In the equation for inverse variation, $y = \dfrac{k}{x}$, suppose you want to solve for k. Multiply both sides of the equation by x.

$$x \cdot y = \frac{k}{\cancel{x}} \cdot \cancel{x}$$

$$xy = k$$

Therefore, depending on the information you are given, you can use either of the two equations to solve for the unknown. Look at two examples: one in which x and y do not vary inversely and another in which they do.

Example 1   Determine if the following data varies inversely.

x	5	10	15	20
y	–10	–20	–30	–40

$xy = k$

$(5)(-10) = k$

$-50 = k$

Step 1: First, notice that as x increases, y decreases. Now you must determine if the second condition is met: each pair of x and y must fit the form $y = \dfrac{k}{x}$ or $xy = k$. Because you are given x and y values, use the equation $xy = k$ to see if the constant of variation is actually constant. If it is not, then this data does not vary inversely. Using $xy = k$ and the first set of values for x and y, substitute 5 and –10 respectively for x and y.

$xy = k$

$(10)(-20) = k$

$-200 = k$

Step 2: The constant of variation, k, is –50. Test the next set of values, 10 and –20, to see if you get the same value for k.

Answer: This time the value of k is –200. The values for k are different after the first two substitutions, so you do not need to proceed any further. Because k is not constant, this data does not vary inversely.

Example 2 Determine if y varies inversely with x.

x	-2	5	-4
y	-10	4	-5

$xy = k$

$(-2)(-10) = 20$

$(5)(4) = 20$

$(-4)(-5) = 20$

Step 1: Whether the numbers are increasing or decreasing is not immediately noticeable, so test the pairs of x and y values using $xy = k$.

Answer: The constant of variation remains constant throughout, so you can conclude that this data varies inversely or that "y varies inversely with x."

Example 3 H is inversely proportional to J. If $H = 4$ when $J = 5$, find H when $J = 2$.

$H = \dfrac{k}{J}$

$k = HJ$

Step 1: You are already told that these values vary inversely, so use the equation $xy = k$. You are not given x and y values, so replace them with H and J.

$k = (4)(5)$

$k = 20$

Step 2: Substitute the given values into the equation.

$H = \dfrac{k}{J}$

$H = \dfrac{20}{2}$

$H = 10$

Step 3: Find the value of H when J is 2 by substituting the known values into the first equation.

Answer: When J is 2, H is 10.

Problem Set

1. Tell whether y varies inversely as x:

x	4	5	6
y	15	12	10

Yes   No

2. Tell whether y varies inversely as x:

x	2	4	8
y	4	8	16

Yes   No

3. Tell whether y varies inversely as x:

x	3	1	6
y	4	12	2

No   Yes

4. Tell whether y varies inversely as x:

x	8	6	24
y	12	15	4

No   Yes

5. Tell whether y varies inversely as x:

x	6	2	3
y	7	21	14

No   Yes

6. Tell whether y varies inversely as x:

x	3	9	3
y	30	10	15

No   Yes

7. If y varies inversely as x, and $y = 18$ when $x = 2$, find y when $x = 9$.

8. If y varies inversely as x, and $y = 10$ when $x = 10$, find y when $x = 4$.

9. If y varies inversely as x, and $y = 3$ when $x = 3$, find y when $x = 1$.

10. If y varies inversely as x, and $y = 12$ when $x = 8$, find y when $x = 16$.

11. Tell whether y varies inversely as x:

x	−1	−3	4
y	−12	4	−3

No   Yes

12. Tell whether y varies inversely as x:

x	−2	3	−6
y	−12	8	−4

Yes   No

13. Tell whether y varies inversely as x:

x	−2	4	−1
y	8	−4	16

No   Yes

14. Tell whether y varies inversely as x:

x	3	−5	3
y	−5	6	10

No   Yes

15. Tell whether y varies inversely as x:

x	5	−1	55
y	11	55	1

No   Yes

16. If y varies inversely as x, and $y = 180$ when $x = 2$, find y when $x = 45$.

17. If y varies inversely as x, and $y = -2$ when $x = 3$, find y when $x = 6$.

18. Time varies inversely as speed if the distance is constant. If a trip takes 6.5 hours when traveling at 50 miles per hour (mph), what speed must the driver maintain in order to complete the return trip in 5 hours?

19. The height (h) of triangles of fixed area varies inversely as the base (b). The height of a triangle is 240 cm and its base is 240 cm. What will be its height when its base is 160 cm?

20. The height (h) of triangles of fixed area varies inversely as the base (b). The height of a triangle is 10 cm and its base is 200 cm. What will be its height when its base is 125 cm?

HA1-455: Solving Systems of Linear Equations by Graphing

In previous lessons, we learned to graph linear equations in two variables. Recall that a linear equation in two variables is an equation of the form $Ax + By = C$, with A and B not both zero. Also recall that a linear equation in two variables has an infinite number of solutions, and that the solutions are all points, (x, y), in the coordinate plane that satisfy the equation.

Many problems in real life situations can be solved using one or more linear equation. Two or more linear equations form a system of linear equations.

System of Linear Equations	Two or more linear equations that use the same variables

The set of equations $2x - 3y = 1$ and $3x - 2y = 4$ is a system of two linear equations in two variables because it consists of two linear equations in two variables. However, the set of equations $3x^2 + y = -4$ and $5x - 2y = 3$ is not a system of linear equations because the first equation is of second degree.

To find the solutions to a system of linear equations in two variables means that we need to find all ordered pairs (x, y), in the coordinate plane, that will satisfy both equations simultaneously. That is, we need to find all the solutions (or ordered pairs) that the two equations have in common.

Solution Set to a System of Two Linear Equations	All ordered pairs, (x, y), in the coordinate plane that satisfy both equations simultaneously.

We can easily verify whether an ordered pair is a solution to a given system of equations by substituting the values of x and y into each equation of the system.

Example 1   Determine whether the ordered pairs (4, 1) and (3, 2) are solutions to the system.

$$x + y = 5$$
$$x - y = 3$$

First equation **Second equation**   **Step 1:** Substitute $x = 4$ and $y = 1$ into each equation.

$x + y = 5$ $x - y = 3$

$4 + 1 \overset{?}{=} 5$ $4 - 1 \overset{?}{=} 3$ *Note: The ordered pair (4, 1) satisfies both equations.*

$5 = 5 \checkmark$ $3 = 3 \checkmark$

First equation **Second equation**   **Step 2:** Substitute $x = 3$ and $y = 2$ into each equation.

$x + y = 5$ $x - y = 3$

$3 + 2 \overset{?}{=} 5$ $3 - 2 \overset{?}{=} 3$ *Note: The ordered pair (3, 2) satisfies the first equation, but it*

$5 = 5 \checkmark$ $1 \neq 3$ *does not satisfy the second equation.*

Answer: The ordered pair (4, 1) is a solution to the given system because it satisfies both equations simultaneously.
The order pair (3, 2) is not a solution to the given system because it does not satisfy the second equation.

There are many methods that we can use to find the solution set of a system of linear equations. In this lesson, we will use the graphing method following two steps.

1. Graph each equation on the same grid using any method.

2. Find the point or points of intersection of the two lines. The solution set is the points of intersection.

Example 2   Solve the system of linear equations by graphing. $x + y = 5$
$2x - y = 1$

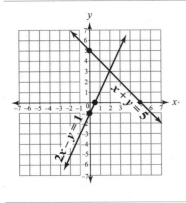

Step 1:   Graph each equation on the same grid using any method.

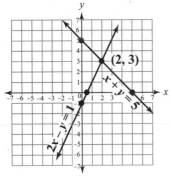

Step 2:   Find the point(s) of intersection of the two lines.

First equation   **Second equation**

$x + y = 5$ $2x - y = 1$

$2 + 3 \overset{?}{=} 5$ $2(2) - 3 \overset{?}{=} 1$

$5 = 5 \checkmark$ $1 = 1 \checkmark$

Step 3:   Verify that the ordered pair (2, 3) is the solution to the given system by substituting $x = 2$ and $y = 3$ into each equation of the system.

Answer: Since the ordered pair satisfies both equations, the solution set of the given system of linear equations is (2, 3).

Note that the above system of linear equations has one solution.

| Consistent and Independent | A system of linear equations that is consistent and independent has one solution. |

Example 3   Solve the system of equations by graphing. $6x + 3y = -6$

$2x + y = 6$

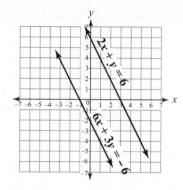

Step 1: Graph each equation on the same grid using any method.

It appears that the two lines are parallel. Since parallel lines never intersect, the two lines do not have any points in common.

Step 2: Find the point(s) of intersection of the two lines.

Answer: The given system has no solution.

Note that the above system of linear equations has no solution.

Inconsistent	A system of linear equations that is inconsistent has no solution.

Recall that parallel lines have equal slopes. Therefore, we can confirm that the two lines are parallel by verifying that they have equal slopes.

Write each equation in slope-intercept form, $y = mx + b$ where m = slope and y-intercept = $(0, b)$, and compare the slopes.

$$6x + 3y = -6$$
$$-6x + 6x = -6x - 6$$
$$3y = -6x - 6$$
$$\frac{3y}{3} = \frac{-6x}{3} - \frac{6}{3}$$
$$y = -2x - 2$$

$$2x + y = 6$$
$$-2x + 2x + y = -2x + 6$$
$$y = -2x + 6$$

Since the two lines have the same slope, $m = -2$, they are parallel.

Example 4   Solve the system of equations by graphing. $6x + 3y = -6$
$$2x + y = -2$$

Step 1: Graph each equation on the same grid using any method.

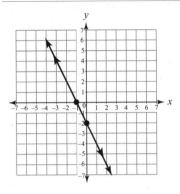

Clearly, the two lines coincide. Therefore, we may conclude that the two lines have an infinite number of points in common.

Step 2: Find the point(s) of intersection of the two lines.

Answer: The system of equations has an infinite number of solutions.

Note that the above system of linear equations has an infinite number of solutions.

Consistent and Dependent	A system of linear equations that is consistent and dependent has an infinite number of solutions

We may confirm that two lines coincide by verifying that they have equal slopes and equal y-intercepts. We write each equation in slope-intercept form, $y = mx + b$, where m = slope and $(0, b)$ is the y-intercept, by solving for y:

$$6x + 3y = -6$$
$$-6x + 6x = -6x - 6$$
$$3y = -6x - 6$$
$$\frac{3y}{3} = \frac{-6x}{3} - \frac{6}{3}$$
$$y = -2x - 2$$

$$2x + y = -2$$
$$-2x + 2x + y = -2x - 2$$
$$y = -2x - 2$$

Since the two lines have the same slope, $m = -2$, they are parallel.

Since the two lines have the same slope, $m = -2$ and the same y-intercept, $(0, -2)$, they are the same line, or the two lines coincide.

Example 5 Given the following system of linear equations, determine whether it is consistent and independent, inconsistent, or consistent and dependent.

$$2x - 5y = 3$$
$$x - y = 3$$

First equation	Second equation	**Step 1:** Write each equation in slope-intercept form, $y = mx + b$, by solving for y.
$2x - 5y = 3$	$x - y = 3$	
$-5y = -2x + 3$	$-y = -x + 3$	
$\dfrac{-5x}{-5} = \dfrac{-2x}{-5} + \dfrac{3}{-5}$	$\dfrac{-y}{-1} = \dfrac{-x}{-1} + \dfrac{3}{-1}$	
$y = \dfrac{2}{5}x - \dfrac{3}{5}$	$y = x - 3$	

First equation	Second equation	**Step 2:** Find the slope and y-intercepts for each equation.
$m = \dfrac{2}{5}$	$m = 1$	
y-intercept $= \left(0, -\dfrac{3}{5}\right)$	y-intercept $= (0, -3)$	

The system has different slopes, and intersects at one point. Therefore, the system has one solution.	**Step 3:** Determine the number of solutions of the system.

Answer: A system of linear equations having one solution is consistent and independent.

The following table will help you summarize the information provided in this lesson.

Graphs of Equations	Number of Solutions or Points of Intersection	Type of System
Intersecting lines	One	Consistent and independent
Parallel Lines	None	Inconsistent
Same Line	Infinitely many	Consistent and dependent

Problem Set

1. Given the following system of linear equations, is the ordered pair (1, 3) a solution? Why or why not?

$$3x - 2y = -3$$
$$x + 4y = 11$$

2. Given the following system of linear equations, is the ordered pair (–2,–1) a solution? Why or why not?

$$-3x - 2y = 8$$
$$x + 3y = -5$$

3. Given the following system of linear equations, is the ordered pair (4, –1) a solution? Why or why not?

$$x + 2y = -6$$
$$5x + 5y = 25$$

4. Given the following system of linear equations, is the ordered pair (–3, 4) a solution? Why or why not?

$$2x - y = -2$$
$$3x + 2y = -1$$

5. Given the following system of linear equations, is the ordered pair (0,–2) a solution? Why or why not?

$$x + y = -2$$
$$x - y = -2$$

6. Given the following system of linear equations, is the ordered pair (–6, 0) a solution? Why or why not?

$$x + 2y = -6$$
$$-x + 4y = 6$$

7. Given the following system of linear equations, is the ordered pair (–3, 3) a solution? Why or why not?

$$x - y = 0$$
$$3x + 2y = 6$$

8. Given the following system of linear equations, is the ordered pair (6, –2) a solution? Why or why not?

$$-x - 2y = -10$$
$$3x - 2y = 22$$

9. Determine which graph represents a system of linear equations that is consistent and independent.

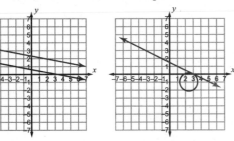

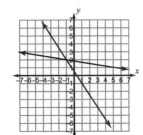
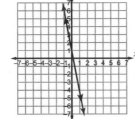

10. Determine which graph represents a system of linear equations that is inconsistent.

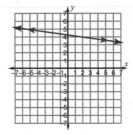
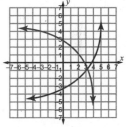

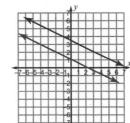
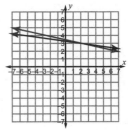

11. Determine which graph represents a system of linear equations that is consistent and dependent.

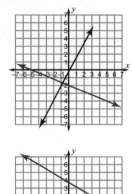

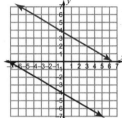

12. Determine which graph represents a system of linear equations that is consistent and independent.

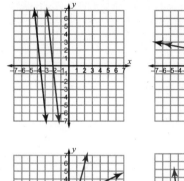

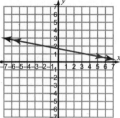

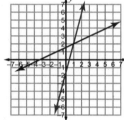

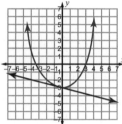

13. Determine which graph represents a system of linear equations that is inconsistent.

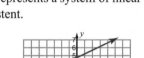

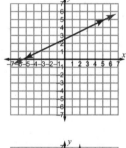

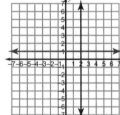

14. Determine which graph represents a system of linear equations that is consistent and dependent.

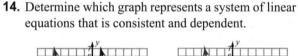

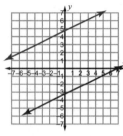

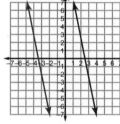

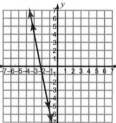

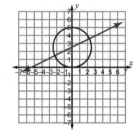

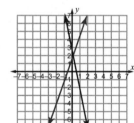

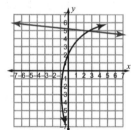

15. Determine which graph represents a system of linear equations that is consistent and independent.

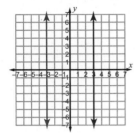 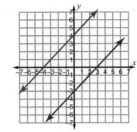

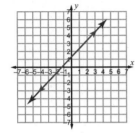 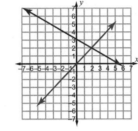

16. Determine which type of system is given below:

$$3x + y = 2$$
$$-4x + y = -7$$

Consistent and dependent

Consistent and independent

Inconsistent

Inconsistent and independent

17. Determine which type of system is given below:

$$2x + y = 1$$
$$2x + y = -3$$

Inconsistent

Consistent and dependent

Consistent and independent

Inconsistent and independent

18. Determine which type of system is given below:

$$y = -4x - 9$$
$$4x + y = -9$$

Consistent and independent

Inconsistent

Consistent and dependent

Inconsistent and independent

19. Determine which type of system is given below:

$$x + 6y = -12$$
$$3x + y = 9$$

Inconsistent

Consistent and independent

Consistent and dependent

Inconsistent and independent

20. Determine which type of system is given below:

$$3x + y = 5$$
$$6x + 2y = -5$$

Inconsistent and independent

Consistent and dependent

Consistent and independent

Inconsistent

21. Determine which type of system is given below:

$$3x - 2y - 6 = 0$$
$$-3x + 2y = -6$$

Inconsistent and independent

Consistent and independent

Consistent and dependent

Inconsistent

22. Determine which type of system is given below:

$$4x - 2y = 6$$
$$y = 5x - 9$$

Consistent and dependent

Inconsistent and independent

Inconsistent

Consistent and independent

23. Determine which type of system is given below:

$$x + y = 5$$
$$2x + 2y = -8$$

Consistent and independent

Consistent and dependent

Inconsistent

Inconsistent and independent

Solve the following systems of equations by graphing:

24. $y = x + 4$
$y = -2x + 4$

25. $2x + y = -1$
$x + y = 0$

26. $y = 3x - 2$
$3x - y = -4$

27. $-2x + y = 4$
$y = 2x - 3$

28. $6x + 3y = 6$
$2x + y = 2$

29. $y = -x + 1$
$x + y = 4$

30. $x - y = -4$
$2x + y = 1$

31. $y = \frac{1}{2}x + 4$
$\frac{1}{2}x + \frac{3}{2}y = 1$

32. $\frac{1}{2}x - \frac{1}{3}y = -1$
$x + y = 3$

33. $\frac{1}{2}y = x$
$\frac{2}{3}x + \frac{2}{3}y = 2$

34. $y - \frac{1}{2}x = 1$
$\frac{1}{2}x - \frac{1}{4}y = -1$

35. $2x - \frac{1}{2}y = 3$
$4x - y = -2$

36. $y = \frac{2}{3}x - 4$
$2x - 3y = 6$

37. $\frac{1}{4}x - \frac{1}{2}y = 0$
$-x + 2y = 4$

38. $6x + 3y = 12$
$\frac{1}{4}y = -\frac{1}{2}x + 1$

39. $\frac{1}{3}x - \frac{1}{3}y = 1$
$y = x - 3$

40. $2y = x + 4$
$\frac{-1}{2}x + y = 2$

Consider the following system of equations: $\begin{cases} y = 3x - 1 \\ 7x + 2y = 37 \end{cases}$

If you attempt to solve this system by graphing, you will soon find that it is awkward to draw the picture. It is far better to solve the system algebraically. When one of the equations is solved for either x or y, a good approach is the **substitution method**, which is outlined in this lesson. In the given system the first equation is solved for y. The equation says that y and $3x - 1$ are equal quantities. The idea is that you substitute $3x - 1$ for y in the second equation as follows.

Example 1   Solve using the substitution method: $\begin{cases} y = 3x - 1 \\ 7x + 2y = 37 \end{cases}$

$7x + 2(3x - 1) = 37$	**Step 1:** Isolate one variable from either equation. In this case, the variable y is already isolated in the first equation. Therefore, simply substitute $3x - 1$ for y in the second equation.

$$7x + 6x - 2 = 37$$
$$13x - 2 = 37$$
$$13x - 2 + 2 = 37 + 2$$
$$\frac{13x}{13} = \frac{39}{13}$$
$$x = 3$$

Step 2: Simplify the equation and solve for x.

$$y = 3x - 1$$
$$= 3(3) - 1$$
$$= 9 - 1$$
$$= 8$$

Step 3: Having found the value of x, you can use one of the original equations to find y. You can use either equation, but you should determine which one will be easier to use. In this case the first equation is easier because it is solved for y.

$$y = 3x - 1 \qquad 7x + 2y = 37$$
$$(8) = 3(3) - 1 \qquad 7(3) + 2(8) = 37$$
$$8 = 9 - 1 \qquad 21 + 16 = 37$$
$$8 = 8 \qquad 37 = 37$$

Step 4: Check your work by substituting into the original system of equations. Replace x with 3 and y with 8 to see if the ordered pair (3, 8) makes both equations true.

Answer: Therefore, the ordered pair (3, 8) is a solution to this system of equations.

Example 2   Solve $\begin{cases} 5x - y = 20 \\ y = 3x \end{cases}$ using the substitution method.

$5x - (3x) = 20$	**Step 1:** In this example, the second equation is solved for y. Since y and $3x$ are equal quantities, substitute $3x$ for y in the first equation.

$5x - 3x = 20$ $\dfrac{2x}{2} = \dfrac{20}{2}$ $x = 10$	**Step 2:** Solve for x.

$y = 3(10)$ $y = 30$	**Step 3:** Now find y by replacing x with 10 in the second equation.

$y = 3x$ $30 = 3(10)$ $30 = 30$ $\quad$ $5x - y = 20$ $5(10) - (30) = 20$ $50 - 30 = 20$ $20 = 20$	**Step 4:** Check your answer by replacing x by 10 and y by 30.

Answer: The ordered pair (10, 30) is a solution to this system of equations.

The next example shows how to recognize an inconsistent system when solving systems algebraically.

Example 3   Solve $\begin{cases} x - 2y = 4 \\ 4y - 2x = 7 \end{cases}$ using the substitution method.

$x - 2y = 4$ $x - 2y + 2y = 4 + 2y$ $x = 4 + 2y$	**Step 1:** In order to solve by substitution, one of the equations must be solved for either x or y. In this system it seems easiest to solve the first equation for x by adding $2y$ to each side.

$x = 4 + 2y$ $4y - 2x = 7$	**Step 2:** Substitute the new equation for the first equation.

$4y - 2(4 + 2y) = 7$	**Step 3:** Substitute $4 + 2y$ for x in the second equation.

$4y - 8 - 4y = 7$ $-8 \neq 7$	**Step 4:** Simplify.

Answer: If you get a false statement, such as $-8 = 7$, it means there is no solution; that is, the solution set is a null set: $\varnothing$. Recall that when solving by graphing, you get no solution when the lines are parallel. You can check that solving the above system by graphing yields parallel lines.

The next example is intended to show how to recognize a dependent system when solving systems algebraically.

Example 4 Solve $\begin{cases} 4x - 2y = 12 \\ y = 2x - 6 \end{cases}$ using the substitution method.

$4x - 2(2x - 6) = 12$ | **Step 1:** Since the second equation is solved for y, substitute $2x - 6$ for y in the first equation.

$4x - 4x + 12 = 12$
$12 = 12$
$12 - 12 = 12 - 12$
$0 = 0$

Step 2: Solve the equation.

Answer: After substituting, if you get an equation that simplifies to $0 = 0$, it means that the original system is dependent. A dependent system has infinitely many solutions. Recall that when solving systems by graphing, a system is dependent if both lines have that same graph. You can check that this is the case for this example by graphing equations.

Example 5 Solve $\begin{cases} 3x - 5y = -14 \\ 4x + 2y = 16 \end{cases}$ using the substitution method.

$4x + 2y = 16$
$4x - 4x + 2y = 16 - 4x$
$ 2y = 16 - 4x$
$\dfrac{2y}{2} = \dfrac{16 - 4x}{2}$
$\phantom{\dfrac{2y}{2}} y = 8 - 2x$

Step 1: One of the equations must be solved either for x or for y. Solving the first equation for either variable will introduce fractions. You should always look for the easiest solution. In this problem, it is easier to solve the second equation for y.

$3x - 5y = -14$
$y = 8 - 2x$

Step 2: Substitute the new equation for the second equation.

$3x - 5(8 - 2x) = -14$
$3x - 40 + 10x = -14$
$13x - 40 = -14$
$13x - 40 + 40 = -14 + 40$
$13x = 26$
$\dfrac{13x}{13} = \dfrac{26}{13}$
$x = 2$

Step 3: Substitute $8 - 2x$ for y in the first equation and solve for x.

$y = 8 - 2(2)$
$y = 4$

Step 4: Now use the equation $y = 8 - 2x$ to find y.

$$3(2) - 5(4) = -14$$
$$6 - 20 = -14$$
$$-14 = -14$$

$$4(2) + 2(4) = 16$$
$$8 + 8 = 16$$
$$16 = 16$$

Step 5: Finally, check the answer using the original equations. Do not check the solution in the system you actually solved, because you may have made a mistake in deriving that system. Replace x with 2 and y with 4.

Answer: Since each equation yields a true statement, the solution (2, 4) is correct.

Problem Set

1. Solve the equation for x:
$$x - 2y = 20$$

2. Solve the equation for x:
$$x - 3y = -11$$

3. Solve the equation for x:
$$x - 2y = -9$$

4. Solve the equation for x:
$$2x - 4y = -16$$

5. Solve the equation for x:
$$7x + 7y = 21$$

6. Is (3, 2) a solution of the following system of linear equations? Answer yes or no.
$$x - y = 1$$
$$3x - y = 7$$

7. Is (3, 1) a solution of the following system of linear equations? Answer yes or no.
$$x - y = 2$$
$$x - 2y = 4$$

8. Is (−2, 3) a solution of the following system of linear equations? Answer yes or no.
$$x + y = 1$$
$$x + 5y = 13$$

9. Is (1, −4) a solution of the following system of linear equations? Answer yes or no.
$$3x - 3y = 15$$
$$x + 5y = -18$$

10. Is (−2, −2) a solution of the following system of linear equations? Answer yes or no.
$$2x + 3y = -10$$
$$3x - y = -6$$

Solve the following systems of linear equations using the substitution method:

11. $y = x - 3$
$3x - y = 7$

12. $x = y + 1$
$2x - y = 6$

13. $x = 2y + 1$
$3x - y = 13$

14. $x - y = -1$
$5x + y = 19$

15. $x - y = 1$
$5x + y = 17$

16. $x - y = -8$
$x + 5y = 22$

17. $x - y = 3$
$3x + 3y = 39$

18. $2x + 2y = -4$
$3x + 2y = -7$

19. $2x - 4y = -16$
$3x - 2y = -12$

20. $4x - 8y = -12$
$3x - 4y = -3$

HA1-465: Solving Systems of Linear Equations by the Addition/Subtraction Method

This lesson introduces another approach to solving systems of equations, known as the **addition/subtraction method**. The reason for learning different approaches is that different problems tend to work out more easily using one method rather than another. In practice a problem is solved using the method that appears easiest for the problem.

Example 1
$$\begin{cases} 7x - 5y = 52 \\ 2x + 5y = 47 \end{cases}$$

Notice that the coefficients of y are opposites (-5 and 5). If either the x-terms or y-terms are opposites, you add the corresponding sides of the equations.

$$\begin{array}{r} 7x - 5y = 52 \\ 2x + 5y = 47 \\ \hline 9x = 99 \end{array}$$

Step 1: Add the two equations to eliminate y. This method is also known as the elimination method.

$$\frac{9x}{9} = \frac{99}{9}$$

$$x = 11$$

Step 2: Solve for x.

$$2x + 5y = 47$$
$$2(11) + 5y = 47$$
$$22 + 5y = 47$$
$$22 + 5y - 22 = 47 - 22$$
$$5y = 25$$
$$\frac{5y}{5} = \frac{25}{5}$$
$$y = 5$$

Step 3: Having determined x, you can now use one of the original equations to determine y. Either equation can be used. The usual rule applies when you have a choice: choose the equation that looks easier to handle. In this example, if you use the second equation, you replace x with 11 and then use the resulting equation to determine y.

$$7x - 5y = 52$$
$$7(11) - 5(5) = 52$$
$$77 - 25 = 52$$
$$52 = 52$$

Step 4: Check your answer. Since y was found using the second equation, the answer is checked using the first equation. Replace x with 11 and y with 5.

Answer: This is a true statement; the solution (11, 5) is correct.

Example 2 $\begin{cases} 8x + 4y = 22 \\ -2x + 4y = 17 \end{cases}$ In this example, the y terms are the same. This means that if you subtract corresponding sides of the equations, the y-terms will be eliminated.

$8x - (-2x) + 4y - 4y = 22 - 17$ **Step 1:** Subtract the equations to eliminate the y-terms.

$$8x + 2x = 5$$
$$10x = 5$$
$$\frac{10x}{10} = \frac{5}{10}$$
$$x = \frac{1}{2}$$

Step 2: Simplify and solve for x.

$$8\left(\frac{1}{2}\right) + 4y = 22$$
$$4 + 4y = 22$$
$$4 - 4 + 4y = 22 - 4$$
$$4y = 18$$
$$\frac{4y}{4} = \frac{18}{4}$$
$$y = \frac{9}{2}$$

Step 3: Now use one of the original equations to determine y. In this example, the first equation is used. Substitute the value found for x and solve for y.

$$-2\left(\frac{1}{2}\right) + 4\left(\frac{9}{2}\right) = 17$$
$$-\frac{2}{2} + \frac{36}{2} = 17$$
$$-1 + 18 = 17$$
$$17 = 17$$

Step 4: Since the first equation was used to determine y, check the answer in the second equation.

Answer: This is a true statement; the solution $\left(\frac{1}{2}, \frac{9}{2}\right)$ is correct.

Since it is easy to make an arithmetic error when dealing with negative numbers, it is a good idea to begin by multiplying each side of one of the equations by -1. If you do this, it will make the y terms opposites and then the equations can be solved by adding corresponding sides.

Example 3 $\begin{cases} 8x + 4y = 22 \\ -2x + 4y = 17 \end{cases}$

$$8x + 4y = 22$$
$$-1(-2x + 4y) = -1(17)$$

Step 1: Multiply each side of the second equation by -1.

$$8x + 4y = 22$$
$$2x - 4y = -17$$

Step 2: The system is now simplified.

$$10x = 5$$

Step 3: Now add the corresponding sides.

Step 4: From this point on, the steps are identical to the steps in Example 2, so they will not be repeated.

Answer: The solution is $\left(\frac{1}{2}, \frac{9}{2}\right)$.

When solving a problem, it is a good idea to attempt to figure out which operations will make subsequent steps easier. Since y-terms are the same, subtracting corresponding sides will eliminate y. Adding is usually easier, but the coefficients of the y-terms would need to be opposites. This is accomplished by multiplying each side of the first equations by -1. Then, the addition method can be used.

Example 4 $\begin{cases} 3x - 2y = 5 \\ 5x = 2y + 9 \end{cases}$

$$3x - 2y = 5$$
$$5x - 2y = 9$$

Step 1: Write the equations with the variable aligned.

$$-1(3x - 2y) = -1(5)$$
$$5x - 2y = 9$$

Step 2: Multiply each side of the first equation by -1.

$$\begin{aligned} -3x + 2y &= -5 \\ 5x - 2y &= 9 \\ \hline 2x &= 4 \end{aligned}$$

Step 3: Simplify and then add.

$$\frac{2x}{2} = \frac{4}{2}$$
$$x = 2$$

Step 4: Now solve to determine x.

$$3(2) - 2y = 5$$
$$6 - 2y = 5$$
$$6 - 6 - 2y = 5 - 6$$
$$-2y = -1$$
$$\frac{-2y}{-2} = \frac{-1}{-2}$$
$$y = \frac{1}{2}$$

Step 5: Having found x, use one of the original equations to determine y. This example uses the first equation.

$$5(2) = 2\left(\frac{1}{2}\right) + 9$$
$$10 = 1 + 9$$
$$10 = 10$$

Step 6: Since y was found using the first equation, the answer is checked using the second equation. Replace x with 2 and y with $\frac{1}{2}$.

Answer: This is a true statement; the solution $(2, \frac{1}{2})$ is correct.

Problem Set

1. What would be the best first step to solve the following system?

$$x + y = 6$$
$$x - y = -2$$

Graph each equation on the same set of axes.

Add or subtract the terms in one equation.

Add or subtract the given equations to eliminate one of the variables.

Solve for the first variable, then substitute the value into the first equation.

2. What would be the best first step to solve the following system?

$$2x = y - 5$$
$$3x - y = -3$$

Rewrite the second equation in standard form.

Solve for the first variable, then substitute the value into the first equation.

Rewrite the first equation in standard form.

Add or subtract the terms in one equation.

Solve the following systems of equations using the addition or substitution method:

3. $x + y = -3$
   $x - y = 3$

4. $x - y = 5$
   $x + y = 7$

5. $5x - 3y = -24$
   $x + 3y = -6$

6. $x + y = 10$
   $2x = y - 4$

7. $2x + 3y = 4$
   $-2y = 2x - 8$

8. $4x + 2y = -2$
   $2y = 4x + 6$

9. $2x + 4y = 8$
   $2x - 3y = 1$

10. $2x + 4y = 12$
    $x + 4y = 8$

HA1-470: Solving Systems of Linear Equations by the Multiply/Add/Subtract Method

In the previous lesson you saw how to solve systems of linear equations in two variables when it was possible to eliminate a variable by adding or subtracting the corresponding sides of the equations. Consider the following

system: $\begin{cases} 3x + 2y = 23 \\ x - y = 6 \end{cases}$

Example 1 Solve: $\begin{cases} 3x + 2y = 23 \\ x - y = 6 \end{cases}$

$3x + 2y = 23$ $2(x - y) = 2(6)$	**Step 1:** Notice that if you multiply each side of the second equation by 2, you get a pair of equations in which the y terms are opposites.

$3x + 2y = 23$ $\underline{2x - 2y = 12}$ $5x \quad\quad = 35$	**Step 2:** Simplify and add the equations.

$5x = 35$ $\dfrac{5x}{5} = \dfrac{35}{5}$ $x = 7$	**Step 3:** Now solve this equation to find x.

$7 - y = 6$ $7 - 7 - y = 6 - 7$ $-y = -1$ $y = 1$	**Step 4:** Having found x, the procedure is the same as for the addition/subtraction method. Use one of the original equations to find y. In this case, use the second equation.

$3(7) + 2(1) = 23$ $21 + 2 = 23$ $23 = 23$	**Step 5:** Since the second equation was used to find y, check the answer using the first equation.

Answer: This is a true statement; the solution $(7,1)$ is correct.

Example 2 Solve: $\begin{cases} 2x + 3y = 17 \\ 3x + 2y = 18 \end{cases}$

$3(2x + 3y) = 3(17)$ $-2(3x + 2y) = -2(18)$	**Step 1:** The objective is to make either the x-terms or the y-terms opposites by multiplying each side of the equation by some number. As a general rule, do what seems easier. Suppose you choose to make the x-terms opposites. Find the least common multiple of the coefficients of x. In this case, it is the least common multiple of 2 and 3, which is 6. You now make the coefficients of x be 6 and –6. It does not matter which one is negative. To do this, multiply each side of the first equation by 3 and each side of the second equation by –2.

$$6x + 9y = 51$$
$$-6x - 4y = -36$$
$$5y = 15$$

Step 2: Simplify and add the equations.

$$\frac{5y}{5} = \frac{15}{5}$$
$$y = 3$$

Step 3: Now solve this equation to find y.

$$2x + 3(3) = 17$$
$$2x + 9 = 17$$
$$2x + 9 - 9 = 17 - 9$$
$$\frac{2x}{2} = \frac{8}{2}$$
$$x = 4$$

Step 4: Now use one of the original equations to find x.

$$3(4) + 2(3) = 18$$
$$12 + 6 = 18$$
$$18 = 18$$

Step 5: Since the first equation was used to find x, check the answer using the second equation.

Answer: This is a true statement; the solution (4,3) is correct.

Recall that when solving systems by substitution, some of the systems turned out to be inconsistent or dependent. The same can happen when you solve using the addition method.

Example 3   Solve: $\begin{cases} -4x + 6y = 5 \\ 6x - 9y = 7 \end{cases}$

$$3(-4x + 6y) = 3(5)$$
$$2(6x - 9y) = 2(7)$$

Step 1: Suppose you decide to make the x-terms opposites. The least common multiple of 4 and 6 is 12, so multiply each side of the first equation by 3 and each side of the second equation by 2.

$$-12x + 18y = 15$$
$$12x - 18y = 14$$
$$0 \neq 29$$

Step 2: Simplify and add the equations.

Answer: As in the substitution method, if you get a false statement, then there are no solutions. The system is inconsistent and there are no solutions.

Suppose Example 3 had been the following: $\begin{cases} -4x + 6y = 8 \\ 6x - 9y = -12 \end{cases}$

Example 4   Solve: $\begin{cases} -4x + 6y = 8 \\ 6x - 9y = -12 \end{cases}$

$3(-4x + 6y) = 3(8)$

$2(6x - 9y) = 2(-12)$

Step 1:   Suppose you decide to make the x-terms opposites. The least common multiple of 4 and 6 is 12, so multiply each side of the first equation by 3 and each side of the second equation by 2.

$-12x + 18y = 24$

$12x - 18y = -24$

$0 = 0$

Step 2:   Simplify and add the equations.

Answer: As in the substitution method, if you obtain $0 = 0$, then the system is dependent. There are infinitely many solutions.

Problem Set

1. What would be the best first step to solve the following system?

$$3m + n = 5$$
$$m = 2n - 4$$

Multiply the second equation by 3.

Multiply the first equation by –2.

Rewrite the equation $m = 2n - 4$ in standard form.

Add or subtract the two equations.

2. What would be the best first step to solve the following system?

$$7x - 3y = 4$$
$$x - y = -5$$

Graph each equation on the same set of axes.

Multiply the second equation by –7.

Rewrite each equation in standard form.

Add or subtract the two equations.

Rewrite each equation in standard form.

3. What would be the best first step to solve the following system?

$$3y = 2x + 9$$
$$2x = 3y - 4$$

Multiply each equation by 2.

Multiply each equation by 3.

Rewrite each equation in standard form.

Add or subtract the two equations.

4. What would be the best first step to solve the following system?

$$2x - 3y = -11$$
$$5x - y = -1$$

Multiply the second equation by –3.

Add or subtract the two equations.

Rewrite each equation in standard form.

Graph each equation on the same set of axes.

5. What would be the best first step to solve the following system?

$$5x + 3y = 8$$
$$x - 4y = -2$$

Rewrite each equation in standard form.

Multiply the second equation by 3.

Add or subtract the two equations.

Multiply the second equation by –5.

6. Solve the system for y.

$$3x + 9y = -20$$
$$-3x - 3y = 2$$

7. Solve the system for a.

$$12a + 15b = 38$$
$$-2a - 15b = 42$$

8. Solve the system for n.

$$6m + 15n = 56$$
$$-6m + 10n = 19$$

9. Solve the system for t.

$$14s + 2t = 37$$
$$-14s - 11t = -1$$

10. Solve the system for b.

$$-12a + 8b = 34$$
$$12a - 5b = -19$$

Solve each system of equations:

11. $2x + 2y = -13$
$-4x + y = -9$

12. $3x - y = 14$
$-2x + 3y = 7$

13. $5x + 3y = 14$
$-10x - 6y = -2$

14. $6m + 6n = 12$
$m + 3n = 4$

15. $12x + 3y = 27$
$-4x - y = -9$

16. $x - 3y = 13$
$4x - 7y = 2$

17. $4x + 2y = 2$
$-2x + 6y = -8$

18. $14x + 2y = 6$
$-21x - 3y = 13$

19. $-2x + 3y = 30$
$3x - 2y = -5$

20. $-3x + 7y = -8$
$5x - 11y = 16$

HA1-475: Graphing the Solution Set of a System of Linear Inequalities

You have already seen how a linear inequality in two variables is graphed. The graph consists of all ordered pairs for which the inequality is true. The line that divides the coordinate plane into two regions is called a boundary line. A half-plane is the region formed when the boundary line divides the coordinate plane. The boundary line is either dashed or solid. It is dashed if the inequality is "greater than" or "less than" and it is solid if the inequality is "greater than or equal to" or "less than or equal to." Two or more linear inequalities are called a **system of linear inequalities**.

System of Linear Inequalities	A system that consists of two or more linear inequalities in the same variables

An example of a system of linear inequalities is $\begin{matrix} x + y \geq 4 \\ y \geq 2x - 5 \end{matrix}$. The graph of a system of linear inequalities consists of all the ordered pairs for which both inequalities are true. The solution set of the system is graphed by plotting the graphs of both inequalities on the same coordinate plane; the solution set of the system is the region where the solution sets of the inequalities overlap or intersect.

Solution of a System of Linear Inequalities	An ordered pair (x, y) that is a solution of each inequality in the system

---

Example 1   Solve the system of inequalities by graphing.

$$x > -2$$
$$y \leq 3$$

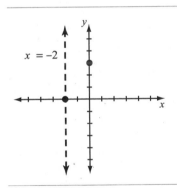

Step 1: Graph the boundary line $x = -2$. Since the x-values for $x > -2$ include the quantities greater than -2, the line is dashed.

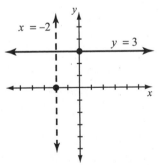

Step 2: Graph the boundary line $y = 3$. Since the y-values for $y \leq 3$ include the quantities less than or equal to 3, the line is solid.

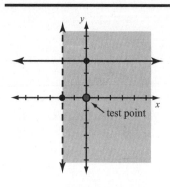

Step 3: Use the test point (0, 0) to test the inequality $x > -2$. Since $0 > -2$ is a true statement, shade to the right of the boundary line.

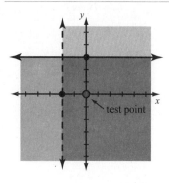

Step 4: Use the test point (0, 0) to test the inequality $y \leq 3$. Since $0 \leq 3$ is a true statement, shade below the boundary line.

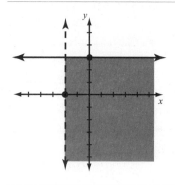

Step 5: Examine the graph to see where the two graphs intersect. The ordered pairs in that region are the solutions to the system.

Answer: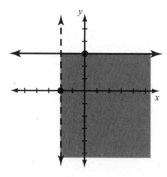

Example 2   Determine whether or not the point (0, 1) is a solution to the system.

$$y > -2x - 1$$
$$y \le -2x + 2$$

$y > -2x - 1$ $1 > -2(0) - 1$ $1 > 0 - 1$ $1 > -1 \quad \text{true}$	**Step 1:** Substitute the point (0, 1) into the first inequality to determine if it is a true statement.
$y \le -2x + 2$ $1 \le -2(0) + 2$ $1 \le 0 + 2$ $1 \le 2 \quad \text{true}$	**Step 2:** Substitute the point (0, 1) into the second inequality to determine if it is a true statement.
	Step 3: Since the point (0, 1) satisfies both inequalities, it is a solution to the system of inequalities.
	Answer: The point (0, 1) is a solution to the system.

Example 3   Solve the system of inequalities by graphing:

$$x + y \ge 4$$
$$y \ge 2x - 5$$

x	y
0	4
4	0

Step 1: Graph the boundary line $x + y = 4$ or $y = -x + 4$ by finding a set of ordered pairs.

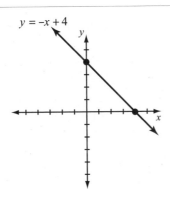

$y = -x + 4$

Step 2: Since the y-values for $y \ge -x + 4$ include the quantities greater than or equal to $-x + 4$, the line is solid.

x	y
0	−5
2	−1
3	1

Step 3: Graph the boundary line $y = 2x - 5$ by finding a set of ordered pairs.

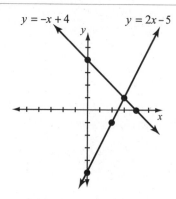

Step 4: Since the y-values for $y \geq 2x - 5$, include the quantities greater than or equal to $2x - 5$, the line is solid.

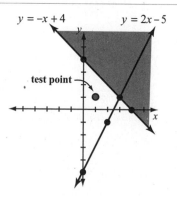

Step 5: Use the test point $(1, 1)$ to test the inequality $x + y \geq 4$. Since $2 \geq 4$ is a false statement, shade above of the boundary line.

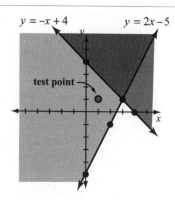

Step 6: Use the test point $(1, 1)$ to test the inequality $y \geq 2x - 5$. Since $1 \geq -3$ is a true statement, shade to the left of the boundary line.

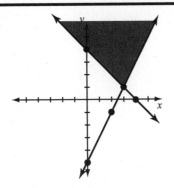

Step 7: Examine the graph to see where the two graphs intersect. The ordered pairs in that region are the solutions to the system.

Answer:

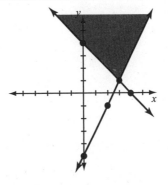

Example 4   Graph the solution set to the system of linear inequalities.

$$y \leq -x + 3$$
$$2x + y > 1$$
$$x \geq 1$$

x	y
0	3
3	0

Step 1: Graph the boundary line $y = -x + 3$ by finding a set of ordered pairs.

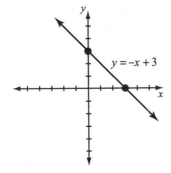

$y = -x + 3$

Step 2: Since the y-values for $y \leq -x + 3$ include the quantities less than or equal to $-x + 3$, the line is solid.

x	y
0	1
1	-1
-1	3

Step 3: Graph the boundary line $2x + y = 1$ or $y = -2x + 1$ by finding a set of ordered pairs.

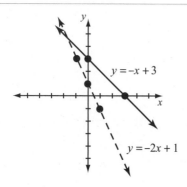

Step 4: Since the y-values for $y > -2x + 1$ include the quantities greater than $-2x + 1$, the line is dashed.

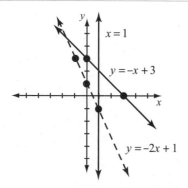

Step 5: Graph the boundary line $x = 1$. Since the x-values for $x \geq 1$ include the quantities greater than or equal to 1, the line is solid.

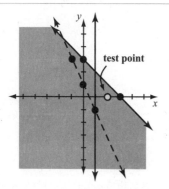

Step 6: Use the test point $(2,0)$ to test the inequality $y \leq -x + 3$. Since $0 \leq 1$ is a true statement, shade below the boundary line.

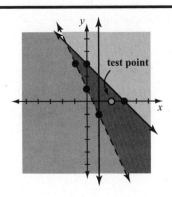

Step 7: Use the test point (2, 0) to test the inequality $2x + y > 1$. Since $4 > 1$ is a true statement, shade above the boundary line.

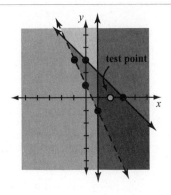

Step 8: Use the test point (2, 0) to test the inequality $x \geq 1$. Since $2 \geq 1$ is a true statement, shade to the right of the boundary line.

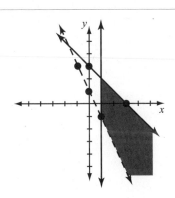

Step 9: Examine the graph to see where the three graphs intersect. The ordered pairs in that region are the solutions to the system.

Answer:

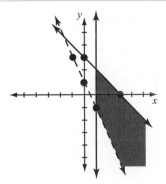

Example 5   A farmer wants to plant corn and sugar cane. She must plant at least 500 acres of corn and at least 625 acres of sugar cane. There are 1,750 acres available for planting. Prepare a graph that will represent all of the possible combinations of planting the available acres under these conditions.

Let c represent the acres of corn.
Let s represent the acres of sugar cane.

Step 1: Set up inequalities to represent the information in the question.

$$c \geq 500$$
$$s \geq 625$$
$$s + c \leq 1,750$$

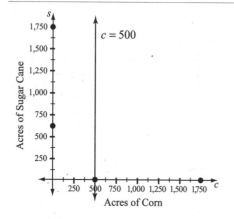

Step 2: Graph the boundary line $c = 500$. Since the c-values for $c \geq 500$ include the quantities greater than or equal to 500, the line is solid.

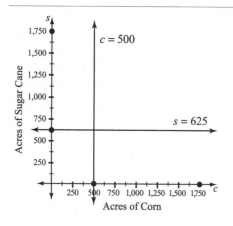

Step 3: Graph the boundary line $s = 625$. Since the s-values for $s \geq 625$ include the quantities greater than or equal to 625, the line is solid.

c	s
0	1,750
1,750	0

Step 4: Graph the boundary line $s + c = 1,750$ or $s = -c + 1,750$ by finding a set of ordered pairs.

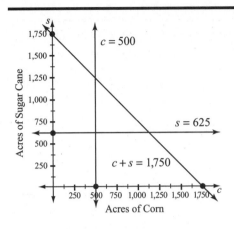

Step 5: Since the s-values for $s \geq -c + 1{,}750$ include the quantities greater than or equal to $-c + 1{,}750$, the line is solid.

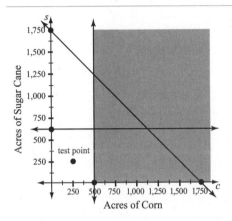

Step 6: Use the test point $(250, 250)$ to test the inequality $c \geq 500$. Since $250 \geq 500$ is a false statement, shade to the right the boundary line.

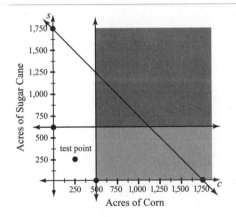

Step 7: Use the test point $(250, 250)$ to test the inequality $s \geq 625$. Since $250 \geq 625$ is a false statement, shade above the boundary line.

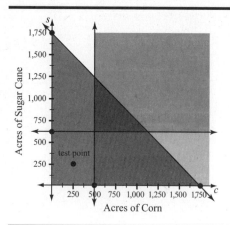

Step 8: Use the test point (250, 250) to test the inequality $s + c \leq 1{,}750$. Since $500 \leq 1{,}750$ is a true statement, shade below the boundary line.

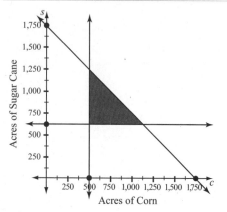

Step 9: Examine the graph to see where the three graphs intersect. The ordered pairs in that region are the solutions to the system.

Answer:

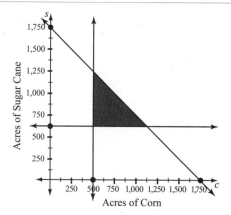

Problem Set

Solve the following:

1. Solve the system of inequalities by graphing.

$$x > 4$$
$$y \leq 2$$

2. Solve the system of inequalities by graphing.

$$x > 4$$
$$y \geq -5$$

3. Solve the system of inequalities by graphing.

$$y \leq x$$
$$y > 2x + 1$$

4. Solve the system of inequalities by graphing.

$$y < x$$
$$y > -3x + 2$$

5. Determine whether or not the point $(3, 4)$ is a solution to the system.

$$2x + y > 3$$
$$4x - y > 4$$

Solution   Not a solution

6. Determine whether or not the point $(0, 2)$ is a solution to the system.

$$x + y < 3$$
$$x - y > -3$$

Not a solution   Solution

7. Determine which point is a solution to the following system.

$$y > 2x - 4$$
$$x + y \le -5$$

$(2, 6)$ $(-4, -5)$
$(6, 3)$ $(1, -10)$

8. Determine which point is a solution to the following system.

$$y > 2x - 4$$
$$x + y \le 5$$

$(9, 0)$ $(1, 3)$
$(3, 5)$ $(4, -2)$

9. Solve the system of inequalities by graphing.

$$x - y > -2$$
$$2x + y > 1$$

10. Solve the system of inequalities by graphing.

$$2x - y > 0$$
$$x + 3y < 2$$

11. Solve the system of inequalities by graphing.

$$3x - y < 2$$
$$x + y > -1$$

12. Solve the system of inequalities by graphing.

$$x - y \le -2$$
$$x + y \ge 4$$

13. Solve the system of inequalities by graphing.

$$y \ge 3$$
$$y > x + 3$$
$$2x + y > 2$$

14. Solve the system of inequalities by graphing.

$$y \ge -3$$
$$x \le 3$$
$$x + 2y \le 4$$

15. Solve the system of inequalities by graphing.

$$y \ge -2$$
$$x \ge 2$$
$$x + y \le 4$$

16. Solve the system of inequalities by graphing.

$$x + y \le 4$$
$$x - y \le -2$$
$$y \le 3$$

17. A jeans store plans to purchase ads on a local radio station to advertise upcoming sales. The operating budget will allow them to spend no more than $10,000 on these advertisements. They plan to run no more than 10 ads. The cost of an ad to air on weekdays is $500 and the cost of an ad to air on a weekend is $1,000. Prepare a graph that will represent all of the possible combinations of ads under these conditions.

18. A local charity plans to publish brochures for their next event. The publications budget allows them to spend less than $500 on brochures. They plan to order no more than 300 brochures. The cost of printing a color brochure is $2 each and the cost of printing a black and white brochure is $1 each. Prepare a graph that will represent all of these possible combinations of brochures under these conditions.

19. A farmer want so plant wheat and green beans. He must plant no more than 900 acres of wheat and no more than 1,200 acres of green beans. He has 1,500 acres available for planting. Prepare a graph that will represent all of the possible combinations of planting the available acres under these conditions.

20. Angie wants to spend no more than $1,200 for hotels while on vacation. She wants to stay at a luxury hotel for at least two nights and at a discount hotel for the remainder of her stay. The luxury hotel is $150 per night, and the discount hotel is $75 per night. She plans to vacation for at least 10 days. Prepare a graph that will represent all of the possible combinations of her stay under these conditions.

HA1-480: Finding the Square Roots of Rational Numbers

We have learned about squaring numbers. Now we will look at the inverse of squaring a number, which is finding the square root of a number. For example, if we know that $3^2 = 9$, then 3 is called the principal square root of 9.

Let's look at some terms used when finding square roots:

$$\text{Radical}\begin{cases} & \text{Radical sign} \\ \sqrt{x} & \\ & \text{Radicand} \end{cases}$$

The **radical** is an expression in the form $\sqrt{x}$. The **radical sign** is the symbol used to express a radical. The **radicand** is the group of number(s) or variable(s) or both under the radical sign.

Example 1   Simplify: $\sqrt{81}$

$\sqrt{81} = \sqrt{9^2}$	**Step 1:** Write the expression as a square.
$= 9$	**Step 2:** Simplify.
	Answer: 9

Now, let's look at two properties which will be helpful in simplifying square roots.

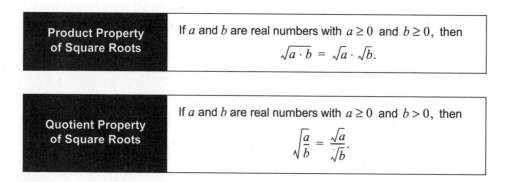

Product Property of Square Roots	If a and b are real numbers with $a \geq 0$ and $b \geq 0$, then $$\sqrt{a \cdot b} = \sqrt{a} \cdot \sqrt{b}.$$
Quotient Property of Square Roots	If a and b are real numbers with $a \geq 0$ and $b > 0$, then $$\sqrt{\frac{a}{b}} = \frac{\sqrt{a}}{\sqrt{b}}.$$

Example 2   Simplify: $\sqrt{576}$

$\sqrt{576} = \sqrt{9 \cdot 64}$	**Step 1:** Factor the expression.
$= \sqrt{9} \cdot \sqrt{64}$	**Step 2:** Use the Product Property of Square Roots.
$= 3 \cdot 8$	**Step 3:** Simplify.
$= 24$	
	Answer: 24

Example 3	Simplify: $-\sqrt{\dfrac{16}{25}}$

$-\sqrt{\dfrac{16}{25}} = -\dfrac{\sqrt{16}}{\sqrt{25}}$	**Step 1:** Use the Quotient Property of Square Roots.
$= -\dfrac{4}{5}$	**Step 2:** Simplify.

Answer: $-\dfrac{4}{5}$

Problem Set

Find the following square roots:

1. $-\sqrt{1}$

2. $\sqrt{441}$

3. $\sqrt{484}$

4. $\pm\sqrt{81}$

5. $-\sqrt{100}$

6. $\pm\sqrt{225}$

7. $\sqrt{-144}$

8. $\sqrt{-256}$

9. $\pm\sqrt{121}$

10. $\pm\sqrt{256}$

11. $\sqrt{\dfrac{1}{9}}$

12. $\sqrt{\dfrac{100}{225}}$

13. $\sqrt{\dfrac{9}{16}}$

14. $-\sqrt{\dfrac{1}{4}}$

15. $\pm\sqrt{\dfrac{25}{49}}$

16. $-\sqrt{\dfrac{81}{100}}$

17. $\sqrt{\dfrac{25}{144}}$

18. $\sqrt{0.36}$

19. $\sqrt{0.49}$

20. $-\sqrt{25 \cdot 81}$

HA1-485: Writing Rational Numbers as Decimals or Fractions

Recall the classification of numbers. The set of whole numbers contains all the natural numbers $\{1, 2, 3, 4...\}$ and zero. Integers are natural numbers, their opposites $\{...-3, -2, -1, 0, 1, 2, 3....\}$, and zero. Rational numbers are numbers that can be written in the form $\frac{a}{b}$ where a and b are both integers and $b \neq 0$. Remember that dividing by zero is not mathematically possible. Notice, however, that a can equal 0.

The following table lists some examples of numbers and why they can or cannot be considered rational numbers.

7	This is a rational number because it can be written as $\frac{7}{1}$.
$5\frac{1}{3}$	This is a rational number because it can be written as $\frac{16}{3}$.
7.2	This is a rational number because it can be written as $7\frac{2}{10}$, which converts to $\frac{72}{10}$.
$\frac{\sqrt{25}}{3}$	This is a rational number because it can be written as $\frac{5}{3}$.
$\frac{\sqrt{3}}{2}$	This is *not* a rational number because the value of $\sqrt{3}$ is not an integer.

In certain situations it is helpful to know how to convert a rational number into its equivalent decimal value. Any rational number can be written as a **terminating decimal** or a **repeating decimal**.

Terminating Decimal	A decimal that has a finite number of decimal places (the decimal value does not have any repeating digits)

Repeating Decimal	A decimal with one or more digits repeating without end

The stock market, for example, quotes stock prices in fractional form. You often hear that Company Z went up $\frac{3}{8}$ today. If you own stock in this company, you will want to know how much money you earned per share. To do so, you must calculate the decimal value of $\frac{3}{8}$.

Note: **It is important to realize that a fraction implies division. Set up your problem as you read the fraction from top to bottom. For example, the fraction $\frac{3}{8}$ means 3 divided by 8 and is written as $8\overline{)3}$ NOT $3\overline{)8}$. Be sure that you set up the problem correctly, or your resulting decimal value will not be equivalent to the fraction.**

Example 1   Convert $\frac{3}{8}$ to a decimal.

$$\frac{3}{8} = 8\overline{)3.000}$$

$$\begin{array}{r} 0.375 \\ \underline{24} \\ 60 \\ \underline{56} \\ 40 \\ \underline{40} \\ 0 \end{array}$$

Step 1:   Divide 3 by 8.

Answer: $\frac{3}{8}$ is equal to the decimal 0.375.

Notice that the division stops once you get a remainder of 0; therefore, it is a terminating decimal.

Example 2   Convert $\frac{4}{9}$ to a decimal.

$$\frac{4}{9} = 9\overline{)4.000}$$

$$\begin{array}{r} 0.444 \\ \underline{36} \\ 40 \\ \underline{36} \\ 40 \\ \underline{36} \\ 4 \end{array}$$

Step 1:   Divide 4 by 9.

Note: After dividing several times, you should be able to see the pattern. You will never reach a remainder of zero. Once a pattern is established, you can stop dividing and write your answer like this: $0.\overline{4}$.

Answer: $0.\overline{4}$

The bar over the digit or set of digits indicates that you have one or more repeating number(s). You must place the bar over only those digits that repeat.

Because all rational numbers can be written as fractions, they can also be written as equivalent terminating or repeating decimals. Naturally, you will sometimes have a decimal value that you want to convert to a corresponding fractional value. Look at the following examples

Example 3   Write 0.5 as a fraction.

$0.5 = \dfrac{5}{10}$	**Step 1:** The decimal 0.5 is read as "5 tenths" because the 5 is in the tenths place. Rewrite the fraction to correspond to the decimal value.
$\dfrac{5}{10} = \dfrac{1}{2}$	**Step 2:** The fraction can be reduced and rewritten.
	Answer: $\dfrac{1}{2}$

Example 4   Write 0.27 as a fraction.

$0.27 = \dfrac{27}{100}$	**Step 1:** The decimal 0.27 is read as "27 hundredths" because the last digit, 7, is in the hundredths place. Rewrite the fraction to correspond to the decimal value. *Note: This fraction cannot be reduced any further.*
	Answer: $\dfrac{27}{100}$

The next example is a repeating decimal. Let's proceed through the conversion process.

Example 5   Write $0.\overline{7}$ as a fraction.

$x = 0.\overline{7}$	**Step 1:** Let $x = 0.\overline{7}$, the repeating decimal.
$10x = 0.\overline{7}(10)$ $10x = 7.\overline{7}$	**Step 2:** Multiply both sides of the equation by 10^a where a is the number of repeating digits. In this example, only one digit is repeating, so use 10^1, which equals 10. *Note: Remember that you are really multiplying 0.777... and 10.*
$\begin{aligned} 10x &= 7.\overline{7} \\ -x &= -0.\overline{7} \\ \hline 9x &= 7.0 \end{aligned}$	**Step 3:** Subtract the first equation from this new one.
$\dfrac{9x}{9} = \dfrac{7}{9}$ $x = \dfrac{7}{9}$	**Step 4:** The resulting equation is $9x = 7$. Divide both sides of the equation by 9 to isolate x.
	Answer: The decimal $0.\overline{7}$ is equivalent to $\dfrac{7}{9}$.

Example 6 Convert $0.\overline{54}$ to a fraction.

$x = 0.\overline{54}$	**Step 1:** Set x equal to the repeating decimal.
$(100)x = 0.\overline{54}(100)$	**Step 2:** Multiply both sides of the equation by 10^2, or 100.
$100x = 54.\overline{54}$ $-x = -0.\overline{54}$ $\overline{99x = 54}$	**Step 3:** Subtract the first equation from this new one.
$\dfrac{99x}{99} = \dfrac{54}{99}$ $x = \dfrac{54}{99}$	**Step 4:** Solve for x.
$x = \dfrac{54}{99} = \dfrac{6}{11}$	**Step 5:** This fraction can be reduced by dividing both the numerator and denominator by 9.

Answer: Thus, the decimal $0.\overline{54}$ can be written as $\dfrac{6}{11}$ in fraction form.

Problem Set

Express the rational number as a decimal:

1. $\dfrac{3}{11}$ **2.** $-\dfrac{7}{5}$ **3.** $\dfrac{2}{11}$ **4.** $\dfrac{14}{5}$

5. $\dfrac{12}{5}$ **6.** $\dfrac{5}{12}$ **7.** $\dfrac{5}{16}$ **8.** $\dfrac{7}{11}$

9. $\dfrac{7}{6}$ **10.** $-\dfrac{7}{3}$

Write the decimal in the form $\dfrac{a}{b}$, where $b \neq 0$.

11. $3.\overline{2}$ **12.** $4.\overline{6}$ **13.** $5.\overline{4}$ **14.** $0.8\overline{6}$

15. $0.\overline{2}$ **16.** $0.\overline{8}$ **17.** $7.\overline{5}$ **18.** $0.\overline{125}$

19. $0.\overline{69}$ **20.** $0.\overline{155}$

To simplify square roots of non-perfect squares, you must use the product property, and you must remove any perfect square factors from the radicand. A perfect square is a number that is equal to some whole number squared. Nine is a perfect square because it is equal to three squared. The product property states that $\sqrt{mn} = \sqrt{m} \cdot \sqrt{n}$, where m ≥ 0 and n ≥ 0.

Example 1   Simplify: $\sqrt{z^7}$

$\sqrt{z^7} = \sqrt{z \cdot z \cdot z \cdot z \cdot z \cdot z \cdot z}$ $= \sqrt{z^6 \cdot z}$	**Step 1:** Factor the base.
$= \sqrt{z^6 \cdot z}$	**Step 2:** Use the Product Property of Square Roots.
$= z^3 \sqrt{z}$	**Step 3:** Simplify.
	Answer: $z^3 \sqrt{z}$

Example 2   Simplify: $-\sqrt{16m^3 n^4}$

$-\sqrt{16m^3 n^4} = -\sqrt{16 \cdot m^2 \cdot m \cdot n^4}$ $= -\sqrt{16m^2 n^4 m}$	**Step 1:** Factor the base.
$= -\sqrt{16m^2 n^4} \cdot \sqrt{m}$	**Step 2:** Use the Product Property of Square Roots.
$= -4mn^2 \sqrt{m}$	**Step 3:** Simplify.
	Answer: $-4mn^2 \sqrt{m}$

Example 3   Simplify: $\sqrt{250m^8 n^5}$

$\sqrt{250m^8 n^5} = \sqrt{25 \cdot 10 \cdot m^8 \cdot n^4 \cdot n}$	**Step 1:** Factor the base.
$= \sqrt{25 \cdot m^8 \cdot n^4} \cdot \sqrt{10n}$	**Step 2:** Use the Product Property of Square Roots.

$$= 5m^4n^2\sqrt{10n}$$

Step 3: Simplify.

Answer: $5m^4n^2\sqrt{10n}$

Problem Set

Simplify:

1. $\sqrt{60}$ **2.** $\sqrt{27}$ **3.** $\sqrt{126}$

4. $\sqrt{b^8}$ **5.** $\sqrt{n^{18}}$ **6.** $\sqrt{50}$

7. $\sqrt{96}$ **8.** $\sqrt{90}$ **9.** $\sqrt{c^{16}}$

10. $\sqrt{108}$ **11.** $\sqrt{72n^9}$ **12.** $\sqrt{45x^{11}}$

13. $\sqrt{99a^{17}}$ **14.** $\sqrt{12a^{17}}$ **15.** $\sqrt{162k^5}$

16. $\sqrt{1,400}$ **17.** $\sqrt{3,400}$ **18.** $\sqrt{a^6b^5c^4}$

19. $\sqrt{343x^3y^5}$ **20.** $\sqrt{207k^9m^8n^7}$

HA1-492: Simplifying Square and Cube Roots

Square roots are used to find a number if its square is given.

<table>
<tr><td>**Square Root**</td><td>Let x be a real number and y be a non-negative real number such that

$$x^2 = y$$

Then x **is the square root of** y. If $x \geq 0$, it is called the principal square root of y and it is denoted as

$$x = \sqrt{y} .$$

with radical sign pointing to $\sqrt{}$ and radicand pointing to y.

Square roots may also be written as

$$\sqrt{y} = y^{\frac{1}{2}}$$</td></tr>
</table>

Remember, the square root of a negative number is not defined. Note that a positive number, y, has two square roots:

$$\text{Positive square root: } \sqrt{y} = y^{\frac{1}{2}}$$

$$\text{Negative square root: } -\sqrt{y} = -y^{\frac{1}{2}}$$

If asked to find a square root in words, give both the positive and negative square roots.

<table>
<tr><td>**Properties of Square Roots**</td><td>Let x and y be positive real numbers and n be a positive integer. Then

$$\sqrt{x^2} = x \quad \text{or} \quad (x^2)^{\frac{1}{2}} = x$$

$$\sqrt{xy} = \sqrt{x} \cdot \sqrt{y} \quad \text{or} \quad (xy)^{\frac{1}{2}} = (x)^{\frac{1}{2}} \cdot (y)^{\frac{1}{2}}$$

$$\sqrt{\frac{x}{y}} = \frac{\sqrt{x}}{\sqrt{y}} \quad \text{or} \quad \left(\frac{x}{y}\right)^{\frac{1}{2}} = \frac{(x)^{\frac{1}{2}}}{(y)^{\frac{1}{2}}}$$

$$\sqrt{x^n} = (\sqrt{x})^n \quad \text{or} \quad (x^n)^{\frac{1}{2}} = \left(x^{\frac{1}{2}}\right)^n = x^{\frac{n}{2}}$$</td></tr>
</table>

Similarly, cube roots can be used to find a number when its cube is given.

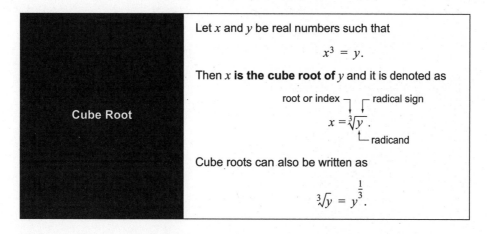

Cube Root	Let x and y be real numbers such that
	$$x^3 = y.$$
	Then x **is the cube root of** y and it is denoted as
	root or index ⌝ ⌜ radical sign
	$$x = \sqrt[3]{y}.$$
	∟ radicand
	Cube roots can also be written as
	$$\sqrt[3]{y} = y^{\frac{1}{3}}.$$

There is only one cube root of a number. The radicand can be positive, negative, or zero.

Properties of Cube Roots	Let x and y be positive real numbers and n be a positive integer. Then
	$\sqrt[3]{x^3} = x$ or $(x^3)^{\frac{1}{3}} = x$
	$\sqrt[3]{xy} = \sqrt[3]{x} \cdot \sqrt[3]{y}$ or $(xy)^{\frac{1}{3}} = (x)^{\frac{1}{3}} \cdot (y)^{\frac{1}{3}}$
	$\sqrt[3]{\dfrac{x}{y}} = \dfrac{\sqrt[3]{x}}{\sqrt[3]{y}}$ or $\left(\dfrac{x}{y}\right)^{\frac{1}{3}} = \dfrac{(x)^{\frac{1}{3}}}{(y)^{\frac{1}{3}}}$
	$\sqrt[3]{x^n} = \left(\sqrt[3]{x}\right)^n$ or $(x^n)^{\frac{1}{3}} = \left(x^{\frac{1}{3}}\right)^n = x^{\frac{n}{3}}$

Example 1   Simplify: $\sqrt{144}$

$\sqrt{144} = \sqrt{(12)^2}$	**Step 1:** Express the given number as a perfect square of a non-negative number.
$\sqrt{(12)^2} = 12$	**Step 2:** Use the definition of square root to get the principal square root.
	Answer: $\sqrt{144}$ simplifies to 12.

Example 2   Simplify: $\sqrt[3]{z^9}$

$\sqrt[3]{z^9} = (z^9)^{\frac{1}{3}}$	**Step 1:** Express the cube root as the $\frac{1}{3}$ power.
$= z^{\frac{9}{3}}$	**Step 2:** Use the property $(x^n)^{\frac{1}{3}} = \left(x^{\frac{1}{3}}\right)^n = x^{\frac{n}{3}}$
$= z^3$	**Step 3:** Simplify the exponent.
	Answer: $\sqrt[3]{z^9}$ simplifies to z^3.

Example 3   Simplify $\sqrt{64a^6b^{14}}$, where a and b are positive real numbers.

$\sqrt{64a^6b^{14}} = (64a^6b^{14})^{\frac{1}{2}}$	**Step 1:** Express the square root as the $\frac{1}{2}$ power.
$= (64)^{\frac{1}{2}} \cdot (a^6)^{\frac{1}{2}} \cdot (b^{14})^{\frac{1}{2}}$	**Step 2:** Use the property $(xy)^{\frac{1}{2}} = (x)^{\frac{1}{2}} \cdot (y)^{\frac{1}{2}}$.
$= (8^2)^{\frac{1}{2}} \cdot (a^6)^{\frac{1}{2}} \cdot (b^{14})^{\frac{1}{2}}$	**Step 3:** Express 64 as a perfect square.
$= 8^{\frac{2}{2}} \cdot a^{\frac{6}{2}} \cdot b^{\frac{14}{2}}$	**Step 4:** Use the property $(x^n)^{\frac{1}{2}} = \left(x^{\frac{1}{2}}\right)^n = x^{\frac{n}{2}}$.
$= 8a^3b^7$	**Step 5:** Simplify the exponents.
	Answer: $\sqrt{64a^6b^{14}}$ simplifies to $8a^3b^7$.

Example 4   Simplify: $\left(\dfrac{125x^9y^{15}}{27z^{12}}\right)^{\frac{1}{3}}$

$\left(\dfrac{125x^9y^{15}}{27z^{12}}\right)^{\frac{1}{3}} = \dfrac{(125x^9y^{15})^{\frac{1}{3}}}{(27z^{12})^{\frac{1}{3}}}$	**Step 1:** Use the property $\left(\dfrac{x}{y}\right)^{\frac{1}{3}} = \dfrac{(x)^{\frac{1}{3}}}{(y)^{\frac{1}{3}}}$.
$= \dfrac{(125)^{\frac{1}{3}} \cdot (x^9)^{\frac{1}{3}} \cdot (y^{15})^{\frac{1}{3}}}{(27)^{\frac{1}{3}} \cdot (z^{12})^{\frac{1}{3}}}$	**Step 2:** Use the property $(xy)^{\frac{1}{3}} = (x)^{\frac{1}{3}} \cdot (y)^{\frac{1}{3}}$ in both the numerator and the denominator.
$= \dfrac{(5^3)^{\frac{1}{3}} \cdot (x^9)^{\frac{1}{3}} \cdot (y^{15})^{\frac{1}{3}}}{(3^3)^{\frac{1}{3}} \cdot (z^{12})^{\frac{1}{3}}}$	**Step 3:** Express 125 and 27 as perfect cubes.

$$= \frac{5^{\frac{3}{3}} \cdot x^{\frac{9}{3}} \cdot y^{\frac{15}{3}}}{3^{\frac{3}{3}} \cdot z^{\frac{12}{3}}}$$

Step 4: Use the property $(x^n)^{\frac{1}{3}} = \left(x^{\frac{1}{3}}\right)^n = x^{\frac{n}{3}}$ in both the numerator and the denominator.

$$= \frac{5x^3y^5}{3z^4}$$

Step 5: Simplify the exponents.

Answer: $\left(\dfrac{125x^9y^{15}}{27z^{12}}\right)^{\frac{1}{3}}$ simplifies to $\dfrac{5x^3y^5}{3z^4}$.

Example 5   The volume, V, of a cube equals $64x^3y^9$ where x and y are positive real numbers. Find the area, A, of the top side of the cube.

$V = 64x^3y^9$

Step 1: The volume of the cube is given.

$V = l^3$

Step 2: Formula for the volume of the cube where l is the length of an edge of the cube.

$l^3 = 64x^3y^9$

Step 3: Since both l^3 and $64x^3y^9$ are equal to V, they are equal to each other.

$l^3 = \sqrt[3]{64x^3y^9}$

Step 4: Apply the definition of a cube root.

$l = (64x^3y^9)^{\frac{1}{3}}$

Step 5: Express the cube root as the $\frac{1}{3}$ power.

$l = (64)^{\frac{1}{3}} \cdot (x^3)^{\frac{1}{3}} \cdot (y^9)^{\frac{1}{3}}$

Step 6: Use the property $(xy)^{\frac{1}{3}} = (x)^{\frac{1}{3}} \cdot (y)^{\frac{1}{3}}$.

Step 7: Express 64 as a perfect cube.

$l = (4^3)^{\frac{1}{3}} \cdot (x^3)^{\frac{1}{3}} \cdot (y^9)^{\frac{1}{3}}$

$l = 4^{\frac{3}{3}} \cdot x^{\frac{3}{3}} \cdot y^{\frac{9}{3}}$

Step 8: Use the property $(x^n)^{\frac{1}{3}} = \left(x^{\frac{1}{3}}\right)^n = x^{\frac{n}{3}}$.

$l = 4xy^3$

Step 9: Simplify the exponents to get the length, l, of an edge of the cube.

$A = l^2$

Step 10: Recall the formula for the area, A, of a square. All sides (and also the top side) of a cube are squares. The length of a side of the square equals the length, l, of an edge of the cube.

$A = (4xy^3)^2$	**Step 11:** Replace l with the value found in Step 9.
$A = 16x^2y^6$	**Step 12:** Simplify the expression.

Answer: The area of the top side of the given cube is $16x^2y^6$.

Problem Set

1. Simplify: $\sqrt[3]{-512}$

2. Simplify: $\sqrt[3]{729}$

3. Simplify: $\sqrt[3]{-1,000}$

4. Simplify: $\sqrt{256}$

5. Simplify: $\sqrt{196}$

6. Simplify: $(441)^{\frac{1}{2}}$

7. Simplify: $(512)^{\frac{1}{3}}$

8. Simplify $(x^{14})^{\frac{1}{2}}$ where x is a positive real number.

9. Simplify $(a^{24})^{\frac{1}{2}}$ where a is a positive real number.

10. Simplify $\sqrt{b^8}$ where b is a positive real number.

11. Simplify $\sqrt{z^{20}}$ where z is a positive real number.

12. Simplify $(x^{21})^{\frac{1}{3}}$ where x is a real number.

13. Simplify $(y^{24})^{\frac{1}{3}}$ where y is a real number.

14. Simplify $\sqrt[3]{x^{12}}$ where x is a real number.

15. Simplify $\sqrt[3]{c^{27}}$ where c is a real number.

16. Simplify $\sqrt{4a^6b^4}$ where a and b are positive real numbers.

17. Simplify $\sqrt{81x^8y^{14}}$ where x and y are positive real numbers.

18. Simplify $\sqrt{9a^{12}b^2c^{10}}$ where a, b, and c are positive real numbers.

19. Simplify $\sqrt{25p^{16}q^{14}r^8}$ where p, q, and r are positive real numbers.

20. Simplify $\sqrt[3]{64x^9y^{15}}$ where x and y are real numbers.

21. Simplify $\sqrt[3]{27a^{18}b^6}$ where a and b are real numbers.

22. Simplify $\sqrt[3]{125p^{21}q^{12}r^9}$ where p, q, and r are real numbers.

23. Simplify $\sqrt[3]{216x^{21}y^{24}z^{18}}$ where x, y, and z are real numbers.

24. Simplify $\left(\dfrac{25x^8}{49y^{10}}\right)^{\frac{1}{2}}$ where x and y are positive real numbers and $y \neq 0$.

25. Simplify $\left(\dfrac{36a^{16}}{121b^{12}}\right)^{\frac{1}{2}}$ where a and b are positive

real numbers and $b \neq 0$.

26. Simplify $\left(\dfrac{16x^{12}}{25y^6z^4}\right)^{\frac{1}{2}}$ where x, y, and z are

positive real numbers, $y \neq 0$, and $z \neq 0$.

27. Simplify $\left(\dfrac{144x^6y^4}{169z^{16}}\right)^{\frac{1}{2}}$ where x, y and z are positive

real numbers and $z \neq 0$.

28. Simplify $\left(\dfrac{343x^{15}}{64y^{30}}\right)^{\frac{1}{3}}$ where x and y are real

numbers and $y \neq 0$.

29. Simplify $\left(\dfrac{8a^{21}b^{15}}{125c^{27}}\right)^{\frac{1}{3}}$ where a, b and c are real

numbers and $c \neq 0$.

30. Simplify $\left(\dfrac{216x^{12}}{27y^6z^9}\right)^{\frac{1}{3}}$ where x, y and z are real

numbers, $y \neq 0$, and $z \neq 0$.

31. The volume of a cube is given by $V = 64x^{15}$. Find the length of each edge a.

32. The volume of a cube is given by $V = 216y^{21}$. Find the length of each edge a.

33. The volume of a cube is given by $V = 27p^{30}q^{18}$. Find the length of each edge a.

34. The volume of a cube is given by $V = 8u^{18}v^{21}w^{24}$. Find the length of each edge a.

35. The volume of a cube is given by $V = 729x^{45}$. Find the length of each edge a.

36. The area of a square is given by $A = 64x^{16}$. Find the length of each side a.

37. The area of a square is given by $A = 121c^{18}$. Find the length of each side a.

38. The area of a square is given by $A = 81x^{26}y^{22}$. Find the length of each side a.

39. The area of a square is given by $A = 36x^8y^{10}z^{12}$. Find the length of each side a.

40. The area of a square is given by $A = 400x^{36}$. Find the length of each side a.

HA1-495: Simplifying Sums and Differences of Radicals

When simplifying sums and differences of radicals, remember the saying "You can't add apples and oranges." This means that in order to add or subtract radical expressions, each radical must have the same root and the same radicand. These are called **like radicals**. In this lesson, we will only add or subtract square roots; therefore, each square root must contain the same radicand. When adding or subtracting radicals, first make sure that each radical is in its simplest form. You can further simplify the expression by identifying and combining "like radicals."

Like Radicals	Radicals that have the same root (index) and the same radicand

Unlike Radicals	Radicals that have a different root (index) and/or different radicand

Consider the following examples of like and unlike radicals:

Like Radicals	Unlike Radicals
$4\sqrt{2}$ and $-3\sqrt{2}$	$7\sqrt{5}$ and $-6\sqrt{3}$
$-\sqrt{5}$ and $2\sqrt{5}$	$-4\sqrt{2}$ and $-9\sqrt{6}$
$\sqrt{12}$ and $5\sqrt{3}$ (simplify $\sqrt{12}$ to $2\sqrt{3}$)	

Example 1 Simplify: $3\sqrt{x} - 2\sqrt{x}$

$3\sqrt{x} - 2\sqrt{x} = (3-2)\sqrt{x}$	**Step 1:** Combine like terms using the Distributive Property.
$= \sqrt{x}$	**Step 2:** Simplify the expression.
	Answer: $\sqrt{x}$

Example 2 Simplify: $7\sqrt{5} + 2\sqrt{5} - \sqrt{5}$

$7\sqrt{5} + 2\sqrt{5} - \sqrt{5} = (7+2-1)\sqrt{5}$	**Step 1:** Combine like terms using the Distributive Property.
$= 8\sqrt{5}$	**Step 2:** Simplify the expression.
	Answer: $8\sqrt{5}$

Example 3   Simplify: $2\sqrt{27} + 4\sqrt{12}$

$$2\sqrt{27} + 4\sqrt{12} = 2\sqrt{9 \cdot 3} + 4\sqrt{4 \cdot 3}$$
$$= 2 \cdot 3\sqrt{3} + 4 \cdot 2\sqrt{3}$$
$$= 6\sqrt{3} + 8\sqrt{3}$$

Step 1:   Express each radical in simplest form.

$$= (6 + 8)\sqrt{3}$$

Step 2:   Combine like terms using the Distributive Property.

$$= 14\sqrt{3}$$

Step 3:   Simplify the expression.

Answer: $14\sqrt{3}$

Example 4   Simplify: $2\sqrt{20} + 3\sqrt{45} - \sqrt{5}$

$$2\sqrt{20} + 3\sqrt{45} - \sqrt{5} = 2\sqrt{4 \cdot 5} + 3\sqrt{9 \cdot 5} - \sqrt{5}$$
$$= 2 \cdot 2\sqrt{5} + 3 \cdot 3\sqrt{5} - \sqrt{5}$$
$$= 4\sqrt{5} + 9\sqrt{5} - \sqrt{5}$$

Step 1:   Express each radical in simplest form.

$$= (4 + 9 - 1)\sqrt{5}$$

Step 2:   Combine like terms using the Distributive Property.

$$= 12\sqrt{5}$$

Step 3:   Simplify the expression.

Answer: $12\sqrt{5}$

Example 5   Simplify: $3\sqrt{54} - 5\sqrt{28} + 4\sqrt{63} - 2\sqrt{24}$

$$3\sqrt{54} - 5\sqrt{28} + 4\sqrt{63} - 2\sqrt{24}$$
$$= 3\sqrt{9 \cdot 6} - 5\sqrt{4 \cdot 7} + 4\sqrt{9 \cdot 7} - 2\sqrt{4 \cdot 6}$$
$$= 3 \cdot 3\sqrt{6} - 5 \cdot 2\sqrt{7} + 4 \cdot 3\sqrt{7} - 2 \cdot 2\sqrt{6}$$
$$= 9\sqrt{6} - 10\sqrt{7} + 12\sqrt{7} - 4\sqrt{6}$$

Step 1:   Express each radical in simplest form.

$$= 9\sqrt{6} - 4\sqrt{6} - 10\sqrt{7} + 12\sqrt{7}$$

Step 2:   Determine the like radicals.

$$= (9 - 4)\sqrt{6} + (-10 + 12)\sqrt{7}$$

Step 3:   Combine like terms using the Distributive Property.

$$= 5\sqrt{6} + 2\sqrt{7}$$

Step 4:   Simplify the expression.

Answer: $5\sqrt{6} + 2\sqrt{7}$

Problem Set

Simplify:

1. $9\sqrt{6} + 4\sqrt{6} - \sqrt{6}$

2. $8\sqrt{6} + 12\sqrt{6} + \sqrt{6}$

3. $7\sqrt{10} - 3\sqrt{10}$

4. $8\sqrt{7} - 4\sqrt{7}$

5. $4\sqrt{3} + 9\sqrt{3}$

6. $7\sqrt{2} + 4\sqrt{2} + 8\sqrt{2}$

7. $8\sqrt{5} + 11\sqrt{5}$

8. $9\sqrt{x} + 2\sqrt{x}$

9. $\sqrt{45} + \sqrt{80}$

10. $\sqrt{54} - \sqrt{24}$

11. $3\sqrt{8} + 6\sqrt{2}$

12. $3\sqrt{20} + 5\sqrt{45}$

13. $8\sqrt{45} - 2\sqrt{20}$

14. $8\sqrt{32} - 4\sqrt{50}$

15. $2\sqrt{20} + 3\sqrt{5} + 2\sqrt{5}$

16. $6\sqrt{5} + 7\sqrt{5} - 3\sqrt{20}$

17. $\sqrt{12} + 4\sqrt{3} + 2\sqrt{27}$

18. $3\sqrt{48} + 2\sqrt{80} + 5\sqrt{27} + 3\sqrt{75}$

19. $2\sqrt{18} + \sqrt{108} + \sqrt{50}$

20. $2\sqrt{32x} + \sqrt{18x} + \sqrt{48x}$

HA1-500: Simplifying Products of Radicals

When multiplying expressions involving radicals, several properties of real numbers will be used. In a previous lesson the Product Property of Square Roots was used to simplify expressions containing square roots. This property is shown in the following example:

$$\sqrt{36} = \sqrt{4 \cdot 9}$$
$$= \sqrt{4} \cdot \sqrt{9}$$
$$= 2 \cdot 3$$
$$= 6$$

This property suggests that $\sqrt{36}$ can be written as $\sqrt{4} \cdot \sqrt{9}$. This property can also be used to multiply radical expressions:

$$\sqrt{4} \cdot \sqrt{9} = \sqrt{4 \cdot 9}$$
$$= \sqrt{36}$$
$$= 6$$

To multiply two expressions with the same root, multiply the radicands and simplify the result. The result should have the same root as each term of the product.

The Product Property of Square Roots	For all real numbers a and b, where $a \geq 0$ and $b \geq 0$, $\sqrt{ab} = \sqrt{a} \cdot \sqrt{b}$.

Note: It is possible to multiply expressions with different roots, but this process will be examined in another course.

Example 1   Simplify: $\sqrt{2} \cdot \sqrt{14}$

$\sqrt{2} \cdot \sqrt{14} = \sqrt{2 \cdot 14}$	**Step 1:** Rewrite the radical expressions using the Product Property of Square Roots.
$= \sqrt{2 \cdot 2 \cdot 7}$ $= 2\sqrt{7}$	**Step 2:** Simplify.
	Answer: $2\sqrt{7}$

Example 2   Simplify: $\left(\sqrt{5}\right)^2$

$\left(\sqrt{5}\right)^2 = \sqrt{5} \cdot \sqrt{5}$	**Step 1:** Multiply the square root by itself.
$= \sqrt{5 \cdot 5}$	**Step 2:** Rewrite the radical expressions using the Product Property of Square Roots.

$= 5$

Step 3: Simplify.

Answer: 5

The Commutative and Associative Properties for multiplication can also be used when multiplying radical expressions. This is shown in the next example.

Example 3   Simplify: $(2\sqrt{7})(3\sqrt{21})$

$(2\sqrt{7})(3\sqrt{21}) = (2 \cdot 3) \cdot (\sqrt{7} \cdot \sqrt{21})$

Step 1: Use the Commutative and Associative Properties to rewrite the radical expressions.

$= (2 \cdot 3) \cdot (\sqrt{7 \cdot 21})$

Step 2: Rewrite the radical expressions using the Product Property of Square Roots.

$= 2 \cdot 3 \cdot \sqrt{7 \cdot 7 \cdot 3}$

Step 3: Factor the terms under the radical.

$= 2 \cdot 3 \cdot 7 \cdot \sqrt{3}$

Step 4: Simplify.

$= 42\sqrt{3}$

Answer: $42\sqrt{3}$

Now consider the process necessary to complete the following product: $\sqrt{3}(2\sqrt{5} + \sqrt{11})$.

First, you should recognize from previous lessons that in this problem a monomial is multiplied by an expression of two terms (a binomial). In this case you must use the Distributive Property to complete the product. The process would look like this:

$$\sqrt{3}(2\sqrt{5} + \sqrt{11}) = \sqrt{3} \cdot 2\sqrt{5} + \sqrt{3} \cdot \sqrt{11}$$

Consider the following example.

Example 4   Simplify: $\sqrt{3}(2 - 3\sqrt{6})$

$\sqrt{3}(2 - 3\sqrt{6}) = \sqrt{3} \cdot 2 - \sqrt{3} \cdot 3\sqrt{6}$
$= 2\sqrt{3} - 3\sqrt{3 \cdot 6}$

Step 1: Multiply the monomial by the binomial expression using the Distributive Property.

$= 2\sqrt{3} - 3\sqrt{3 \cdot 2 \cdot 3}$

Step 2: Factor the terms under the radical.

$= 2\sqrt{3} - 3 \cdot 3\sqrt{2}$

Step 3: Simplify.

$= 2\sqrt{3} - 9\sqrt{2}$

Answer: $2\sqrt{3} - 9\sqrt{2}$

When multiplying two binomial expressions, recall that you must use the FOIL method (First Outer Inner Last).

Example 5 Simplify: $(3 + \sqrt{5})(3 - \sqrt{5})$

F $3 \cdot 3 = 9$	**Step 1:** Multiply the first terms of each binomial.
O $3 \cdot (-\sqrt{5}) = -3\sqrt{5}$	**Step 2:** Multiply the outer terms of each binomial.
I $\sqrt{5} \cdot 3 = 3\sqrt{5}$	**Step 3:** Multiply the inner terms of each binomial.
L $\sqrt{5} \cdot (-\sqrt{5}) = -5$	**Step 4:** Multiply the last terms of each binomial.
$(3 + \sqrt{5})(3 - \sqrt{5}) = 9 - 3\sqrt{5} + 3\sqrt{5} - 5$	**Step 5:** Combine all the terms together.
$\qquad = 9 - 5$ $\qquad = 4$	**Step 6:** Simplify.
	Answer: 4

Problem Set

Simplify:

1. $\sqrt{5} \cdot \sqrt{7}$

2. $\sqrt{2} \cdot \sqrt{14}$

3. $\sqrt{3} \cdot \sqrt{27}$

4. $\sqrt{10} \cdot \sqrt{2}$

5. $\sqrt{2} \cdot \sqrt{8}$

6. $\sqrt{2} \cdot \sqrt{9}$

7. $(\sqrt{2})^2$

8. $(\sqrt{4})^2$

9. $(\sqrt{8})^2$

10. $(\sqrt{9})^2$

11. $2\sqrt{3} \cdot \sqrt{2}$

12. $3\sqrt{2} \cdot 4\sqrt{3}$

13. $8\sqrt{6} \cdot 4\sqrt{18}$

14. $-5\sqrt{6} \cdot 3\sqrt{2}$

15. $(-3\sqrt{8})(-4\sqrt{6})$

16. $\sqrt{5}(\sqrt{2} - \sqrt{3})$

17. $\sqrt{4}(2\sqrt{3} + 5)$

18. $(10 + \sqrt{6})(10 - \sqrt{6})$

19. $5\sqrt{2x} \cdot 6\sqrt{2x}$

20. $\sqrt{30x^2} \cdot \sqrt{2x^2 y}$

In a previous lesson, you learned the Quotient Property of Square Roots: If a and b are real numbers with $a \geq 0$ and $b > 0$, then $\sqrt{\dfrac{a}{b}} = \dfrac{\sqrt{a}}{\sqrt{b}}$. With this property, you could solve problems like $\sqrt{\dfrac{5}{4}}$, which simplifies to $\dfrac{\sqrt{5}}{\sqrt{4}} = \dfrac{\sqrt{5}}{2}$.

Now consider the following expressions: $\dfrac{3}{\sqrt{2}}$ and $\sqrt{\dfrac{4}{5}}$. These are not in simplest form because there is a radical in the denominator. To put these in simplest form, you will use a process called rationalizing the denominator.

Rationalizing the Denominator	Multiply both the numerator and denominator of the fraction by the factor (radical) needed to eliminate the radical from the denominator.

Note: **When both the numerator and denominator are multiplied by the same radical expression we are using the fundamental principle of fractions because $\dfrac{\sqrt{a}}{\sqrt{a}} = 1$.**

Example 1 Rationalize the denominator of $\dfrac{3}{\sqrt{2}}$.

$\dfrac{3}{\sqrt{2}} = \dfrac{3}{\sqrt{2}} \cdot \dfrac{\sqrt{2}}{\sqrt{2}}$

Step 1: Multiply both the numerator and denominator by $\sqrt{2}$ to eliminate the radical in the denominator. Remember, $\sqrt{2} \cdot \sqrt{2} = \sqrt{2^2} = 2$.

$= \dfrac{3\sqrt{2}}{\sqrt{4}}$

Step 2: Simplify the numerator and denominator.

$= \dfrac{3\sqrt{2}}{2}$

Answer: $\dfrac{3\sqrt{2}}{2}$

Example 2 Rationalize the denominator of $\sqrt{\dfrac{4}{5}}$.

$\sqrt{\dfrac{4}{5}} = \dfrac{\sqrt{4}}{\sqrt{5}}$

Step 1: Use the Quotient Property of Square Roots.

$= \dfrac{\sqrt{4}}{\sqrt{5}} \cdot \dfrac{\sqrt{5}}{\sqrt{5}}$

Step 2: Multiply both the numerator and denominator by $\sqrt{5}$ to eliminate the radical in the denominator.

$$= \frac{2\sqrt{5}}{5}$$

Step 3: Simplify the numerator and denominator.
Note: The 5's cannot be cancelled because one is 5 and the other is the square root of 5.

Answer: $\dfrac{2\sqrt{5}}{5}$

Example 3   Simplify: $\dfrac{3\sqrt{2}}{\sqrt{x}}$

$$\frac{3\sqrt{2}}{\sqrt{x}} = \frac{3\sqrt{2}}{\sqrt{x}} \cdot \frac{\sqrt{x}}{\sqrt{x}}$$

Step 1: Rationalize the denominator to eliminate the radical.

$$= \frac{3\sqrt{2x}}{x}$$

Step 2: Multiply.

Answer: $= \dfrac{3\sqrt{2x}}{x}$

Example 4   Simplify: $\dfrac{7\sqrt{6}}{2\sqrt{14}}$

$$\frac{7\sqrt{6}}{2\sqrt{14}} = \frac{7\sqrt{6}}{2\sqrt{14}} \cdot \frac{\sqrt{14}}{\sqrt{14}}$$

Step 1: Rationalize the denominator to eliminate the radical.

$$= \frac{7\sqrt{6 \cdot 14}}{2 \cdot 14}$$

Step 2: Multiply. Note the product under the radical sign in the numerator:
$$6 \cdot 14 = 2 \cdot 3 \cdot 2 \cdot 7 = 4 \cdot 21$$

$$= \frac{7 \cdot 2\sqrt{21}}{28}$$

$$= \frac{14\sqrt{21}}{28}$$

$$= \frac{\sqrt{21}}{2}$$

Step 3: Simplify.

Answer: $= \dfrac{\sqrt{21}}{2}$

Now let's look at problems where there is a binomial with a radical in the denominator. First recall the product of a sum and difference, for example $(\sqrt{2}-3)(\sqrt{2}+3)$. When the FOIL method is applied to this product we get $(\sqrt{2}-3)(\sqrt{2}+3) = \sqrt{4}+3\sqrt{2}-3\sqrt{2}-9$, which simplifies to $2-9$ or -7 when the radical has been eliminated. These are special binomials called **conjugates**. Compare the two binomials; notice that the terms are the same, but the signs are opposite.

Example 5   What is the conjugate of $\sqrt{5} - 1$?

$\sqrt{5} + 1$

Step 1: The conjugate of the binomial will have the same terms but opposite sign.

Answer: $\sqrt{5} + 1$

Example 6   Simplify: $\dfrac{3}{7 - \sqrt{2}}$

$\dfrac{3}{7 - \sqrt{2}} = \dfrac{3}{(7 - \sqrt{2})} \cdot \dfrac{(7 + \sqrt{2})}{(7 + \sqrt{2})}$

Step 1: Rationalize the denominator by multiplying both the numerator and denominator by the conjugate of $7 - \sqrt{2}$.

$= \dfrac{21 + 3\sqrt{2}}{49 + 7\sqrt{2} - 7\sqrt{2} - \sqrt{4}}$

Step 2: Use the distributive property in the numerator and the FOIL method in the denominator.

$= \dfrac{21 + 3\sqrt{2}}{47}$

Step 3: Simplify.

Answer: $= \dfrac{21 + 3\sqrt{2}}{47}$

Example 7   Simplify: $\dfrac{\sqrt{3} - 1}{5 + \sqrt{2}}$

$\dfrac{\sqrt{3} - 1}{5 + \sqrt{2}} = \dfrac{(\sqrt{3} - 1)}{(5 + \sqrt{2})} \cdot \dfrac{(5 - \sqrt{2})}{(5 - \sqrt{2})}$

Step 1: Rationalize the denominator by multiplying both the numerator and denominator by the conjugate of $5 + \sqrt{2}$.

$= \dfrac{5\sqrt{3} - \sqrt{6} - 5 + \sqrt{2}}{25 - 5\sqrt{2} + 5\sqrt{2} - \sqrt{4}}$

Step 2: Use the FOIL method in both the numerator and the denominator to simplify.

$= \dfrac{5\sqrt{3} - \sqrt{6} - 5 + \sqrt{2}}{25 - \sqrt{4}}$

$= \dfrac{5\sqrt{3} - \sqrt{6} - 5 + \sqrt{2}}{25 - 2}$

$= \dfrac{5\sqrt{3} - \sqrt{6} - 5 + \sqrt{2}}{23}$

Step 3: Combine any like terms.

Answer: $= \dfrac{5\sqrt{3} - \sqrt{6} - 5 + \sqrt{2}}{23}$

Problem Set

Simplify:

1. $\sqrt{\dfrac{24}{x}}$

2. $\sqrt{\dfrac{20}{x}}$

3. $\sqrt{\dfrac{2}{5}}$

4. $\sqrt{\dfrac{4}{9}}$

5. $\sqrt{\dfrac{1}{2}}$

6. $\sqrt{\dfrac{3}{8}}$

7. $\sqrt{\dfrac{3}{4}}$

8. $\dfrac{7}{\sqrt{13}}$

9. $\dfrac{18}{\sqrt{3}}$

10. $\dfrac{2\sqrt{7}}{\sqrt{2}}$

11. $6\sqrt{\dfrac{1}{5}}$

12. $4\sqrt{\dfrac{6}{11}}$

13. $\dfrac{\sqrt{32}}{\sqrt{3}}$

14. $\dfrac{2}{\sqrt{27}}$

15. $\dfrac{7\sqrt{18}}{3\sqrt{45}}$

16. $\dfrac{5\sqrt{6}}{2\sqrt{15}}$

17. $\dfrac{15}{\sqrt{50}}$

18. $\dfrac{\sqrt{7}+2}{\sqrt{7}-2}$

19. $\dfrac{\sqrt{5}+4}{\sqrt{5}-4}$

20. $\dfrac{3}{4-\sqrt{6}}$

HA1-510: Solving Radical Equations

In other lessons, you have solved equations for the variable using a set of procedures. When equations involve a variable that is a part of a radical expression, you have what is called a radical equation. Solving a radical equation involves a set of procedures similar to solving other types of equations.

To solve a radical equation:

Step 1: Isolate the radical sign on one side of the equation.

Step 2: Use the appropriate exponent to eliminate the radical.

Step 3: Isolate the variable and solve the equation.

Step 4: Check the solution.

The following examples illustrate this process involving a variety of radical equations.

Example 1   Solve: $\sqrt{x} = 5$

$\sqrt{x} = 5$	**Step 1:** Isolate the radical sign on one side of the equation.
$(\sqrt{x})^2 = (5)^2$	**Step 2:** Use the appropriate exponent to eliminate the radical.
$x = 25$	**Step 3:** Isolate the variable and solve the equation.
$\sqrt{25} = 5$ $5 = 5$	**Step 4:** Check the solution.
	Answer: The solution set is $\{25\}$.

Example 2   Solve: $\sqrt{x+1} - 4 = 10$

$\sqrt{x+1} - 4 + 4 = 10 + 4$ $\sqrt{x+1} = 14$	**Step 1:** Isolate the radical sign on one side of the equation.
$(\sqrt{x+1})^2 = (14)^2$ $x+1 = 196$	**Step 2:** Use the appropriate exponent to eliminate the radical.
$x+1-1 = 196-1$ $x = 195$	**Step 3:** Isolate the variable and solve the equation.

$$\sqrt{x+1} - 4 = 10$$
$$\sqrt{195+1} - 4 = 10$$
$$\sqrt{196} - 4 = 10$$
$$14 - 4 = 10$$
$$10 = 10$$

Step 4: Check the solution.

Answer: The solution set is $\{195\}$.

Example 3   Solve: $4\sqrt[3]{x} + 3 = 19$

$$4\sqrt[3]{x} + 3 - 3 = 19 - 3$$
$$4\sqrt[3]{x} = 16$$
$$\frac{4\sqrt[3]{x}}{4} = \frac{16}{4}$$
$$\sqrt[3]{x} = 4$$

Step 1: Isolate the radical sign on one side of the equation.

$$(\sqrt[3]{x})^3 = (4)^3$$

Step 2: Use the appropriate exponent to eliminate the radical.

$$x = 64$$

Step 3: Isolate the variable and solve the equation.

$$4\sqrt[3]{x} + 3 = 19$$
$$4\sqrt[3]{64x} + 3 = 19$$
$$4(4) + 3 = 19$$
$$16 + 3 = 19$$
$$19 = 19$$

Step 4: Check the solution.

Answer: The solution set is $\{64\}$.

Example 4   Solve: $3\sqrt{2x+1} = -9$

$$\frac{3\sqrt{2x+1}}{3} = \frac{-9}{3}$$
$$\sqrt{2x+1} = -3$$

Step 1: Isolate the radical sign on one side of the equation.

$$(\sqrt{2x+1})^2 = (-3)^2$$
$$2x + 1 = 9$$

Step 2: Use the appropriate exponent to eliminate the radical.

$$2x + 1 - 1 = 9 - 1$$

$$2x = 8$$

$$\frac{2x}{2} = \frac{8}{2}$$

$$x = 4$$

Step 3: Isolate the variable and solve the equation.

$$3\sqrt{2x + 1} = -9$$

$$3\sqrt{2(4) + 1} = -9$$

$$3\sqrt{8 + 1} = -9$$

$$3\sqrt{9} = -9$$

$$9 \neq -9$$

Step 4: Check the solution.

Answer: There is no solution.

Example 5 Solve: $\sqrt{3x + 18} = x$

$$\sqrt{3x + 18} = x$$

Step 1: Isolate the radical sign on one side of the equation.

$$(\sqrt{3x + 18})^2 = x^2$$

$$3x + 18 = x^2$$

Step 2: Use the appropriate exponent to eliminate the radical.

$$x^2 - 3x - 18 = 0$$

$$(x - 6)(x + 3) = 0$$

Step 3: Isolate the variable and solve the equation. This is a quadratic equation, so it must be factored to be solved.

$$x - 6 = 0 \qquad x + 3 = 0$$

$$x = 6 \qquad x = -3$$

$$\sqrt{3(6) + 18} = 6 \qquad \sqrt{3(-3) + 18} = -3$$

$$\sqrt{18 + 18} = 6 \qquad \sqrt{-9 + 18} = -3$$

$$\sqrt{36} = 6 \qquad \sqrt{9} = -3$$

$$6 = 6 \qquad 3 \neq -3$$

Step 4: Check the solution.

Answer: The solution set is {6}.

Problem Set

Solve:

1. $\sqrt{d} = 6$

2. $\sqrt{a} = 12$

3. $\sqrt{y} = 18$

4. $\sqrt{y} = -3$

5. $3 + \sqrt{x} = 4$

6. $-8 + \sqrt{y} = 3$

7. $\sqrt{x} - 6 = -6$

8. $\sqrt{y} - 7 = 7$

9. $\sqrt{x} = 50$

10. $\sqrt{y} = \dfrac{2}{3}$

11. $\sqrt{n-5} + 3 = 12$

12. $\sqrt{x+4} + 8 = 3$

13. $3 + 2\sqrt{x} = 7$

14. $-3 - \sqrt{y} = 2$

15. $\sqrt{\dfrac{n}{3}} = 2$

16. $10 - 2\sqrt{x} = -2$

17. $\sqrt{x - 10} = 2$

18. $-8 - 6\sqrt{y} = -20$

19. After eliminating the radical, which equation will be the result?

$$2 + 4\sqrt{3n} = 10$$

$9n = 4$ $4 + 48n = 100$

$54n = 64$ $3n = 4$

20. $\sqrt{2a - 2} + 4 = 8$

You have been introduced to certain types of triangles such as isosceles triangles, equilateral triangles, and right triangles. The sum of the interior angles of a triangle is 180°, and a right triangle is a triangle that contains exactly one right (90°) angle. For a right triangle, the two sides adjacent to the 90° angle are called the **legs** of the right triangle, while the side opposite the 90° angle is called the **hypotenuse** of the right triangle.

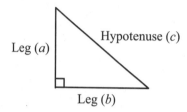

Leg (a)   Hypotenuse (c)

Leg (b)

You may already have heard of the **Pythagorean Theorem**. This theorem describes the relationship among the lengths of the three sides of a right triangle.

Pythagorean Theorem	The sum of the squares of the two legs of a right triangle is equal to the square of the hypotenuse, that is, if a and b are legs of a right triangle with hypotenuse c, then: $$a^2 + b^2 = c^2 \text{ or, } \text{leg}^2 + \text{leg}^2 = \text{hypotenuse}^2.$$

While the Greek mathematician Pythagoras is recognized for discovering the Pythagorean Theorem, the logic of the theorem was well known long before the time of Pythagoras; however, he was the first to represent such logic in terms of a mathematical equation. So, how did the Greeks come up with this invaluable mathematical equation? Well, after many trials, they supposed that if squares are erected on both of the legs and the hypotenuse of a right triangle, then the sum of the areas of the two squares on both legs is equal to the area of the square on the hypotenuse.

Example 1   Find the length of the hypotenuse of a right triangle if the legs have lengths of 3 and 4 inches.

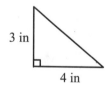

3 in

4 in

$a^2 + b^2 = c^2$	**Step 1:** Write the formula for the Pythagorean Theorem.
$\sqrt{c^2} = \sqrt{a^2 + b^2}$ $c = \sqrt{a^2 + b^2}$	**Step 2:** Solve for c by taking the square root of both sides of the equation.
$c = \sqrt{3^2 + 4^2}$	**Step 3:** Substitute the given information for the appropriate variables in the equation.
$c = \sqrt{9 + 16}$	**Step 4:** Simplify the expression under the radical.
$c = \sqrt{25}$	**Step 5:** Take the square root of the number in the radical.

$c = 5$ inches | **Step 6:** Ensure the answer is properly labeled.

Answer: 5 inches

Note: **The principal square root is used to determine the result, since distance is represented as a positive number.**

Example 2 | If the legs of a triangle are 7 inches and 8 inches, with a hypotenuse of 10 inches, is this triangle a right triangle?

$a^2 + b^2 = c^2$	**Step 1:** Write the formula for the Pythagorean Theorem.
$8^2 + 7^2 = 10^2$ $64 + 49 = 100$	**Step 2:** Substitute the given information for the appropriate variables in the equation.
$113 \neq 100$	**Step 3:** Simplify the expression.

Answer: The statement is false; therefore, the figure above is not a right triangle.

Example 3 | If one of the legs of a right triangle has a length of 5 feet and the hypotenuse has a length of 13 feet, find the length of the remaining leg.

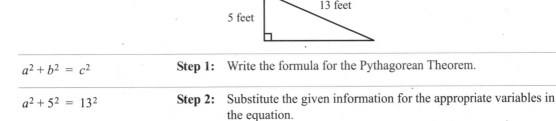

$a^2 + b^2 = c^2$	**Step 1:** Write the formula for the Pythagorean Theorem.
$a^2 + 5^2 = 13^2$	**Step 2:** Substitute the given information for the appropriate variables in the equation.
$a^2 + 25 = 169$	**Step 3:** Evaluate the exponents on each side of the equation.
$a^2 + 25 - 25 = 169 - 25$ $a^2 = 144$ $a = \sqrt{144}$	**Step 4:** Solve for a^2.
$a = 12$	**Step 5:** Take the square root.
$a = 12$ feet	**Step 6:** Make sure that the answer is properly labeled. *Note: Taking the square root of a number or variable reverses the squaring process.*

Answer: 12 feet

Problem Set

1. The lengths of the sides of a triangle are given. Determine whether or not the triangle is a right triangle.

3, 4, 5

2. The lengths of the sides of a triangle are given. Determine whether or not the triangle is a right triangle.

6, 8, 10

3. The lengths of the sides of a triangle are given. Determine whether or not the triangle is a right triangle.

5, 7, 9

4. The lengths of the sides of a triangle are given. Determine whether or not the triangle is a right triangle.

5, 12, 13

5. Assume c is the measure of the hypotenuse of a right triangle. Find b if $a = 9$ and $c = 15$.

6. Assume c is the measure of the hypotenuse of a right triangle. Find b if $a = 24$ and $c = 26$.

7. Assume c is the measure of the hypotenuse of a right triangle. Find b if $a = 24$ and $c = 25$.

8. Assume c is the measure of the hypotenuse of a right triangle. Find b if $a = 8$ and $c = 10$.

9. Assume c is the measure of the hypotenuse of a right triangle. Find a if $b = 20$ and $c = 25$.

10. Assume c is the measure of the hypotenuse of a right triangle. Find c if $a = 24$ and $b = 7$.

11. Assume c is the measure of the hypotenuse of a right triangle. Find a if $b = 9$ and $c = 10$.

12. Assume c is the measure of the hypotenuse of a right triangle. Find c if $a = 5$ and $b = 2$.

13. Assume c is the measure of the hypotenuse of a right triangle. Find b if $a = 1$ and $c = 2$.

14. Find the length of the unknown side.

15. Find the length of the unknown side.

16. Find the length of the unknown side.

17. Find the length of the unknown side.

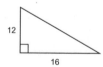

18. A hiker leaves his camp in the morning. After walking 4 miles due south and 8 miles due east, how far is he from his camp?

19. Find the length of the diagonal, z, in the square below.

20. Find the length of the side, x, in the rectangle below.

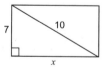

HA1-516: Applications of the Pythagorean Theorem

The **Pythagorean Theorem** states that in any right triangle the square of the hypotenuse (longer side) equals the sum of the squares of the lengths of the legs (shorter sides). The Pythagorean Theorem can be written as a formula, $a^2 + b^2 = c^2$, where the variables a and b each represent one leg of the right triangle, and the variable c always represents the length of the hypotenuse.

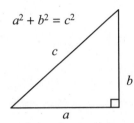

$a^2 + b^2 = c^2$

If a, b, and c are the lengths of the sides of a triangle, and $a^2 + b^2 = c^2$, then the triangle is a right triangle with legs of length a and b and hypotenuse of length c. This theorem is known as the **Converse of the Pythagorean Theorem**.

Example 1   Charlotte, NC is 78 miles north of Columbia, SC. Charleston, SC is 63 miles east of Columbia. How far is it from Charlotte, NC to Charleston, SC (to the nearest mile)?

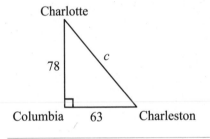

	Step 1: Sketch a picture showing that the distance from Charleston to Columbia is 63 miles and that the distance from Columbia to Charlotte is 78 miles. The distance from Charlotte to Charleston is unknown.

$c^2 = a^2 + b^2$

Step 2: Since the sketch forms a right triangle, we can use the Pythagorean Theorem.

Let $a = 78$ and $b = 63$.

$c^2 = 78^2 + 63^2$

Step 3: Substitute the given values.

$c^2 = 6,084 + 3,969$

$\quad = 10,053$

Step 4: Simplify.

$c = \pm\sqrt{10,053}$

$\quad \approx \pm 100$

Step 5: Take the square root of both sides.

$c \approx 100$

Step 6: Since distance is always positive, choose the positive square root.

Answer: It is approximately 100 miles from Charlotte, NC to Charleston, SC.

Example 2   A 10-foot board is leaning against a wall. If the top of the board is 7 feet up the wall, how far out is the bottom of the board from the wall (to the nearest tenth of a foot)?

Step 1: Sketch a picture of a board leaning against the wall.

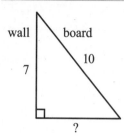

$a^2 + b^2 = c^2$

Step 2: Since the sketch forms a right triangle, we can use the Pythagorean Theorem.

Let $a = 7$, $b = ?$, and $c = 10$.
$7^2 + b^2 = 10^2$

Step 3: Substitute the given values.

$49 + b^2 = 100$
$b^2 = 100 - 49$
$= 51$

Step 4: Simplify and then solve for b^2.

$b = \pm\sqrt{51}$
$\approx \pm 7.1$

Step 5: Take the square root of both sides.

$b \approx \pm 7.1$

Step 6: Since length is always positive, choose the positive square root.

Answer: The base of the board is approximately 7.1 feet from the wall.

Example 3   A run through the park consists of running 200 meters south of point x, then 150 meters east, then back to point x on a straight line. How many total meters are traveled during this run?

Step 1: Sketch a picture showing a distance of 200 meters south from point x and then 150 meters east. The other distance is unknown.

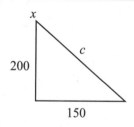

$c^2 = a^2 + b^2$

Step 2: Since the sketch forms a right triangle, we can use the Pythagorean Theorem.

Let $a = 200$ and $b = 150$
$c^2 = 200^2 + 150^2$

Step 3: Substitute the given values.

$c^2 = 40,000 + 22,500$

$\quad = 62,500$

Step 4: Simplify.

$c = \pm\sqrt{62,500}$

$\quad = \pm 250$

Step 5: Take the square root of both sides.

$c = 250$

Step 6: Since distance is always positive, choose the positive square.

$P = a + b + c$

Step 7: Since we know the lengths of each of the sides, we can use the formula for the perimeter of a triangle to determine the total meters traveled.

$P = 200 + 150 + 250$

Step 8: Substitute the values.

$P = 600$

Step 9: Simplify.

Answer: The total meters traveled is 600 meters.

Example 4   A triangle with sides that are 2 inches, 3 inches, and 4 inches is cut out of a piece of construction paper. Is the triangle a right triangle?

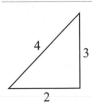

Step 1: Draw a triangle with sides 2, 3, and 4.

Let $a = 2$, $b = 3$, and $c = 4$.

Step 2: Determine the lengths of the hypotenuse and of each side. Let c represent the hypotenuse; a and b represent the lengths of each of the legs.

$a^2 + b^2 = c^2$

$2^2 + 3^2 \overset{?}{=} 4^2$

Step 3: Substitute the given values into the Pythagorean Theorem.

$4 + 9 \overset{?}{=} 16$

$13 \neq 16$

Step 4: Simplify both sides.

Answer: Since $13 \neq 16$, the triangle is not a right triangle.

| **Example 5** | A boy rode his scooter 5 miles south and 3 miles west. What is the difference between the distance he rode and the distance he was from his starting point at the end of the trip? |

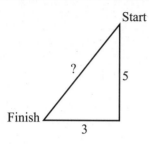

	Step 1:	Sketch a picture of the boy traveling 5 miles south and 3 miles west. The distance from the start to the finish is unknown.
$c^2 = a^2 + b^2$	**Step 2:**	Since the sketch forms a right triangle, we can use the Pythagorean Theorem.
Let $a = 5$ and $b = 3$. $c^2 = 5^2 + 3^2$	**Step 3:**	Substitute the given values.
$c^2 = 25 + 9$ $ = 34$	**Step 4:**	Simplify.
$c = \pm\sqrt{34}$ $ \approx \pm 5.831$	**Step 5:**	Take the square root of both sides.
$c \approx 5.831$	**Step 6:**	Since distance is always positive, choose the positive square root. Therefore, the distance from start to finish is approximately 5.831 miles.
Distance rode: $5 + 3 = 8$	**Step 7:**	Determine the distance the boy rode.
Distance: $\approx 8 - 5.831$ $ \approx 2.169$	**Step 8:**	Determine the difference between the distance he rode and the distance from start to finish.
	Answer:	The difference between the distances is approximately 2.169 miles.

Problem Set

1. A man walks 5 miles north and 12 miles west. What is the straight line distance from his starting point to his ending point?

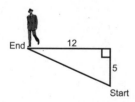

2. If a piece of square tile is 11 inches on each side, how long is the diagonal of the tile? Round your answer to the nearest hundredth.

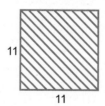

3. A rectangular-shaped flower garden has a length of 4 feet and a width of 3 feet. The gardener divides the garden into two congruent right triangles by placing bricks across the diagonal. What is the total length of the line of bricks?

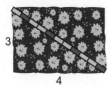

4. The top of a 12-foot ramp is resting against an 8-foot wall, forming a right triangle. What is the length from the base of the wall to the base of the ramp? Round your answer to the nearest hundredth.

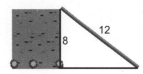

5. Each side of a baseball field is 90 feet. A baseball player walks straight across the field from 1st base to 3rd base. How far did the player walk? Round your answer to the nearest hundredth.

6. A rectangular pool has a length of 100 meters and a width of 40 meters. If a man swims directly from corner X to corner Y, how far does he swim? Round your answer to the nearest hundredth.

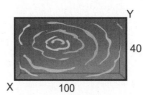

7. An advertisement for a computer monitor states that it is 17 inches. This means the diagonal of the monitor is 17 inches. What is the width of the monitor if the length is 13 inches? Round your answer to the nearest hundredth.

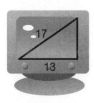

8. A piece of wire is extended from the top of a 60-foot pole to a stake placed 95 feet away from the pole. What is the length of this wire? Round your answer to the nearest hundredth.

9. A carpenter is building a shed that has a rectangular floor. The width of the floor is 15 feet. The diagonal of the floor measures 25 feet. What is the length of the floor?

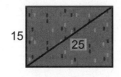

10. For an experiment in math class, Jason is required to construct a right triangle. One leg of the triangle is 18 feet and the hypotenuse of the right triangle is 28 feet. Find the length of the other leg of the triangle. Round your answer to the nearest hundredth.

11. A 26-foot rope is attached to a tree trunk 11 feet from the ground. The other end of the rope is tied to a stake in the ground. To the nearest foot, what is the distance from the base of the tree to the stake?

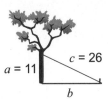

12. A man is standing 75 meters away from a pond and flying a kite that is floating 110 meters directly over the pond. To the nearest meter, what is the length of the kite string?

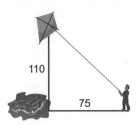

13. A man flying a kite is holding an 80-foot piece of string that is attached to the kite. The man is 40 feet away from a tree and the kite is directly over the tree. To the nearest foot, how far is the kite from the base of the tree?

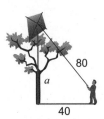

14. A baseball team wants to sell triangular-shaped pennants that contain a right angle and two congruent legs that measure 22 centimeters each. To the nearest centimeter, how long is the hypotenuse of the team pennants?

15. A 10-foot flagpole casts a shadow in the shape of a right triangle. The distance from the top of the flagpole to the end of the shadow is 23 feet. To the nearest foot, what is the length of the shadow?

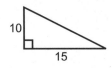

16. A right triangle has a hypotenuse of 17 inches. One of the legs is 8 inches. What is the perimeter of this triangle?

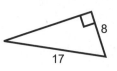

17. A right triangle has legs whose lengths are 10 inches and 15 inches. What is the perimeter of the triangle? Round your answer to the nearest hundredth.

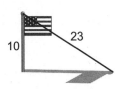

18. A right triangle has a hypotenuse of 34 centimeters. One of the legs is 30 centimeters. What is the perimeter of this triangle?

19. A right triangle has legs with lengths of 15 inches and 36 inches. What is the perimeter of the triangle?

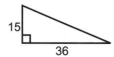

20. A flower bed is shaped like a right triangle. How many feet of border material are needed if the longest side is 70 inches and another side is 42 inches?

21. A path through the park extends 21 meters north of point A, then 28 meters east, and then back to point A on a straight line. How many total meters would a person walking this path travel?

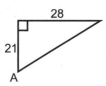

22. A right triangle has a hypotenuse of length 60 inches and one leg that is 36 inches. What is the perimeter of the triangle?

23. The legs of a right triangle are 2 decimeters and 1.5 decimeters, respectively. What is the perimeter of the right triangle?

24. A rug is shaped like a triangle. Its sides are 39 feet, 80 feet, and 89 feet. Is the rug a right triangle? Answer yes or no.

25. The sail of a boat is shaped like a triangle. Its sides are 33 feet, 44 feet, and 50 feet. Is the sail shaped like a right triangle? Answer yes or no.

26. A gardener is laying a border for a flower bed in the shape of a right triangle. The legs are 12 meters and 15 meters in length. The gardener has 39 meters of border. How much more border does he need to buy in order to have enough border for the flower bed? Round your answer to the nearest hundredth.

27. A right triangular frame is to be constructed by cutting three sections from a piece of wood that is 9 feet long. If the longest side is 3 feet long and one of the other sides is 2 feet long, how much wood will be left over after constructing the frame? Round your answer to the nearest hundredth.

28. A rhombus has four sides, each of which is 7 centimeters in length. If a diagonal is $7\sqrt{2}$ centimeters long, is the rhombus a square? Answer yes or no.

29. A piece of tile is shaped like a triangle with equal legs of length 9 inches. The hypotenuse is 13 inches. Is the tile a right triangle? Answer yes or no.

30. A man wants to buy gas at the marina for his boat. The marina is diagonally across the lake from the boat. In order to get gas for the boat, the boater must travel by car 5 miles north and then 12 miles east. If the boat had gas and was able to travel directly to the marina, how many miles could he save by traveling in the boat?

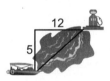

31. A driver needs to get to a destination that is located diagonally across a lake. To do this, the car must travel on a bridge 4.5 miles south and then travel 6 miles east. How many miles shorter would his trip have been if his car could cross the lake diagonally?

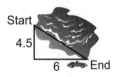

32. A camp group needs to get from Campsite A to Campsite B. They walk south to Campsite C and then east to Campsite B. The distance from Campsite A to Campsite C is 10 meters. The distance from Campsite C to Campsite B is 7.5 meters. How many meters shorter would the group's trip have been if they had traveled by boat across the lake?

33. Two truck drivers leave City A traveling to City C. Driver 1 travels 63 miles south to City B and then 16 miles east to City C. Driver 2 travels on a direct path from City A to City C. Find the difference in miles traveled by the two drivers.

34. Two cars leave an airport traveling two different routes to the same restaurant. The green car travels 16 miles west and then 30 miles north. The red car travels along a road directly to the restaurant. Find the difference in miles traveled by the two cars.

35. A man must run a cable 12 feet down the side of a house, and then to a box 35 feet directly east of the base of the house. How many feet of cable would he save if he could run the cable directly from the top of the house to the box?

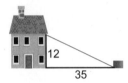

36. A group of friends is playing a game on a piece of graph paper in which the length of each block represents one centimeter. The goal is to get to the destination point by covering the least distance. A player moves 6 blocks down and 8 blocks across. How many centimeters shorter would the trip have been if the player had moved diagonally?

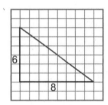

37. A woman walks home by traveling 20 meters north, 25 meters east, and then 5 more meters north. If she could walk home along a straight line, how many fewer meters would she need to walk? Round to the nearest hundredth.

38. A city block is shaped like a square. A bike path passes across the diagonal of the square, which is 150 meters in length. To get from A to B, how many meters would a bicyclist save riding along the diagonal instead of riding along the streets? Round to the nearest hundredth.

39. A girl rode her bicycle 5 miles south and 7 miles west. What is the difference between the distance she rode and the distance she was from her starting point? Round to the nearest hundredth.

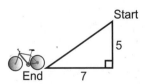

40. A rectangle is separated into two right triangles by drawing a diagonal. The diagonal drawn is 15 centimeters in length, and one leg of the rectangle is 7 centimeters in length. Find the difference between the perimeter of the rectangle and the length of the diagonal of the rectangle. Round your answer to the nearest hundredth.

HA1-520: Finding the Distance Between Two Points on a Coordinate Plane

Recall that to find the distance between any two points on a number line, you simply take the absolute value of the difference of the two numbers. In this lesson, you will learn how to find the distance between two points on a coordinate plane.

Consider two points on the coordinate plane.

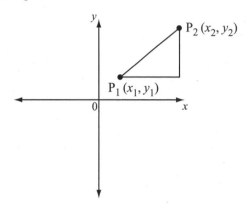

You want to find the distance between these two points. If you construct a right triangle as shown above, you can see that the length of the vertical leg of the triangle is $(y_2 - y_1)$, or $|y_2 - y_1|$ and the length of the horizontal leg of the triangle is $(x_2 - x_1)$ or $|x_2 - x_1|$. By the Pythagorean Theorem, you have $(\text{hypotenuse})^2 = (\text{leg})^2 + (\text{leg})^2$, or $(\text{hypotenuse})^2 = (x_2 - x_1)^2 + (y_2 - y_1)^2$, and taking the square root of both sides, you are left with hypotenuse $= \sqrt{(x_2 - x_1)^2 + (y_2 - y_1)^2}$, where the hypotenuse of the triangle is the distance between P_1 and P_2.

Distance Between Two Points on a Coordinate Plane	The distance between any two points is given by $d = \sqrt{(x_2 - x_1)^2 + (y_2 - y_1)^2}$, where d is the distance between points P_1 and P_2.

Example 1   Find the distance between the points (5, 5) and (8, 9) on a coordinate plane.

$d = \sqrt{(x_2 - x_1)^2 + (y_2 - y_1)^2}$

$d = \sqrt{(8 - 5)^2 + (9 - 5)^2}$

Step 1:   Substitute the coordinates of the points for the correct variables.

$d = \sqrt{3^2 + 4^2}$

$d = \sqrt{25}$

$d = 5$

Step 2:   Simplify.

Answer: 5

Example 2 Find the distance between the origin and $(1, 2)$ on a coordinate plane.

$d = \sqrt{(x_2 - x_1)^2 + (y_2 - y_1)^2}$

$d = \sqrt{(1 - 0)^2 + (2 - 0)^2}$

Step 1: Substitute the coordinates of the points for the correct variables.

$d = \sqrt{1^2 + 2^2}$

$d = \sqrt{5}$

Step 2: Simplify.

Answer: $\sqrt{5}$

Example 3 Find the distance between the points $(2, 5)$ and $(12, 15)$ on a coordinate plane.

$d = \sqrt{(x_2 - x_1)^2 + (y_2 - y_1)^2}$

$d = \sqrt{(12 - 2)^2 + (15 - 5)^2}$

Step 1: Substitute the coordinates of the points for the variables.

$d = \sqrt{10^2 + 10^2}$

$d = \sqrt{200} = 10\sqrt{2}$

Step 2: Simplify.

Answer: $10\sqrt{2}$

Example 4 Find the distance between the points $(-3, -1)$ and $(8, -9)$ on a coordinate plane.

$d = \sqrt{(x_2 - x_1)^2 + (y_2 - y_1)^2}$

$d = \sqrt{(8 - (-3))^2 + (-9 - (-1))^2}$

Step 1: Substitute the coordinates of the points for the variables.

$d = \sqrt{11^2 + (-8)^2}$

$d = \sqrt{121 + 64}$

$d = \sqrt{185}$

Step 2: Simplify.

Note: $(-8)^2 \neq -8^2$

Answer: $\sqrt{185}$

Problem Set

Find the distance between the given points:

1. $(5, 6)$ and $(3, 4)$ **2.** $(0, 6)$ and $(7, 0)$ **3.** $(0, 2)$ and $(6, 0)$ **4.** $(4, 2)$ and $(0, 7)$

5. $(8, 6)$ and $(6, 3)$ **6.** $(7, 9)$ and $(10, 13)$ **7.** $(18, 14)$ and $(23, 21)$ **8.** $(0, 6)$ and $(9, 0)$

9. $(2, 1)$ and $(8, 5)$ **10.** $(2, -3)$ and $(-1, 3)$

Solve the following:

11. Find the distance between the given points A and C.

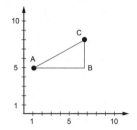

12. Find the distance between the given points A and B.

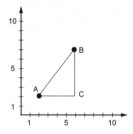

13. Find the distance between the given points B and C.

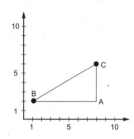

14. Find the distance between the given points R and S.

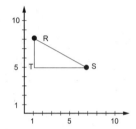

15. Find the distance between the given points A and B.

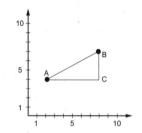

16. Find the distance between the given points D and E.

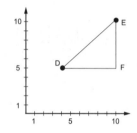

17. Find the distance between the given points H and J.

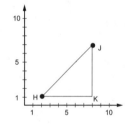

18. Ronda is attending a conference that is 222 miles east and 182 miles south of her home. If Ronda travels in a straight line from her home to the conference, how far will she have traveled?

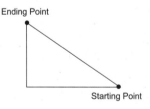

19. Over a 12-week period, Bryan jogged 42 miles west and 38 miles north. If Bryan jogged in a straight line, how far will he have jogged?

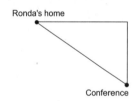

20. A small-engine plane flew 160 miles west and 90 miles south. If the small-engine plane flew in a straight line, how far will it have traveled? Round your answer to the nearest hundredth.

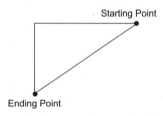

Most equations in previous lessons focused on one or more linear equations. Since linear equations are of order 1, each has exactly one solution. An example is the equation $x - 1 = 0$, where $x = 1$ is the solution. In this lesson, you will concentrate on solving quadratic equations—equations of order 2 that have exactly two solutions.

Quadratic Equation	An equation of the form $ax^2 + bx + c = 0$, where a, b, and c are constants and $a \neq 0$

The equations presented in this lesson involve perfect square expressions. Any quadratic equation in the form $x^2 = c$ where $c \geq 0$ can be solved by applying the square root property.

Square Root Property	If $x^2 = c$ and $c \geq 0$, then $x = \pm\sqrt{c}$.

To solve quadratic equations involving perfect square expressions, you must isolate the variable or squared expression and take the square root of both sides of the equation to find the two solutions.

Consider the first example.

Example 1 Solve: $(x + 2)^2 = 36$

$(x + 2) = \pm\sqrt{36}$	**Step 1:** Take the square root of both sides to eliminate the squared term.
$x + 2 = \pm\sqrt{36}$ $x + 2 = \pm 6$	**Step 2:** Solve the square roots.
$x = -2 \pm 6$	**Step 3:** Solve for x. Since x can equal $(-2 + 6)$ or $(-2 - 6)$, you will have two solutions.
$x = -2 + 6$ or $x = -2 - 6$	**Step 4:** Expand the two solutions.
$x = 4$ or $x = -8$	**Step 5:** Solve for x.
$[(4) + 2]^2 = 36$ $[(-8) + 2]^2 = 36$ $(6)^2 = 36$ $(-6)^2 = 36$ $36 = 36$ $36 = 36$	**Step 6:** Substitute each solution into the original equation to determine if it is part of the solution set.
	Answer: The solution set is $\{-8, 4\}$.

Example 2   Solve: $3x^2 - 75 = 0$

$3x^2 = 75$	**Step 1:** Isolate the squared term.
$\dfrac{3x^2}{3} = \dfrac{75}{3}$ $x^2 = 25$	**Step 2:** Divide both sides by 3.
$x = \pm\sqrt{25}$	**Step 3:** Solve for x by taking the square root of both sides.
$x = \pm 5$ $x = 5 \ \text{ or } \ x = -5$	**Step 4:** Simplify.

$3(5)^2 - 75 = 0$	$3(-5)^2 - 75 = 0$	**Step 5:** Substitute each solution into the original equation to determine if it is part of the solution set.
$3(25) - 75 = 0$	$3(25) - 75 = 0$	
$75 - 75 = 0$	$75 - 75 = 0$	
$0 = 0$	$0 = 0$	

Answer: The solution set is $\{-5, 5\}$.

Example 3   Solve: $6(x - 5)^2 = 12$

$\dfrac{6(x-5)^2}{6} = \dfrac{12}{6}$	**Step 1:** Divide both sides by 6.
$(x-5)^2 = 2$ $x - 5 = \pm\sqrt{2}$	**Step 2:** Take the square root of both sides to eliminate the squared term.
$x = 5 \pm \sqrt{2}$	**Step 3:** Simplify the squared expression using the square root property.
$x = 5 + \sqrt{2} \ \text{ or } \ x = 5 - \sqrt{2}$	**Step 4:** Solve for x.

$6[(5 + \sqrt{2}) - 5]^2 = 12$	$6[(5 - \sqrt{2}) - 5]^2 = 12$	**Step 5:** Substitute each solution into the original equation to determine if it is a part of the solution set.
$6(\sqrt{2})^2 = 12$	$6(-\sqrt{2})^2 = 12$	
$6(2) = 12$	$6(2) = 12$	
$12 = 12$	$12 = 12$	

Answer: The solution set is $\{5 + \sqrt{2}, 5 - \sqrt{2}\}$.

Problem Set

Solve the following equations:

1. $2a^2 = 162$

2. $8a^2 = 72$

3. $2x^2 = 72$

4. $8x^2 = 32$

5. $3x^2 = 27$

6. $4c^2 - 23 = 301$

7. $3x^2 + 13 = 88$

8. $3x^2 + 42 = 150$

9. $6y^2 + 6 = 30$

10. $10x^2 + 40 = -50$

11. $(y-8)^2 = 144$

12. $(g-12)^2 = 81$

13. $(x-4)^2 = 225$

14. $(y+2)^2 = 9$

15. $(n-6)^2 = 64$

16. $(g-6)^2 = 81$

17. $(m+3)^2 = 16$

18. $(x-1)^2 + 15 = 6$

19. $3(b-8)^2 + 10 = 13$

20. $5(c-2)^2 - 8 = 17$

HA1-530: Solving Quadratic Equations by Completing the Square

As you continue solving quadratic equations, you must use all the skills you've learned. Remember that a quadratic equation has an unknown variable, squared and in the form $ax^2 + bx = c$. Prior to this lesson, you solved quadratic equations of the form $x^2 = c$ if $c \geq 0$ by applying the square root property.

Example 1   Solve the equation: $x^2 + 6 = 31$

$x^2 + 6 - 6 = 31 - 6$	**Step 1:** Subtract 6 from both sides to get the variable on one side.
$x^2 = 25$	
$\sqrt{x^2} = \sqrt{25}$	**Step 2:** Take the square root of both sides to eliminate the squared term.
$x = \pm\sqrt{25}$	**Step 3:** Simplify
$x = \pm 5$	
$x = \{5, -5\}$	**Answer:** The solution is $\{5, -5\}$.

You would then check the solutions to make sure $\{5, -5\}$ are actually part of the solution set. You have also gone through lessons where you learned to factor an equation.

Example 2   Solve the equation: $x^2 + 10x + 21 = 0$

$(x + 3)(x + 7) = 0$	**Step 1:** Factor the quadratic expression.
$x + 3 = 0$	**Step 2:** Solve for x.
$x = -3$	
$x + 7 = 0$	
$x = -7$	
$x = \{-3, -7\}$	**Answer:** The solution is $\{-3, -7\}$.

Consider the equation $x^2 - x - 8 = 0$. This equation cannot be factored, nor can it be solved by applying the square root property. To solve these types of quadratic equations, you will use a method called completing the square. This method is used to turn an equation into a perfect square trinomial, or to find a missing third term if the equation is not already a perfect square trinomial.

To complete the square:
- Find half the coefficient of the second term.
- Square the result of the above.
- Add the result of the above as the third term in the equation.

Practice completing the square to find the third term of the trinomial.

Example 3   Complete the square: $x^2 + 6x + ?$

$\dfrac{6}{2} = 3$	**Step 1:** Take half of the coefficient of the second term.
$3^2 = 9$	**Step 2:** Square the result you just found.
$x^2 + 6x + 9$	**Step 3:** Rewrite the expression, including the third term.
	Answer: The third term is 9.

Example 4   Complete the square: $x^2 - 10x + ?$

$\dfrac{-10}{2} = -5$	**Step 1:** Take half of the coefficient of the second term.
$(-5)^2 = 25$	**Step 2:** Square the result you just found.
$x^2 - 10x + 25$	**Step 3:** Rewrite the expression including the third term.
	Answer: The third term is 25.

When completing the square, the concept of finding the third term of a perfect square trinomial is useful. Before you can solve quadratic equations by completing the square, the following conditions must be met:

- Arrange the equation so that the terms containing x^2 and x are on one side of the equation and the constant is on the other.

- Ensure that the coefficient of x^2 is one. If the coefficient of the x^2 term is not 1, you must divide each term of the equation by that coefficient before beginning the process.

- When adding a quantity to one side of the equation, you must add the same quantity to the other side of the equation as well.

Example 5   Solve the equation: $x^2 - 4x = 5$

$x^2 - 4x = 5$	**Step 1:** Determine if the equation meets these conditions: • Are the x^2 and x terms on one side of the equation in descending order, and the constant, or c term, on the opposite side? Yes. • Is 1 the coefficient of x^2? Yes. • Since both conditions are met, the process can begin.
$\left(-\dfrac{4}{2}\right)^2 = (-2)^2 = 4$	**Step 2:** Find half of the coefficient of the x term and square it. Next, simplify the expression but remember that the number, -2, which is one half the coefficient, is part of the binomial square; therefore, -2 will be the constant in the binomial that you square.

$$x^2 - 4x + 4 = 5 + 4$$
$$x^2 - 4x + 4 = 9$$
$$(x - 2)^2 = 9$$

Step 3: Now, add the result of Step 2 to both sides of the original equation and rewrite the left side of the equation as a perfect square. Remember to use the (–2) from the second step.

$$(x - 2) = \pm\sqrt{9}$$
$$x - 2 = \pm\sqrt{9}$$
$$x - 2 = \pm 3$$

Step 4: To solve for x, you must eliminate the squared term. Take the square root of both sides of the equation.

$$x - 2 = 3 \qquad x - 2 = -3$$
$$x - 2 + 2 = 3 + 2 \text{ or } x - 2 + 2 = -3 + 2$$
$$x = 5 \qquad\qquad x = -1$$

Step 5: Solve for x.

$$(5)^2 - 4(5) = 5 \qquad (-1)^2 - 4(-1) = 5$$
$$25 - 20 = 5 \qquad\quad 1 - (-4) = 5$$
$$5 = 5 \qquad\qquad\quad 5 = 5$$

Step 6: As usual, the solutions must be tested to ensure that they are part of the solution set.

Answer: The solution set is $\{5, -1\}$.

Since both solutions satisfy the equation, they are part of the solution set. The equation could have been factored, even though the process of completing the square was used. In the next example, you are forced to complete the square since the equation will not factor.

Example 6 Solve the equation: $x^2 - x - 8 = 0$ Note the equation meets the necessary conditions.

$$x^2 - x = 8$$

Step 1: Rewrite the terms with the x's in descending order on the left side of the equation. Place the constant, or c term, on the right side.

$$\left(-\frac{1}{2}\right)^2 = \left(\frac{1}{2}\right)^2$$

Step 2: Take half of the x coefficient and square the term. Do not simplify the expression at this point.

$$x^2 - x + \left(\frac{1}{2}\right)^2 = 8 + \left(\frac{1}{2}\right)^2$$

Step 3: Add the result found in Step 2 to both sides of the equation.

$$\left(x - \frac{1}{2}\right)^2 = 8 + \frac{1}{4}$$
$$\left(x - \frac{1}{2}\right)^2 = \frac{33}{4}$$

Step 4: Write the left side of the equation as a perfect square.

$$\left(x - \frac{1}{2}\right) = \pm\sqrt{\frac{33}{4}}$$

Step 5: Take the square root of both sides to eliminate the square.

$$x - \frac{1}{2} = \pm\frac{\sqrt{33}}{2}$$

Step 6: Simplify to the lowest terms. Remember:
$$\sqrt{\frac{33}{4}} = \frac{\sqrt{33}}{\sqrt{4}} = \frac{\sqrt{33}}{2}$$

$$x = \frac{1}{2} \pm \frac{\sqrt{33}}{2}$$

$$x = \frac{1 - \sqrt{33}}{2} \quad \text{or} \quad x = \frac{1 + \sqrt{33}}{2}$$

Step 7: Solve for x.

$$\left(\frac{1 - \sqrt{33}}{2}\right)^2 - \left(\frac{1 - \sqrt{33}}{2}\right) - 8 = 0$$

$$(1 - \sqrt{33})^2 - 2 + 2\sqrt{33} - 32 = 0$$

$$1 - 2\sqrt{33} + 33 - 2 + 2\sqrt{33} - 32 = 0$$

$$0 = 0$$

$$\left(\frac{1 + \sqrt{33}}{2}\right)^2 - \left(\frac{1 + \sqrt{33}}{2}\right) - 8 = 0$$

$$\frac{1 + 2\sqrt{33} + 33}{4} - \left(\frac{1 + \sqrt{33}}{2}\right) - 8 = 0$$

$$1 + 2\sqrt{33} + 33 - 2 - 2\sqrt{33} - 32 = 0$$

$$0 = 0$$

Step 8: Check to determine if both solutions are part of the solution set.

Answer: Since both solutions satisfy the equation, the solution set is $\left\{ \dfrac{1 - \sqrt{33}}{2}, \dfrac{1 + \sqrt{33}}{2} \right\}$.

Now consider a case where the coefficient of x^2 is not 1.

| Example 7 | Solve the equation: $3x^2 - 2x - 5 = 0$ |

$$3x^2 - 2x = 5$$

Step 1: Rewrite the terms with x's in descending order on the left side of the equation. Place the constant, or c term, on the right side.

$$\frac{3x^2 - 2x}{3} = \frac{5}{3}$$

$$\frac{3x^2}{3} - \frac{2x}{3} = \frac{5}{3}$$

Step 2: Divide both sides of the equation by the coefficient of x^2. In this case, divide by 3.

$$x^2 - \frac{2}{3}x = \frac{5}{3}$$

$$x^2 - \frac{2}{3}x + \frac{1}{9} = \frac{5}{3} + \frac{1}{9}$$

Step 3: Take half of the coefficient of x, square it, and add it to both sides.

Note: $\left(\frac{1}{2} \cdot \frac{2}{3}\right)^2 = \left(\frac{2}{6}\right)^2 = \left(\frac{1}{3}\right)^2 = \frac{1}{9}$

$$\left(x - \frac{1}{3}\right)^2 = \frac{15}{9} + \frac{1}{9}$$

$$\left(x - \frac{1}{3}\right)^2 = \frac{16}{9}$$

Step 4: Rewrite the left side as a perfect square. Obtain the common denominator and add the right side.

$$x - \frac{1}{3} = \pm\sqrt{\frac{16}{9}}$$

Step 5: Take the square root of both sides.

$$x - \frac{1}{3} = \pm\frac{4}{3}$$

$$x = \frac{1}{3} \pm \frac{4}{3}$$

$$x = \frac{1}{3} + \frac{4}{3} \qquad x = \frac{1}{3} - \frac{4}{3}$$

$$\text{or}$$

$$x = \frac{5}{3} \qquad x = -\frac{3}{3}$$

$$x = -1$$

Step 6: Solve for x.

$$3\left(\frac{5}{3}\right)^2 - 2\left(\frac{5}{3}\right) - 5 = 0$$

$$3\left(\frac{25}{9}\right) - \frac{10}{3} - 5 = 0$$

$$\frac{25}{3} - \frac{10}{3} - \frac{15}{3} = 0$$

$$0 = 0$$

Step 7: Check to determine if both solutions are part of the solution set.

$$3(-1)^2 - 2(-1) - 5 = 0$$

$$3(1) + 2 - 5 = 0$$

$$3 + 2 - 5 = 0$$

$$0 = 0$$

Answer: Since both solutions satisfy the equation, the solution set is $\{\frac{5}{3}, -1\}$.

Problem Set

1. Find the value of c to complete the square.

$$n^2 + 3n + c$$

2. Find the value of c to complete the square.

$$x^2 + 4x + c$$

3. Find the value of c to complete the square.

$$m^2 - 18m + c$$

4. Find the value of c to complete the square.

$$y^2 - 7y + c$$

5. Find the value of c to complete the square.

$$n^2 + 5n + c$$

6. Solve: $p^2 - 10p = -16$

7. Solve: $k^2 + 6k = 16$

8. Solve: $p^2 - 2p = 3$

9. Solve: $h^2 + 6h + 7 = 0$

10. Solve: $h^2 + 6h + 3 = 0$

11. Given one of the steps of completing the square for the problem below, find the missing term.

$$3x^2 - 18x + 2 = 0, (x - \underline{\quad})^2 = \frac{25}{3}$$

12. Given one of the steps of completing the square for the problem below, find the missing term.

$$5x^2 - 10x + 4 = 0, (x - \underline{\quad})^2 = \frac{1}{5}$$

13. Given one of the steps of completing the square for the problem below, find the missing term.

$$3m^2 - 12m - 1 = 0, (m - \underline{\quad})^2 = \frac{13}{3}$$

In previous lessons, we learned several methods used to solve quadratic equations written in standard form.

Standard Form of a Quadratic Equation	A quadratic equation of the form $ax^2 + bx + c = 0$ where a, b, and c are real numbers and $a \neq 0$

In this lesson we will look at another method called the quadratic formula. Recall that the method of factoring can only be used to solve quadratic equations that are factorable. To solve equations that are not factorable, we used the method of completing the square. Recall that this method can be used to solve all quadratic equations.

Using the method of completing the square, we can derive the quadratic formula by solving the standard form of the quadratic equation.

$$\text{Solve } ax^2 + bx + c = 0.$$

$$ax^2 + bx + c - c = 0 - c$$

$$ax^2 + bx = -c$$

$$\frac{a}{a}x^2 + \frac{b}{a}x = \frac{-c}{a}$$

$$x^2 + \frac{b}{a}x = \frac{-c}{a}$$

$$x^2 + \frac{bx}{a} + \left(\frac{b}{2a}\right)^2 = \left(\frac{b}{2a}\right)^2 - \frac{c}{a}$$

$$\left(x + \frac{b}{2a}\right)^2 = \frac{b^2}{4a^2} - \frac{c}{a}$$

$$\left(x + \frac{b}{2a}\right)^2 = \frac{b^2 - 4ac}{4a^2}$$

$$\sqrt{\left(x + \frac{b}{2a}\right)^2} = \pm\sqrt{\frac{b^2 - 4ac}{4a^2}}$$

$$x + \frac{b}{2a} = \pm\frac{\sqrt{b^2 - 4ac}}{2a}$$

$$x + \frac{b}{2a} - \frac{b}{2a} = -\frac{b}{2a} \pm \frac{\sqrt{b^2 - 4ac}}{2a}$$

$$x = \frac{-b \pm \sqrt{b^2 - 4ac}}{2a}$$

	For a quadratic equation $ax^2 + bx + c = 0$, the
Quadratic Formula	solutions are $x = \dfrac{-b \pm \sqrt{b^2 - 4ac}}{2a}$ where $a \neq 0$.

Example 1 Write the quadratic equation $x^2 = 8x + 10$ in standard form and identify the values of a, b, and c.

$ax^2 + bx + c = 0$	**Step 1:** Recall the standard form a quadratic equation.
$x^2 = 8x + 10$ $x^2 - 8x = 8x - 8x + 10$ $x^2 - 8x = 10$	**Step 2:** Subtract $8x$ from both sides of the equation and simplify.
$x^2 - 8x - 10 = 10 - 10$ $x^2 - 8x - 10 = 0$	**Step 3:** Subtract 10 from both sides of the equation and simplify. The quadratic equation is now in standard form.
$a = 1,\ b = -8,\ c = -10$	**Step 4:** Identify the values of a, b, and c in the standard form of the quadratic equation.
	Answer: $x^2 - 8x - 10 = 0$ $a = 1,\ b = -8,\ c = -10$

Example 2 Determine the values of a, b, and c, and write the quadratic formula that represents the following quadratic equation: $x^2 = 5x - 6$.

$x^2 = 5x - 6$ $x^2 - 5x = 5x - 5x - 6$ $x^2 - 5x = -6$ $x^2 - 5x + 6 = -6 + 6$ $x^2 - 5x + 6 = 0$	**Step 1:** Write the equation in standard form.
$a = 1,\ b = -5,\ c = 6$	**Step 2:** Identify the values of a, b, and c.
$x = \dfrac{-b \pm \sqrt{b^2 - 4ac}}{2a} = \dfrac{-(-5) \pm \sqrt{(-5)^2 - 4(1)(6)}}{2(1)}$	**Step 3:** Substitute these values into the quadratic formula.
	Answer: $\dfrac{-(-5) \pm \sqrt{(-5)^2 - 4(1)(6)}}{2(1)}$

Example 3   Use the quadratic formula to solve the following quadratic equation: $3x^2 + 5x - 2 = 0$.

$a = 3$, $b = 5$, $c = -2$

Step 1: Identify the values of a, b, and c in the equation.

$x = \dfrac{-b \pm \sqrt{b^2 - 4ac}}{2a}$

$x = \dfrac{-5 \pm \sqrt{5^2 - 4(3)(-2)}}{2(3)}$

Step 2: Substitute these values into the quadratic formula.

$x = \dfrac{-5 \pm \sqrt{25 + 24}}{6}$

$x = \dfrac{-5 \pm \sqrt{49}}{6}$

$x = \dfrac{-5 \pm 7}{6}$

$x = \dfrac{-5 + 7}{6} = \dfrac{2}{6} = \dfrac{1}{3}$ or $x = \dfrac{-5 - 7}{6} = -\dfrac{12}{6} = -2$

Step 3: Simplify.

Answer: The solution set is $\left\{ \dfrac{1}{3}, -2 \right\}$.

Example 4   Use the quadratic formula to solve $3x^2 = 6x - 1$; write the solutions in decimal form approximated to the nearest tenth.

$3x^2 = 6x - 1$

$3x^2 - 6x = 6x - 6x - 1$

$3x^2 - 6x = -1$

$3x^2 - 6x + 1 = -1 + 1$

$3x^2 - 6x + 1 = 0$

Step 1: Write the equation in standard form.

$a = 3$, $b = -6$, $c = 1$

Step 2: Identify the values of a, b, and c in the equation.

$x = \dfrac{-b \pm \sqrt{b^2 - 4ac}}{2a}$

$x = \dfrac{-(-6) \pm \sqrt{(-6)^2 - 4(3)(1)}}{2(3)}$

Step 3: Substitute these values into the quadratic formula.

$$x = \frac{6 \pm \sqrt{36-12}}{6}$$

$$x = \frac{6 \pm \sqrt{24}}{6}$$

$$x = \frac{6 \pm \sqrt{4 \cdot 6}}{6}$$

$$x = \frac{6 \pm 2\sqrt{6}}{6}$$

$$x = \frac{2(3 \pm \sqrt{6})}{6}$$

$$x = \frac{3 \pm \sqrt{6}}{3}$$

Step 4: Simplify.

$$x = \frac{3 + \sqrt{6}}{3} \approx 1.8 \quad \text{or} \quad x = \frac{3 - \sqrt{6}}{3} \approx 0.2$$

Step 5: Write the solutions in decimal form.

Answer: $x = 1.8$ or $x = 0.2$

Example 5   A ball is thrown upward from the ground with an initial velocity of 192 ft/sec. How many seconds will it take the object to reach a height of 512 ft the second time? Use the formula $h = vt - 16t^2$.

$h = 512$ ft and $v = 192$ ft/sec.

Step 1: Identify the given values in the problem.

$h = vt - 16t^2$
$512 = 192t - 16t^2$

Step 2: Substitute these values into the formula $h = vt - 16t^2$.

$512 = 192t - 16t^2$
$16t^2 - 192t + 512 = 0$

Step 3: Write the quadratic equation in standard form.

$a = 16, \ b = -192, \ c = 512$

Step 4: Identify the values of a, b, and c in the equation.

$$x = \frac{-b \pm \sqrt{b^2 - 4ac}}{2a}$$

$$x = \frac{-(-192) \pm \sqrt{(-192)^2 - 4(16)(512)}}{2(16)}$$

Step 5: Substitute these values into the quadratic formula.

$$x = \frac{192 \pm \sqrt{36,864 - 32,768}}{32}$$

$$x = \frac{192 \pm \sqrt{4096}}{32}$$

$$x = \frac{192 \pm 64}{32}$$

$$x = \frac{192 + 64}{32} = \frac{256}{32} = 8 \quad \text{or} \quad x = \frac{192 - 64}{32} = \frac{128}{32} = 4$$

Answer: It will take 8 seconds for the ball to reach a height of 512 feet the second time.

Problem Set

Solve the following:

1. Rewrite the following equation in standard form and identify the values of a, b, and c.

$$x^2 = 3x - 5$$

2. Rewrite the following equation in standard form and identify the values of a, b, and c.

$$x^2 = 5x - 4$$

3. Rewrite the following equation in standard form and identify the values of a, b, and c.

$$-3x + 6 = -2x^2$$

4. Rewrite the following equation in standard form and identify the values of a, b, and c.

$$2x^2 = 5x - 7$$

5. Determine the values for a, b, and c and choose the quadratic formula that represents the following quadratic equation:

$$5x^2 = 9x + 2$$

$$x = \frac{-(-9) \pm \sqrt{(-9)^2 - 4(5)(-2)}}{2(5)}$$

$$x = \frac{-9 \pm \sqrt{9^2 - 4(5)(2)}}{2(5)}$$

$$x = \frac{-9 \pm \sqrt{(-9)^2 - 4(5)(-2)}}{2(1)}$$

$$x = \frac{-9 \pm \sqrt{(-9)^2 + 4(5)(2)}}{2(5)}$$

6. Determine the values for a, b, and c and choose the quadratic formula that represents the following quadratic equation:

$$x^2 = 9x - 8$$

$$x = \frac{-9 \pm \sqrt{(-9)^2 - 4(1)(-8)}}{2(1)}$$

$$x = \frac{-9 \pm \sqrt{(-9)^2 - 4(1)(8)}}{2(1)}$$

$$x = \frac{-(-9) \pm \sqrt{(-9)^2 - 4(1)(8)}}{2(1)}$$

$$x = \frac{-9 \pm \sqrt{9^2 - 4(1)(-8)}}{2(1)}$$

7. Determine the values for a, b, and c and choose the quadratic formula that represents the following quadratic equation:

$$3 = 4x - x^2$$

$$x = \frac{-(-4) \pm \sqrt{(-4)^2 - 4(1)(3)}}{2(1)}$$

$$x = \frac{-(-4) \pm \sqrt{(-4)^2 + 4(1)(3)}}{2(1)}$$

$$x = \frac{-4 \pm \sqrt{(-4)^2 - 4(1)(3)}}{2(1)}$$

$$x = \frac{-4 \pm \sqrt{4^2 - 4(-1)(3)}}{2(1)}$$

8. Determine the values for a, b, and c and choose the quadratic formula that represents the following quadratic equation:

$$2x^2 = -3x + 2$$

$$x = \frac{-(-3) \pm \sqrt{(-3)^2 - 4(-2)(2)}}{2(-2)}$$

$$x = \frac{-3 \pm \sqrt{3^2 - 4(2)(-2)}}{2(2)}$$

$$x = \frac{-(-3) \pm \sqrt{(-3)^2 - 4(2)(-2)}}{2(2)}$$

$$x = \frac{-3 \pm \sqrt{3^2 - 4(2)(2)}}{2(2)}$$

9. Use the quadratic formula to solve the following quadratic equation:

$$4x^2 + x - 3 = 0$$

10. Use the quadratic formula to solve the following quadratic equation:

$$x^2 + 10x + 9 = 0$$

11. Use the quadratic formula to solve the following quadratic equation:

$$3x^2 - 11x + 5 = 0$$

12. Use the quadratic formula to solve the following quadratic equation:

$$2x^2 - 4x + 1 = 0$$

13. Use the quadratic formula to solve $4x - 3 = -2x^2$. Write the solutions in simplest rational form.

14. Use the quadratic formula to solve $-7x = 7 - 5x^2$. Write the solutions in simplest rational form.

15. Use the quadratic formula to solve $x - 4 = -2x^2$. Approximate the solutions to the nearest tenth.

16. Use the quadratic formula to solve $4x - 2 = -3x^2$. Approximate the solutions to the nearest tenth.

17. An object is shot upward from the earth's surface with an initial velocity of 35 m/sec. How many seconds will it take the object to reach a height of 20 m the first time? Use the formula $h = vt - 5t^2$ and round your answer to the nearest tenth of a second.

18. A model rocket is shot upward from the earth's surface with an initial velocity of 50 ft/sec. How many seconds will it take the object to reach a height of 35 ft the first time? Use the formula $h = vt - 16t^2$ and round your answer to the nearest tenth of a second.

19. An object is dropped from the top of a cliff. How many seconds will it take the object to travel a distance of 24 m? Use the formula $d = 5t^2$ and round your answer to the nearest tenth of a second.

20. A coin is dropped from the top of a wishing well. The distance from the top of the wishing well to the bottom of the wishing well is 50 feet. How many seconds will it take the coin to reach the bottom of the wishing well? Use the formula $d = 16t^2$ and round your answer to the nearest tenth of a second.

Quadratic equations like $x^2 - 8x - 9 = 0$ can be solved using the TI-83 Plus™ graphing calculator. Using the graphing ability of the calculator, we will consider the graph of the equation $y = x^2 - 8x - 9$. This means we are trying to find the places on the graph where the y-coordinate is 0. In other words, we are looking for the places where the graph intersects the x-axis.

The process has five steps:

- Step 0: (Settings) Initialize the calculator to a standard set of values so that we have a common starting point.
- Step 1: (Enter the expression) Enter the symbolic form of the quadratic equation to be solved Y_1 and enter 0 in Y_2.
- Step 2: (Graph) Obtain a graph of the two equations Y_1 and Y_2.
- Step 3: (Check) Use the graphing calculator's ability to find intersection points.
- Step 4: (Solve) Use information about the intersection points to solve the initial equation.

Note: Before doing any of these examples you should check your calculator's settings to be sure that it will function as described above.

Press the MODE key and be sure that your settings appear as shown below.

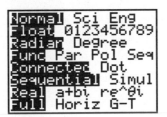

Next press the 2nd ZOOM keys and be sure that your settings appear as shown below.

Next press the ZOOM key then the 6 key to select the standard window setting.

Press the WINDOW key to get the following screen.

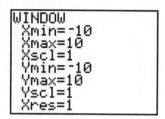

Example 1   Use the graphing calculator to solve the quadratic equation $x^2 - 7x - 18 = 0$.

Step 0: (Settings) Make sure you have the default settings as described above.

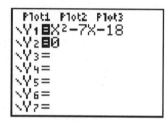

Step 1: (Enter the expression) Press the Y= key and enter the expression $x^2 - 7x - 18$ into the Y_1 slot and put 0 into the Y_2 slot.

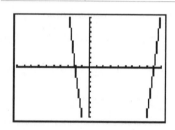

Step 2: (Graph) Press the GRAPH key. From the graph, we see that the x-intercepts are $(-2, 0)$ and $(9, 0)$.

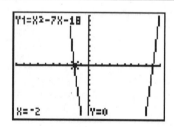

Step 3: (Check) Check to see that $(-2, 0)$ and $(9, 0)$ are the intercepts. To do that, press TRACE and then − 2, and finally ENTER, and you will get the screen to the left. Notice that at the bottom of the screen we see that when $x = -2$, $y = 0$. This verifies the first attempt.

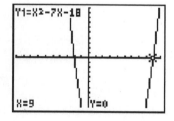

Now type in 9 followed by ENTER, and at the bottom of the screen we see that when $x = 9$ that $y = 0$. This verifies the second attempt.

Step 4: (Solve) Since the intercepts are (–2, 0) and (9, 0), we know that the two solutions of the equation $x^2 - 7x - 18 = 0$ are: $x = -2$ and $x = 9$.

Answer: The solutions of the equation $x^2 - 7x - 18 = 0$ are $x = -2$ and $x = 9$.

Example 2   Use the graphing calculator to solve the equation $2x^2 + 3x - 20 = 0$.

Step 0: (Settings) Make sure you have the default settings as described in the beginning of the lesson.

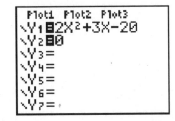

Step 1: (Enter the expression) Press the ⟨Y=⟩ key and enter the expression $2x^2 + 3x - 20$ into the Y_1 slot and 0 into the Y_2 slot.

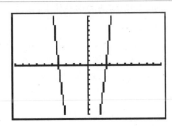

Step 2: (Graph) Press the ⟨GRAPH⟩ key. From the graph, we see that one x-intercepts falls between $x = 2$ and $x = 3$, and one falls near $x = -4$.

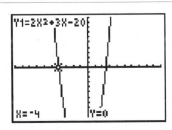

Step 3: (Check) Verify the intercept at (–4, 0) as we did in the previous example. To do this, press ⟨TRACE⟩ and then ⟨–⟩⟨4⟩ followed by ⟨ENTER⟩ to get the screen to the left.

This verifies that (–3, 0) is one of the intercepts. The second intercept isn't as easy to guess, so we will use an alternative method of finding the intercept.

Find the place where the graph of Y_1 and Y_2 intersect (this will be the second x-intercept). This is done by pressing [2nd][TRACE] followed by [5].

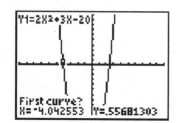

You will be prompted for the first curve with a screen like the one to the left. Press [ENTER].

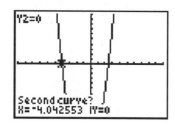

You will be prompted for the second curve with a screen like the one to the left. Press [ENTER] again.

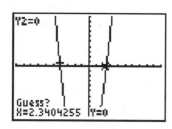

You will be prompted for a guess with a screen like the one to the left. Use the [◄] and [►] keys to move the highlighted point as close as possible to the intercept you are trying to verify and press [ENTER].

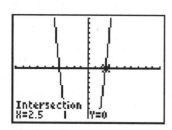

The calculator should display a screen like the one to the left, verifying that the second intercept is at the point $x = 2.5$.

Step 4: (Solve) Since the intercepts are $(2.5, 0)$ and $(-4, 0)$, we know that the two solutions to $2x^2 + 3x - 20 = 0$ are $x = 2.5$ and $x = -4$.

Answer: The two solutions to $2x^2 + 3x - 20 = 0$ are $x = 2.5$ and $x = -4$.

Example 3   Use the graphing calculator to solve the quadratic equation $4x^2 + 7x - 15 = 0$.

Step 0:   (Settings) Make sure you have the default settings as described in the beginning of the lesson.

Step 1:   (Enter the expression) Press the $\boxed{Y=}$ key and enter the expression $4x^2 + 7x - 15$ into the Y_1 slot and put 0 into the Y_2 slot.

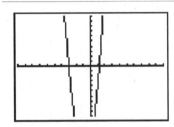

Step 2:   (Graph) Press the $\boxed{\text{GRAPH}}$ key. We see that one x-intercepts falls between $x = 1$ and $x = 2$, and one falls near $x = -3$.

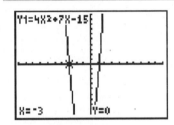

Step 3:   (Check) Verify the intercept at $(-3, 0)$. To do this, press $\boxed{\text{TRACE}}$ and then $\boxed{-}\boxed{3}$ followed by $\boxed{\text{ENTER}}$, and you will get the screen to the left.

This verifies that $(-3, 0)$ is one of the intercepts. The second intercept isn't as easy to guess, so we will use an alternative method of finding it.

Next, find the place where the graphs of Y_1 and Y_2 intersect (this will be the second x-intercept). You can do this by pressing $\boxed{\text{2nd}}\boxed{\text{TRACE}}$ followed by $\boxed{5}$.

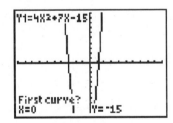

You will be prompted for the first curve with a screen like the one to the left. Press $\boxed{\text{ENTER}}$.

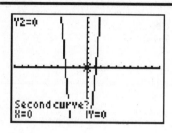

You will be prompted for the second curve with a screen like the one to the left. Press [ENTER] again.

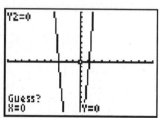

You will be prompted for a guess with a screen like the one to the left. Use the ◄ and ► keys to move the highlighted point as close as possible to the intercept you are trying to verify and press [ENTER].

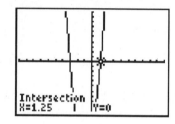

The calculator should display a screen like the one to the left, verifying that the second intercept is at the point $(1.25, 0)$.

Step 4: (Solve) Since the intercepts are $(1.25, 0)$ and $(-3, 0)$, we know that the solutions of the equation $4x^2 + 7x - 15 = 0$ are $x = 1.25$ and $x = -3$.

Answer: The solutions of the equation $4x^2 + 7x - 15 = 0$ are $x = 1.25$ and $x = -3$.

Problem Set

1. Solve using the graphing calculator:
$$x^2 + 6x + 8 = 0$$

2. Solve using the graphing calculator:
$$b^2 + 19b - 66 = 0$$

3. Solve using the graphing calculator:
$$x^2 - 12x = -20$$

4. Solve using the graphing calculator:
$$-x^2 - 13x = 42$$

5. Solve using the graphing calculator:
$$m(m - 3) = 54$$

6. Solve using the graphing calculator:
$$2x^2 + 5x - 7 = 0$$

7. Solve using the graphing calculator:
$$a^2 + 6a - 187 = 0$$

8. Solve using the graphing calculator:
$$9x^2 - 15x - 14 = 0$$

9. Solve using the graphing calculator:
$$12x^2 + 7x - 12 = 0$$

10. Solve using the graphing calculator:
$$-x^2 + 12x - 36 = 0$$

HA1-537: Solving Systems of Linear and Nonlinear Equations

This lesson introduces students to solving nonlinear systems of equations. Students substitute coordinates into a quadratic equation describing a circle to determine if the point lies on the circle. Given a nonlinear system of equations, students substitute coordinates into the equations of the system to determine if a point is a solution. Students solve simple quadratic-linear systems of equations by graphing. Students solve simple quadratic-linear systems of equations algebraically using substitution. Students write and solve simple quadratic-linear systems of equations from real-life situations and interpret the solution in appropriate terms.

Linear Equation	An equation that can be written in slope-intercept form $y = mx + b$
Quadratic Equation	An equation that can be written in the form $Ax^2 + Bxy + Cy^2 + Dx + Ey + F = 0$ where not all A, B, C equal zero
System of Equations	A group of equations is referred to as a system. Solving a system of equations in two variables requires finding the ordered pair (or ordered pairs) that satisfy all the equations in the system.
Nonlinear System	A system of equations that contains at least one equation whose graph is not a line
Quadratic-linear System	A system of equations that contains at least one linear equation and at least one quadratic equation (and no non-linear, non-quadratic equations)
Real Solutions to a System of Equations	The points where the graphs of the equations of a system of equations intersect, if any, represent real solutions to the system of equations. Conversely, the real solutions to a system of equations represent intersection points on the graphs of the equations in the system.

Example 1   Consider the equation $x^2 + y^2 = 1$. Is the point $\left(\dfrac{9}{41}, -\dfrac{40}{41} \right)$ on the circle?

$$x^2 + y^2 = 1$$
$$\left(\frac{9}{41} \right)^2 + \left(-\frac{40}{41} \right)^2 = 1$$

Step 1:   Substitute the coordinates into the equation.

$$\left(\frac{9}{41}\right)\left(\frac{9}{41}\right) + \left(-\frac{40}{41}\right)\left(-\frac{40}{41}\right) = 1$$

$$\frac{81}{1,681} + \frac{1,600}{1,681} = 1$$

$$\frac{1,681}{1,681} = 1$$

$$1 = 1$$

Step 2: Simplify and observe if the resulting mathematical statement is true or false.

Answer: Yes, the point $\left(\frac{9}{41}, -\frac{40}{41}\right)$ is on the circle $x^2 + y^2 = 1$.

Example 2   Consider the nonlinear system of equations.

$$\begin{cases} y = 2x^2 \\ y = 2x + 4 \end{cases}$$

Verify that the ordered pair $(-1, 2)$ is a solution to the system of equations.

$y = 2x^2$

$2 = 2(-1)^2$

$2 = 2(-1)(-1)$

$2 = 2(1)$

$2 = 2$

Step 1: Substitute the coordinates into the quadratic equation and simplify to see if the result is a true or false mathematical statement.

$y = 2x + 4$

$2 = 2(-1) + 4$

$2 = -2 + 4$

$2 = 2$

Step 2: Substitute the coordinates into the linear equation and simplify to see if the result is a true or false mathematical statement.

Answer: Yes, the ordered pair is a solution to the system because it satisfies both equations.

Example 3   Solve the nonlinear system of equations by graphing.

$$\begin{cases} y = \frac{1}{4}x^2 \\ y = -\frac{1}{2}x + 2 \end{cases}$$

$y = \frac{1}{4}x^2$ $y = \frac{1}{4}x^2$

$y = \frac{1}{4}(2)^2$ $y = \frac{1}{4}(4)^2$

$y = \frac{1}{4}(4)$ $y = \frac{1}{4}(16)$

$y = 1$ $y = 4$

$(2, 1)$ $(4, 4)$

Step 1: The vertex of the parabola is the origin. Find other points on the parabola by substituting a few positive x-values into the quadratic equation. Substituting two and four lead to the points $(2, 1)$ and $(4, 4)$ respectively.

 (−2, 1)   (−4, 4)

Step 2: Use symmetry to find symmetrical points on the parabola. The *y*-axis is a line of symmetry. If (x, y) is a point on the parabola, then $(-x, y)$ is a point on the parabola.

Step 3: Plot the points $(0, 0)$, $(2, 1)$, $(4, 4)$, $(-2, 1)$, and $(-4, 4)$; then sketch the parabola.

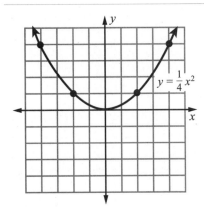

Step 4: Begin graphing the line. The *y*-intercept value is 2. Place a point at $(0, 2)$.

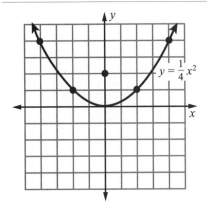

Step 5: Graph the line using the slope. Start at $(0, 2)$ and then use the slope $-\dfrac{1}{2}$, as a ratio of vertical change to horizontal change, to find another point. Remember that exactly one change must be in a negative direction for the slope to be negative, that is, $-\dfrac{1}{2} = \dfrac{-1}{2} = \dfrac{1}{-2}$.

For instance, start at $(0, 2)$ and then fall vertically one unit and run horizontally to the right two units to find another point $(2, 1)$ on the line. Or start at $(0, 2)$, then rise vertically one unit and run horizontally to the left two units to find another point, $(-2, 3)$, on the line. Sketch the line through these points.

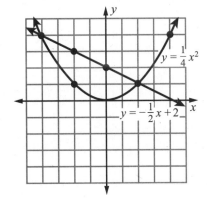

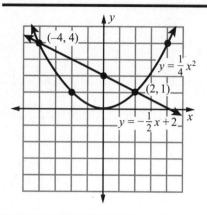

Step 6: Note the intersection points.

Answer: The solutions to the nonlinear system of equations are (–4, 4) and (2, 1).

Example 4 Solve the nonlinear system of equations algebraically.

$$\begin{cases} x^2 + y^2 = 5 \\ y = 3x - 5 \end{cases}$$

$$x^2 + y^2 = 5$$
$$x^2 + (3x - 5)^2 = 5$$

Step 1: Substitute the linear expression for y into the quadratic equation.

$$x^2 + (3x - 5)(3x - 5) = 5$$
$$x^2 + 9x^2 - 15x - 15x + 25 = 5$$
$$10x^2 - 30x + 25 = 5$$
$$10x^2 - 30x + 25 - 5 = 5 - 5$$
$$10x^2 - 30x + 20 = 0$$

Step 2: Square the binomial, add like terms, and set the resulting quadratic equation equal to zero.

$$10x^2 - 30x + 20 = 0$$
$$10(x^2 - 3x + 2) = 0$$
$$10(x - 1)(x - 2) = 0$$

Step 3: Factor the trinomial.

$$x - 1 = 0 \qquad x - 2 = 0$$
$$x - 1 + 1 = 0 + 1 \quad x - 2 + 2 = 0 + 2$$
$$x = 1 \qquad\qquad x = 2$$

Step 4: Set each factor with a variable expression equal to zero and solve independently.

$$y = 3x - 5 \qquad y = 3x - 5$$
$$y = 3(1) - 5 \qquad y = 3(2) - 5$$
$$y = 3 - 5 \qquad\quad y = 6 - 5$$
$$y = -2 \qquad\qquad y = 1$$
$$(1, -2) \qquad\quad (2, 1)$$

Step 5: Substitute the x-coordinates into the linear equation to find the corresponding y-coordinates. Be sure to substitute into the line, as opposed to the quadratic equation, especially if the quadratic equation does not describe a function.

Answer: (1, –2) and (2, 1)

Example 5   A civil engineer is working on the design of a city park. The park has a flagpole in its center. For his design, the engineer uses the points of the compass as the axes and the flagpole as the origin of a Cartesian coordinate plane. The engineer wants a circular bike path with a radius of $40\sqrt{5}$ meters centered at the park's flagpole. The engineer also wants a linear walking trail with a slope of 2 starting at the flagpole and extending in two directions. Help the engineer by writing a system of equations to describe the paths in the park and then find the points where the walking path intersects the bike path.

$x^2 + y^2 = r^2$ $x^2 + y^2 = (40\sqrt{5})^2$ $x^2 + y^2 = 8,000$	**Step 1:** Write an equation to describe the circular bike path. The radius is $40\sqrt{5}$ meters.
$y = mx + b$ $y = 2x + 0$ $y = 2x$	**Step 2:** Write an equation to describe the linear walking path. The walking path starts at the flagpole, which is the origin, so the y-intercept is zero. The slope is two.
$\begin{cases} x^2 + y^2 = 8,000 \\ y = 2x \end{cases}$	**Step 3:** Write the equations together to represent the system of equations.
$x^2 + y^2 = 8,000$ $x^2 + (2x)^2 = 8,000$ $x^2 + (2x)(2x) = 8,000$ $x^2 + 4x^2 = 8,000$ $5x^2 = 8,000$ $\dfrac{5x^2}{5} = \dfrac{8,000}{5}$ $x^2 = 1,600$ $\sqrt{x^2} = \sqrt{1,600}$ $x = \pm 40$	**Step 4:** Substitute the linear expression for y into the quadratic equation and solve for x.
$\begin{array}{ll} y = 2x & y = 2x \\ y = 2(40) & y = 2(-40) \\ y = 80 & y = -80 \\ (40, 80) & (-40, -80) \end{array}$	**Step 5:** Substitute the x-values into the linear equation to find the coordinating y-values.

Answer: $\begin{cases} x^2 + y^2 = 8,000 \\ y = 2x \end{cases}$

Solutions: $(40, 80)$ and $(-40, -80)$

Problem Set

Simplify:

1. Consider the equation $x^2 + y^2 = 16$. Is $(-4, 0)$ on the circle?

   Yes   No

2. Consider the equation $x^2 + y^2 = 25$. Which point lies on the circle?

   $(3, -4)$ $(-2, 3)$

   $(4, 0)$ $(5, 4)$

3. Consider the equation $x^2 + y^2 = 2$.

   Is $\left(-\dfrac{6}{5}, \dfrac{8}{5}\right)$ on the circle?

   Yes   No

4. Consider the equation $x^2 + y^2 = 4$.

   Is $\left(\dfrac{10}{13}, \dfrac{24}{13}\right)$ on the circle?

   Yes   No

5. Consider the equation $x^2 + y^2 = 1$.

   Is $\left(\dfrac{7}{25}, \dfrac{24}{25}\right)$ on the circle?

   Yes   No

6. Consider the equation $x^2 + y^2 = 1$.

   Is $\left(\dfrac{7}{9}, \dfrac{5}{9}\right)$ on the circle?

   Yes   No

7. Consider the equation $x^2 + y^2 = 169$. Which point lies on the circle?

   $(172, -3)$ $(13, 1)$

   $(12, -5)$ $(-2, 11)$

8. Consider the nonlinear system of equations.

$$\begin{cases} y = 2x^2 \\ y = 2x + 4 \end{cases}$$

   Which point is a solution to the system?

   $(-2, 0)$ $(2, 8)$

   $(0, 4)$ $(-3, 18)$

9. Consider the nonlinear system of equations.

$$\begin{cases} x^2 + y^2 = 41 \\ y = -x - 1 \end{cases}$$

   Which point is a solution to the system?

   $(-7, 6)$ $(4, -5)$

   $(4, 5)$ $(3, -4)$

10. Consider the nonlinear system of equations.

$$\begin{cases} x^2 + y^2 = 26 \\ x - y = 6 \end{cases}$$

   Which point is a solution to the system?

   $(-2, -8)$ $(6, 0)$

   $(10, 4)$ $(1, -5)$

11. Consider the nonlinear system of equations.

$$\begin{cases} x^2 + y^2 = 53 \\ x - y = 5 \end{cases}$$

Which point is a solution to the system?

    (58, 53)   (5, 0)

    (−2, −7)   (2, 7)

12. Consider the nonlinear system of equations.

$$\begin{cases} y = -2x^2 \\ 6x + y = 4 \end{cases}$$

Is (1, −2) a solution to the system?

    Yes   No

13. Consider the nonlinear system of equations.

$$\begin{cases} y = -3x^2 \\ 3x - y = 6 \end{cases}$$

Is (2, −12) a solution to the system?

    Yes   No

14. Consider the nonlinear system of equations.

$$\begin{cases} y = \dfrac{1}{4}x^2 \\ 3x + 2y = 8 \end{cases}$$

Is (2, 1) a solution to the system?

    Yes   No

15. Match the nonlinear system of equations with its graph.

$$\begin{cases} y = -\dfrac{1}{2}x^2 \\ y = -x - 4 \end{cases}$$

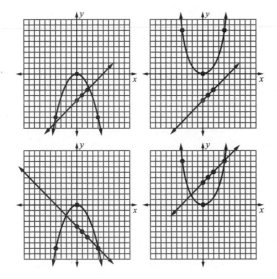

16. Match the nonlinear system of equations with its graph.

$$\begin{cases} y = \dfrac{1}{2}x^2 \\ y = -x + 4 \end{cases}$$

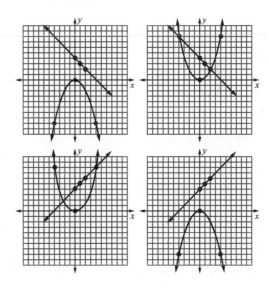

17. Match the nonlinear system of equations with its graph.

$$\begin{cases} x^2 + y^2 = 100 \\ y = x + 2 \end{cases}$$

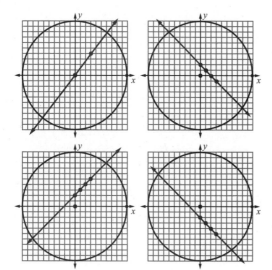

18. Match the nonlinear system of equations with its graph.

$$\begin{cases} x^2 + y^2 = 1 \\ x + y = 1 \end{cases}$$

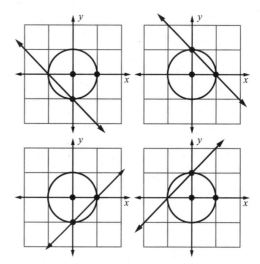

19. Match the nonlinear system of equations with its graph.

$$\begin{cases} x^2 + y^2 = 4 \\ y = x + 2 \end{cases}$$

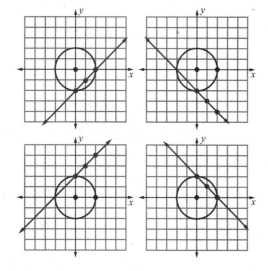

20. Match the nonlinear system of equations with its graph.

$$\begin{cases} x^2 + y^2 = 9 \\ y = -x - 3 \end{cases}$$

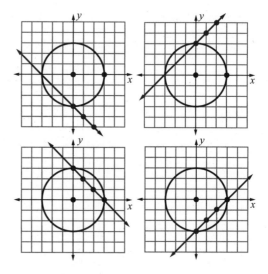

21. Match the nonlinear system of equations with its graph.

$$\begin{cases} y = x^2 \\ y = -x \end{cases}$$

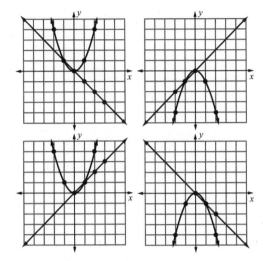

22. Solve the system of equations.

$$\begin{cases} y = x^2 \\ y = -3x \end{cases}$$

23. Solve the system of equations.

$$\begin{cases} x^2 + y^2 = 45 \\ y = x - 3 \end{cases}$$

24. Solve the system of equations.

$$\begin{cases} x^2 + y^2 = 10 \\ y = 3x \end{cases}$$

25. Solve the system of equations.

$$\begin{cases} x^2 + y^2 = 41 \\ y = x + 1 \end{cases}$$

26. Solve the system of equations.

$$\begin{cases} x^2 + y^2 = 3 \\ y = x + 4 \end{cases}$$

27. Solve the system of equations.

$$\begin{cases} x^2 + y^2 = 36 \\ y = x - 6 \end{cases}$$

28. Solve the system of equations.

$$\begin{cases} x^2 + y^2 = 325 \\ y = -x + 25 \end{cases}$$

29. A computer game features a target planet surrounded by a circular force field projected onto a computer screen. The object of the game is for players to shoot missiles directly towards the planet in an effort to break the force field.

Will a player hit the force field if the radius of the force field is 5 units and he fires a missile that follows the trajectory described by $y = 3x - 5$?

Yes   No

30. A computer game features a target planet surrounded by a circular force field projected onto a computer screen. The object of the game is for players to shoot missiles directly towards the planet in an effort to break the force field.

Will a player hit the force field if the radius of the force field is 5 units and he fires a missile that follows the trajectory described by $y = x + 8$?

Yes   No

31. Air traffic control systems project data from radar to a computer screen. Suppose that the location of an air traffic control station serves as the origin of a coordinate system using miles as units and that $y = \frac{7}{17}x + \frac{169}{17}$ describes the trajectory of a particular jet flying through the air space of this air traffic control system whose radar reaches 13 miles in all directions.

Write a system of equations whose solutions represent the intersection of the jet's trajectory with the extreme range of the radar.

32. Sam needs to find two numbers to solve a puzzle. If Sam squares each number and then adds the result, the sum will be 41. Moreover, the larger number is one unit larger than the smaller number. Write a system of equations to represent this situation.

33. A civil engineer is working on the design of a city park. The park has a flagpole in its center. For his design, the engineer uses the points of the compass as the axes and the flagpole as the origin of a Cartesian coordinate plane. The engineer wants a circular bike path, centered at the park's flagpole, with a radius of $\sqrt{226}$ meters and a linear walking trail starting at the flagpole and extending in two directions with a slope of 15. Help the engineer by writing a system of equations to describe the paths in the park.

34. Air traffic control systems project data from radar to a computer screen. Suppose that the location of an air traffic control station serves as the origin of a coordinate system using miles as units and that $y = x + 7$ describes the trajectory of a particular jet flying through the air space of this air traffic control system whose radar reaches 17 miles in all directions.

Find the points where the jet enters and leaves the air space of the air traffic control system as projected on the computer screen.

35. A computer game features a target planet surrounded by a circular force field projected onto a computer screen. The object of the game is for players to shoot missiles directly towards the planet in an effort to break the force field.

A player fires a missile that follows a trajectory described by $y = x + 1$ at the force field whose radius is 5. Will he hit the force field?

Yes   No

HA1-605: Interpreting the Correlation Coefficient of a Linear Fit

In this lesson, students will investigate the relationship between two variables using scatterplots and the correlation coefficient of a linear fit. Students will use technology to create scatterplots, compute regression lines, and to calculate linear correlation coefficients. Students will informally estimate a line of fit from a scatterplot and analyze residuals to assess whether a proposed linear model fits a set of data points. Students will distinguish between interpolation and extrapolation and will use a line of best fit to make predictions appropriate to available data.

Scatterplot	A display in a Cartesian coordinate plane of the ordered pairs collected in a sample
Correlation	The degree to which two variables show a tendency to vary together is the correlation. **Positive correlation** describes a relationship where an increase in one variable tends to accompany an increase in the other variable. **Negative correlation** describes a relationship where an increase in one variable tends to accompany a decrease in the other variable.
Residual	The difference between y and the y-value predicted by a proposed linear model is the **residual**, e, of a data point (x, y). Using y_p to denote the predicted y-value, the residual of a data point is $e = y - y_p$.
Least-squares Criterion	A rule proposing that the straight line that best fits a set of data is the one having the smallest possible sum of squared residuals
Regression Line or Line of Best Fit	The straight line, and/or its equation, that meets the least-squares criterion as the best fit for a set of data points out of all the possible lines
Predictor Variable	If $y_p = ax + b$ is a regression line equation, then the independent variable, x, is called the **predictor variable**.
Predicted Variable	If $y_p = ax + b$ is a regression line equation, then the dependent variable, y_p, is called the **predicted variable**, or **response variable**.

Residual Plot	A plot of the ordered pairs (x, e), where e is the residual of the data point (x, y), is referred to as a residual plot. Linear regression is reasonable when the residual plot roughly forms a horizontal band centered and symmetric about the x-axis (for adequate sample sizes).
Linear Correlation Coefficient	Also called the **Pearson product moment correlation coefficient**, and denoted r, this statistic measures the correlation between two variables. The linear correlation coefficient always lies between, or is equal to, -1 and 1. Values close to -1 or 1 indicate a strong linear relationship between the variables. Values near zero indicate no correlation.
Interpolation	Suppose $y_p = ax + b$ describes the line that best fits a sample of data points. **Interpolation** is making predictions with this equation using x-values within the range of x-values of the sample: greater than or equal to the minimum x-value, but less than or equal to the maximum x-value that appears in the sample.
Extrapolation	Suppose $y_p = ax + b$ describes the line that best fits a sample of data points. **Extrapolation** is making predictions using x-values outside the range of x-values that appear in the sample. Extrapolation is not a valid statistical procedure because it relies on x-values that are not represented in the data.

Example 1   Refer to the scatterplot and describe the correlation between x and y.

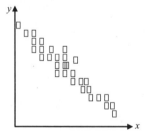

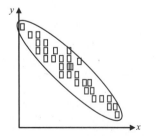

Step 1: Try encompassing the majority of the points within an ellipse leaving as little empty space as possible. Correlation is roughly a function of the elongation of the ellipse containing the majority of the data points most efficiently: the more elongate the ellipse, the stronger the correlation.

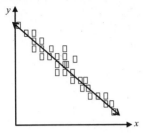

Step 2: Draw a negatively-sloped line through the scatterplot.

Notice that the points in the scatterplot seem to cluster in a band around the line. This indicates negative correlation.

Answer: The relationship exhibits negative correlation.

Example 2 Suppose the linear correlation coefficient for a set of data points is $r = 0.13$. Describe the correlation between the variables.

$0 \leq 0.13 < 0.3$

Step 1: Note that $0 \leq r < 0.3$. In general, if $0 \leq r < 0.3$, or if $-0.3 < r \leq 0$, then the variables exhibit no correlation.

Answer: The variables exhibit no correlation.

Example 3 Estimate a line that fits the data in the table.

x	3	4	5	5	5	6	7	9	11	12
y	6	8	10	11	12	14	16	21	26	28

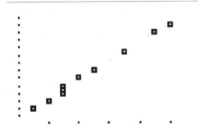

Step 1: Create a scatterplot. First, press STAT and then press ENTER. This accesses the list editor of the calculator. Use the list editor to enter the *x*-values into list one and the *y*-values into list two. Press ZOOM. Press 9. If the calculator does not display a scatterplot, press 2nd STAT PLOT ENTER. Next, highlight **On** and then highlight the scatterplot icon for the **Type** of graph. Enter **L1** and **L2** as the **XList** and **YList** respectively. Then, press ZOOM 9.

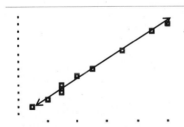

Step 2: Superimpose a line over the scatterplot and identify two points on the line.

The line passes through (5, 11) and (11, 26).

$$m = \frac{y_2 - y_1}{x_2 - x_1}$$

$$= \frac{26 - 11}{11 - 5}$$

$$= \frac{15}{6}$$

$$= \frac{3 \cdot 5}{3 \cdot 2}$$

$$= \frac{5}{2}$$

$$= 2.5$$

Step 3: Calculate the slope of the line.

$$y = mx + b$$
$$11 = m \cdot 5 + b$$
$$11 = 2.5 \cdot 5 + b$$
$$11 = 12.5 + b$$
$$11 - 12.5 = 12.5 - 12.5 + b$$
$$-1.5 = b$$

Step 4: Calculate the y-intercept of the line.

Answer: $y = 2.5x - 1.5$

Example 4 Sociologists interested in the correlation between government revenue and the life expectancy of citizens collect the data in the table.

Country	A	B	C	D	E	F	G	H	I	J
Government Revenue as a Percent of Gross Domestic Product (GDP)	17	28	16	15	16	22	13	40	22	32
Life Expectancy in Years	67	74	70	70	69	73	63	79	77	78

Assume the sample is large enough and find the linear correlation coefficient for this sample. Determine if a correlation exists and if so, what type of correlation.

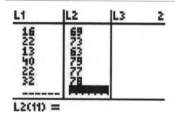

Step 1: Enter the data into the calculator. Press [STAT] and then press [ENTER]. This accesses the list editor of the calculator. Use the list editor to enter the government revenue data into list one and the life expectancy data into list two.

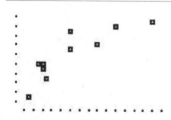

Step 2: Create a scatterplot. First, press [ZOOM] and then press [9]. If the calculator does not display a scatterplot, press [2nd][STAT PLOT][ENTER]. Next, highlight **On** and then highlight the scatterplot icon for the **Type** of graph. Enter **L1** and **L2** as the **XList** and **YList** respectively. Then, press [ZOOM][9].

LinReg
y=ax+b
a=.5066239627
b=60.80361042

Step 3: Compute the line of best fit. Press $\boxed{\text{STAT}}$. Use the arrow keys to move the cursor to the **CALC** menu. The fourth item is linear regression. Press $\boxed{4}$. Press $\boxed{\text{ENTER}}$.

r
   .8606845503

Step 4: Compute the linear correlation coefficient. Press $\boxed{\text{VARS}}$. The fifth item on the menu is for statistics. Press $\boxed{5}$. Use the arrow keys to move the cursor to the **EQ** menu. The seventh item on the menu is r, the linear correlation coefficient. Press $\boxed{7}$. Then, press $\boxed{\text{ENTER}}$.

Answer: The linear correlation coefficient is
$r = 0.8606845503$. The variables exhibit strong positive correlation because a correlation coefficient between 0.8 and 1 indicates strong positive correlation.

Example 5 An economist studying the relationship between family income and the amount of money spent on food gathers the data in the table.

Income (in thousands of dollars)	30	36	27	20	16	24	19	25
Amount of Money Spent Yearly on Food (in hundreds of dollars)	55	60	42	40	37	39	39	43

If appropriate, use a line of best fit to predict the amount of money spent on food in a family with income of $29,000.00.

The income data is reported in thousands of dollars, so 29,000 would be 29 in the data set. Making predictions based on an income value of 29 is interpolation because the data includes income values below and above 29.

Step 1: Decide if the prediction would be interpolation or extrapolation.

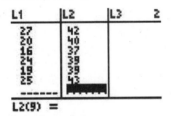

Step 2: Enter the data into the calculator. Press $\boxed{\text{STAT}}$ and then press $\boxed{\text{ENTER}}$ to access the list editor of the calculator. Use the list editor to enter the income data into list one and the food expenditure data into list two.

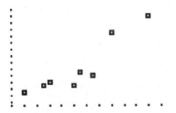

Step 3: Create a scatterplot. First, press $\boxed{\text{ZOOM}}$ and then press $\boxed{9}$. If the calculator does not display a scatterplot, press $\boxed{\text{2nd}}\boxed{\text{STAT PLOT}}\boxed{\text{ENTER}}$. Next, highlight **On** and then highlight the scatterplot icon for the **Type** of graph. Enter **L1** and **L2** as the **XList** and **YList** respectively. Then, press $\boxed{\text{ZOOM}}\boxed{9}$.

The data points cluster in a band that mimics an oblique line with a positive slope. The variables exhibit positive correlation.

The line of best fit is close to

$y_p \approx 1.186x + 15.173$.

r

.9098051965

$y_p \approx 1.186x + 15.173$

$\approx 1.186(29) + 15.173$

$\approx 34.394 + 15.173$

≈ 49.567

Food expenditure data is reported in hundreds of dollars, so 49.567 is $4,956.70.

Step 4: Compute the line of best fit. Press [STAT]. Use the arrow keys to move the cursor to the **CALC** menu. The fourth item is linear regression. Press [4]. Then, press [ENTER].

Step 5: Compute the linear correlation coefficient in order to determine if the correlation is strong enough for interpolation to be valid. Press [VARS]. The fifth item on the menu is for statistics. Press [5]. Use the arrow keys to move the cursor to the **EQ** menu. The seventh item on the menu is r, the linear correlation coefficient. Press [7]. Then, press [ENTER].

Step 6: Substitute 29 for the predictor variable and solve for the predicted variable.

Answer: According to the data, a family with income of $29,000.00 will spend $4,956.70 annually on food.

Problem Set

Solve:

1. Consider the scatterplot below. Describe the correlation between x and y.

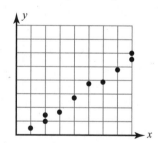

2. Consider the scatterplot below. Describe the correlation between x and y.

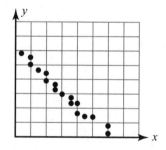

3. Consider the scatterplot below. Describe the correlation between x and y.

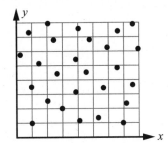

4. Which scatterplot exhibits positive correlation between x and y?

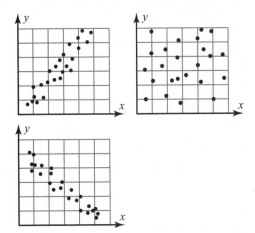

5. Which scatterplot exhibits negative correlation between x and y?

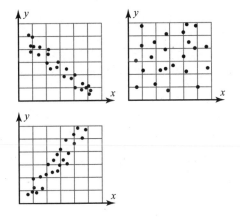

6. Which scatterplot exhibits no correlation between x and y?

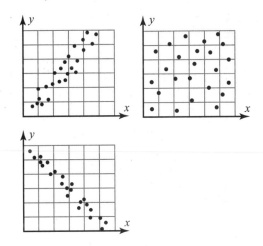

7. Which scatterplot exhibits perfect positive correlation?

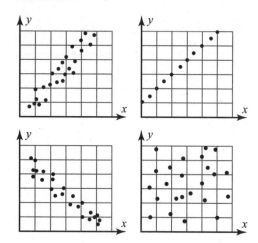

8. Consider the scatterplot and the corresponding linear correlation coefficient. Describe the correlation between x and y.

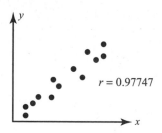

9. Which linear correlation coefficient suggests strong positive correlation?

$r = 0.0101$ $r = 0.89$

$r = -0.8$ $r = 0.2499$

10. Which linear correlation coefficient suggests strong positive correlation?

$r = 0.1999$ $r = 0.309$

$r = -0.63$ $r = 0.99$

11. Use the given linear correlation coefficient to describe the correlation between x and y for the data in the scatterplot.

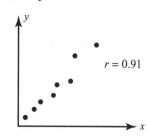

12. Which linear correlation coefficient suggests strong negative correlation?

$r = 1$ $r = -0.143267$

$r = -0.856$ $r = 0.87$

13. Which linear correlation coefficient suggests strong negative correlation?

$r = 0.97$ $r = -0.869702$

$r = -0.3$ $r = -0.2$

14. Use the given linear correlation coefficient to describe the correlation between x and y for the data in the scatterplot.

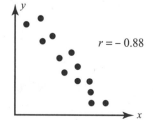

15. Which line reasonably fits the data in the scatterplot?

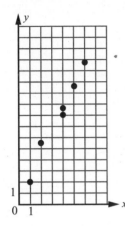

$y = 2x$

$y = 0.5x$

$y = 6x - 2$

$y = -2x$

16. Which line reasonably fits the data in the scatterplot?

$y = -x + 8$

$y = -x$

$y = -6x + 8$

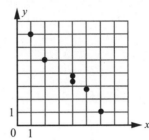

$y = 1.1x + 1.6$

17. Which line reasonably fits the data in the scatterplot?

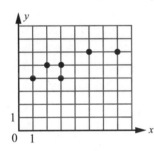

$y = -\dfrac{1}{6}x - \dfrac{5}{6}$

$y = \dfrac{1}{6}x$

$y = -\dfrac{1}{3}x + \dfrac{11}{3}$

$y = \dfrac{1}{3}x + \dfrac{11}{3}$

18. Which line reasonably fits the data in the scatterplot?

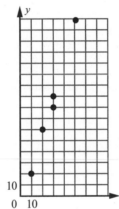

$y = -3x + 60$

$y = 3x$

$y = 30x$

$y = x + 30$

19. Which line reasonably fits the data in the scatterplot?

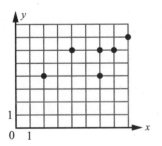

$y = 2x + 3$

$y = -2x$

$y = 0.5x + 3$

$y = -0.5x + 3$

20. Which line reasonably fits the data in the scatterplot?

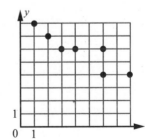

$y = 0.5x + 8$

$y = -0.5x + 8$

$y = 0.5x - 8$

$y = -2x + 8$

21. Which line reasonably fits the data in the scatterplot?

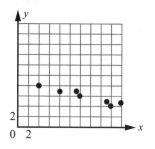

$y = -4x + 9$

$y = -0.25x + 9$

$y = 0.5x + 3$

$y = -0.5x + 4$

22. Economists interested in the correlation between the average annual household expenditure on a particular product in Europe and America collect the data in the table.

Average Annual Expenditure (in equivalent U.S Dollars) for Product		
Year	Europe	America
1998	$48	$41
1999	$52	$43
2000	$60	$47
2001	$65	$52
2002	$75	$58
2003	$77	$70
2004	$84	$78
2005	$86	$82
2006	$85	$84
2007	$90	$91
2008	$93	$93
2009	$94	$95

Assume the sample is large enough and find the linear correlation coefficient for this sample. Determine if a correlation exists and if so, what type of correlation.

23. Economists interested in the correlation between the average annual household expenditure on a particular product in Europe and America collect the data in the table.

Average Annual Expenditure (in equivalent U.S Dollars) for Product		
Year	Europe	America
1998	$39	$47
1999	$52	$98
2000	$54	$41
2001	$65	$101
2002	$74	$12
2003	$78	$29
2004	$84	$78
2005	$86	$98
2006	$90	$34
2007	$92	$78
2008	$94	$51
2009	$96	$66

Assume the sample is large enough and find the linear correlation coefficient for this sample. Determine if a correlation exists and if so, what type of correlation.

24. Climatologists use the table to record the average rate of growth in atmospheric levels of carbon dioxide in parts per million per year (ppm/y) using 1961 as year 1.

Average Rate of Growth in Atmospheric Levels of Carbon Dioxide (in parts per million per year)	
Year	Growth Rate of CO_2
1	0.95
2	0.69
3	0.73
4	0.29
5	0.98
6	1.23
7	0.75
8	1.02
9	1.34
10	1.02
11	0.82
12	1.76

Assume the sample is large enough and find the linear correlation coefficient for this sample. Determine if a correlation exists and if so, what type of correlation.

25. Climatologists use the table to record the average rate of growth in atmospheric levels of carbon dioxide in parts per million per year (ppm/y) using 1961 as year 1.

Average Rate of Growth in Atmospheric Levels of Carbon Dioxide (in parts per million per year)	
Year	Growth Rate of CO_2
1	1.02
2	0.43
3	1.35
4	1.90
5	1.98
6	1.19
7	1.96
8	2.93
9	0.94
10	1.74
11	1.59
12	2.56

Assume the sample is large enough and find the linear correlation coefficient for this sample. Determine if a correlation exists and if so, what type of correlation.

26. Climatologists use the table to record the average rate of growth in atmospheric levels of carbon dioxide in parts per million per year (ppm/y) using 1991 as year 1.

Average Rate of Growth in Atmospheric Levels of Pollutant (in parts per million per year)	
Year	Growth Rate of Pollutant
1	1.22
2	1.30
3	1.37
4	1.46
5	1.55
6	1.63
7	1.70
8	1.77
9	1.88
10	1.92
11	2.02
12	2.09

Assume the sample is large enough and find the linear correlation coefficient for this sample. Determine if a correlation exists and if so, what type of correlation.

27. Climatologists use the table to to record the average monthly high temperature for two cities.

Average High Temperature (°F)		
Month	City 1	City 2
Jan	34	76
Feb	47	72
Mar	52	69
Apr	55	62
May	57	53
Jun	73	41
Jul	74	40
Aug	74	39
Sep	55	49
Oct	49	62
Nov	48	67
Dec	37	71

Assume the sample is large enough and find the linear correlation coefficient for this sample. Determine if a correlation exists and if so, what type of correlation.

28. Climatologists use the table to to record the average monthly high temperature for two cities.

Average High Temperature (°F)		
Month	City 1	City 2
Jan	42	43
Feb	53	57
Mar	57	56
Apr	58	59
May	63	64
Jun	74	74
Jul	77	78
Aug	82	77
Sep	69	70
Oct	70	60
Nov	51	51
Dec	39	38

Assume the sample is large enough and find the linear correlation coefficient for this sample. Determine if a correlation exists and if so, what type of correlation.

29. Climatologists have computed
$y = 1.385x + 324.31$ as the line of best fit for the data in the table, which records annual atmospheric pollutant levels (in parts per million).

Years since 1970	PPM of Pollutant
2	327.3
4	330
6	332
8	335.3
10	338.5

The linear correlation coefficient computed for the linear fit is $r = 0.966$.

If appropriate, use the line of best fit to predict the pollutant level in 1975. Assume the sample size is large enough.

30. Climatologists have computed
$y = 5.025x + 189.63$ as the line of best fit for the data in the table, which records annual atmospheric pollutant levels (in parts per million).

Years since 1990	PPM of Pollutant
2	200.1
4	210.2
6	217.5
8	231.3
10	239.8

The linear correlation coefficient computed for the linear fit is $r = 0.996179$.

If appropriate, use the line of best fit to predict the pollutant level in 1997. Assume the sample size is large enough.

31. Appraisers working for an insurance company have computed $y = -18.41x + 164.6$ as the line of best fit for the data in the table regarding make T, model C automobiles.

Age of Vehicle in years	Value of Vehicle in hundreds of $
2	125.6
2	127.8
3	103.9
5	77.3
5	79.7
6	55.4
7	36.8
8	10.4

The linear correlation coefficient computed for the linear fit is $r = -0.993$.

If appropriate, use the line of best fit to predict the value of a make T, model C automobile that is four years old.

32. Appraisers working for an insurance company have computed $y = -26.9x + 170.35$ as the line of best fit for the data in the table regarding make T, model V automobiles.

Age of Vehicle in years	Value of Vehicle in hundreds of $
1	137.6
2	129.8
2	111.9
4	60.5
5	34.8
5	36.7
5	35.4
6	9.1

The linear correlation coefficient computed for the linear fit is $r = -0.993$.

If appropriate, use the line of best fit to predict the value of a make T, model V automobile that is three years old.

33. Appraisers working for an insurance company have computed $y = -24.405x + 212.7925$ as the line of best fit for the data in the table regarding make M, model R automobiles.

Age of Vehicle in years	Value of Vehicle in hundreds of $
1	188.6
2	166.7
2	163.6
4	113.6
4	114.9
4	112.9
5	88.6
6	70.1

The linear correlation coefficient computed for the linear fit is $r = -0.9986$.

If appropriate, use the line of best fit to predict the value of a make M, model R automobile that is three years old.

34. Appraisers working for an insurance company have computed $y = -24.1x + 211.85$ as the line of best fit for the data in the table regarding make M, model R automobiles.

Age of Vehicle in years	Value of Vehicle in hundreds of $
1	188.5
2	166
2	163.5
4	113.5
4	115
4	113
5	88.5
6	72

The linear correlation coefficient computed for the linear fit is $r = -0.99799$.

If appropriate, use the line of best fit to predict the value of a make M, model R automobile that is seven years old.

35. Appraisers working for an insurance company have computed $y = -26.4x + 214.5$ as the line of best fit for the data in the table regarding make M, model R automobiles.

Age of Vehicle in years	Value of Vehicle in hundreds of $
3	135.5
3	138
3	132.5
5	83
5	82.5
5	81.5
6	56.5
7	29.5

The linear correlation coefficient computed for the linear fit is $r = -0.99925$.

If appropriate, use the line of best fit to predict the value of a make M, model R automobile that is one year old.

In this lesson, you will factor trinomials of the form $x^2 + bx + c$, where b is the coefficient of the x term and c is a constant. When factoring a trinomial, you are asked to find the binomial factors that equal the trinomial. The product of the factors of the trinomial must equal c, and the sum of the factors must equal b. When the coefficient of the x^2 term is one, there are some useful rules to determine which factors to use.

    1. The product of the first terms in the binomial is the first term in the trinomial.

    2. The product of the last terms in the binomial is the last term in the trinomial.

    3. The sum of the last terms in the binomials is equal to the coefficient of x, or b.

The following table will help determine the appropriate sign to use for each of the factors.

	$c > 0$	$c < 0$
$b > 0$	Both factors positive	Larger factor positive
$b < 0$	Both factors negative	Larger factor negative

In order to check the answer, we can use the FOIL method. Recall that the FOIL method is used to multiply two binomials.

FOIL Method	A method used to multiply two binomials, in the following order:		
	F	First	Multiply the first terms of each binomial.
	O	Outer	Multiply the outer terms: the first term of the first binomial and the second term of the second binomial.
	I	Inner	Multiply the inner terms: the second term of the first binomial and the first term of the second binomial.
	L	Last	Multiply the last terms of each binomial.

Example 1   Find the missing term: $x^2 + 9x + 20 = (x + 4)(x + ?)$

Factors of 20	Sum of Factors
1, 20	21
2, 10	12
4, 5	**9**

Step 1: Determine which two numbers will have a product of 20 and a sum of 9.

$(x + 4)(x + \underline{5})$

Step 2: Use the factors from Step 1 to determine the missing term.

Answer: The missing term is 5.

Example 2   Factor: $x^2 + 11x + 24$

$x \cdot x$

Step 1: Determine which factors are multiplied to get x^2.

Factors of 24	Sum of Factors
1, 24	25
2, 12	14
3, 8	**11**
4, 6	10

Step 2: Determine which two numbers will have a product of 24 and a sum of 11.

$(x + 3)(x + 8)$

Step 3: Show the factors in binomial form.

Step 4: Use the FOIL method to check.

F $x \cdot x = x^2$

O $x \cdot 8 = 8x$

I $3 \cdot x = 3x$

L $3 \cdot 8 = 24$

$x^2 + 8x + 3x + 24 = x^2 + 11x + 24$

Answer: $(x + 3)(x + 8)$

Example 3   Factor: $x^2 - 8x + 16$

$x \cdot x$

Step 1: Determine which factors are multiplied to get x^2.

Factors of 16	Sum of Factors
−1, −16	−17
−2, −8	−10
−4, −4	**−8**

Step 2: Determine which two numbers will have a product of 16 and a sum of −8.

$(x-4)(x-4)$

Step 3: Show the factors in binomial form.

Step 4: Use the FOIL method to check.

F $\quad x \cdot x = x^2$

O $\quad x \cdot (-4) = -4x$

I $\quad -4 \cdot x = -4x$

L $\quad -4 \cdot (-4) = 16$

$x^2 - 4x - 4x + 16 = x^2 - 8x + 16$

Answer: $(x-4)(x-4)$

Example 4 If the area of a rectangle is $x^2 + 27x + 50$ and the length is $(x+25)$, find the width.

Area $=$ length $\times$ width

$\quad = (x+25)(\quad)$

Step 1: Recall the formula for the area of a rectangle and substitute the given information into the formula.

Factors of 50	Sum of Factors
1, 50	51
2, 25	**27**
5, 10	15

Step 2: Determine which two numbers will have a product of 50 and a sum of 27.

$(x+25)(x+2)$

Step 3: Show the factors in binomial form.

$x^2 + 27 + 50 = (x+25)(\underline{x+2})$

Step 4: Determine the width from the factors in the binomial, since the length was given as $(x+25)$.

Answer: The width of the rectangle is $(x+2)$.

Example 5 Factor: $x^2 - 14x - 32$

$x \cdot x$

Step 1: Determine which factors are multiplied to get x^2.

Factors of 32	Sum of Factors
1, −32	−31
2, −16	**−14**
4, −8	−4

Step 2: Determine which two numbers will have a product of −32 and a sum of −14.

$(x + 2)(x − 16)$

Step 3: Show the factors in binomial form.

Step 4: Use the FOIL method to check.

F $x \cdot x = x^2$

O $x \cdot (-16) = -16x$

I $2 \cdot x = 2x$

L $2 \cdot (-16) = -32$

$x^2 - 16x + 2x - 32 = x^2 - 14x - 32$

Answer: $(x + 2)(x − 16)$

Problem Set

Factor:

1. $x^2 + 4x + 4$

2. $x^2 + 11x + 10$

3. $x^2 + 11x + 18$

4. $x^2 + 10x + 24$

5. $x^2 + 12x + 32$

6. $x^2 + 13x + 30$

7. $x^2 + 13x + 40$

8. $z^2 + 20z + 64$

9. $x^2 + 12x + 20$

10. $x^2 + 20x + 99$

11. $x^2 - 6x + 8$

12. $w^2 - 5w + 6$

13. $y^2 - 11y + 28$

14. $x^2 - 8x + 7$

15. $a^2 - 9a + 18$

16. $r^2 - 4r + 4$

17. $z^2 - 12z + 35$

18. $x^2 + 5x - 36$

19. $x^2 - 4x - 96$

20. $x^2 + 11x - 60$

HA1-805: Applying Algebra Concepts

You've learned how to solve word problems involving equations and inequalities, and we've looked at some applications of linear functions. Now it's time to put those skills together and work on applying algebra concepts to word problems that involve systems, tables, linear functions, and quadratic equations.

Example 1 Kayla likes to buy snacks with her allowance. Last week, she bought two bags of chips and one bag of cookies for $2. This week, she bought one bag of chips and two bags of cookies for $2.50. Find the price for each bag of chips and each bag of cookies.

x = price for each bag of chips
y = price for each bag of cookies

$$\begin{cases} 2x + y = 2 \\ x + 2y = 2.50 \end{cases}$$

Step 1: Set up the equations. Let x be the price for each bag of chips and y be the price for each bag of cookies. On the first week, she bought two bags of chips and one bag cookies for $2. Therefore, the equation is $2x + y = 2$. On the next week, she bought one bag of chips and two bag of cookies for $2.50. Therefore, the equation is $x + 2y = 2.50$.

$$\begin{cases} 2x + y = 2 \\ -2(x + 2y = 2.50) \end{cases}$$

Step 2: Solve the equation using the Elimination Method.

$$\begin{aligned} 2x + y &= 2 \\ + (-2x) - 4y &= -5 \\ \hline -3y &= -3 \\ y &= 1 \end{aligned}$$ Price for a bag of cookies

$$\begin{aligned} 2x + (1) &= 2 \\ 2x &= 1 \\ x &= \frac{1}{2} = 0.50 \end{aligned}$$ Price for a bag of chips

Answer: The price for each bag of chips is $0.50 and the price for each bag of cookies is $1.

Example 2 A total of 500 seats were sold for a play. The floor seats cost $25.00. The balcony seats cost $15.00. The play brought in a total of $10,000. Find the number of tickets sold on the floor and the number of seats tickets on the balcony.

$$\begin{aligned} x + y &= 500 \\ 25x + 15y &= 10,000 \end{aligned}$$

Step 1: Set up the equations.

$y = 500 - x$

$$25x + 15(500 - x) = 10,000$$
$$25x + 7,500 - 15x = 10,000$$
$$10x + 7,500 = 10,000$$
$$10x = 2,500$$
$$x = 250$$

$y = 500 - 250$
$\quad = 250$

Step 2: Solve the equations using the Substitution Method.

Answer: There were 250 tickets sold for the first floor and 250 tickets sold for the balcony.

Example 3 What are the dimensions of a rectangular box, if its perimeter is 34 inches and its area is 60 square inches?

$P = 2l + 2w$

$A = lw$

Let **length** $= x$
$\quad$ **width** $= y$
Therefore,
$2x + 2y = 34$
$\quad xy = 60$

Step 1: Set up the equations. Recall that the Perimeter $= 2l + 2w$ and Area $= lw$.

$2y = 34 - 2x$
$\quad y = 17 - x$

$x(17 - x) = 60$
$17x - x^2 = 60$
$x^2 - 17x + 60 = 0$
$(x - 12)(x - 5) = 0$

$x = 5$ or $x = 12$

Since length is greater than width, $x = 12$
and $y = 5$

Step 2: Solve the equations using the Substitution Method.

Answer: Therefore, the length of the box is 12 inches and the width of the box is 5 inches.

Problem Set

1. A carpenter braces a 6×8 foot wall by nailing a board diagonally across the wall. How long is the bracing board?

6

8

2. Sizes of TV screens and computer monitors are given according to the length of the diagonal. If a monitor screen is a rectangle which is 12 inches by 5 inches, how long is the diagonal?

5

12

3. If a piece of square tile is 16 inches on a side, how long is the diagonal of the tile? Round your answer to the nearest hundredth.

16

16

4. A surveyor needs to find the distance across a lake from point C to point B. He measures the distance from A to C to be 170 meters, and the distance from A to B to be 80 meters. Find the distance across the lake.

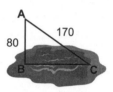

A

170

80

B   C

5. A hot-air balloon is rising vertically but it is attached to a 34-meter cord. When the balloon reaches its maximum height of 34 meters, an observer uses a laser to determine that the distance between him and the balloon is 36 meters. How far is he from the point of liftoff of the balloon? Round the answer to the nearest hundredth.

36

34

6. The area of a rectangle is 84 square feet. If the length is 17 feet more than the width, find the length of the rectangle.

7. The width of a rectangle rug is 3 feet less than its length. If the area of the rug is 80 feet, find the width of the rug. Round your answer to the nearest tenth.

8. The length of a rectangular swimming pool is 15 feet longer than its width. If the area of the pool is 127 square feet, what are the length and width of the pool?

9. Alvin sold 80 tickets for the school play. He gave the treasurer $460. If adult tickets cost $8 each and child tickets cost $4 each, how many of each did he sell?

10. A large bag of flour weighs 3 pounds more than three small bags of flour. Find the weight of each if 4 large bags and 4 small bags weigh 60 pounds.

Solving a system of linear equations means finding the point (x, y) where the two lines intersect. Systems of equations can be solved using the TI-83 Plus™ graphing calculator. Using the calculator, we can consider each equation and find the x-coordinate and y-coordinate of the point where the graphs intersect. There may be occasions where the lines are parallel and therefore never intersect (no solution) or where the two lines are the same (infinite number of solutions).

The process has five steps:

- Step 0: (Settings) Initialize the calculator to a standard set of values so that we have a common starting point.
- Step 1: (Enter the expressions) Enter the symbolic form of the two sides of the equation into the calculator.
- Step 2: (Graph) Obtain the graphs of the two equations Y_1 and Y_2.
- Step 3: (Identify Intersection Point) Use other Intersect feature to verify the x-coordinate and y-coordinate of the point where the graphs intersect.
- Step 4: (Solve) Use information about the x-coordinate and y-coordinate of the intersection point to solve the original system of equations.

Note: **Before doing any of these examples, you should check your calculator's settings to be sure that it will function as described above.**

Press the MODE key and be sure that your settings appear as shown below.

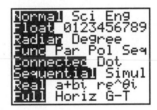

Next press the 2nd ZOOM keys and be sure that your settings appear as shown below.

Next press the ZOOM key then the 6 key to select the standard window setting.

Press the WINDOW key to get the following screen.

```
WINDOW
 Xmin=-10
 Xmax=10
 Xscl=1
 Ymin=-10
 Ymax=10
 Yscl=1
 Xres=1
```

Example 1   Use the graphing calculator to solve the system of equations: $\begin{cases} y = 2x - 5 \\ y = 4 - x \end{cases}$.

Step 0: (Settings) Make sure you have the default settings as described above.

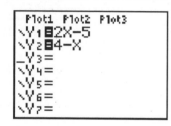

Step 1: (Enter the expression) Press the Y= key and enter the expression $2x - 5$ into the Y_1 slot and $4 - x$ into the Y_2 slot.

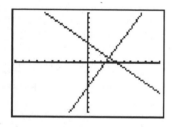

Step 2: (Graph) Press the GRAPH key. We can see that the two graphs intersect at a point in the first quadrant.

Step 3: (Identify Intersection Point) Next, we will find the place where the graph of Y_1 and Y_2 intersect (the x-coordinate of this point is the solution to our original equation). Press 2nd TRACE followed by 5.

You will be prompted for the first curve with a screen like the one to the left. Press ENTER.

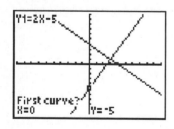

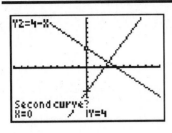

You will be prompted for the second curve with a screen like the one to the left. Press ENTER again.

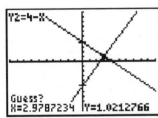

You will be prompted for a guess with a screen like the one to the left. Use the ◄ and ► keys to move the highlighted point as close as possible to the intercept you are trying to verify and press ENTER.

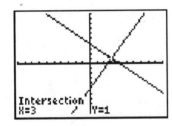

The calculator should display a screen like the one to the left. This gives us an intersection point whose x-coordinate is 3 and whose y-coordinate is 1.

Step 4: (Solve) The solution of the system of equations $\begin{cases} y = 2x - 5 \\ y = 4 - x \end{cases}$ is

the point (3, 1), or $x = 3$ and $y = 1$.

Answer: The solution of the system of equations $\begin{cases} y = 2x - 5 \\ y = 4 - x \end{cases}$ is

the point (3, 1), that is $x = 3$ and $y = 1$.

Example 2   Use the graphing calculator to solve the system of equations: $\begin{cases} y = 0.2x + 1.5 \\ y = 1.1x - 3.2 \end{cases}$.

Step 0: (Settings) Make sure you have the default settings as described at the beginning of the lesson.

Step 1: (Enter the expression) Press the Y= key and enter the expression $0.2x + 1.5$ into the Y_1 slot and $1.1x - 3.2$ into the Y_2 slot.

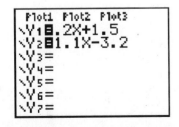

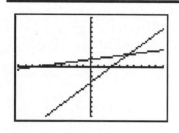

Step 2: (Graph) Press the GRAPH key. We see that the two graphs intersect at a point in the first quadrant.

Step 3: (Identify Intersection Point) Next, we will find the place where the graphs of Y_1 and Y_2 intersect (the *x*-coordinate of this point is the solution to our original equation). Press 2nd TRACE followed by 5.

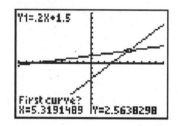

You will be prompted for the first curve with a screen like the one to the left. Press ENTER.

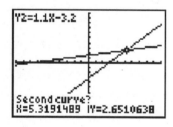

Now you will be prompted for the second curve with a screen like the one to the left. Press ENTER again.

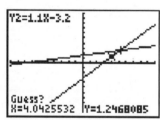

You will be prompted for a guess with a screen like the one to the left. Use the ◄ and ► keys to move the highlighted point as close as possible to the intercept you are trying to verify and press ENTER.

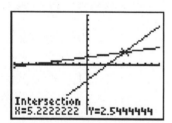

The calculator should display a screen like the one to the left.

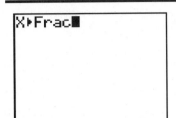

This gives us an intersection whose *x*-coordinate is 5.22222... and whose *y*-coordinate is 2.54444...   You can convert these into fraction form. Press the keys [2nd] [MODE] to return to the home screen. Next, press the keys [X,T,Θ,*n*] [MATH] [1] and you should see a screen like the one to the left.

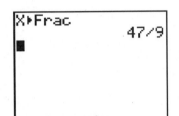

Press [ENTER] and you will get a screen like the one to the left.

Press the [VARS] key followed by the [▶] to get to the Y-VARS menu on the calculator.

Select [1] or press [ENTER].

We want to convert this to a fraction. Press [MATH] [1] followed by [ENTER].

Here we can see that, as fractions, we have $x = \dfrac{47}{9}$ and $y = \dfrac{229}{90}$.

Step 4: (Solve) The system of equations $\begin{cases} y = 0.2x + 1.5 \\ y = 1.1x - 3.2 \end{cases}$ has solution

$(5.2\bar{2}, 2.54\bar{4})$ or, in fraction form, $\left(\dfrac{47}{9}, \dfrac{229}{90}\right)$.

Answer: The solution of the system of equations $\begin{cases} y = 0.2x + 1.5 \\ y = 1.1x - 3.2 \end{cases}$ is

$(5.2\bar{2}, 2.54\bar{4})$ or, in fraction form, $\left(\dfrac{47}{9}, \dfrac{229}{90}\right)$.

Example 3 Use the graphing calculator to solve the system of equations: $\begin{cases} y = 5x - 23 \\ y = 40 - 2x \end{cases}$.

Step 0: (Settings) Make sure you have the default settings as described at the beginning of the lesson.

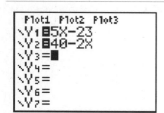

Step 1: (Enter the expression) Press the $\boxed{\text{Y=}}$ key and enter the expression $5x - 23$ into the Y_1 slot and $40 - 2x$ into the Y_2 slot.

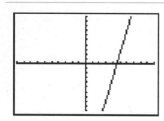

Step 2: (Graph) Press the $\boxed{\text{GRAPH}}$ key. We can only see one graph. The other graph (and the intersection point) must not be visible in this window.

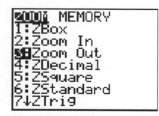

Resize the window by using the $\boxed{\text{ZOOM}}\boxed{3}$ keys and then pressing $\boxed{\text{ENTER}}$ again.

You should now see the other graph appear in the display.

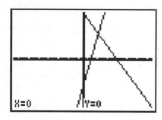

Step 3: (Identify Intersection Point) Next, we will find the place where the graphs of Y_1 and Y_2 intersect (the x-coordinate of this point is the solution to our original equation). Press $\boxed{\text{2nd}}$ $\boxed{\text{TRACE}}$ followed by $\boxed{5}$.

You will be prompted for the first curve with a screen like the one to the left. Press $\boxed{\text{ENTER}}$.

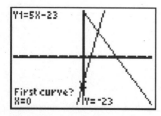

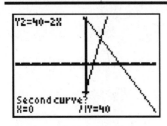

You will be prompted for the second curve with a screen like the one to the left. Press $\boxed{\text{ENTER}}$ again.

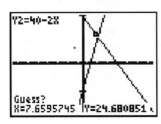

You will be prompted for a guess with a screen like the one to the left. Use the $\boxed{\blacktriangleleft}$ and $\boxed{\blacktriangleright}$ keys to move the highlighted point as close as possible to the intercept you are trying to verify and press $\boxed{\text{ENTER}}$.

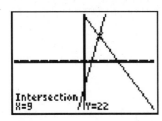

The calculator should display a screen like the one to the left. This gives us an intersection point whose x-coordinate is 9 and whose y-coordinate is 22.

Step 4: (Solve) The system of equations $\begin{cases} y = 5x - 23 \\ y = 40 - 2x \end{cases}$ has solution $(9, 22)$

or $x = 9$ and $y = 22$.

Answer: The solution of the system of equations $\begin{cases} y = 5x - 23 \\ y = 40 - 2x \end{cases}$ is $(9, 22)$

or $x = 9$ and $y = 22$.

Problem Set

Use the graphing calculator to solve the systems of equations:

1. $y = -2x - 3$
$y = x + 3$

2. $y = -\dfrac{3}{4}x - 4$
$y = \dfrac{3}{5}x - 4$

3. $y = -\dfrac{2}{7}x + \dfrac{3}{4}$
$y = \dfrac{3}{7}x - \dfrac{1}{2}$

4. $v = \dfrac{4}{15}u + 10$
$v = -\dfrac{7}{15}u + 32$

5. $y = -\dfrac{13}{23}x - 7$
$y = -\dfrac{17}{23}x - 5$

6. $y = \dfrac{7}{4}x - 3$
$y = 1.75x + 2$

7. $y = 0.85x + 3.25$
$y = \dfrac{17}{20}x + \dfrac{13}{4}$

8. $5x - 2y = 7$
$4x - 5y = 9$

9. $-42x + 37y = 444$
$18x + 26y = 898$

10. $6x + 7y = 259$
$x + y = 39$

HA1-820: Graphing Exponential Functions

Previously we learned about linear and quadratic functions. Recall that a **linear function** is a function of the form $y = mx + b$ where m and b are constants and a **quadratic function** is a function of the form $y = ax^2 + bx + c$, where a, b, and c are constants and $a \neq 0$. Now we are going to learn about another function called an **exponential function**. It is defined as a function of the form $y = ab^x$, $a \neq 0$, $b > 0$, $b \neq 1$.

Exponential Function	A function of the form $y = ab^x$, $a \neq 0$, $b > 0$, $b \neq 1$

In exponential functions, the exponent is a variable and the base is a constant. In linear or quadratic functions, the exponent is a constant and the base is a variable. Examples of each are shown in the following table.

Function	Type of Function
$y = 2x^2$	Quadratic
$y = 2^x$	Exponential
$y = x + 2$	Linear

Let's look at some examples involving exponential functions.

Example 1   Evaluate the function $f(x) = 2(6)^x$ for $f(2)$.

$f(x) = 2(6)^2$	**Step 1:** Substitute 2 for x in the function.
$\begin{aligned} &= 2(6)^2 \\ &= 2(36) \\ &= 72 \end{aligned}$	**Step 2:** Solve.

Answer: 72

Example 2 Does the function $y = 3\left(\frac{1}{2}\right)^x$ represent the data in the table below?

x	-2	-1	0	1
y	12	6	3	1.5

For $x = -2$: For $x = -1$:

Step 1: Substitute the values for x and solve for y.

$y = 3\left(\frac{1}{2}\right)^{-2}$ $y = 3\left(\frac{1}{2}\right)^{-1}$

$= 3(4)$ $= 3(2)$

$= 12$ $= 6$

For $x = 0$: For $x = 1$:

$y = 3\left(\frac{1}{2}\right)^{0}$ $y = 3\left(\frac{1}{2}\right)^{1}$

$= 3(1)$ $= 3\left(\frac{1}{2}\right)$

$= 3$

$= \frac{3}{2}$

x	-2	-1	0	1
y	12	6	3	1.5

Step 2: Examine the table to see if the values for x and y correspond to the table.

Answer: Yes, $y = 3\left(\frac{1}{2}\right)^x$ represents the data in the table.

Now let's look at the list of characteristics of exponential functions before graphing.

Characteristics of exponential functions in the form $y = a(b)^x$:

1. The domain is the set of all real numbers.

2. The x-axis x-axis is an asymptote of the graph.

3. The range is the set of all positive numbers if $a > 0$ and all negative numbers if $a < 0$.

4. The y-intercept is at $(0, a)$.

5. The graphs of $y = ab^x$ and $y = a\left(\frac{1}{b}\right)^x$ are reflections across the y-axis.

6. If $0 < b < 1$ then the function is decreasing, and if $b > 1$ then the function is increasing.

Example 3   Graph the function $y = 4^x$ and state the domain and range.

x	y
-1	$\frac{1}{4}$
0	1
1	4

Step 1:   Set up a table to graph the function.

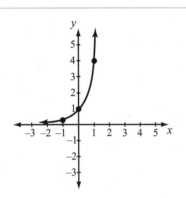

Step 2:   Plot the points from the table and draw a smooth curve through the points.

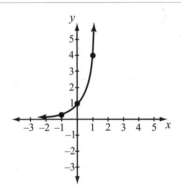

Step 3:   Examine the graph and determine the domain and range.

Domain: all real numbers
Range: all positive numbers

Answer: Domain: all real numbers
Range: all positive numbers

Example 4   Graph the function $y = 2\left(\dfrac{1}{4}\right)^x$.

x	y
-1	8
0	2
1	$\frac{1}{2}$

Step 1:   Set up a table to graph the function.

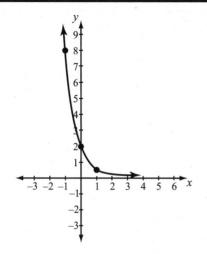

Step 2: Plot the points from the table and draw a smooth curve through the points.

Answer:

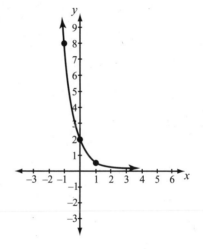

Example 5   Graph the function $y = \frac{1}{3}(3)^x$ and determine if the graph is increasing or decreasing.

Step 1: Set up a table to graph the function.

x	y
-1	$\frac{1}{9}$
0	$\frac{1}{3}$
1	1
3	9

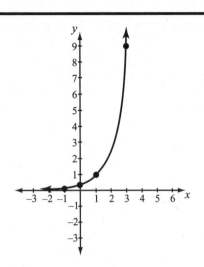

Step 2: Plot the points from the table and draw a smooth curve through the points.

Since the graph grows from left to right, the graph is increasing.

Step 3: Examine the graph to determine if the graph is increasing or decreasing.

Answer: Increasing

Problem Set

Evaluate for the given values of the variables:

1. Evaluate the function.

$f(x) = 4(2)^x$ for $f(-4)$

2. Evaluate the function.

$f(x) = 3(4)^x$ for $f(3)$

3. Evaluate the function.

$f(x) = 9\left(\dfrac{1}{3}\right)^x$ for $f(1)$

4. Evaluate the function.

$f(x) = -2\left(\dfrac{1}{4}\right)^x$ for $f(-3)$

Solve:

5. Determine which exponential function represents the data shown in the table.

x	−1	0	1	2	3
y	3	1	0.333...	0.111...	0.037...

$y = 3^x$ $y = \left(\dfrac{1}{3}\right)^x$

$y = 2^x$ $y = 0.5^x$

6. Determine which exponential function represents the data shown in the table.

x	−1	0	1	2	3
y	5	1	0.2	0.04	0.008

$y = \left(\dfrac{1}{4}\right)^x$ $y = 4^x$

$y = 5^x$ $y = 0.2^x$

7. Determine which exponential function represents the data shown in the table.

x	−1	0	1	2	3
y	0.333...	1	3	9	27

$$y = 4^x \qquad y = 0.25^x$$

$$y = 3^x \qquad y = \left(\frac{1}{3}\right)^x$$

8. Determine which exponential function represents the data shown in the table.

x	−1	0	1	2	3
y	0.2	1	5	25	125

$$y = 0.5^x \qquad y = 5^x$$

$$y = 2^x \qquad y = \left(\frac{1}{5}\right)^x$$

9. Graph the function $y = \left(\frac{1}{2}\right)^x$.

10. Graph the function $y = 4^x$.

11. Graph the function $y = 2 \cdot 3^x$.

12. Graph the function $y = 2\left(\frac{1}{4}\right)^x$.

13. Graph the function $y = -3 \cdot 2^x$ and state the domain and range of the function.

14. Graph the function $y = 3 \cdot 2^x$ and state the domain and range of the function.

15. Graph the function $y = 2^x + 2$ and state the domain and range of the function.

16. Graph the function $y = 2\left(\frac{1}{2}\right)^x - 1$ and state the domain and range of the function.

17. Graph the function $y = 2 \cdot 3^x$ and determine which statement is not true.

The domain of the function is the set of all real numbers.

The range is the set of all negative numbers.

The graph of the function increases from left to right.

The y-intercept is at $(0, 2)$.

18. Graph the function $y = 2 \cdot 2^x$ and determine which statement is not true.

The range is the set of all positive numbers.

The y-intercept is at $(0, 4)$.

The domain of the function is the set of all real numbers.

The graph of the function increases from left to right.

19. Graph the function $y = 0.25^x$ and determine which statement is not true.

The y-intercept is at $(0, 1)$.

The range is the set of all positive numbers.

The graph of the function increases from left to right.

The domain of the function is the set of all real numbers.

20. Graph the function $y = 2\left(\frac{1}{2}\right)^x$ and determine which statement is not true.

The domain of the function is the set of all real numbers.

The graph of the function decreases from left to right.

The y-intercept is at $(0, 2)$.

The range is the set of all real numbers.

Previously we learned about exponential functions and how to graph them. Recall that an **exponential function** is defined as a function of the form $y = ab^x$, $a \neq 0$, $b > 0$, $b \neq 1$. This function can increase or grow from left to right, which is defined as an **exponential growth function**, or could decrease or decay from left to right, which is defined as an **exponential decay function**.

Exponential Function	A function of the form $y = ab^x$, $a \neq 0$, $b > 0$, $b \neq 1$

Exponential Growth Function	A function in the form $y = ab^x$ if $a > 0$ and $b > 1$

Exponential Decay Function	A function in the form $y = ab^x$ if $a > 0$ and $0 < b < 1$

Let's look at the graphs of the growth and the decay functions. In the graph below, the growth function is represented by the function $y = 2^x$ since it increases from left to right, and the decay function is represented by the function $y = 3\left(\frac{1}{2}\right)^x$ since it decreases from left to right.

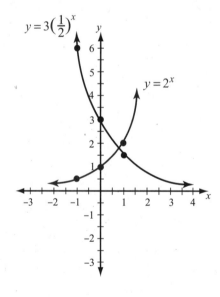

The exponential growth function is represented by a specific model called the **exponential growth model**. It is defined as $y = a(1 + r)^t$, where r represents the percent increase (or rate of growth) and $(1 + r)$ represents the growth factor.

Exponential Growth Model	$y = a(1 + r)^t$ where a is the initial amount, t is the time, r is the percent of increase expressed as a decimal (or rate of growth), and $1 + r$ is the growth factor.

The exponential decay function has a specific model that represents it called the **exponential decay model**. It is defined as $y = a(1 - r)^t$, where r represents the percent increase (or rate of decay) and $(1 - r)$ represents the decay factor.

Exponential Decay Model	$y = a(1 - r)^t$ where a is the initial amount, t is the time, r is the percent of decrease expressed as a decimal (or rate of decay), and $1 - r$ is the decay factor.

Let's look at the following examples.

Example 1   Does the model $y = 6(0.32)^t$ represent an exponential decay model?

$y = ab^x$

$y = 6(0.32)^t$

Step 1: Determine if the function is an exponential function. An exponential function is in the form

$y = ab^x, \ a \neq 0, b > 0, b \neq 1$

Exponential Decay Model

$y = ab^x$ if $a > 0$ and $0 < b < 1$

$a = 6$

$b = 0.32$

Step 2: Determine if the model represents an exponential decay function.

Answer: Yes, the model represents an exponential decay function.

Example 2   In the exponential growth model $y = 9,000(4)^t$, what are the initial amount and the growth factor?

$y = a(1 + r)^t$

$y = 9,000(4)^t,$

Step 1: Compare the model to the exponential growth model.

$a = 9,000$

Step 2: Identify the initial amount.

$1 + r = 4$ **Step 3:**   Identify the growth factor.

                                   Answer: Initial amount = \$9,000
                                                 Growth factor = 4

Example 3   The population in County X was 1,370,000 in 2000 and increased at a rate of 29.2% per year until
2006. Write an equation to represent this situation.

$y = a(1 + r)^t$ **Step 1:**   Since the population is increasing, use the model for
                                                 exponential growth.

$a = 1,370,000 \rightarrow$ initial population   **Step 2:**   Define the variables.
$r = 29.2\%$ or $0.292 \rightarrow$ percent increase
$t =$ time

$y = 1,370,000(1 + 0.292)^t$ **Step 3:**   Substitute the variables into the model.

$y = 1,370,000(1.292)^t$ **Step 4:**   Simplify.

                                   Answer: $y = 1,370,000(1.292)^t$

Example 4   A certain type of bacteria triples in population every day. Given that there are approximately 100
bacteria to start with, how many bacteria will there be after one week?

$y = a(1 + r)^t$ **Step 1:**   Since the bacteria are increasing, use the model for
                                                 exponential growth.

$A = 100$ bacteria   **Step 2:**   Define the variables.
$r = 300\%$ or 3 (triples in size)
$t = 7$ (number of bacteria after one week)

$y = 100(1 + 3)^t$ **Step 3:**   Substitute the values into the model.

$y = 100(4)^7$ **Step 4:**   Simplify.
$y = 100(16,384)$
$y = 1,638,400$

                                   Answer: There will be 1,638,400 bacteria after one week.

There is a specific type of growth application called compound interest. It is defined as $A = P\left(1 + \dfrac{r}{n}\right)^{nt}$ where P is the principal amount, r is the rate of interest, n is the number of times per year the interest is compounded, t is the number of years, and A is the final amount. The number of times the interest can be compounded per year can be annually, semi-annually, quarterly, monthly, or daily.

Below is a chart that represents the value of n for the various intervals at which the interest is compounded.

Compounded	n
Annually	1
Semi-annually	2
Quarterly	4
Monthly	12
Daily	365

Let's look at an example of this type of problem.

Example 5   Janice deposited $10,000 into a money market account that pays an annual interest rate of 5% compounded daily.   If no other deposits are made, what will the account total in 15 years?

$A = P\left(1 + \dfrac{r}{n}\right)^{nt}$	**Step 1:** Use the compound interest formula.
$P = 10,000 \rightarrow$ principal amount $r = 5\%$ or $0.05 \rightarrow$ percent increase $n = 365 \rightarrow$ number of times the interest is compounded per year. $t = 15 \rightarrow$ time $A =$ final amount	**Step 2:** Define the variables.
$A = 10,000\left(1 + \dfrac{0.05}{365}\right)^{(365)(15)}$	**Step 3:** Substitute the values into the formula.
$A \approx 21{,}168.91$	**Step 4:** Simplify.
	Answer: $21,168.91

Problem Set

Solve:

1. Which of the following functions represents an exponential growth function?

$$y = 0.36(0.5)^x \qquad y = 0.36(20)^x$$
$$y = 0.36x^2 \qquad y = 20(0.36)^x$$

2. Which of the following functions represents an exponential growth function?

$$y = 0.5(0.4)^x \qquad y = 400(15x)$$
$$y = 400(0.5)^x \qquad y = 400(15)^x$$

3. Which of the following functions represents an exponential decay function?

$$y = 0.5(1,000)^x \qquad y = 5(1,000)^x$$
$$y = 1,000(x)^{0.05} \qquad y = 1,000(0.5)^x$$

4. Which of the following represents an exponential decay function?

$$y = 0.5(20,000)^x \qquad y = 20,000x^{0.5}$$
$$y = 20,000(5)^x \qquad y = 20,000(0.5)^x$$

5. Given the exponential decay model, $y = 24,000(0.70)^t$, determine the decay factor and the decay rate.

6. Given the exponential decay model, $y = 56,000(0.45)^t$, determine the initial amount and the decay factor.

7. Given the exponential growth model, $y = 70,000(1.25)^t$, determine the growth factor and the growth rate.

8. Given the exponential growth model, $y = 6,100(1.07)^t$, determine the initial amount and the growth factor.

9. The population in Eastside County was 48,500 in 1965 and is decreasing at a rate of 8% per year. Which equation best fits the situation?

$$y = 48,500(1 + 0.08)t$$
$$y = 48,500(1 - 0.08)^t$$
$$y = 48,500(0.08)^t$$
$$y = 48,500(1 - 8)^t$$

10. The fish population in the lake was 64,000 in 2000 and is decreasing at a rate of 4% per year. Which equation best fits this situation?

$$y = 64,000(1 + 0.04)^t$$
$$y = 64,000(0.04)^t$$
$$y = 64,000(1 - 0.04)^t$$
$$y = 64,000(1 - 4)^t$$

11. The population in Westside County was 63,000 in 1995 and is increasing at a rate of 15% per year. Which equation best fits this situation?

$$y = 63,000(1 + 0.15)^t$$
$$y = 63,000(1 - 0.15)^t$$
$$y = 63,000(115)^t$$
$$y = 63,000(0.85)^t$$

12. David has $20,000 in a savings account that is growing 3% per year. Which equation best fits this situation?

$$y = 20,000(0.97)^t$$
$$y = 20,000(1 - 0.03)^t$$
$$y = 20,000(1 + 0.03)^t$$
$$y = 20,000(103)^t$$

13. An entomologist estimates that the population of a beehive is 150 and that it is increasing at a rate of 12% per week.

  a.) Write the equation that models the population change.

  b.) What is the expected population after 10 weeks?

14. A marine biologist estimates that the population of dolphins in the bay is 200 and that it is decreasing at a rate of 20% per year.

  a.) Write the equation that models the population change.

  b.) What is the expected population after 4 years?

15. Brad bought a new car for $26,800 in 2005. The car is depreciating at a rate of 15% per year.

  a.) Write the equation that models the value of the car.

  b.) What is the expected value of the car after 3 years?

16. Maria has $1,000 in a savings account that earns an interest of 5.5% per year.

  a.) Write the equation that models the amount in the savings account.

  b.) What is the expected amount in the account in 4 years?

17. When Sam was born, his parents deposited $5,000 into a college savings account paying 8% interest compounded monthly. If no other deposits are made, how much will be in the account when he is 18 years old?

18. When Zoe turned 24 years old, she deposited $25,000 into an investment account paying 6% interest compounded monthly. If no other deposits are made, how much will be in her account when she turns 29 years old?

19. Charlotte bought a Certificate of Deposit for $3,000 that pays an annual interest rate of 4.5% compounded quarterly. How much will the CD be worth after 6 years?

20. Hector bought a Certificate of Deposit for $10,000 that pays an annual interest rate of 6.5% compounded daily. How much will the CD be worth after 10 years?

HA1-840: Introduction to Matrices

It is often convenient to arrange numbers in rows and columns for keeping records, comparing data, and other everyday situations. Rectangular arrangements of numbers can be expressed mathematically using matrices. This lesson introduces matrices and the terminology associated with matrices.

Matrix (matrices)	A rectangular arrangement of elements in rows and columns that is enclosed in brackets

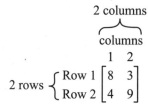

For example, consider the matrix below:

Quiz grades

Weeks

	1	2	3
Lang. Arts	9	8	7
Math	9	9	6
Science	8	7	9
History	10	9	9
Health	6	7	8

In the example above, each number inside the brackets represents a quiz score. A number in a matrix is also called an **element.**

Elements	Entries in a matrix

Each row in the matrix above represents one of five courses: language arts, mathematics, science, history, and health. For example, the science quiz grades in the third row are 8, 7, and 9.

Row	A horizontal line of numbers

Each column represents the quiz grades in a week. For example, the quiz grades during the second week are in the second column and are 8, 9, 7, 9, and 7.

Column	A vertical line of numbers

The dimensions of a matrix give the numbers of rows and columns.

Dimensions of a Matrix	The number of rows and columns. A matrix with m rows and n columns is an "$m \times n$" or "m-by-n" matrix.

The matrix has dimensions of 5×3.

Example 1   What are the dimensions of the following matrix?
$$\begin{bmatrix} 1 & 4 & 2 \\ 3 & 4 & 9 \\ 5 & 7 & 10 \\ 7 & 3 & 6 \end{bmatrix}$$

4 rows $\begin{cases} \text{Row 1} \\ \text{Row 2} \\ \text{Row 3} \\ \text{Row 4} \end{cases}$ $\begin{bmatrix} 1 & 4 & 2 \\ 3 & 4 & 9 \\ 5 & 7 & 10 \\ 7 & 3 & 6 \end{bmatrix}$

Step 1: The dimensions of a matrix give the number of rows and columns in the matrix. First, determine the number of rows. There are four horizontal lines of elements, therefore, this matrix has four rows.

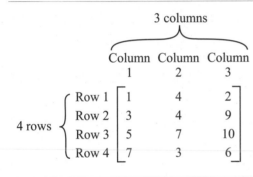

Step 2: Next, determine the number of columns in the matrix. A column is a vertical line of elements, so this matrix has three columns.

Answer: Therefore, the dimensions of the matrix are 4×3.

Example 2   What is the position of the number 3 in the following matrix?
$$\begin{bmatrix} 2 & 5 \\ 4 & 4 \\ 5 & 0 \\ 7 & \mathbf{3} \\ 0 & 6 \\ 9 & 9 \end{bmatrix}$$

$\begin{matrix} \text{Row 1} \\ \text{Row 2} \\ \text{Row 3} \\ \textbf{Row 4} \\ \text{Row 5} \\ \text{Row 6} \end{matrix}$ $\begin{bmatrix} 2 & 5 \\ 4 & 4 \\ 5 & 0 \\ 7 & \mathbf{3} \\ 0 & 6 \\ 9 & 9 \end{bmatrix}$

Step 1: First, determine the row position of the number. The number 3 is in Row 4.

Column Column
1   2

$$\begin{bmatrix} 2 & 5 \\ 4 & 4 \\ 5 & 0 \\ 7 & 3 \\ 0 & 6 \\ 9 & 9 \end{bmatrix}$$

Step 2: Next, determine the column position of the number. The number 3 is in Column 2.

Answer: Therefore, the number 3 is in row 4, Column 2.

Example 3   On four consecutive days, a track coach timed and ranked his four sprinters to determine how he would order them in a relay.

	Jason	Michael	Alex	Jesse
Monday	1st	3rd	2nd	4th
Tuesday	2nd	4th	1st	3rd
Wednesday	1st	2nd	4th	3rd
Thursday	2nd	3rd	1st	4th

Construct a matrix that shows how many times each person placed in each position.

	Jason	Michael	Alex	Jesse
1st	2			
2nd	2			
3rd	0			
4th	0			

Step 1: To solve this problem, find the number of times each person placed 1st, 2nd, 3rd, and 4th, and write the results in the matrix. Jason placed 1st twice, so write 2 in the first row, first column. He placed 2nd twice, so write 2 in the second row, first column. He did not place either 3rd or 4th, so write 0 in the third and fourth rows of the first column.

	Jason	Michael	Alex	Jesse
1st	2	0		
2nd	2	1		
3rd	0	2		
4th	0	1		

Step 2: Michael did not place 1st on any day, so write 0 in the first row, second column. He placed 2nd once, so write 1 in the second row, second column. He placed 3rd twice, so write 2 in the third row, second column. He placed 4th once, so write 1 in the fourth row, second column.

	Jason	Michael	Alex	Jesse
1st	2	0	2	
2nd	2	1	1	
3rd	0	2	0	
4th	0	1	1	

Step 3: Repeat the process for Alex.

	Jason	Michael	Alex	Jesse
1st	2	0	2	0
2nd	2	1	1	0
3rd	0	2	0	2
4th	0	1	1	2

Step 4: Repeat the process for Jesse.

Answer: Therefore, this is the desired matrix:

	Jason	Michael	Alex	Jesse
1st	2	0	2	0
2nd	2	1	1	0
3rd	0	2	0	2
4th	0	1	1	2

Example 4 Four pre-K students are assessed each day on their behavior and given a summary report at the end of each week. The grades for the first two weeks are shown in the table below.

	Week 1					Week 2				
	M	T	W	T	F	M	T	W	T	F
Jane	A	B	B	A	C	A	B	C	B	A
Michelle	B	A	A	C	B	B	B	B	C	B
Randy	C	C	B	B	B	B	B	C	B	A
Jackson	B	B	B	B	A	B	B	B	C	A

Complete the following 4×6 matrix showing the students' reports. The column headings refer to the number of times a student received that letter grade during the week.

	Week 1			Week 2		
	A	B	C	A	B	C
Jane						
Michelle						
Randy						
Jackson						

Step 1: Start with Jane's grades. Find the total number of A's, B's, and C's Jane received the first week. She received two A's, two B's, and one C, so write 2, 2, and 1 in Jane's row of the matrix for the first week. For the second week, Jane again received two A's, two B's, and one C, so write 2, 2, and 1 in the matrix for the second week.

	Week 1			Week 2		
	A	B	C	A	B	C
Jane	2	2	1	2	2	1
Michelle						
Randy						
Jackson						

	Week 1			Week 2		
	A	B	C	A	B	C
Jane	2	2	1	2	2	1
Michelle	2	2	1	0	4	1
Randy						
Jackson						

Step 2: Complete Michelle's row in the same manner. Michelle received two A's, two B's, and one C in the first week, so write 2, 2, and 1 in Michelle's row of the matrix for the first week. For the second week, Michelle received no A's, 4 B's, and one C, so write 0, 4, and 1 in the matrix for the second week.

	Week 1			Week 2		
	A	B	C	A	B	C
Jane	2	2	1	2	2	1
Michelle	2	2	1	0	4	1
Randy	0	3	2	1	3	1
Jackson						

Step 3: Randy received no A's, three B's, and two C's in the first week, so write 0, 3, and 2 in Randy's row of the matrix for the first week. For the second week, Randy received one A, three B's, and one C, so write 1, 3, and 1 in the matrix for the second week.

	Week 1			Week 2		
	A	B	C	A	B	C
Jane	2	2	1	2	2	1
Michelle	2	2	1	0	4	1
Randy	0	3	2	1	3	1
Jackson	1	4	0	1	3	1

Step 4: Jackson received one A, four B's, and no C's in the first week, so write 1, 4, and 0 in Jackson's row of the matrix for the first week. For the second week, Jackson received one A, three B's, and one C, so write 1, 3, and 1 in the matrix for the second week.

Answer: Therefore, this is the desired matrix:

	Week 1			Week 2		
	A	B	C	A	B	C
Jane	2	2	1	2	2	1
Michelle	2	2	1	0	4	1
Randy	0	3	2	1	3	1
Jackson	1	4	0	1	3	1

Example 5 Last Saturday, the track team had a fund-raiser for an end-of-season party at a water park. Each athlete solicited sponsors to donate $1 for each lap. The three highest money-raisers were Jimmy, with six sponsors and sixteen laps; Caroline, with five sponsors and fourteen laps; and Jasmine, with four sponsors and eleven laps. Construct a matrix to organize this information, including the total amount earned for each athlete. Also, find the total amount earned by the three athletes.

	Sponsors	Laps	Earnings
Jimmy			
Caroline			
Jasmine			

Step 1: Set up a matrix with rows that represent each athlete. Let the columns represent the number of sponsors, the number of laps, and the amount earned in dollars.

	Sponsors	Laps	Earnings
Jimmy	6	16	96
Caroline			
Jasmine			

Step 2: Fill in Jimmy's row with 6 sponsors and 16 laps. Jimmy earned 6 × 16, or 96 dollars.

	Sponsors	Laps	Earnings
Jimmy	6	16	96
Caroline	5	14	70
Jasmine			

Step 3: Fill in Caroline's row with 5 sponsors and 14 laps. Caroline earned 5 × 14, or 70 dollars.

	Sponsors	Laps	Earnings
Jimmy	6	16	96
Caroline	5	14	70
Jasmine	4	11	44

Step 4: Fill in Jasmine's row with 4 sponsors and 11 laps. Jasmine earned 4 × 11, or 44 dollars.

The total earnings for these athletes is $96 + 70 + 44$, or 210 dollars.

Step 5: The total amount earned by the three athletes is the sum of the three elements in the "Earnings" column.

Answer: The desired matrix is shown in Step 4, and the total amount earned by the three athletes is $210.

Problem Set

Solve:

1. What are the dimensions of the following matrix?

$$\begin{bmatrix} 3 & 2 & 7 & 4 & 19 \\ 10 & 13 & 15 & 3 & 6 \\ 11 & 8 & 12 & 9 & 18 \\ 17 & 16 & 14 & 0 & 5 \end{bmatrix}$$

2. What are the dimensions of the following matrix?

$$\begin{bmatrix} 4 & 8 & 0 \\ 3 & 7 & 1 \end{bmatrix}$$

3. What are the dimensions of the following matrix?

$$\begin{bmatrix} 12 & 5 & 6 & 4 \\ 2 & 1 & 7 & 3 \\ 11 & 18 & 8 & 20 \\ 27 & 23 & 0 & 25 \\ 17 & 19 & 9 & 21 \end{bmatrix}$$

4. What are the dimensions of the following matrix?

$$\begin{bmatrix} 10 & 17 & 8 & 1 & 9 & 2 & 11 \\ 14 & 7 & 16 & 15 & 0 & 12 & 4 \\ 1 & 6 & 13 & 0 & 5 & 3 & 2 \\ 7 & 5 & 8 & 4 & 7 & 32 & 20 \\ 22 & 0 & 9 & 2 & 25 & 9 & 16 \end{bmatrix}$$

5. What are the dimensions of the following matrix?

$$\begin{bmatrix} 3 & 8 & 6 & 5 \\ 11 & 7 & 9 & 1 \end{bmatrix}$$

6. What are the dimensions of the following matrix?

$$\begin{bmatrix} 2 & 7 & 3 & 1 & 5 \\ 4 & 8 & 9 & 9 & 12 \\ 6 & 7 & 5 & 11 & 3 \end{bmatrix}$$

7. What are the dimensions of the following matrix?

$$\begin{bmatrix} 2 & 1 & 8 & 7 \\ 5 & 10 & 9 & 4 \\ 3 & 5 & 22 & 1 \\ 6 & 16 & 19 & 3 \end{bmatrix}$$

8. What is the position of the number "9" in the following matrix?

$$\begin{bmatrix} 5 & 3 & 6 & 2 \\ 4 & 5 & 5 & 7 \\ 6 & 9 & 8 & 1 \end{bmatrix}$$

9. What is the position of the number "8" in the following matrix?

$$\begin{bmatrix} 6 & 11 \\ 2 & 8 \\ 9 & 3 \\ 5 & 4 \\ 1 & 2 \\ 7 & 4 \end{bmatrix}$$

10. What is the position of the number "13" in the following matrix?

$$\begin{bmatrix} 14 & 2 & 3 & 9 \\ 8 & 1 & 10 & 5 \\ 17 & 6 & 11 & 13 \end{bmatrix}$$

11. What is the position of the number "1" in the following matrix?

$$\begin{bmatrix} 2 & 13 & 5 & 12 & 8 \\ 7 & 6 & 14 & 1 & 19 \end{bmatrix}$$

12. What is the position of the number "3" in the following matrix?

$$\begin{bmatrix} 2 & 3 & 4 \\ 4 & 5 & 2 \\ 0 & 7 & 8 \end{bmatrix}$$

13. What is the position of the number "23" in the following matrix?

$$\begin{bmatrix} 2 & 5 & 6 & 4 \\ 2 & 1 & 7 & 3 \\ 13 & 8 & 8 & 20 \\ 7 & 23 & 0 & 5 \\ 17 & 19 & 9 & 21 \end{bmatrix}$$

14. What is the position of the number "4" in the following matrix?

$$\begin{bmatrix} 5 & 9 & 0 \\ 2 & 7 & 4 \end{bmatrix}$$

15. What is the position of the number "4" in the following matrix?

$$\begin{bmatrix} 3 & 11 & 4 \\ 16 & 5 & 12 \\ 9 & 17 & 8 \end{bmatrix}$$

16. Mr. Bearden gave his top three students a prize based on their overall participation each day of the week.

Daily Prize Table

	Student A	Student B	Student C
M	balloon	pen	balloon
T	pen	pen	pen
W	balloon	balloon	balloon
TH	pencil	balloon	pencil
F	pencil	pen	pencil

Using the rows and columns defined below, write a matrix that describes how many times each student received a pen, pencil, and balloon.

	Student A	Student B	Student C
pen			
pencil			
balloon			

17. Rochelle and Myra compared grades on their English quizzes for each day of the week.

Daily English Quiz Table

	Rochelle	Myra
M	B	A
T	A	A
W	A	C
TH	B	B
F	C	C

Using the rows and columns defined below, write a matrix that describes how many times each student received an A, B, and C.

	Rochelle	Myra
A		
B		
C		

18. A weather forecaster displayed the weekly weather conditions for two cities over a 6-week period.

	Genoa City	Pine Valley
Week 1	snow	sunny
Week 2	snow	rain
Week 3	rain	sunny
Week 4	rain	rain
Week 5	sunny	rain
Week 6	sunny	snow

Using the rows and columns defined below, write a matrix that describes how many times each city received rain, snow, and sunny weather.

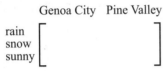

Genoa City   Pine Valley

rain
snow
sunny

19. Daryl and Phoebe compared stamps that they collected each day.

Daily Stamps Collected

	Daryl	Phoebe
M	Heritage	Heritage
T	Breast cancer	American flag
W	American flag	American flag
TH	Heritage	Breast cancer
F	Heritage	Heritage

Using the rows and columns defined below, write a matrix that describes how many times Daryl and Phoebe received a heritage, breast cancer, and American flag stamp.

Daryl   Phoebe

Heritage
Breast cancer
American flag

20. A local hospital's daily report showed the following information for patients A, B, and C.

Daily Medicine Distribution

	Patient A	Patient B	Patient C
day 1	aspirin	multi-vitamin	multi-vitamin
day 2	aspirin	iron	aspirin
day 3	iron	iron	iron
day 4	multi-vitamin	multi-vitamin	aspirin
day 5	iron	aspirin	aspirin

Using the rows and columns defined below, write a matrix that describes how many times Patient A, Patient B, and Patient C received aspirin, iron, and a multi-vitamin.

Patient A   Patient B   Patient C

aspirin
iron
mulit-vitamin

21. Kelly and Michelle displayed the type of vehicles they leased each year.

Leased Vehicle Table

	Kelly	Michelle
Year 1	SUV	car
Year 2	truck	car
Year 3	car	truck
Year 4	SUV	truck
Year 5	truck	SUV

Using the rows and columns defined below, write a matrix that describes how many of the leased vehicles were SUVs, trucks, and cars.

Kelly   Michelle

SUV
truck
car

22. At a major electronics store, the four month sales report showed the following information for Group A and Group B.

	Group A	Group B
November	profit loss	profit gain
December	profit loss	profit gain
January	profit loss	profit loss
February	profit gain	profit loss

Using the rows and columns defined below, write a matrix that describes how many times Group A and Group B received a profit gain and a profit loss.

$$
\begin{array}{cc} & \text{Group A} \quad \text{Group B} \\ \begin{array}{c} \text{profit gain} \\ \text{profit loss} \end{array} & \left[\quad\quad\quad\quad\quad \right] \end{array}
$$

23. The weekly on-off chart for two network computers is given below. Create a 2×2 matrix showing the total on-off usage for the week. Let the first column represent Computer A and the second column represent Computer B. Let the first row represent the number of computers "on" and the second row represent the number of computers "off".

	Computer A	Computer B
Week 1	on	on
Week 2	on	off
Week 3	off	on
Week 4	off	on
Week 5	off	on

24. At Simply Tea®, Shelby is responsible for testing the temperature of three types of teas. The hourly temperature chart for each type of tea is given below. Create a 3×3 matrix showing the different temperatures. Let the first column represent Tea 1, the second column represent Tea 2, and the third column represent Tea 3. Let the first row represent the tea that is hot, the second row represent the tea that is warm, and the third row represent the tea that is cold.

	Tea 1	Tea 2	Tea 3
7:00	hot	hot	hot
8:00	hot	warm	hot
9:00	warm	warm	warm
10:00	warm	cold	cold
11:00	cold	cold	cold

25. The top two candidates running for governor are given below. Create a 2×2 matrix showing the responses of six cities. Let the first column represent Republican and the second column represent Democrat. Let the first row represent the "for" votes, and the second row represent the "against" votes.

	Republican	Democrat
City A	for	against
City B	against	for
City C	against	for
City D	against	for
City E	against	for
City F	for	against

26. The answers for two students' history quizzes are given below. Create a 2×2 matrix showing the responses for questions one through five. Let the first column represent Jason's quiz responses and the second column represent Nicholas' quiz responses. Let the first row represent the true responses and the second row represent the false responses.

	Jason	Nicholas
Question 1	TRUE	TRUE
Question 2	TRUE	TRUE
Question 3	FALSE	FALSE
Question 4	TRUE	TRUE
Question 5	FALSE	TRUE

27. The results from a light bulb testing company are listed below. Create a 2×2 matrix showing the results of good and bad light bulbs. Let the first column represent Batch A and the second column represent Batch B. Let the first row represent the good light bulbs and the second row represent the bad light bulbs.

	Batch A	Batch B
Bulb 1	Good	Bad
Bulb 2	Bad	Bad
Bulb 3	Good	Bad
Bulb 4	Bad	Good
Bulb 5	Bad	Bad
Bulb 6	Good	Good

28. The plays by quarter that Thomas and Bryce contributed to the basketball game are listed below. Create a 3×2 matrix showing the different plays of the basketball game. Let the first column represent Thomas' plays and the second column represent Bryce's plays. Let the first row represent the number of free throws, the second row represent the number of jump shots, and the third row represent the number of lay-ups.

	Thomas	Bryce
1st quarter	Free throw	Lay-up
2nd quarter	Jump shot	Free throw
3rd quarter	Lay-up	Jump shot
4th quarter	Jump shot	Free throw

29. The results from a loan department are given below. Create a 2×3 matrix showing the outcome of the three customers. Let the first column represent Customer A, the second column represent Customer B, and the third column represent Customer C. Let the first row represent the approved results and the second row represent the denied results.

	Customer A	Customer B	Customer C
Officer 1	approved	denied	denied
Officer 2	approved	approved	approved
Officer 3	denied	denied	denied
Officer 4	approved	approved	approved
Officer 5	approved	denied	approved

30. The report cards for three students are given below. Create a 3×3 matrix showing the grades of the students. Let the first column represent Ann, the second column represent Cameron, and the third column represent Darren. Let the first row represent the A's, the second row represent the B's, and the third row represent the C's.

	Ann	Cameron	Darren
Spanish	A	A	B
History	B	A	A
Reading	C	C	B

31. Leslie and Michelle are stock market investors. The total number of stocks they purchased each year is shown below.

What is the total number of stocks each one purchased for these five years?

$$
\begin{array}{c}
 \begin{array}{cc} \text{Leslie} & \text{Michelle} \end{array} \\
\begin{array}{c} 2000 \\ 2001 \\ 2002 \\ 2003 \\ 2004 \end{array}
\begin{bmatrix} 13 & 14 \\ 16 & 15 \\ 13 & 16 \\ 14 & 17 \\ 15 & 14 \end{bmatrix}
\end{array}
$$

32. Nancy and Gerald are training for the Breast Cancer Awareness Marathon. Listed in the matrix are the miles they ran each day.

What was the average distance in miles Nancy and Gerald each ran?

	Nancy	Gerald
Monday	4.5	2.5
Tuesday	3.5	3.8
Wednesday	4.2	5.2
Thursday	4.8	3.5
Friday	3.0	2.0

33. Keisha works part-time at a boutique. Her wages for the past two weeks are shown in the matrix below.

What is her total wages earned for each week?

	Week 1	Week 2
Monday	$45	$54
Tuesday	$48	$52
Wednesday	$35	$56
Thursday	$54	$59
Friday	$58	$59
Saturday	$68	$52
Sunday	$65	$70

34. The Candy Company® receives numerous orders for Valentine's Day. Listed below are the totals from the past four years.

What is the total number of each type of dessert ordered?

	Cakes	Cookies	Pies
2002	50	65	80
2003	45	70	64
2004	65	76	50
2005	40	60	65

35. Judy and her sister Jasmine clipped coupons each day from the newspaper. Curious to see who saved the most money this month, they decided to compare grocery bills. The following information is shown in the matrix below.

What is the total amount of money Judy and her sister each saved?

	Judy	Jasmine
Bill 1	$4.50	$9.90
Bill 2	$11.80	$12.50
Bill 3	$7.50	$8.25
Bill 4	$6.50	$6.00
Bill 5	$9.25	$10.30

36. Betty and Tyler collected money for their class trip. At the end of eight hours, they compared the total amount they collected. The information is shown in the matrix below.
What is the total amount of money Betty and Tyler each collected?

	Betty	Tyler
Hour 1	$10	$12
Hour 2	$18	$13
Hour 3	$16	$15
Hour 4	$15	$14
Hour 5	$12	$18
Hour 6	$18	$16
Hour 7	$19	$12
Hour 8	$11	$17

37. At summer camp, Trisha, Leah, Marc, Nathan, and Troy were playing a game. At the end of the day, they compared the total number of wins and losses for each round. The information is shown in the matrix below.

What is the total win-loss record?

	Win	Loss
Trisha	4	2
Leah	3	3
Marc	1	5
Nathan	5	1
Troy	6	0

38. Dairy Mart® displayed their milk prices over a seven-week period.

If Maya bought a gallon of whole milk and a gallon of skim milk each week for seven weeks, what is the total amount of money she spent on each type of milk?

	Whole	Skim
Week 1	$2.14	$2.28
Week 2	$2.09	$2.29
Week 3	$2.11	$2.30
Week 4	$2.15	$2.30
Week 5	$2.11	$2.39
Week 6	$2.20	$2.27
Week 7	$2.29	$2.25

39. A weather forecaster displayed the seven day forecast for a town.

What are the average high-low temperatures for these seven days?

	High	Low
Thurs.	89°	72°
Fri.	88°	71°
Sat.	90°	73°
Sun.	91°	73°
Mon.	77°	58°
Tues.	76°	56°
Wed.	77°	59°

40. Katie and Andrea compared Spanish test scores at the end of the semester. Their test scores for the semester are shown in a matrix below.

What is the average Spanish test score for each student?

	Katie	Andrea
Test 1	88	90
Test 2	92	87
Test 3	85	79
Test 4	99	94

HA1-845: Operations with Matrices

This lesson describes how to perform basic operations with matrices.

Operation	A mathematical process of deriving one expression from other expressions according to a rule

Two matrix operations are addition and subtraction.

Matrix Addition (or Subtraction)	An operation in which corresponding elements of two matrices with the same dimensions are added (or subtracted) to form a matrix with the same dimensions as the original matrices

For example, to add $\begin{bmatrix} 2 & -4 & 6 \\ -8 & 10 & -12 \end{bmatrix}$ and $\begin{bmatrix} 0 & 1 & 3 \\ -5 & -7 & -9 \end{bmatrix}$, add corresponding elements. As shown in the equations

below, the element 2 in the first matrix and the element 0 in the second matrix are both in the first row and first column of their respective matrices, so 2 + 0, or 2, is in the first row and first column of the matrix that represents the sum. Find the other elements in the sum by adding the other five pairs of corresponding elements, as shown below:

$$\begin{bmatrix} 2 & -4 & 6 \\ -8 & 10 & -12 \end{bmatrix} + \begin{bmatrix} 0 & 1 & 3 \\ -5 & -7 & -9 \end{bmatrix} = \begin{bmatrix} 2+0 & -4+1 & 6+3 \\ -8+(-5) & 10+(-7) & -12+(-9) \end{bmatrix}$$

$$= \begin{bmatrix} 2 & -3 & 9 \\ -13 & 3 & -21 \end{bmatrix}$$

Another matrix operation is scalar multiplication.

Scalar	A number or constant (as opposed to a 1-by-1 matrix)

Scalar Multiplication	An operation in which each element of a matrix is multiplied by a scalar to form a matrix with the same dimensions as the original matrix

For example, to multiply $\begin{bmatrix} 1 & -1 \\ 2 & 3 \end{bmatrix}$ by the scalar 5, multiply each element of the matrix by 5, as follows:

$$5 \begin{bmatrix} 1 & -1 \\ 2 & 3 \end{bmatrix} = \begin{bmatrix} 5(1) & 5(-1) \\ 5(2) & 5(3) \end{bmatrix}$$

$$= \begin{bmatrix} 5 & -5 \\ 10 & 15 \end{bmatrix}$$

Example 1 Given matrices C and B, find $C + B$.

$$C = \begin{bmatrix} 2 & 5 \\ 3 & 7 \\ 6 & 4 \end{bmatrix} \qquad B = \begin{bmatrix} 1 & 2 \\ 4 & 6 \\ 8 & 5 \end{bmatrix}$$

$$C + B = \begin{bmatrix} 2 & 5 \\ 3 & 7 \\ 6 & 4 \end{bmatrix} + \begin{bmatrix} 1 & 2 \\ 4 & 6 \\ 8 & 5 \end{bmatrix}$$

Step 1: Replace the variables in $C + B$ with the matrices represented by C and B.

$$= \begin{bmatrix} 2+1 & 5+2 \\ 3+4 & 7+6 \\ 6+8 & 4+5 \end{bmatrix}$$

Step 2: Add the corresponding elements of the matrices.

$$= \begin{bmatrix} 3 & 7 \\ 7 & 13 \\ 14 & 9 \end{bmatrix}$$

Step 3: Find the sums.

Answer:

$$C + B = \begin{bmatrix} 3 & 7 \\ 7 & 13 \\ 14 & 9 \end{bmatrix}$$

Example 2 Given the matrix A, find $-4A$.

$$A = \begin{bmatrix} 3 & -2 \\ 5 & 4 \\ -9 & 6 \\ 7 & 8 \end{bmatrix}$$

$$A = -4 \begin{bmatrix} 3 & -2 \\ 5 & 4 \\ -9 & 6 \\ 7 & 8 \end{bmatrix}$$

Step 1: Replace the variable in $-4A$ with the matrix represented by A.

$$= \begin{bmatrix} -4(3) & -4(-2) \\ -4(5) & -4(4) \\ -4(-9) & -4(6) \\ -4(7) & -4(8) \end{bmatrix}$$

Step 2: Multiply each element in the matrix by the scalar -4.

$$= \begin{bmatrix} -12 & 8 \\ -20 & -16 \\ 36 & -24 \\ -28 & -32 \end{bmatrix}$$

Step 3: Find the products.

Answer:

$$-4A = \begin{bmatrix} -12 & 8 \\ -20 & -16 \\ 36 & -24 \\ -28 & -32 \end{bmatrix}$$

Example 3 Given the matrices A and B, find $4A - B$.

$$A = \begin{bmatrix} -2 & 3 & 1 \\ -8 & 6 & -2 \end{bmatrix} \qquad B = \begin{bmatrix} 2 & 4 & 2 \\ 4 & -7 & -1 \end{bmatrix}$$

$$4A - B = 4\begin{bmatrix} -2 & 3 & 1 \\ -8 & 6 & -2 \end{bmatrix} - \begin{bmatrix} 2 & 4 & 2 \\ 4 & -7 & -1 \end{bmatrix}$$

Step 1: Replace the variables in $4A - B$ with the matrices represented by A and B.

$$= 4\begin{bmatrix} -2 & 3 & 1 \\ -8 & 6 & -2 \end{bmatrix} + \begin{bmatrix} -2 & -4 & -2 \\ -4 & 7 & 1 \end{bmatrix}$$

Step 2: Subtract matrix B by changing the subtraction sign to an addition sign and changing each element in B to its opposite.

$$= \begin{bmatrix} 4(-2) & 4(3) & 4(1) \\ 4(-8) & 4(6) & 4(-2) \end{bmatrix} + \begin{bmatrix} -2 & -4 & -2 \\ -4 & +7 & +1 \end{bmatrix}$$

Step 3: Multiply each element in matrix A by the scalar 4.

$$= \begin{bmatrix} -8 & 12 & 4 \\ -32 & 24 & -8 \end{bmatrix} + \begin{bmatrix} -2 & -4 & -2 \\ -4 & +7 & +1 \end{bmatrix}$$

Step 4: Find the products in the first matrix.

$$= \begin{bmatrix} -8+(-2) & 12+(-4) & 4+(-2) \\ -32+(-4) & 24+7 & -8+1 \end{bmatrix}$$

Step 5: Add the corresponding elements of the matrices.

$$= \begin{bmatrix} -10 & 8 & 2 \\ -36 & 31 & -7 \end{bmatrix}$$

Step 6: Find the sums.

Answer:

$$4A - B = \begin{bmatrix} -10 & 8 & 2 \\ -36 & 31 & -7 \end{bmatrix}$$

Example 4   Given matrices D, E, and F, find $D + 3E - 2F$.

$$D = \begin{bmatrix} 2 & 5 \\ -3 & 6 \end{bmatrix} \quad E = \begin{bmatrix} 4 & 8 \\ 5 & 9 \end{bmatrix} \quad F = \begin{bmatrix} -1 & 2 \\ -3 & -5 \end{bmatrix}$$

$D + 3E - 2F = \begin{bmatrix} 2 & 5 \\ -3 & 6 \end{bmatrix} + 3\begin{bmatrix} 4 & 8 \\ 5 & 9 \end{bmatrix} - 2\begin{bmatrix} -1 & 2 \\ -3 & -5 \end{bmatrix}$	**Step 1:** Replace the variables in $D + 3E - 2F$ with the matrices represented by D, E, and F.
$= \begin{bmatrix} 2 & 5 \\ -3 & 6 \end{bmatrix} + 3\begin{bmatrix} 4 & 8 \\ 5 & 9 \end{bmatrix} + 2\begin{bmatrix} 1 & -2 \\ 3 & 5 \end{bmatrix}$	**Step 2:** Subtract $2F$ by changing the subtraction sign to an addition sign and changing each element in F to its opposite.
$= \begin{bmatrix} 2 & 5 \\ -3 & 6 \end{bmatrix} + \begin{bmatrix} 3(4) & 3(8) \\ 3(5) & 3(9) \end{bmatrix} + \begin{bmatrix} 2(1) & 2(-2) \\ 2(3) & 2(5) \end{bmatrix}$	**Step 3:** Multiply each element in matrix E by the scalar 3, and multiply each element in matrix F by the scalar 2.
$= \begin{bmatrix} 2 & 5 \\ -3 & 6 \end{bmatrix} + \begin{bmatrix} 12 & 24 \\ 15 & 27 \end{bmatrix} + \begin{bmatrix} 2 & -4 \\ 6 & 10 \end{bmatrix}$	**Step 4:** Find the products in the second and third matrices.
$= \begin{bmatrix} 2 + 12 + 2 & 5 + 24 + (-4) \\ -3 + 15 + 6 & 6 + 27 + 10 \end{bmatrix}$	**Step 5:** Add the corresponding elements of the three matrices.
$= \begin{bmatrix} 16 & 25 \\ 18 & 43 \end{bmatrix}$	**Step 6:** Find the sums.

Answer: $D + 3E - 2F = \begin{bmatrix} 16 & 25 \\ 18 & 43 \end{bmatrix}$

Example 5   This table shows the number of vehicles sold last month by three salesmen at a local dealership:

Number of Vehicles Sold

Name	Cars	SUVs	Trucks
Abbott	8	11	7
Buddy	11	12	9
Charles	9	8	8

If a salesman receives a $100 commission for a car, a $200 commission for a SUV, and a $300 commission for a truck, find the total commission each salesman received last month.

$C = \begin{bmatrix} 8 \\ 11 \\ 9 \end{bmatrix} \quad S = \begin{bmatrix} 11 \\ 12 \\ 8 \end{bmatrix} \quad T = \begin{bmatrix} 7 \\ 9 \\ 8 \end{bmatrix}$	**Step 1:** Define three 3-by-1 matrices whose elements are the number of each type of vehicle sold by the salesmen. Matrix C is the number of cars, matrix S is the number of SUVs, and matrix T is the number of trucks sold.

$\dfrac{\text{Total}}{\text{commissions}}$ = \$100C + \$200S + \$300T	**Step 2:** Find the total commissions by multiplying the number of cars sold by \$100, the number of SUVs sold by \$200, and the number of trucks sold by \$300, and then add the results.
$= 100 \begin{bmatrix} 8 \\ 11 \\ 9 \end{bmatrix} + 200 \begin{bmatrix} 11 \\ 12 \\ 8 \end{bmatrix} + 300 \begin{bmatrix} 7 \\ 9 \\ 8 \end{bmatrix}$	**Step 3:** Replace the variables in $100C + 200S + 300T$ with the matrices represented by C, S, and T.
$= \begin{bmatrix} 100(8) \\ 100(11) \\ 100(9) \end{bmatrix} + \begin{bmatrix} 200(11) \\ 200(12) \\ 200(8) \end{bmatrix} + \begin{bmatrix} 300(7) \\ 300(9) \\ 300(8) \end{bmatrix}$	**Step 4:** Multiply each element of C by the scalar 100, each element of S by the scalar 200, and each element of T by the scalar 300.
$= \begin{bmatrix} 800 \\ 1,100 \\ 900 \end{bmatrix} + \begin{bmatrix} 2,200 \\ 2,400 \\ 1,600 \end{bmatrix} + \begin{bmatrix} 2,100 \\ 2,700 \\ 2,400 \end{bmatrix}$	**Step 5:** Find the products in each matrix.
$= \begin{bmatrix} 800 + 2,200 + 2,100 \\ 1,100 + 2,400 + 2,700 \\ 900 + 1,600 + 2,400 \end{bmatrix}$	**Step 6:** Add the corresponding elements of the three matrices.
$= \begin{bmatrix} 5,100 \\ 6,200 \\ 4,900 \end{bmatrix}$	**Step 7:** Find the sums.

Answer: The total commission for each salesman is shown in the matrix below.

$$\begin{matrix} \text{Abbott} \\ \text{Buddy} \\ \text{Charles} \end{matrix} \begin{bmatrix} \$5,100 \\ \$6,200 \\ \$4,900 \end{bmatrix}$$

Problem Set

Solve:

1. Given matrices A and B, find $A + B$.

$$A = \begin{bmatrix} 3 & 9 \\ 4 & 8 \end{bmatrix} \qquad B = \begin{bmatrix} 3 & 4 \\ 9 & 5 \end{bmatrix}$$

2. Given matrices A and B, find $A + B$.

$$A = \begin{bmatrix} 1 & 2 & 1 \\ 6 & 3 & 4 \\ 9 & 8 & 7 \end{bmatrix} \qquad B = \begin{bmatrix} 4 & 6 & 4 \\ 1 & 3 & 2 \\ 0 & 4 & 5 \end{bmatrix}$$

3. Given matrices C and D, find $C + D$.

$$C = \begin{bmatrix} 2 & 5 \\ 8 & 7 \end{bmatrix} \quad D = \begin{bmatrix} 6 & 2 \\ 3 & 5 \end{bmatrix}$$

4. Given matrices A and B, find $A + B$.

$$A = \begin{bmatrix} 3 & 5 & 8 \\ 0 & 8 & 7 \\ 4 & 3 & 1 \end{bmatrix} \quad B = \begin{bmatrix} 1 & 2 & 8 \\ 8 & 1 & 4 \\ 5 & 3 & 4 \end{bmatrix}$$

5. Given matrices R and S, find $R + S$.

$$R = \begin{bmatrix} 1 & 2 & 1 & 2 \\ 1 & 2 & 1 & 2 \\ 1 & 2 & 1 & 2 \\ 1 & 2 & 1 & 2 \end{bmatrix} \quad S = \begin{bmatrix} 2 & 1 & 2 & 1 \\ 2 & 1 & 2 & 1 \\ 2 & 1 & 2 & 1 \\ 2 & 1 & 2 & 1 \end{bmatrix}$$

6. Given matrices M and N, find $M + N$.

$$M = \begin{bmatrix} 3 & 7 \\ 8 & 8 \end{bmatrix} \quad N = \begin{bmatrix} 1 & 9 \\ 7 & 2 \end{bmatrix}$$

7. Given matrices A and B, find $A + B$.

$$A = \begin{bmatrix} 3 & 2 & 1 \\ 1 & 2 & 3 \\ 2 & 4 & 2 \end{bmatrix} \quad B = \begin{bmatrix} 1 & 2 & 3 \\ 4 & 5 & 6 \\ 7 & 8 & 9 \end{bmatrix}$$

8. Given matrices F and G, find $F + G$.

$$F = \begin{bmatrix} 1 & 2 & 3 & 4 \\ 1 & 2 & 3 & 4 \\ 1 & 2 & 3 & 4 \\ 1 & 2 & 3 & 4 \end{bmatrix} \quad G = \begin{bmatrix} 5 & 6 & 7 & 8 \\ 5 & 6 & 7 & 8 \\ 5 & 6 & 7 & 8 \\ 5 & 6 & 7 & 8 \end{bmatrix}$$

9. Given matrix H, find $3H$.

$$H = \begin{bmatrix} 3 & 3 \\ 1 & 1 \\ 1 & 3 \\ 4 & 1 \\ 3 & 3 \\ 1 & 2 \end{bmatrix}$$

10. Given matrix C, find $6C$.

$$C = \begin{bmatrix} 2 & 6 & 3 & 1 & 2 & 6 \\ 4 & 5 & 2 & 1 & 0 & 1 \end{bmatrix}$$

11. Given matrix D, find $2D$.

$$D = \begin{bmatrix} 4 & 1 \\ 3 & 2 \\ 4 & 1 \\ 2 & 5 \end{bmatrix}$$

12. Given matrix D, find $3D$.

$$D = \begin{bmatrix} 4 & 2 \\ 3 & 8 \\ 1 & 1 \\ 2 & 0 \end{bmatrix}$$

13. Given matrix S, find $4S$.

$$S = \begin{bmatrix} 3 & 9 & 0 \\ 7 & 5 & 2 \\ 0 & 6 & 4 \end{bmatrix}$$

14. Given matrix J, find $2J$.

$$J = \begin{bmatrix} 6 & 4 \\ 2 & 1 \\ 3 & 5 \\ 4 & 3 \\ 2 & 2 \end{bmatrix}$$

15. Given matrix X, find $3X$.

$$X = \begin{bmatrix} 5 & 4 \\ 3 & 2 \end{bmatrix}$$

16. Given matrices A and G, find $A + 2G$.

$$A = \begin{bmatrix} 3 & 2 \\ 5 & -2 \end{bmatrix} \quad G = \begin{bmatrix} 2 & -6 \\ 3 & 2 \end{bmatrix}$$

17. Given matrices C and E, find $2C + 2E$.

$$C = \begin{bmatrix} 6 & 4 & 1 \\ 6 & 2 & 3 \\ 6 & 5 & 1 \end{bmatrix} \quad E = \begin{bmatrix} 1 & 3 & 5 \\ 7 & 2 & 3 \\ 8 & 3 & 4 \end{bmatrix}$$

18. Given matrices U and V, find $3U + 2V$.

$$U = \begin{bmatrix} 2 & 4 \\ 3 & 2 \end{bmatrix} \quad V = \begin{bmatrix} 2 & 5 \\ 3 & 4 \end{bmatrix}$$

19. Given matrices G and J, find $2G + J$.

$$G = \begin{bmatrix} -4 & -4 \\ 8 & -6 \end{bmatrix} \quad J = \begin{bmatrix} -3 & 2 \\ -2 & -1 \end{bmatrix}$$

20. Given matrices J and K, find $J + 2K$.

$$J = \begin{bmatrix} -4 & 3 \\ -9 & 6 \end{bmatrix} \quad K = \begin{bmatrix} 3 & 2 \\ 2 & 1 \end{bmatrix}$$

21. Given matrices R and Q, find $2R + 2Q$.

$$R = \begin{bmatrix} 5 & 4 & 1 \\ 5 & 2 & 3 \\ 5 & 5 & 1 \end{bmatrix} \quad Q = \begin{bmatrix} -1 & 3 & 2 \\ 3 & 2 & -3 \\ 5 & -2 & 4 \end{bmatrix}$$

22. Given matrices N and K, find $N + 2K$.

$$N = \begin{bmatrix} 2 & 3 \\ 3 & -4 \end{bmatrix} \quad K = \begin{bmatrix} 4 & 2 \\ 3 & 4 \end{bmatrix}$$

23. Given matrices U and V, find $3U + V$.

$$U = \begin{bmatrix} -6 & 4 & 1 \\ 2 & -4 & 3 \end{bmatrix} \quad V = \begin{bmatrix} 3 & 2 & 7 \\ 6 & 9 & 8 \end{bmatrix}$$

24. Given matrices F and T, find $F + 2T$.

$$F = \begin{bmatrix} 3 & 4 & 1 \\ 2 & 2 & 3 \\ 6 & 5 & 1 \end{bmatrix} \quad T = \begin{bmatrix} 1 & 3 & 5 \\ 7 & 2 & 3 \\ 9 & 3 & 2 \end{bmatrix}$$

25. Given matrices F, G, and H, find $F - 3G + 2H$.

$$F = \begin{bmatrix} 2 & 2 \\ 1 & 1 \end{bmatrix} \quad G = \begin{bmatrix} 3 & 2 \\ 5 & 4 \end{bmatrix} \quad H = \begin{bmatrix} 2 & 1 \\ 4 & 3 \end{bmatrix}$$

26. Given matrices D, E, and F, find $D + 2E - F$.

$$D = \begin{bmatrix} 2 & 4 \\ 1 & 3 \end{bmatrix} \quad E = \begin{bmatrix} 3 & 1 \\ 6 & 4 \end{bmatrix} \quad F = \begin{bmatrix} 9 & 1 \\ 0 & 4 \end{bmatrix}$$

27. Given matrices B, A, and D, find $3B + 2A + D$.

$$B = \begin{bmatrix} 2 & 5 \\ 2 & 3 \end{bmatrix} \quad A = \begin{bmatrix} 3 & 1 \\ 5 & 4 \end{bmatrix} \quad D = \begin{bmatrix} 1 & 2 \\ 2 & 4 \end{bmatrix}$$

28. Given matrices S, E, and T, find $S - 3E + T$.

$$S = \begin{bmatrix} 4 & 1 \\ 1 & 3 \end{bmatrix} \quad E = \begin{bmatrix} 1 & 1 \\ 1 & 1 \end{bmatrix} \quad T = \begin{bmatrix} 3 & 1 \\ 5 & 4 \end{bmatrix}$$

29. Given matrices D, B, and C, find $2D - B + 2C$.

$$D = \begin{bmatrix} 5 & 4 & 2 \\ 3 & 2 & 1 \\ 6 & 3 & 1 \end{bmatrix} \quad B = \begin{bmatrix} 1 & 9 & 7 \\ 6 & 8 & 2 \\ 2 & 5 & 6 \end{bmatrix} \quad C = \begin{bmatrix} 2 & 4 & 2 \\ 1 & 2 & 1 \\ 3 & 1 & 2 \end{bmatrix}$$

30. Given matrices C, E, and T, find $C + E + T$.

$$C = \begin{bmatrix} 8 & 9 \\ 6 & 7 \end{bmatrix} \quad E = \begin{bmatrix} -1 & -1 \\ -1 & -1 \end{bmatrix} \quad T = \begin{bmatrix} 2 & 4 \\ 3 & 2 \end{bmatrix}$$

31. At Crimson University, the total number of male and female students in the math department for two weeks is given below.

Week 1   Class

	A	B
male	25	30
female	10	7

Week 2   Class

	A	B
male	13	5
female	15	23

To estimate the amount of students present in the department over the next fourteen weeks, the department head adds the two matrices above, and then multiplies the sum by seven. Find the resulting matrix.

32. Two neighboring towns are getting ready for their mayoral election. The total number of Democratic and Republican voters in Town A and Town B is given below.

Year 1   Town

	A	B
Dem.	109	200
Rep.	75	318

Year 2   Town

	A	B
Dem.	135	117
Rep.	211	313

To estimate the amount of registered voters over ten years, the mayor adds the two matrices above, and then multiplies the sum by five. Find the resulting matrix.

33. At Big Al's® new and used car lot, the total number of cars and SUVs sold is given below.

Week 1

	new	used
cars	32	34
SUVs	26	22

Week 2

	new	used
cars	16	31
SUVs	36	27

To estimate the amount of vehicles sold over 18 weeks, Al adds the two matrices above, and then multiplies the sum by nine. Find the resulting matrix.

34. The receptionist at the university ordered pencils and pens for her department. The following shows the amount for two months

Month 1

	pens	pencils
blue	234	251
black	228	248

Month 2

	pens	pencils
blue	224	271
black	251	220

To estimate the amount of pens and pencils purchased over 12 months, the receptionist adds the two matrices above, and then multiplies the sum by six. Find the resulting matrix.

35. Miss Tyson has three stocks, HTTD, IRON, and ACE. The annual report shows the total stocks broken down over two business weeks.

Week 1

	HTTD	IRON	ACE
Mon.	52	62	29
Tues.	52	63	29
Wed.	50	61	30
Thur.	52	60	32
Fri.	53	68	31

Week 2

	HTTD	IRON	ACE
Mon.	54	62	29
Tues.	54	64	32
Wed.	55	65	33
Thur.	56	66	33
Fri.	56	66	35

To estimate the price of the stocks over the next eight weeks, Miss Tyson must add the two matrices above, and then multiply the sum by four. Find the resulting matrix.

36. The student teacher ratio between two local high schools for two years is given below.

Year 1   School

	A	B
teachers	119	86
students	875	918

Year 2   School

	A	B
teachers	123	88
students	675	723

To estimate the amount of teachers and students over twelve years, add the two matrices above, and then multiply the sum by six. Find the resulting matrix.

37. The Computer Store® is having their annual clearance sale. Two stores sold the following computers over a two-day period.

Day 1

$$\begin{array}{c} \\ \text{laptop} \\ \text{desktop} \\ \text{tablet pc} \end{array} \begin{array}{cc} \text{Store A} & \text{Store B} \\ \left[\begin{array}{cc} 50 & 27 \\ 66 & 59 \\ 20 & 43 \end{array}\right] \end{array}$$

Day 2

$$\begin{array}{c} \\ \text{laptop} \\ \text{desktop} \\ \text{tablet pc} \end{array} \begin{array}{cc} \text{Store A} & \text{Store B} \\ \left[\begin{array}{cc} 48 & 45 \\ 89 & 68 \\ 48 & 39 \end{array}\right] \end{array}$$

To estimate the number of computers sold over the next twelve days, the store owner adds the two matrices above, and then multiplies the sum by six. Find the resulting matrix.

38. The Music Factor® is having a clearance sale. The following table shows the inventory sold of two types of music.

Week 1

$$\begin{array}{c} \\ \text{Hiphop Music} \\ \text{Country Music} \end{array} \begin{array}{ccc} \text{Cassettes} & \text{LPs} & \text{CDs} \\ \left[\begin{array}{ccc} 234 & 105 & 359 \\ 356 & 87 & 206 \end{array}\right] \end{array}$$

Week 2

$$\begin{array}{c} \\ \text{Hiphop Music} \\ \text{Country Music} \end{array} \begin{array}{ccc} \text{Cassettes} & \text{LPs} & \text{CDs} \\ \left[\begin{array}{ccc} 204 & 105 & 350 \\ 306 & 75 & 222 \end{array}\right] \end{array}$$

To estimate the amount of music to be sold over the next four weeks, the store manager adds the two matrices above, and then multiplies the sum by two. Find the resulting matrix.

39. The total number of dogs and cats adopted for the first two days of Adopt-a-Pet week are listed below.

Day 1

$$\begin{array}{c} \\ \text{dogs} \\ \text{cats} \end{array} \begin{array}{cc} \multicolumn{2}{c}{\text{pound}} \\ \text{A} & \text{B} \\ \left[\begin{array}{cc} 23 & 34 \\ 43 & 32 \end{array}\right] \end{array}$$

Day 2

$$\begin{array}{c} \\ \text{dogs} \\ \text{cats} \end{array} \begin{array}{cc} \multicolumn{2}{c}{\text{pound}} \\ \text{A} & \text{B} \\ \left[\begin{array}{cc} 32 & 31 \\ 48 & 39 \end{array}\right] \end{array}$$

To estimate the number of animals to be adopted over the next four days, add the two matrices above, and then multiply the sum by two. Find the resulting matrix.

40. Two local sporting goods stores report shoe sales for December and January as follows:

December

$$\begin{array}{c} \\ \text{running} \\ \text{walking} \\ \text{basketball} \\ \text{golf} \end{array} \begin{array}{cc} \multicolumn{2}{c}{\text{Store}} \\ \text{A} & \text{B} \\ \left[\begin{array}{cc} 34 & 65 \\ 43 & 23 \\ 54 & 34 \\ 24 & 14 \end{array}\right] \end{array}$$

January

$$\begin{array}{c} \\ \text{running} \\ \text{walking} \\ \text{basketball} \\ \text{golf} \end{array} \begin{array}{cc} \multicolumn{2}{c}{\text{Store}} \\ \text{A} & \text{B} \\ \left[\begin{array}{cc} 24 & 34 \\ 35 & 27 \\ 34 & 32 \\ 29 & 24 \end{array}\right] \end{array}$$

To estimate the number of shoes by type to purchase for the next eight months, the store manager adds the two matrices above, and then multiplies the sum by four. Find the resulting matrix.

Before getting too involved with the applications of the matrix, you should learn the fundamental ideas and concepts.

Matrix	A rectangular array of numbers

The following are some examples of matrices.

$$\begin{bmatrix} 1 & 2 & 3 \\ 4 & 5 & 6 \\ 7 & 8 & 9 \end{bmatrix} \text{ or } \begin{bmatrix} -1 & -2 & 0 & 11 \end{bmatrix} \text{ or } \begin{bmatrix} -2 & -7 \\ -1 & -6 \\ 0 & -5 \\ 1 & -4 \end{bmatrix}$$

Note that in this book matrices are enclosed in brackets. You may also see parentheses used in place of brackets. For example:

$$\begin{pmatrix} 1 & -9 \\ -9 & 1 \end{pmatrix} \text{ or } \begin{pmatrix} 0 \\ -1 \\ -4 \\ -16 \end{pmatrix} \text{ or } \begin{pmatrix} 0 & 6 & 0 \\ 0 & 0 & 6 \end{pmatrix}.$$

The primary application of matrices is to help us solve systems of linear equations and inequalities. They are also used to organize and store data in computers. The objective in this lesson is to introduce the terminology and notation associated with matrices.

It is customary to use capital letters to denote matrices. For example: $A = \begin{bmatrix} 1 & 5 & -2 \\ 6 & 3 & 0 \end{bmatrix}$

The size of a matrix is the number of rows by the number of columns. For example, in the above example, A is a two by three matrix, or in symbols, A is a 2×3 matrix. Here is a 1×4 matrix called B: $B = \begin{bmatrix} -1 & 0 & -2 & 4 \end{bmatrix}$

Each number in a matrix is called an **element** of the matrix.

Element	An element is a number in a matrix.

The location of an element in a matrix is given by the row that contains the element followed by the column. For example, the 3, 2 element of the matrix below is 77, which is in the third row, second column.

$$\begin{bmatrix} 2 & 0 & -1 & 6 \\ 15 & 12 & -4 & 18 \\ 6 & 77 & 2 & 4 \\ -1 & 0 & 3 & 2 \\ 5 & 6 & 9 & 0 \end{bmatrix}$$

Elements are named using the lowercase form of the letter that names the matrix and a double subscript. The double subscript gives the location of the element. For example, if the matrix in the above example is named B, then

$b_{32} = 77$. The following notation can be used to describe a matrix: $M = [m_{pq}]$. This says that the name of the matrix is M and the elements are denoted using m. The location of an element is denoted using p and q. For example, if $p = 3$ then the element is in the third row; if $q = 7$ then the element is in the seventh column.

Example 1   Write down a 2×4 matrix named C with $c_{21} = 1$, $c_{12} = 4$, $c_{23} = 5$, $c_{14} = 6$
and all other elements equal to 0.

$C = \begin{bmatrix} 0 & 4 & 0 & 6 \\ 1 & 0 & 5 & 0 \end{bmatrix}$ In this matrix, c_{21} is the number in the 2nd row and the 1st column, which in this case is 1.

A matrix is a **square matrix** if the number of rows is equal to the number of columns. For a square matrix the **order** is the number of rows (or columns).

Example 2   Write down a matrix of order 3, each of whose element is 6.

$\begin{bmatrix} 6 & 6 & 6 \\ 6 & 6 & 6 \\ 6 & 6 & 6 \end{bmatrix}$ Note that specifying that the order is 3 means that the matrix must be square and 3×3.

A matrix is a **zero matrix** if each of its elements is zero. A zero matrix is denoted by 0 regardless of its size. Usually the size of a zero matrix is determined from its context, otherwise it must be specified. The following is a 4×1 zero matrix.

$$0 = \begin{bmatrix} 0 \\ 0 \\ 0 \\ 0 \end{bmatrix}$$

The **main diagonal** of a square matrix is the diagonal elements from the top left corner to the bottom right corner of the matrix. For example, in the following matrix the elements m_{11}, m_{22} and m_{33} make up the main diagonal:

$$M = \begin{bmatrix} m_{11} & m_{12} & m_{13} \\ m_{21} & m_{22} & m_{23} \\ m_{31} & m_{32} & m_{33} \end{bmatrix}$$

An **identity matrix** is a square matrix where each element on the main diagonal is 1 and all other elements are 0's. An identity matrix is denoted by I. Usually, the size of an identity matrix is clear from its context. Note that in a situation where, for example, all matrices are 3×3, it is understood that I is the matrix.

$$\begin{bmatrix} 1 & 0 & 0 \\ 0 & 1 & 0 \\ 0 & 0 & 1 \end{bmatrix}$$

If the size needs to be specified, it is given using a subscript. For example, each of the following is an identity matrix.

$$I_2 = \begin{bmatrix} 1 & 0 \\ 0 & 1 \end{bmatrix}, I_3 = \begin{bmatrix} 1 & 0 & 0 \\ 0 & 1 & 0 \\ 0 & 0 & 1 \end{bmatrix}, \text{ and } I_4 = \begin{bmatrix} 1 & 0 & 0 & 0 \\ 0 & 1 & 0 & 0 \\ 0 & 0 & 1 & 0 \\ 0 & 0 & 0 & 1 \end{bmatrix}$$

The transpose of a matrix A is the matrix obtained by interchanging the rows and columns of A. The transpose of A is denoted A^t and the symbol A^t is read as "A-transpose." For example:

$$\text{If } A = \begin{bmatrix} 1 & 2 \\ 3 & 4 \\ 5 & 6 \end{bmatrix} \text{ then } A^t = \begin{bmatrix} 1 & 3 & 5 \\ 2 & 4 & 6 \end{bmatrix}$$

Here is a more precise definition of transpose.

Transpose of a Matrix	If A is an $m \times n$ matrix, then B is the transpose of A. B is an $n \times m$ matrix and $b_{ij} = a_{ji}$ for each choice of i and j.

Example 3   Find the transpose of the following matrix:

$$D = \begin{bmatrix} 1 & 9 & 0 \\ 0 & -2 & 8 \\ -4 & -1 & 7 \\ 4 & 6 & 10 \\ 1 & 0 & -1 \end{bmatrix}$$

Answer: $D^t = \begin{bmatrix} 1 & 0 & -4 & 4 & 1 \\ 9 & -2 & -1 & 6 & 0 \\ 0 & 8 & 7 & 10 & -1 \end{bmatrix}$

The next example illustrates how a matrix can be used to organize data.

Example 4   Write a matrix named S corresponding to the following test scores: Adam: 21, 34, 29, 39; Barbara: 93, 98, 79, 86; Carl: 97, 21, 56, 83; Daniel: 34, 67, 85, 57; Eve: 99, 97, 98, 99.
Use rows for the students and columns for the scores. What does s_{43} represent?

$$S = \begin{bmatrix} 21 & 34 & 29 & 39 \\ 93 & 98 & 79 & 86 \\ 97 & 21 & 56 & 83 \\ 34 & 67 & 85 & 57 \\ 99 & 97 & 98 & 99 \end{bmatrix}$$

Step 1:   Since each row gives the score for a particular student and each column gives the scores on a particular test, s_{43} is the score by the fourth student on the third test.

Answer: s_{43} represents Daniel's score on the third test, which is 85.

Problem Set

1. If A is a square matrix of order three and
$a_{11} = 6$, $a_{12} = 3$, and $a_{13} = -3$,
$a_{21} = 9$, $a_{22} = 0$, and $a_{23} = 5$,
$a_{31} = 15$, $a_{32} = -4$, and $a_{33} = -1$, what is A?

2. What is a_{22}?

$$A = \begin{bmatrix} 11 & -9 \\ 2 & -1 \end{bmatrix}$$

3. What is the dimension of A?

$$A = \begin{bmatrix} 2 & -9 \\ 3 & 1 \\ 4 & -1 \\ 8 & -2 \end{bmatrix}$$

4. What element is shown in column three of row A?

$$A = \begin{bmatrix} 2 & 13 & 11 & 9 & 0 \end{bmatrix}$$

5. What is a_{22}?

$$A = \begin{bmatrix} -2 & 11 \\ 0 & 12 \\ 1 & 24 \end{bmatrix}$$

6. What element is in row three of A?

$$A = \begin{bmatrix} 11 \\ -9 \\ 0 \\ 3 \\ 5 \end{bmatrix}$$

7. What is a_{13}?

$$A = \begin{bmatrix} 2 & 15 & 4 \\ 0 & 6 & 7 \\ 5 & 7 & 13 \end{bmatrix}$$

8. What is the dimension of the A?

$$A = \begin{bmatrix} 24 & 3 & -9 \\ 0 & 5 & 7 \end{bmatrix}$$

9. What is row one of A?

$$A = \begin{bmatrix} 3 & 2 \\ 5 & 4 \\ 7 & 6 \\ 9 & 8 \end{bmatrix}$$

10. What is row three of A?

$$A = \begin{bmatrix} 4 & 2 \\ 5 & 4 \\ 9 & 6 \\ 8 & 4 \end{bmatrix}$$

11. Which of the following matrices is a 1 by 5 zero matrix?

$$\begin{bmatrix} 1 & 0 & 1 & 0 & 1 \end{bmatrix} \qquad \begin{bmatrix} 0 \\ 0 \\ 0 \\ 0 \\ 0 \end{bmatrix}$$

$$\begin{bmatrix} 1 & 1 & 1 & 1 & 1 \end{bmatrix} \qquad \begin{bmatrix} 0 & 0 & 0 & 0 & 0 \end{bmatrix}$$

12. What is the transpose of A?

$$A = \begin{bmatrix} 1 & 12 & 0 \\ -8 & 9 & 4 \\ 11 & 9 & -9 \\ 0 & 7 & 12 \end{bmatrix}$$

13. Find B^t.

$$B = \begin{bmatrix} 11 & 0 \\ 0 & 11 \end{bmatrix}$$

14. Which of the following matrices is a 2 by 3 zero matrix?

$$\begin{bmatrix} 1 & 0 & 1 \\ 0 & 1 & 0 \end{bmatrix} \qquad \begin{bmatrix} 0 & 0 & 0 \\ 0 & 0 & 0 \end{bmatrix}$$

$$\begin{bmatrix} 1 & 0 & 0 \\ 0 & 0 & 1 \end{bmatrix} \qquad \begin{bmatrix} 0 & 0 \\ 0 & 0 \\ 0 & 0 \end{bmatrix}$$

15. Which of the following matrices is a 2 by 4 zero matrix?

$$\begin{bmatrix} 0 & 0 & 0 & 0 \\ 0 & 0 & 0 & 0 \end{bmatrix} \qquad \begin{bmatrix} 0 & 0 \\ 0 & 0 \\ 0 & 0 \\ 0 & 0 \end{bmatrix}$$

$$\begin{bmatrix} 0 & 0 & 0 \\ 0 & 0 & 0 \\ 0 & 0 & 0 \end{bmatrix} \qquad \begin{bmatrix} 0 & 0 & 0 \\ 0 & 0 & 0 \end{bmatrix}$$

16. Which of the following matrices is an identity matrix of order two?

$$\begin{bmatrix} 0 & 0 \\ 1 & 1 \end{bmatrix} \qquad \begin{bmatrix} 1 & 1 \\ 1 & 1 \end{bmatrix}$$

$$\begin{bmatrix} 0 & 1 \\ 1 & 0 \end{bmatrix} \qquad \begin{bmatrix} 1 & 0 \\ 0 & 1 \end{bmatrix}$$

17. Which of the following matrices is a 1 by 2 zero matrix?

$$\begin{bmatrix} 0 & 0 \end{bmatrix} \qquad \begin{bmatrix} 0 & 0 \\ 0 & 0 \end{bmatrix}$$

$$\begin{bmatrix} 0 \\ 0 \end{bmatrix} \qquad \begin{bmatrix} 1 & 0 \\ 0 & 1 \end{bmatrix}$$

18. A matrix A is called symmetric if $A^t = A$. Determine whether A is symmetric or not.

$$A = \begin{bmatrix} 1 & 0 & 0 & 2 \\ 0 & 1 & 2 & 3 \\ 0 & 2 & 0 & 2 \\ 2 & 3 & 1 & 0 \end{bmatrix}$$

19. Matrix A has the corresponding home runs scored by each player in five ball games.

Babe: 0, 2, 2, 2, 1
Ken: 2, 0, 1, 0, 0
Mark: 1, 2, 2, 3, 1

Use rows for the players. What does a_{35} represent?

20. What is the matrix of order four whose main diagonal is 21, 10, 5, –2 and all other elements are 1?

$$\begin{bmatrix} 21 & 10 & 5 & -2 \\ 1 & 1 & 1 & 1 \\ 1 & 1 & 1 & 1 \\ 1 & 1 & 1 & 1 \end{bmatrix} \qquad \begin{bmatrix} 1 & 1 & 1 & 21 \\ 1 & 1 & 10 & 1 \\ 1 & 5 & 1 & 1 \\ -2 & 1 & 1 & 1 \end{bmatrix}$$

$$\begin{bmatrix} 21 & 1 & 1 & 1 \\ 10 & 1 & 1 & 1 \\ 5 & 1 & 1 & 1 \\ -2 & 1 & 1 & 1 \end{bmatrix} \qquad \begin{bmatrix} 21 & 1 & 1 & 1 \\ 1 & 10 & 1 & 1 \\ 1 & 1 & 5 & 1 \\ 1 & 1 & 1 & -2 \end{bmatrix}$$

HA1-851: Performing Row Operations on Matrices

The row operations introduced in this lesson will be used in later lessons when solving systems of equations. The objective here is to explain what row operations are and the notation used to describe them. The following matrix will be used to demonstrate the various row operations:

$$M = \begin{bmatrix} 6 & -3 & 9 & 0 & 12 \\ 1 & 9 & 4 & 11 & -5 \\ -2 & 7 & 8 & 3 & 0 \\ 6 & 0 & -1 & 4 & 9 \end{bmatrix}$$

Example 1   Interchange rows 2 and 3 of the matrix:

Step 1:   Rewrite the original matrix.

$$M = \begin{bmatrix} 6 & -3 & 9 & 0 & 12 \\ 1 & 9 & 4 & 11 & -5 \\ -2 & 7 & 8 & 3 & 0 \\ 6 & 0 & -1 & 4 & 9 \end{bmatrix}$$

$R_2 \leftrightarrow R_3$

Step 2:   Write down the operation you are going to perform.

Step 3:   Write the matrix produced by the row operation.

$$\begin{bmatrix} 6 & -3 & 9 & 0 & 12 \\ -2 & 7 & 8 & 3 & 0 \\ 1 & 9 & 4 & 11 & -5 \\ 6 & 0 & -1 & 4 & 9 \end{bmatrix}$$

Example 2   Multiply row 4 of M by -6.

Step 1:   Rewrite the original matrix.

$$M = \begin{bmatrix} 6 & -3 & 9 & 0 & 12 \\ 1 & 9 & 4 & 11 & -5 \\ -2 & 7 & 8 & 3 & 0 \\ 6 & 0 & -1 & 4 & 9 \end{bmatrix}$$

$R_4 \rightarrow (-6) \cdot R_4$

Step 2:   Write the operation you are going to perform.

Step 3:   Write the matrix produced by the row operation.

$$\begin{bmatrix} 6 & -3 & 9 & 0 & 12 \\ 1 & 9 & 4 & 11 & -5 \\ -2 & 7 & 8 & 3 & 0 \\ 6(-6) & 0(-6) & (-1)(-6) & 4(-6) & 9(-6) \end{bmatrix}$$

Step 4:   Simplify the matrix.

$$\begin{bmatrix} 6 & -3 & 9 & 0 & 12 \\ 1 & 9 & 4 & 11 & -5 \\ -2 & 7 & 8 & 3 & 0 \\ -36 & 0 & 6 & -24 & -54 \end{bmatrix}$$

You can also divide a row by a non-zero number. This means that each element in a row is divided by the same non-zero number.

Example 3   Divide row 1 of M by 3. Note that this is the same as multiplying row 1 by $\frac{1}{3}$.

$$M = \begin{bmatrix} 6 & -3 & 9 & 0 & 12 \\ 1 & 9 & 4 & 11 & -5 \\ -2 & 7 & 8 & 3 & 0 \\ 6 & 0 & -1 & 4 & 9 \end{bmatrix}$$

Step 1: Rewrite the original matrix.

$R_1 \rightarrow R_1 \div 3$

Step 2: Write the operation you are going to perform.

Step 3: Write the matrix produced by the row operation.

$$\begin{bmatrix} \frac{6}{3} & \frac{-3}{3} & \frac{9}{3} & \frac{0}{3} & \frac{12}{3} \\ 1 & 9 & 4 & 11 & -5 \\ -2 & 7 & 8 & 3 & 0 \\ 6 & 0 & -1 & 4 & 9 \end{bmatrix}$$

Step 4: Simplify the matrix.

$$\begin{bmatrix} 2 & -1 & 3 & 0 & 4 \\ 1 & 9 & 4 & 11 & -5 \\ -2 & 7 & 8 & 3 & 0 \\ 6 & 0 & -1 & 4 & 9 \end{bmatrix}$$

The next row operation is to add a multiple of one row to another row as shown in the following.

Example 4   Add –6 times row 2 of M to row 4.

Step 1: $M = \begin{bmatrix} 6 & -3 & 9 & 0 & 12 \\ 1 & 9 & 4 & 11 & -5 \\ -2 & 7 & 8 & 3 & 0 \\ 6 & 0 & -1 & 4 & 9 \end{bmatrix}$ Rewrite the original matrix.

Step 2: Write the operation you are going to perform. $R_4 \rightarrow R_4 + (-6)R_2$

Step 3: Write the matrix produced by the row operation. Note that each element of row 2 is multiplied by –6 and the resulting product is added to the corresponding element in row 4.

$$\begin{bmatrix} 6 & -3 & 9 & 0 & 12 \\ 1 & 9 & 4 & 11 & -5 \\ -2 & 7 & 8 & 3 & 0 \\ 6+(-6)(1) & 0+(-6)(9) & -1+(-6)(4) & 4+(-6)(11) & 9+(-6)(-5) \end{bmatrix}$$

Step 4: Simplify the matrix.

$$\begin{bmatrix} 6 & -3 & 9 & 0 & 12 \\ 1 & 9 & 4 & 11 & -5 \\ -2 & 7 & 8 & 3 & 0 \\ 0 & -54 & -25 & -62 & 39 \end{bmatrix}$$

It is also possible to subtract a multiple of one row from another row, but it is usually more convenient to add a negative multiple than it is to subtract.

Example 5 Subtract row 2 of M from row 1.

$$M = \begin{bmatrix} 6 & -3 & 9 & 0 & 12 \\ 1 & 9 & 4 & 11 & -5 \\ -2 & 7 & 8 & 3 & 0 \\ 6 & 0 & -1 & 4 & 9 \end{bmatrix}$$

Step 1: Rewrite the original matrix.

$R_1 \rightarrow R_1 - R_2$

Step 2: Write the operation you are going to perform.

$$\begin{bmatrix} 6-1 & -3-9 & 9-4 & 0-11 & 12-(-5) \\ 1 & 9 & 4 & 11 & -5 \\ -2 & 7 & 8 & 3 & 0 \\ 6 & 0 & -1 & 4 & 9 \end{bmatrix}$$

Step 3: Write the matrix produced by the row operation. Note that each element of row 1 is being subtracted by the corresponding element from row 2.

$$\begin{bmatrix} 5 & -12 & 5 & -11 & 17 \\ 1 & 9 & 4 & 11 & -5 \\ -2 & 7 & 8 & 3 & 0 \\ 6 & 0 & -1 & 4 & 9 \end{bmatrix}$$

Step 4: Simplify the matrix.

Note that, with the exception of interchanging two rows, a row operation changes only one row of the matrix and the row that changes is to the left of the arrow in the symbol for the row operation. Usually when performing row operations you have a particular objective in mind. There can be more than one way to achieve the objective as shown in the next example.

Example 6 Given the following matrix, using one row operation transform the element in the first row and first column equal to 1. Give two possible answers, calling the resulting matrices B and C.

$$A = \begin{bmatrix} 5 & 3 & 2 \\ 2 & 1 & 6 \\ 3 & 0 & 4 \\ 6 & 1 & 9 \end{bmatrix}$$

$R_1 \rightarrow R_1 \div 5$

Step 1: Write the operation you are going to perform. One option is to divide row 1 by 5.

Step 2: Write the matrix produced by the row operation.

$$B = \begin{bmatrix} 1 & \frac{3}{5} & \frac{2}{5} \\ 2 & 1 & 6 \\ 3 & 0 & 4 \\ 6 & 1 & 9 \end{bmatrix}$$

$$R_1 \rightarrow R_1 - 2 \cdot R_2$$

Step 3: Write the operation you are going to perform. Another option is to subtract two times row 2 from row 1.

$$C = \begin{bmatrix} 1 & 1 & -10 \\ 2 & 1 & 6 \\ 3 & 0 & 4 \\ 6 & 1 & 9 \end{bmatrix}$$

Step 4: Write the matrix produced by the row operation. Remember to start from the original matrix.

Answer: $B = \begin{bmatrix} 1 & \frac{3}{5} & \frac{2}{5} \\ 2 & 1 & 6 \\ 3 & 0 & 4 \\ 6 & 1 & 9 \end{bmatrix}$ $C = \begin{bmatrix} 1 & 1 & -10 \\ 2 & 1 & 6 \\ 3 & 0 & 4 \\ 6 & 1 & 9 \end{bmatrix}$

Note that the point of the above example illustrates that there may be more than one possible answer, but usually one row operation works out more easily than the others. When working with matrices, you must try to keep the numbers simple so that you can work with them easily.

Problem Set

1. Interchange rows one and two of A.

$$A = \begin{bmatrix} 9 & 1 & 6 \\ 2 & 0 & 0 \\ 3 & 5 & 7 \end{bmatrix}$$

2. Interchange rows two and three of A.

$$A = \begin{bmatrix} 1 & 2 & 0 \\ 4 & 9 & 9 \\ 6 & 1 & 6 \end{bmatrix}$$

3. Interchange rows one and three of A.

$$A = \begin{bmatrix} 3 & 5 & 2 & 4 \\ 0 & 1 & 7 & 8 \\ 6 & 2 & 5 & 8 \\ 0 & 5 & 7 & 2 \end{bmatrix}$$

4. Interchange rows two and four of A.

$$A = \begin{bmatrix} 1 & 2 & 4 \\ 8 & 1 & 7 \\ 0 & 2 & 9 \\ 9 & 0 & 3 \end{bmatrix}$$

5. Add row one to row three.

$$A = \begin{bmatrix} 9 & 2 & 7 \\ 8 & -4 & 2 \\ 4 & -3 & 7 \end{bmatrix}$$

6. Add row three to row two.

$$A = \begin{bmatrix} 1 & 7 & -1 \\ 4 & 6 & 1 \\ 9 & -9 & 0 \end{bmatrix}$$

7. Divide row one by -1.

$$A = \begin{bmatrix} 6 & -4 & 4 \\ -5 & 3 & 2 \\ 7 & 0 & 1 \end{bmatrix}$$

8. Divide row two by 6.

$$A = \begin{bmatrix} 2 & 2 & 4 \\ 6 & -3 & -6 \\ 6 & 7 & 2 \end{bmatrix}$$

9. Multiply row two by 3.

$$A = \begin{bmatrix} 4 & 7 & -1 & 0 \\ -6 & 5 & 3 & 2 \\ 7 & 5 & 6 & 7 \\ 3 & 2 & 3 & 5 \end{bmatrix}$$

10. Multiply row one by 2.

$$A = \begin{bmatrix} 4 & 3 & 4 & 8 \\ -6 & -9 & 3 & -9 \\ 7 & 1 & -1 & 2 \\ 2 & 2 & 1 & 5 \end{bmatrix}$$

11. Interchange two rows of A to produce a matrix B with $b_{23} = 2$.

$$A = \begin{bmatrix} -1 & 3 & -6 \\ -7 & 4 & -3 \\ -12 & 3 & 2 \end{bmatrix}$$

12. Interchange two rows of A to produce a matrix B with $b_{13} = 7$.

$$A = \begin{bmatrix} -13 & 2 & 1 \\ -5 & -9 & 7 \\ 6 & 4 & 3 \end{bmatrix}$$

13. Interchange two rows of A to produce a matrix B with $b_{23} = 2$.

$$A = \begin{bmatrix} -1 & 3 & -6 \\ -7 & 4 & -3 \\ -12 & 3 & 2 \end{bmatrix}$$

14. Interchange two rows of A to produce a matrix B with $b_{31} = 2$.

$$A = \begin{bmatrix} 2 & 1 & 3 \\ 5 & -6 & -3 \\ -12 & 7 & 4 \end{bmatrix}$$

15. Multiply (or divide) row one by a number so that the element a_{12} becomes one.

$$A = \begin{bmatrix} 49 & 7 & 21 \\ 5 & 6 & -2 \\ 0 & 1 & 11 \end{bmatrix}$$

16. Multiply (or divide) row three by a number so that the element a_{33} becomes one.

$$A = \begin{bmatrix} 6 & 9 & -4 & 0 \\ 11 & 12 & -15 & 20 \\ 2 & 18 & \frac{1}{5} & 4 \\ 9 & -9 & 9 & -9 \end{bmatrix}$$

17. Multiply (or divide) row two by a number so that the element a_{24} becomes one.

$$A = \begin{bmatrix} 3 & 9 & 6 & 18 \\ 10 & 100 & 55 & 5 \\ 2 & 4 & 6 & 8 \\ 6 & 12 & 18 & 24 \end{bmatrix}$$

18. Subtract a multiple of row one from row two so that the element a_{21} is zero.

$$A = \begin{bmatrix} 1 & 0 & -9 \\ 16 & 4 & 2 \\ 3 & -1 & 0 \end{bmatrix}$$

19. Subtract a multiple of row three from row one so that the element a_{11} is zero.

$$A = \begin{bmatrix} 4 & 4 & 2 \\ -9 & 6 & 3 \\ 2 & 2 & 1 \end{bmatrix}$$

20. Add a multiple of row two to row one so that element a_{11} is zero.

$$A = \begin{bmatrix} 8 & 2 & 4 \\ -2 & 3 & 6 \\ 9 & 3 & -9 \end{bmatrix}$$

HA1-852: Solving Systems of Linear Equations in Three Variables Using the Gauss-Jordan Method

You have already learned how to solve a system of two equations in two variables. It is now time to learn how to solve linear systems with more than two variables. The problems in this lesson are systems of linear equations in three variables, although the procedures you will learn could be applied to systems of any size. This is a typical example:

$$\begin{cases} 2x + 9y - 6z = 4 \\ x + 2y - 12z = -8 \\ -4x - 3y + z = 0 \end{cases}$$

To make it clear which types of problems are solved in this lesson, a formal definition is needed. The above system of equations fits the following definition:

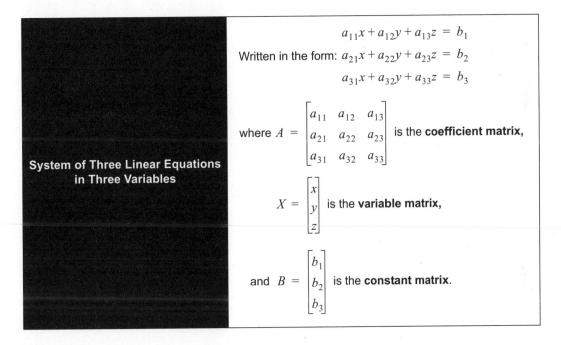

System of Three Linear Equations in Three Variables

Written in the form:
$$a_{11}x + a_{12}y + a_{13}z = b_1$$
$$a_{21}x + a_{22}y + a_{23}z = b_2$$
$$a_{31}x + a_{32}y + a_{33}z = b_3$$

where $A = \begin{bmatrix} a_{11} & a_{12} & a_{13} \\ a_{21} & a_{22} & a_{23} \\ a_{31} & a_{32} & a_{33} \end{bmatrix}$ is the **coefficient matrix,**

$X = \begin{bmatrix} x \\ y \\ z \end{bmatrix}$ is the **variable matrix,**

and $B = \begin{bmatrix} b_1 \\ b_2 \\ b_3 \end{bmatrix}$ is the **constant matrix.**

A well-organized approach is needed to solve systems with more than two variables. The process outlined below is known as **Gauss-Jordan elimination**. The first step is to write down the **augmented matrix**. It is the coefficient matrix and the constant matrix combined into one matrix and separated by a bar, as follows:

$$\begin{bmatrix} 2 & 9 & -6 & | & 4 \\ 1 & 2 & -12 & | & -8 \\ -4 & -3 & 1 & | & 0 \end{bmatrix}$$

The system is solved by using row operations to transform the augmented matrix into a special form known as **row echelon** form. A matrix is in row echelon form if:

1. The first non-zero element in any row is 1. This element is called a leading one.

2. Each leading one is to the right of the leading ones above it.

Here are some examples of row echelon form. The leading ones are in bold.

$$\begin{bmatrix} \mathbf{1} & 0 & -5 & 4 \\ 0 & \mathbf{1} & 3 & 4 \\ 0 & 0 & \mathbf{1} & -9 \end{bmatrix} \quad \begin{bmatrix} \mathbf{1} & 2 & 3 & 4 \\ 0 & \mathbf{1} & -6 & 4 \\ 0 & 0 & 0 & \mathbf{1} \end{bmatrix} \quad \begin{bmatrix} \mathbf{1} & 2 & 3 & 4 \\ 0 & 0 & \mathbf{1} & 4 \\ 0 & 0 & 0 & 0 \end{bmatrix}$$

Example 1   Here is how to transform $\begin{bmatrix} 2 & 9 & -6 & | & 4 \\ 1 & 2 & -12 & | & -8 \\ -4 & -3 & 1 & | & 0 \end{bmatrix}$ into row echelon form. Given an augmented

matrix, you need to be able to write down the corresponding system of equations. At each stage the system is given, although you would not normally do this. One reason for giving the system is to show how row operations correspond to operations with the equations.

$R_1 \leftrightarrow R_2$

$$\begin{bmatrix} 1 & 2 & -12 & | & -8 \\ 2 & 9 & -6 & | & 4 \\ -4 & -3 & 1 & | & 0 \end{bmatrix}$$

Step 1: Make the first element of the first row equal to 1. The easiest way to do this is to interchange rows 1 and 2.

System: $\begin{cases} x + 2y - 12z = -8 \\ 2x + 9y - 6z = 4 \\ -4x - 3y + z = 0 \end{cases}$

Note: Interchanging rows corresponds to writing the equations in a different order.

$R_2 \rightarrow R_2 + (-2)R_1$ and

$R_3 \rightarrow R_3 + 4R_1$

$$\begin{bmatrix} 1 & 2 & -12 & | & -8 \\ 0 & 5 & 18 & | & 20 \\ 0 & 5 & -47 & | & -32 \end{bmatrix}$$

Step 2: The first leading one is now in place. The elements below it must be zero. You make elements zero by adding (or subtracting) multiples of one row to other rows.

System: $\begin{cases} x + 2y - 12z = -8 \\ 5y + 18z = 20 \\ 5y - 47z = -32 \end{cases}$

Note: The first row operation corresponds to multiplying each side of the first equation by –2, and then adding the sides of the resulting equation to the second equation. The second row operation corresponds to multiplying each side of the first equation by 4 and then adding the sides of the resulting equation to the third equation.

$R_2 \rightarrow \dfrac{R_2}{5}$

$$\begin{bmatrix} 1 & 2 & -12 & | & -8 \\ 0 & 1 & \dfrac{18}{5} & | & 4 \\ 0 & 5 & -47 & | & -32 \end{bmatrix}$$

Step 3: Now introduce a leading one into row 2. The easiest way to do this is to divide each element of row 2 by 5.

System: $\begin{cases} x + 2y - 12z = -8 \\ y + \dfrac{18}{5}z = 4 \\ 5y - 47z = -32 \end{cases}$

Note: Dividing the second row by 5 corresponds to dividing each side of the second equation by five. When transforming a matrix to row echelon form, work your way down the matrix. After a leading one is put into place, you work to make the elements below it zero, but you do not perform any operations involving the rows above it.

$R_3 \to R_3 + (-5)R_2$

$$\begin{bmatrix} 1 & 2 & -12 & | & -8 \\ 0 & 1 & \frac{18}{5} & | & 4 \\ 0 & 0 & -65 & | & -52 \end{bmatrix}$$

Step 4: Now, add the product of negative five and row 2 to row 3.

System: $\begin{cases} x + 2y - 12z = -8 \\ y + \frac{18}{5}z = 4 \\ -65z = -52 \end{cases}$

Note: This row operation corresponds to multiplying each side of the second equation by −5 and then adding the sides of the resulting equation to the third equation. Next, divide the row 3 by −65.

$R_3 \to \dfrac{R_3}{-65}$

$$\begin{bmatrix} 1 & 2 & -12 & | & -8 \\ 0 & 1 & \frac{18}{5} & | & 4 \\ 0 & 0 & 1 & | & \frac{4}{5} \end{bmatrix}$$

Step 5: Next, divide row 3 by −65.

System: $\begin{cases} x + 2y - 12z = -8 \\ y + \frac{18}{5}z = 4 \\ z = \frac{4}{5} \end{cases}$

Note: This row operation corresponds to dividing each side of the third equation by −65. The value of z has now been found.

$$y + \frac{18}{5}z = 4$$

$$y + \left(\frac{18}{5}\right)\left(\frac{4}{5}\right) = 4$$

$$y + \frac{72}{25} = 4$$

$$y = \frac{28}{25}$$

Step 6: Substitute the value of z into the second equation to find y.

$$x + 2y - 12z = -8$$

$$x + 2\left(\frac{28}{25}\right) - 12\left(\frac{4}{5}\right) = -8$$

$$x + \frac{56}{25} - \frac{48}{5} = -8$$

$$x - \frac{184}{25} = -8$$

$$x = -\frac{16}{25}$$

Step 7: You can then substitute the values of y and z into the first equation to find x. This process is known as "back substitution".

Answer: Recall that it is standard practice to give the solution of a system in two variables as an ordered pair. For systems in three variables, the answers are given as ordered triples. The solution is $\left(-\frac{16}{25}, \frac{28}{25}, \frac{4}{5}\right)$.

Note: The variables must be in alphabetical order: x, y and z.

When solving a system of two equations, it is possible that the system is inconsistent, meaning that it has no solution. The same is true when solving systems of three equations, as shown in the following example.

Example 2   Solve: $\begin{cases} x + 2y + 4z = 5 \\ 3x + 7y - 2z = 7 \\ -2x - 5y + 6z = 3 \end{cases}$

$\begin{bmatrix} 1 & 2 & 4 & 5 \\ 3 & 7 & -2 & 7 \\ -2 & -5 & 6 & 3 \end{bmatrix}$

Step 1: Write down the augmented matrix.

$R_2 \rightarrow R_2 + (-3)R_1$
and $R_3 \rightarrow R_3 + 2R_1$

$\begin{bmatrix} 1 & 2 & 4 & 5 \\ 0 & 1 & -14 & -8 \\ 0 & -1 & 14 & 13 \end{bmatrix}$

Step 2: The first leading one is already in place, so make the elements below it equal to zero.

$R_3 \rightarrow R_3 + R_2$

$\begin{bmatrix} 1 & 2 & 4 & 5 \\ 0 & 1 & -14 & -8 \\ 0 & 0 & 0 & 5 \end{bmatrix}$

Step 3: Add row 2 to row 3.

$R_3 \rightarrow \dfrac{R_3}{5}$

$\begin{bmatrix} 1 & 2 & 4 & 5 \\ 0 & 1 & -14 & -8 \\ 0 & 0 & 0 & 1 \end{bmatrix}$

Step 4: Divide row 3 by 5. The system of equations corresponding to the row echelon form is also given.

System: $\begin{cases} x + 2y + 4z = 5 \\ y - 14z = -8 \\ 0 \neq 1 \end{cases}$

Answer: Since the third equation gives the false statement that zero and one are equal, the system has no solution. The system is called an inconsistent system; there are no solutions to this system.

It is possible that a system of three linear equations has infinitely many solutions, as shown in the following example.

Example 3   Solve: $\begin{cases} 4x = 5 + 6z - 9y \\ 2y - 3z = 2 - x \\ x = -1 - 3y - 3z \end{cases}$

$4x + 9y - 6z = 5$
$x + 2y - 3z = 2$
$x + 3y + 3z = -1$

Step 1: Write the equations with the variables aligned.

$$\begin{bmatrix} 4 & 9 & -6 & | & 5 \\ 1 & 2 & -3 & | & 2 \\ 1 & 3 & 3 & | & -1 \end{bmatrix}$$

Step 2: Write down the augmented matrix.

$R_1 \leftrightarrow R_2$

Step 3: To get the first leading one in place, interchange rows 1 and 2.

$$\begin{bmatrix} 1 & 2 & -3 & | & 2 \\ 4 & 9 & -6 & | & 5 \\ 1 & 3 & 3 & | & -1 \end{bmatrix}$$

$R_2 \rightarrow R_2 + (-4)R_1$

and $R_3 \rightarrow R_3 + (-1)R_1$

Step 4: Make the elements below the leading one equal to zero.

$$\begin{bmatrix} 1 & 2 & -3 & | & 2 \\ 0 & 1 & 6 & | & -3 \\ 0 & 1 & 6 & | & -3 \end{bmatrix}$$

$R_3 \rightarrow R_3 + (-1)R_2$

Step 5: Multiply row 2 by –1, then add the result to row 3. Note that the system has been reduced to two equations.

$$\begin{bmatrix} 1 & 2 & -3 & | & 2 \\ 0 & 1 & 6 & | & -3 \\ 0 & 0 & 0 & | & 0 \end{bmatrix}$$

System: $\begin{cases} x + 2y - 3z = 2 \\ \quad\quad y + 6z = -3 \\ \quad\quad\quad\quad 0 = 0 \end{cases}$

Answer: To get a solution, you can give z any value and then use back substitution to find x and y. Since z can be any number, there are infinitely many solutions.

When solving a system of three equations in three variables, if there is a row of zeroes in the row echelon form, then the system is dependent.

Example 4   Solve: $\begin{cases} 3x + 2z = 7 \\ y + 3z = 5 \\ 2x - y = 3 \end{cases}$

$$\begin{bmatrix} 3 & 0 & 2 & | & 7 \\ 0 & 1 & 3 & | & 5 \\ 2 & -1 & 0 & | & 3 \end{bmatrix}$$

Step 1: In this example, not all variables appear in all equations. If a variable does not appear in an equation, its coefficient is zero. Write down the augmented matrix.

$R_1 \rightarrow R_1 - R_3$

Step 2: To get the first leading one in place, subtract row 3 from row 1.

$$\begin{bmatrix} 1 & 1 & 2 & | & 4 \\ 0 & 1 & 3 & | & 5 \\ 2 & -1 & 0 & | & 3 \end{bmatrix}$$

$R_3 \rightarrow R_3 - 2R_1$

$$\begin{bmatrix} 1 & 1 & 2 & | & 4 \\ 0 & 1 & 3 & | & 5 \\ 0 & -3 & -4 & | & -5 \end{bmatrix}$$

Step 3: Make the elements below the leading one equal to zero.

$R_3 \rightarrow R_3 + 3R_2$

$$\begin{bmatrix} 1 & 1 & 2 & | & 4 \\ 0 & 1 & 3 & | & 5 \\ 0 & 0 & 5 & | & 10 \end{bmatrix}$$

Step 4: The leading one in the second row is already in place, so make the element below it equal to zero.

$R_3 \rightarrow \dfrac{R_3}{5}$

$$\begin{bmatrix} 1 & 1 & 2 & | & 4 \\ 0 & 1 & 3 & | & 5 \\ 0 & 0 & 1 & | & 2 \end{bmatrix}$$

Step 5: Divide row 3 by 5.

System: $\begin{cases} x + y + 2z = 4 \\ y + 3z = 5 \\ z = 2 \end{cases}$

$y + 3z = 5$

$y + 3(2) = 5$

$y + 6 - 6 = 5 - 6$

$\quad y = -1$

$x + y + 2z = 4$

$x + (-1) + 2(2) = 4$

$\quad\quad x + 3 = 4$

$\quad x + 3 - 3 = 4 - 3$

$\quad\quad\quad x = 1$

Step 6: Now use back substitution.

Answer: The solution is $(1, -1, 2)$.

Problem Set

1. Write the augmented matrix:
$$5x + 3y - 6z = 1$$
$$x - 2y + 2z = 0$$
$$2x - 7y + 8z = 5$$

2. Write the augmented matrix:
$$6x - 2y - 4z = 0$$
$$x + 2y + 4z = 7$$
$$-2x + 9y + 6z = 3$$

3. Write the augmented matrix.
$$x + y + 3z = 4$$
$$x + 2y + 5z = 6$$
$$x + 2y + 6z = 8$$

4. Write the augmented matrix.
$$4y - z = 1$$
$$-x = 2z + 5y - 2$$
$$z = -4y + 4x - 4$$

5. Write the augmented matrix.
$$2y + 3x - 3 = z$$
$$6y - 2x + 4 = 2z$$
$$-2y - 8x - 5 = 4z$$

6. Write a system of equations that corresponds to this augmented matrix. Use variables x, y, and z.
$$\begin{bmatrix} 1 & 2 & 3 & | & 4 \\ 0 & 1 & 4 & | & 6 \\ 0 & 0 & 1 & | & 0 \end{bmatrix}$$

7. Write a system of equations that corresponds to this augmented matrix. Use variables x, y, and z.
$$\begin{bmatrix} 1 & 0 & 5 & | & -8 \\ 0 & 2 & -7 & | & -3 \\ 0 & 0 & 1 & | & 1 \end{bmatrix}$$

8. Write a system of equations that corresponds to this augmented matrix. Use variables x, y, and z.
$$\begin{bmatrix} 1 & 8 & -3 & | & 1 \\ 0 & 1 & 4 & | & -21 \\ 0 & 2 & 0 & | & -1 \end{bmatrix}$$

9. Write a system of equations that corresponds to this augmented matrix. Use variables x, y, and z.
$$\begin{bmatrix} 1 & 2 & -3 & | & -2 \\ 1 & -2 & 5 & | & 10 \\ 5 & -2 & 9 & | & 16 \end{bmatrix}$$

10. Write a system of equations that corresponds to this augmented matrix. Use variables x, y, and z.
$$\begin{bmatrix} 1 & -1 & 7 & | & 4 \\ 0 & 2 & 4 & | & 2 \\ 5 & 0 & -6 & | & 0 \end{bmatrix}$$

11. Solve the system:
$$-x - y - 21z = -16$$
$$2x + 4y - 6z = -2$$
$$-5x + 9y + 9z = -12$$

12. Solve the system:
$$4x + 3y \quad\;\; = 7$$
$$3x + 2y + 2z = 5$$
$$2y + \;\; z = 6$$

13. Solve the system:
$$2x + 3y - 5z = -14$$
$$x + 4y - 8z = -24$$
$$4x - 6y + 9z = 24$$

14. Solve the system:
$$x - y + z = 3$$
$$x + y - z = 3$$
$$x - y + z = 4$$

15. Solve the system:
$$x + 4y - 8 = 6z$$
$$2x - 5 = 3y + z$$
$$5x - 25z = 5 - 21y$$

16. Solve the system:
$$1 = 2x - 3y + 4z$$
$$2 = x - y + 2z$$
$$0 = x - y + z$$

17. Solve the system:
$$x = -2y + 4z$$
$$5y + z = -3x$$
$$4x - 3z = -7y$$

18. Solve the system:
$$0.4x - 0.2y + 0.5z = 0.1$$
$$0.3x - 0.4y + 0.4z = 0.2$$
$$0.5x + 0.3y + 0.3z = 0.1$$

19. Solve the system:
$$2y - \frac{1}{4}z = 6 - x$$
$$2x - \frac{1}{6}z = 5 - \frac{2}{3}y$$
$$3x - \frac{7}{5}y = 4 - \frac{1}{5}z$$

20. Solve the system:
$$\frac{1}{3}x + \frac{1}{4}y + \frac{1}{4}z = \frac{1}{3}$$
$$\frac{2}{3}x - \frac{1}{3}y + \frac{1}{6}z = \frac{1}{3}$$
$$\frac{1}{5}x - \frac{1}{35}y + \frac{1}{7}z = \frac{1}{7}$$

In this lesson, you will learn a new function called the logarithmic function, or "log" for short. The logarithmic function is used in several scientific applications.

The notation is $y = \log_b x$, where b is the base and x is the argument. This is read as "y equals log base b of x."

Note: The argument cannot be negative or zero, but the result of taking the log of a positive number may be positive, negative, or zero.

Logarithm	If b and x are positive numbers ($b \neq 1$ and $b > 0$), $\log_b x = y$ if and only if $b^y = x$. The can be any positive number except 1, since every power of 1 is 1.

Properties of Logarithms:

1. $\log_b M = \log_b N$ if and only if $M = N$.

2. $\log_b 1 = 0$ if and only if $1 = b^0$.

3. $\log_b b = 1$ if and only if $b = b^1$.

4. $\log x = a$ if and only if $x = 10^a$.

Note: A log written without any base means $\log_{10}$.

The log function is related to the exponential function and, because of this, there are properties of logs that are similar to properties of exponents. Here are some examples.

Exponential Form	Logarithmic Form
$2^3 = 8$	$\log_2 8 = 3$
$2^4 = 16$	$\log_2 16 = 4$
$2^0 = 1$	$\log_2 1 = 0$
$2^{-1} = \dfrac{1}{2}$	$\log_2 \dfrac{1}{2} = -1$
$2^k = N$	$\log_2 N = k$

Example 1   Write each equation in exponential form: A) $\log_6 36 = 2$ B) $\log (0.001) = -3$

A) $\log_6 36 = 2$ **Answer:** $6^2 = 36$ Definition of Logarithm

B) $\log_{10} (0.001) = -3$ **Step 1:**   Remember a log written without any base means $\log_{10}$.

$$10^{-3} = 0.001$$

Step 2: Using the definition for logarithms, $\log_b x = y$ if and only if $b^y = x$, let the base $= 10$, $x = 0.001$ and $y = -3$.

Answer: $10^{-3} = 0.001$

Example 2   Write each equation in logarithmic form: A) $6^0 = 1$ B) $8^{\frac{-2}{3}} = \dfrac{1}{4}$

A) $6^0 = 1$ **Answer:** $\log_6 1 = 0$

B) $8^{\frac{-2}{3}} = \dfrac{1}{4}$ **Answer:** $\log_8 \dfrac{1}{4} = -\dfrac{2}{3}$

Example 3   Simplify each logarithm: A) $\log_5 25$ B) $\log_2 8\sqrt{2}$ C) $\log_2 0.125 = x$

A) $\log_5 25 = x$ **Step 1:** Rewrite the equation as an exponential equation.

$$5^x = 25$$
$$5^x = 5^2$$

Step 2: Find a common base.

$$5^x = 5^2$$
$$x = 2$$

Step 3: Set the exponents equal to each other.

Answer: $x = 2$

B) $\log_2 8\sqrt{2} = x$ **Step 1:** Rewrite the equation as an exponential equation.

$$2^x = 8\sqrt{2}$$
$$2^x = 2^3 \cdot 2^{1/2}$$
$$2^x = 2^{7/2}$$

Step 2: Find a common base. Remember the laws of exponents states $a^m \cdot a^n = a^{m+n}$.

$$x = \dfrac{7}{2}$$

Step 3: Set the exponents equal to each other.

Answer: $x = \dfrac{7}{2}$

C) $\log_2 0.125 = x$ **Step 1:** Rewrite the equation as an exponential equation.

$$2^x = 0.125$$

Step 2: Find a common base.

$$2^x = \dfrac{1}{8}$$
$$2^x = \dfrac{1}{2^3}$$

$$2^x = 2^{-3}$$

$$x = -3$$

Step 3: Set the exponents equal to each other.

Answer: $x = -3$

The laws of exponents can be used to derive the laws of logarithms. Let's review the laws of exponents.

$$a^m \cdot a^n = a^{m+n}$$

$$\frac{a^m}{a^n} = a^{m-n}$$

$$(a^m)^n = a^{mn}$$

$$(ab)^n = a^n b^n$$

$$\left(\frac{a}{b}\right)^n = \frac{a^n}{b^n}$$

Laws of Logarithms

Let b be the base of a logarithmic function ($b > 0$, $b \neq 1$). Let n and m be positive numbers.

1. $\log_b (n \cdot m) = \log_b n + \log_b m$

2. $\log_b \left(\dfrac{n}{m}\right) = \log_b n - \log_b m$

3. $\log_b a^n = n \cdot \log_b a$

4. $\log_b b^x = x$

5. $b^{\log_b x} = x$

Example 4 Express $\log_6 n^2 m^3$ in terms of $\log_6 n$ and $\log_6 m$.

$\log_6 n^2 m^3 = \log_6 n^2 + \log_6 m^3$ **Step 1:** Separate the logarithm by adding the log of each factor.

$= 2\log_6 n + 3\log_6 m$ **Step 2:** Make the exponents of the variables become the coefficients of the logarithms.

Answer: $= 2\log_6 n + 3\log_6 m$

Example 5 Express $\log_2 \sqrt{\dfrac{n}{m^5}}$ in terms of $\log_2 n$ and $\log_2 m$.

Step 1: Rewrite the radical as an exponent.

$\log_2 \sqrt{\dfrac{n}{m^5}} = \log_2 \left(\dfrac{n}{m^5}\right)^{\frac{1}{2}}$

$= \dfrac{1}{2}\log_2 \left(\dfrac{n}{m^5}\right)$ **Step 2:** Make that exponent a coefficient of the logarithm.

	Step 3:	Separate the logarithm by subtracting the log of the divisor from the log of the dividend.
$= \frac{1}{2}(\log_2 n - \log_2 m^5)$		

$= \frac{1}{2}(\log_2 n - 5\log_2 m)$	**Step 4:**	Make the exponent of m^5 a coefficient of its logarithm.

Answer: $\frac{1}{2}(\log_2 n - 5\log_2 m)$

Example 6   If log $2 \approx 0.30$ and log $3 \approx 0.48$, find the following: A) log 18   B) $\log\left(\frac{1}{\sqrt[3]{2}}\right)$

A) log 18

Since $18 = 2 \cdot 3^2$,

$\log 18 = \log 2 + \log 3^2$

$= \log 2 + 2\log 3$

Step 1: Rewrite 18 using the factors of 2 and 3. Separate the logarithm by adding the log of each factor. Make the exponents of the variables become the coefficients of the logarithms

$\approx 0.30 + 2(0.48)$

Step 2: Substitute approximate values.

Answer: $\log 18 \approx 1.26$

B) $\log\left(\frac{1}{\sqrt[3]{2}}\right)$

Since $\frac{1}{\sqrt[3]{2}} = \frac{1}{2^{\frac{1}{3}}}$

$= 2^{\frac{-1}{3}}$,

$\log\left(\frac{1}{\sqrt[3]{2}}\right) = \log 2^{\frac{-1}{3}}$

$= -\frac{1}{3}\log 2$

Step 1: Factor $\frac{1}{\sqrt[3]{2}}$ using 2 as the only factor.

Make the exponents of the variable become the coefficient of the logarithms.

$\approx -\frac{1}{3}(0.30)$

Step 2: Substitute the approximate value.

Answer: $\log\left(\frac{1}{\sqrt[3]{2}}\right) \approx -0.10$

We have talked about the common log, log base ten. There is another special log that is used primarily in natural science and it is called the **natural logarithm function**. Its base is the irrational number e, which has the approximate value 2.71828. The natural logarithm of x is sometimes denoted by **$\log_e x$,** but more often by **ln** x.

The exercises in this part of the lesson are just like the previous exercises. The only difference is that the symbol **ln** x is used instead of **log**$_b$ x. The following example illustrates:

Working with base 2 logs	Working with base e logs
1. If $\log_2 x = 5$, then $x = 2^5$.	1. If $\ln x = 5$, then $x = e^5$.
2. If $2^x = 7$, then $x = \log_2 7$.	2. If $e^x = 7$, then $x = \ln 7$.
3. $\log_2 2^5 = 5$ and $2^{\log_2 7} = 7$	3. $\ln e^5 = 5$ and $e^{\ln 7} = 7$

Logarithms and natural logarithms are also related in this way:
$\log_e e = 1$, following Properties of Logarithms 3.
$\log_e = \ln$, following the definition of natural logarithm.
$\ln e = 1$, substituting ln for $\log_e$ for first sentence.

Example 7   Simplify: $\ln \dfrac{1}{e^2}$

$\ln \dfrac{1}{e^2} = \ln e^{-2}$	**Step 1:** Write the logarithm as e to an exponent.
$= -2 \ln e$	**Step 2:** Rewrite the exponent of e as a coefficient of the logarithm.
$= -2(1)$ $= -2$	**Step 3:** Substitute $\ln e = 1$
	Answer: $\ln \dfrac{1}{e^2} = -2$

Example 8   If $\ln 5 \approx 1.61$, $\ln 4 \approx 1.39$, and $\ln 3 \approx 1.10$, find each of the following:

A) $\ln \sqrt[3]{16}$ B) $\ln \dfrac{25}{48}$

A) $\ln \sqrt[3]{16}$

$\sqrt[3]{16} = \sqrt[3]{4^2}$ $\ln \sqrt[3]{16} = \ln \sqrt[3]{4^2}$	**Step 1:** Rewrite $\sqrt[3]{16}$ as an exponent of base 4. Take the natural log of each side.
$= \ln (4^2)^{1/3}$	**Step 2:** Make the exponents become the coefficient of the logarithm.
$= \dfrac{1}{3} \ln 4^2$	
$= \left(\dfrac{1}{3}\right)(2) \ln 4$	
$= \left(\dfrac{2}{3}\right) \ln 4$	

$$\approx \left(\frac{2}{3}\right)(1.39)$$

$$\approx \frac{2.78}{3}$$

$$\approx 0.93$$

Step 3: Substitute the given value for $\ln 4$.

Answer: $\ln \sqrt[3]{16} \approx 0.93$

B) $\ln \frac{25}{48}$

$25 = 5^2$

$48 = 4^2 \cdot 3$

Step 1: Rewrite 25 and 48 using the factors 5, 4, and 3.

$\ln \frac{25}{48} = \ln 25 - \ln 48$

Step 2: Rewrite using the laws of logarithms

$= \ln 5^2 - \ln 4^2 \cdot 3$

$= \ln 5^2 - (\ln 4^2 + \ln 3)$

$= 2\ln 5^2 - (2\ln 4 + \ln 3)$

Step 3: Substitute factorizations for 25 and 48 and apply laws of logarithms.

$\approx 2(1.61) - [2(1.39) + 1.10]$

$\approx 3.22 - (2.78 + 1.10)$

≈ -0.66

Step 4: Substitute given values and simplify.

Answer: $\ln \frac{25}{48} \approx -0.66$

Because logarithms and exponents are related, some interesting things happen when they are together in the same problem. Let's look at two properties which show the canceling effect of logs and exponents together.

Properties of Logarithms that demonstrate the relationships between Logarithms and Exponents:

1. $\log_b b^x = x$
2. $b^{\log_b x} = x$

Example 9 Simplify the following: A) $\log_8 8^x$ B) $9^{\log_9 x}$

A) $\log_8 8^x$

$\log_8 8^x = x\log_8 8$

Step 1: Rewrite the exponent as the coefficient.

$= x(1)$

Step 2: $\log_8 8 = 1$, so substitute.

Answer: $\log_8 8^x = x$

B) $9^{\log_9 x}$ **Answer:** Using Properties of Logarithms (#2 above), $9^{\log_9 x} = x$, so the solution is x.

Problem Set

Evaluate the expression:

1. $\log_2 1$ **2.** $\ln e$ **3.** $\log 10$

Rewrite each expression as the sum or difference of simple logarithms:

4. $\ln (6x)$ **5.** $\log (xyz)$ **6.** $\log_2 \left(\dfrac{x}{y}\right)$ **7.** $\log y^{12}$ **8.** $\log \left(\dfrac{1}{5}\right)$

Solve the following:

9. Evaluate the expression:
$$\log_3 81$$

10. Use the properties of logarithms to simplify:
$$8^{\log_8 x}$$

11. Evaluate the expression given:
$\ln 2 = 0.693$ and $\ln 3 = 1.099$.
$$\ln \left(\frac{2}{3}\right)$$

12. Evaluate the expression given:
$\ln 2 = 0.693$, $\ln 3 = 1.099$, and $\ln 5 = 1.609$
$$\ln 30$$

13. Rewrite the expression as the sum or difference of simple logarithms. Simplify where possible.
$$\ln (e^3 x^2)$$

14. Use the properties of logarithms to simplify:
$$\ln \left(\frac{x^4}{e^3}\right)$$

15. Rewrite the expression as the sum or difference of simple logarithms.
$$\ln \left(\frac{2}{xy}\right)$$

16. Rewrite the expression as the sum or difference of simple logarithms. Simplify where possible.
$$\ln (x^3 e^2)$$

17. Rewrite the expression as the sum or difference of simple logarithms. Simplify where possible.
$$\ln (x^2 y^3)$$

18. Rewrite the expression as the sum or difference of simple logarithms. Simplify where possible.
$$\log \sqrt{\frac{x}{y}}$$

19. Evaluate the expression given.
$\log_5 7 = 1.209$ and $\log_5 3 = 0.683$
$$\log_5 \left(\frac{49}{3}\right)$$

20. Evaluate the expression given.
$\log_5 2 = 0.431$ and $\log_5 3 = 0.683$
$$\log_5 \left(\frac{2}{9}\right)$$

HA1-854: Determining the Value of Common and Natural Logarithms and Irrational Exponents

This lesson shows you how to use a calculator to evaluate some logarithms and exponential expressions. Since calculator models vary, refer to your owner's manual to find the specific keystrokes that your calculator requires.

You already know some properties of logs and exponents, and can evaluate certain expressions without a calculator. However, a calculator is required to evaluate most logarithmic expressions.

Let's review some facts about logarithms and your calculator. The only logs on your calculator are the common and natural ones. Remember that the common log is **log base 10** and is written simply as **log** without a base. The natural log is **log base e** and is written as **ln**.

$$\log_{10} = \log$$
$$\log_e = \ln$$

Example 1 Evaluate each expression. Round decimals to the nearest thousandths.

A) log 4

Step 1: On your calculator, key in $\boxed{4}$ $\boxed{\log}$ $\boxed{=}$

Answer: log $4 \approx 0.602$

B) ln 25

Step 1: On your calculator, key in $\boxed{25}$ $\boxed{\ln}$ $\boxed{=}$

Answer: ln $25 \approx 3.219$

Example 2 Evaluate each expression.

A) log (–3)

Step 1: On your calculator, key in $\boxed{3}$ $\boxed{\pm}$ $\boxed{\log}$ $\boxed{=}$

Answer: Error

B) ln 0

Step 1: On your calculator, key in $\boxed{0}$ $\boxed{\ln}$ $\boxed{=}$

Answer: Error

Remember, you can only take the log or ln of positive numbers.

Example 3 Evaluate each expression.

A) log 1

Step 1: On your calculator, key in $\boxed{1}$ $\boxed{\log}$ $\boxed{=}$

Answer: log $1 = 0$

B) ln 1

Step 1: On your calculator, key in $\boxed{1}$ $\boxed{\ln}$ $\boxed{=}$

Answer: ln $1 = 0$

Remember, the log of any base, or ln, of 1 is zero.

It is a simple matter to evaluate any common or natural log on a calculator—just press the right keys. But there are logarithms to other bases besides 10 and e. How do you evaluate $\log_3 5$, for instance? The following formula can be used to solve the problem.

Change of Base Formula	$\log_b a = \dfrac{\log_c a}{\log_c b}$, where $c = 10$ or $\log_b a = \dfrac{\ln a}{\ln b}$

Example 4   Evaluate $\log_3 5$. Round decimals to nearest thousandths.

$\log_3 5 = \dfrac{\log_{10} 5}{\log_{10} 3}$

$\approx \dfrac{0.699}{0.477}$

Step 1: $\log_b x = \dfrac{\log x}{\log b}$

Step 2:   On your calculator, key in $\boxed{5}$ $\boxed{\log}$ $\boxed{\div}$ $\boxed{3}$ $\boxed{\log}$ $\boxed{=}$

Answer: $\log_3 5 \approx 1.465$

$\log_3 5 = \dfrac{\ln 5}{\ln 3}$

$\approx \dfrac{1.609}{1.099}$

Alternatively:

Step 1: $\log_b x = \dfrac{\ln x}{\ln b}$

Step 2:   On your calculator, key in $\boxed{5}$ $\boxed{\ln}$ $\boxed{\div}$ $\boxed{3}$ $\boxed{\ln}$ $\boxed{=}$

Answer: $\log_3 5 \approx 1.465$

Example 5   Evaluate $\log_7 \dfrac{1}{2}$ Round decimals to nearest thousandths.

$\log_7 \dfrac{1}{2} = \dfrac{\log_{10} \dfrac{1}{2}}{\log_{10} 7}$

$\approx \dfrac{-0.301}{0.845}$

Step 1: $\log_b x = \dfrac{\log x}{\log b}$

Step 2:   On your calculator, key in $\boxed{0}$ $\boxed{.}$ $\boxed{5}$ $\boxed{\log}$ $\boxed{\div}$ $\boxed{7}$ $\boxed{\log}$ $\boxed{=}$

Answer: $\log_7 \dfrac{1}{2} \approx -0.356$

$\log_7 \dfrac{1}{2} = \dfrac{\ln \dfrac{1}{2}}{\ln 7}$

$\approx \dfrac{-0.693}{1.946}$

Alternatively:

Step 1: $\log_b x = \dfrac{\ln x}{\ln b}$

Answer: $\log_7 \dfrac{1}{2} \approx -0.356$

Example 6 Evaluate $\log_4 20 - 2\log_4 6$ Round decimals to nearest thousandths.

$\begin{aligned} \log_4 20 - 2\log_4 6 &= \log_4 20 - \log_4 6^2 \\ &= \log_4 20 - \log_4 36 \\ &= \log_4 \dfrac{20}{36} \end{aligned}$

Step 1: Rewrite the coefficient 2 as an exponent of 6 and apply laws of logarithms.

$= \log_4 \dfrac{5}{9}$

Step 2: Divide the terms of the logarithms.

$\log_4 \dfrac{5}{9} = \dfrac{\log_{10}\frac{5}{9}}{\log_{10}4}$

Step 3: $\log_b x = \dfrac{\log x}{\log b}$

$\begin{aligned} &\approx \dfrac{-0.255}{0.602} \\ &\approx -0.424 \end{aligned}$

Step 4: On your calculator, key in $\boxed{5}\ \boxed{\div}\ \boxed{9}\ \boxed{=}\ \boxed{\log}\ \boxed{\div}\ \boxed{4}\ \boxed{\log}\ \boxed{=}$

Answer: $\log_4 20 - 2\log_4 6 \approx -0.424$

Alternatively:

$\log_4 \dfrac{5}{9} = \dfrac{\ln\frac{5}{9}}{\ln 4}$

Step 1: $\log_b x = \dfrac{\ln x}{\ln b}$

$\approx \dfrac{-0.588}{1.386}$

Step 2: On your calculator, key in $\boxed{5}\ \boxed{\div}\ \boxed{9}\ \boxed{=}\ \boxed{\ln}\ \boxed{\div}\ \boxed{4}\ \boxed{\ln}\ \boxed{=}$

Answer: -0.424

Let's review the definitions of positive, negative, zero, and fractional exponents.

Definitions	Example
$a^n = a_1 \cdot a_2 \cdot a_3 \cdot a_4 \ldots a_n$	$3^4 = 3 \cdot 3 \cdot 3 \cdot 3 = 81$
$a^0 = 1$	$9^0 = 1$
$a^{-n} = \left(\dfrac{1}{a}\right)^n$	$4^{-3} = \left(\dfrac{1}{4}\right)^3 = \dfrac{1}{64}$
$a^{m/n} = \sqrt[n]{a^m} = \left(\sqrt[n]{a}\right)^m$	$81^{3/4} = \sqrt[4]{81^3} = \left(\sqrt[4]{81}\right)^3 = 3^3 = 27$

However, if the numbers are not neat, such as $25^{4/5}$, evaluating them is slightly more complicated. You can use a calculator to find an approximate answer. The table below contains specific keys on the calculator and the operations they perform.

Name of Key	Key on Calculator	Operation performed
Exponent	$\boxed{x^y}$	Allows you to enter any number as a base and enter any number as an exponent.
Root	$\boxed{2nd}$ $\boxed{x^y}$	Allows you to take any root of any number.
Fraction	$\boxed{a^{b/c}}$	Allows you to enter fractions on the calculator.

Example 7 Evaluate the following:

A) $25^{4/5}$ B) $4^{-5/3}$ C) $6^{\sqrt{2}}$ D) $2^{-2.4}$ E) $3^{5+\sqrt{2}}$

Round decimals to the nearest thousandths.

A) $25^{4/5}$ On your scientific calculator, key in $\boxed{2}\boxed{5}\boxed{x^y}\boxed{(}\boxed{4}\boxed{a^{b/c}}\boxed{5}\boxed{)}\boxed{=}$ 13.133
[On the TI-83 calculator: $\boxed{2}\boxed{5}\boxed{\wedge}\boxed{(}\boxed{(}\boxed{4}\boxed{\div}\boxed{5}\boxed{)}\boxed{)}\boxed{ENTER}$]

B) $4^{-5/3}$ On your scientific calculator, key in $\boxed{4}\boxed{x^y}\boxed{(}\boxed{5}\boxed{a^{b/c}}\boxed{3}\boxed{-}\boxed{)}\boxed{=}$ 0.099
[On the TI-83 calculator: $\boxed{4}\boxed{\wedge}\boxed{(}\boxed{(}\boxed{(-)}\boxed{5}\boxed{\div}\boxed{3}\boxed{)}\boxed{)}\boxed{ENTER}$]

C) $6^{\sqrt{2}}$ On your scientific calculator, key in $\boxed{6}\boxed{x^y}\boxed{2}\boxed{\sqrt{}}\boxed{=}$ 12.603
[On the TI-83 calculator: $\boxed{6}\boxed{\wedge}\boxed{(}\boxed{(}\boxed{2nd}\boxed{x^2}\boxed{2}\boxed{)}\boxed{)}\boxed{ENTER}$]

D) $2^{-2.4}$ On your scientific calculator, key in $\boxed{2}\boxed{x^y}\boxed{2}\boxed{.}\boxed{4}\boxed{-}\boxed{=}$ 0.189
[On the TI-83 calculator: $\boxed{2}\boxed{\wedge}\boxed{(}\boxed{(}\boxed{(-)}\boxed{2}\boxed{.}\boxed{4}\boxed{)}\boxed{ENTER}$]

E) $3^{5+\sqrt{2}}$ On your scientific calculator, key in $\boxed{3}\boxed{x^y}\boxed{(}\boxed{5}\boxed{+}\boxed{(}\boxed{2}\boxed{\sqrt{}}\boxed{)}\boxed{)}\boxed{=}$ 1,149.09
[On the TI-83 calculator: $\boxed{3}\boxed{\wedge}\boxed{(}\boxed{(}\boxed{5}\boxed{+}\boxed{2nd}\boxed{x^2}\boxed{2}\boxed{)}\boxed{)}\boxed{ENTER}$]

Problem Set

Evaluate the following expression. Round to the nearest thousandth.

1. $\log 20$
2. $\log 45$
3. $\log e$
4. $\ln 2$

5. $\ln 21$
6. $\ln 100$
7. $7^{\sqrt{2}}$
8. $10^{\sqrt{3}}$

9. $3^{-\sqrt{3}}$
10. $5^{-\sqrt{10}}$
11. $\log_7 2$
12. $\log_7 50$

13. 7^{-e}
14. $e^{\sqrt{2}}$
15. $\log_{\frac{1}{2}} 100$
16. $\ln_{\frac{1}{2}} e$

17. $(\sqrt{3})^{\sqrt{5}}$
18. $5^{\sqrt[3]{7}}$
19. $\log_2 6 + \log_2 10$
20. $\ln_7 e^5$

HA1-855: Solving Exponential Equations

You have worked with variables in expressions and in equations. In this lesson, you will learn to solve equations that have one or more variables in an exponent. Two types of equations have exponents. In the first type, the bases are the same. Let's look at a few examples of this type. If $2^x = 8$, you can solve the equation by converting both sides to the same base. Because $8 = 2^3$, you can say that $2^x = 2^3$. Now that the bases are equal, the exponents must also be equal, so $x = 3$. The preceding argument comes from the following rule: If $a^x = a^y$, then $x = y$.

Let's apply this rule to two examples.

Example 1   Solve: $2^{x+1} = 4^{x-1}$

$2^{x+1} = (2^2)^{x-1}$	**Step 1:** Express both sides of the equation in the same base. *Note: Remember, the Law of Exponents for a Power of a Power is $(a^m)^n = a^{mn}$ for all positive integers.*
$2^{x+1} = 2^{2x-2}$	**Step 2:** Simplify the right side of the equation by multiplying the exponents.
$x + 1 = 2x - 2$	**Step 3:** Because the bases are equal, set the exponents equal.
$x + 3 = 2x$ $3 = x$	**Step 4:** Solve the equation.
	Answer: $x = 3$

Example 2   Solve: $3^a = \dfrac{1}{81}$

$3^a = \dfrac{1}{81}$ $= \dfrac{1}{3^4}$ $= 3^{-4}$	**Step 1:** If possible, express both sides of the equation in the same base.
$3^a = 3^{-4}$	**Step 2:** Because the bases are equal, set the exponents equal.
$a = -4$	**Step 3:** Solve the equation.
	Answer: $a = -4$

Unfortunately, not all exponential equations can be rewritten with the same base. When this happens, you can eliminate the variable from the exponent by using the properties of logarithms. Let's try to solve $3^x = 8$. Because you cannot convert to equivalent bases, you must convert the exponential form to logarithmic form. Therefore, $3^x = 8$ becomes $\log_3 8 = x$, so $x = \log_3 8$

Remember, $\log_3 8 = \dfrac{\log 8}{\log 3}$.

Using a calculator, we find that $x \approx 1.893$.

Now let's try an example. In this example, take the log of both sides to eliminate the variable from the exponent. Then, follow the usual procedures to solve for x.

Example 3   Solve: $4^{x+2} = 6^x$

$\log 4^{x+2} = \log 6^x$	**Step 1:** Because you cannot express both sides of the equation in the same base, take the log of each side.
$(x+2)\log 4 = x\log 6$	**Step 2:** Extract the exponents as factors. Keep $x + 2$ in parentheses.
$x\log 4 + 2\log 4 = x\log 6$	**Step 3:** Distribute $\log 4$ to x and to 2.
$2\log 4 = x\log 6 - x\log 4$	**Step 4:** Collect the terms with x in them on the same side of the equation.
$2\log 4 = x(\log 6 - \log 4)$	**Step 5:** Because the terms on the right side are like terms, factor x out of each term.
$\dfrac{2\log 4}{\log 6 - \log 4} = x$	**Step 6:** Divide both sides by the coefficient of x in order to isolate x.
$x \approx 6.838$	**Step 7:** Find a decimal approximation with a calculator.
	Answer: $x \approx 6.838$

Here's an example with a natural logarithm:

Example 4   Solve: $5^x = e^{x-4}$

$\ln 5^x = \ln e^{x-4}$	**Step 1:** Because we cannot express both sides of the equation in the same base, take the log of each side.
$x\ln 5 = (x-4)\ln e$	**Step 2:** Extract the exponents as factors. Keep $x - 4$ in parentheses.
$x\ln 5 = x - 4$	**Step 3:** $\ln e = 1$
$4 = x - x\ln 5$	**Step 4:** Collect the terms with x in them on the same side of the equation.
$4 = x(1 - \ln 5)$	**Step 5:** Because the terms on the right side are like terms, factor x out of each term.
$\dfrac{4}{1 - \ln 5} = x$	**Step 6:** Divide both sides by the coefficient of x in order to isolate x.
$x \approx -6.563$	**Step 7:** Find a decimal approximation with a calculator.
	Answer: $x \approx -6.563$

Example 5 $6,000 is invested at 7.5% interest compounded monthly. In how many years will the investment reach $18,000?

$A = P\left(1 + \dfrac{r}{n}\right)^{nt}$	**Step 1:** Write the formula for compound interest.

$$18000 = 6000\left(1 + \frac{0.075}{12}\right)^{12t}$$

Step 2: Substitute the variable with given values: $A = 18,000$, $P = 6,000$, $r = 7.5\%$ or 0.075, $n = 12$ because the interest is compounded twelve times per year, and t is the unknown.

$$3 = (1 + 0.00625)^{12t}$$

Step 3: Divide both sides by 6,000 and reduce the fraction in parentheses.

$$\log 3 = \log (1.00625)^{12t}$$

Step 4: Take the log of each side.

$$\log 3 = 12t\log 1.00625$$

Step 5: Extract the exponent on the right, $12t$, as a factor.

$$\frac{\log 3}{12\log 1.00625} = t$$

Step 6: Divide both sides by the coefficient of t.

$$t \approx 14.694$$

Step 7: Find the decimal approximation with a calculator.

Answer: The $6,000 dollar investment will reach $18,000 dollars in approximately 14.7 years.

Here's a problem involving exponential decay:

Example 6   The decay constant of a neutron (before it decays into even smaller subatomic particles) is 0.0011325 for seconds. If a physicist has 15,000,000 neutrons, how many does she have after 10,000 seconds?

$$A_t = A_0 e^{-kt}$$

Step 1: Write the formula for exponential decay.

$$A_t = 15,000,000e^{-(0.0011325)(10,000)}$$

Step 2: Substitute variables for given values: $A_0 = 15,000,000$; $k = 0.0011325$; $t = 10,000$.

$$A_t = 15,000,000e^{-11.325}$$

Step 3: Multiply the factors in the exponent.

$$A_t \approx (15,000,000)(0.1207\times10^{-4})$$

Step 4: Raise e to the product in step 3.

$$A_t \approx 181$$

Step 5: Multiply 15,000,000 by the result.

Answer: Approximately 181 neutrons. Therefore, after about 2.8 hours, approximately 181 neutrons remain from the initial 15,000,000.

Example 7   Plutonium has a half-life of 24,000 years. Nuclear engineers stored 92 grams of plutonium in an underground facility in the year 2000. If the decay constant is 0.000028881, how much plutonium remains in the year 20000?

$$A_t = A_0 e^{-kt}$$

Step 1: Write the formula for exponential decay.

$$A_t = 92e^{-(0.2888\times10^{-4})(18,000)}$$

Step 2: Substitute variables for given values: $A_0 = 92$; $k = 0.000028881$; $t = 20000 - 2000 = 18,000$.

$$A_t = 92e^{-0.519858}$$

Step 3: Multiply the factors in the exponent.

$A_t \approx (92)(0.59460)$ **Step 4:**   Raise e to the product in step 3.

$A_t \approx 54.7$ **Step 5:**   Multiply 92 by the result.

Answer: Approximately 55 grams of plutonium remain after 18 millenniums.

Problem Set

Solve:

1. $5^x = \dfrac{1}{125}$ **2.** $2^x = 8$ **3.** $2^x = \dfrac{1}{8}$ **4.** $4^x = 16$ **5.** $6^x = 36$

6. $6^x = \dfrac{1}{36}$ **7.** $2^x = \dfrac{1}{64}$ **8.** $4^{2x+4} = 16^{3x}$ **9.** $6^{x+3} = 36^x$ **10.** $2^{5x+6} = 16^{2x}$

Solve the equations below and round your answers to the nearest thousandth:

11. $4^x = 14$ **12.** $14^x = 4$ **13.** $e^{x-5} = 13$ **14.** $e^{x-1} = 17$

15. $4^{x+1} = 20^x$ **16.** $6^{x+1} = 30^x$ **17.** $11^{x-2} = 9^x$

18. If \$1,000 is deposited at an interest rate of 3% compounded monthly, how long will it take for the investment to grow to \$2,000? Use the formula below and round your answer to the nearest tenth.

$$A = P\left(1 + \frac{r}{n}\right)^{nt} \text{ where:}$$

A = amount of investment after t years
P = original amount invested
r = interest rate
n = number of times compounded per year
t = time (number of years)

19. The value of the constant of growth for a certain bacteria is 0.08 when time is recorded in minutes. Approximately how long will it take for the bacteria to double in quantity? Use the formula below and round your answer to the nearest whole number.

$$A_t = A_o e^{kt} \text{ where:}$$

A_t = final amount
A_o = initial amount
k = constant
t = time

20. In Harrison County, Mississippi, the population has grown at an average rate of 12% a year. If the rate of growth remains constant, how many years will it take for an area with a current population of 25,000 residents to reach a population of 45,000? Use the formula below and round your answer to the nearest tenth.

$$P_t = P_o e^{kt} \text{ where:}$$

P_t = population after t years
P_o = current population
k = constant
t = time

HA1-856: Translating Exponential and Logarithmic Equations

To continue the discussion of the logarithmic and exponential functions, let's examine their relationship more closely. You know they are related due to the similar properties they have. Logarithmic and exponential functions are inverse functions of each other.

Let $y = \log_b x$

The inverse of $y = \log_b x$ is
$$\log_b y = x$$
$$y = b^x$$

Therefore, $y = \log_b x$ and $\log_b y = x$ are inverse functions.

To understand this relationship, let's look at some other inverse functions that are more familiar.

Let $y = x^2$. The inverse of $y = x^2$ is $y^2 = x$.

Therefore, you can make a general statement: $A^n = B$ if and only if $\sqrt[n]{B} = A$.

Example 1 Solve each equation:

$$A) \sqrt[8]{256} = x \qquad B) \sqrt[5]{-1024} = x$$

A) $\sqrt[8]{256} = x$

$\sqrt[8]{256} = x$	**Step 1:** Find the prime factors of 256.
$x^8 = 256$	
$x^8 = 128 \cdot 2$	
$x^8 = 64 \cdot 2 \cdot 2$	**Step 2:** Because eight x factors are on the left and eight 2 factors are on the right, the eighth root of both sides yields one x on the left and one 2 on the right.
$x^8 = 8 \cdot 8 \cdot 2 \cdot 2$	
$x^8 = 2 \cdot 2 \cdot 2 \cdot 2 \cdot 2 \cdot 2 \cdot 2 \cdot 2$	
$x = 2$	

Answer: $x = 2$

B) $\sqrt[5]{-1024} = x$

$\sqrt[5]{-1024} = x$	**Step 1:** Find the prime factors of -1024.
$x^5 = -1024$	
$x^5 = 256 \cdot -4$	
$x^5 = 64 \cdot -4 \cdot -4$	**Step 2:** Because five x factors are on the left and five -4 factors are on the right, the fifth root of both sides yields one x on the left and one -4 on the right.
$x^5 = 16 \cdot -4 \cdot -4 \cdot -4$	
$x^5 = -4 \cdot -4 \cdot -4 \cdot -4 \cdot -4$	
$x = -4$	

Answer: $x = -4$

Let's look at some examples of a logarithm and its inverse.

Example 2   Solve each equation:

A) $\log_4 2 = x$ B) $\log_x 5 = -1$ C) $\log_{\frac{1}{9}} \sqrt[4]{3} = x$ D) $\log_9 x = \dfrac{3}{2}$

A) $\log_4 2 = x$

$4^x = 2$ **Step 1:** Rewrite the equation in exponential form.

$(2^2)^x = 2$ **Step 2:** Find a common base.

$2^{2x} = 2^1$ **Step 3:** Set the exponents equal to each other and solve for x.

$2x = 1$

$x = \dfrac{1}{2}$

                 Answer: $x = \dfrac{1}{2}$

B) $\log_x 5 = -1$

$x^{-1} = 5$ **Step 1:** Rewrite the equation in exponential form.

$\dfrac{1}{x} = 5$ **Step 2:** Solve.

$1 = 5x$

$\dfrac{1}{5} = x$

                 Answer: $x = \dfrac{1}{5}$

C) $\log_{\frac{1}{9}} \sqrt[4]{3} = x$

$\left(\dfrac{1}{9}\right)^x = \sqrt[4]{3}$ **Step 1:** Rewrite the equation in exponential form.

$\left(\dfrac{1}{3^2}\right)^x = 3^{1/4}$ **Step 2:** Find a common base.

$(3^{-2})^x = 3^{1/4}$

$3^{-2x} = 3^{1/4}$ **Step 3:** Set the exponents equal to each other and solve.

$-2x = \dfrac{1}{4}$

$-8x = 1$ **Answer:** $x = -\dfrac{1}{8}$

$x = -\dfrac{1}{8}$

D) $\log_9 x = \dfrac{3}{2}$

$x = 9^{3/2}$

Step 1: Rewrite the equation in exponential form

$x = \sqrt{9^3}$

$x = 27$

Step 2: Solve.

Answer: $x = 27$

These last examples have been about translating a logarithmic expression into an exponential one in order to evaluate the log expression. However, you can translate logs to exponents for a variety of reasons.

Log Equation	Exponential Equation
$\log_b x = y$	$b^y = x$

Example 3 Translate each exponential equation into a logarithmic equation:

A) $3^{\sqrt{x}} = 2x - 1$ B) $e^{x-4} = y^5$

A) $3^{\sqrt{x}} = 2x - 1$

$\log_3 (2x - 1) = \sqrt{x}$

Answer: The exponent has a base of 3. Take the log (base 3) of both sides.

B) $e^{x-4} = y^5$

$\ln y^5 = x - 4$

Answer: The exponent with a constant base has a base of e. Take the natural log of both sides.

Example 4 Translate each log equation into an exponential equation.

A) $\log_{15} (2x^3 + 4) = x + 7$

$15^{x+7} = 2x^3 + 4$

Answer: The logarithm has a base of 15. Rewrite each as an exponent with a base of 15.

B) $\ln \sqrt{x} = 3x - 1$

$e^{3x-1} = \sqrt{x}$

Answer: The logarithm has a base of e. Rewrite each side as an exponent with a base of e.

Problem Set

Translate the logarithmic equation into an exponential equation:

1. $\log_2 16 = 4$

2. $\log_3 243 = 5$

3. $\log_2 1{,}024 = 10$

4. $\log_3 729 = 6$

5. $\log_5 \dfrac{1}{5} = -1$

6. $\log_{\frac{1}{2}} \dfrac{1}{8} = 3$

7. $\log_5 \dfrac{1}{25} = -2$

8. $\log_{\frac{1}{2}} 1 = 0$

9. $\log_{\sqrt{2}} 16 = 8$

10. $\log_{\sqrt{3}} 27 = 6$

Translate the logarithmic equation into an exponential equation and solve for x:

11. $\log_4 16 = x$

12. $\log_3 27 = x$

13. $\ln e^{\sqrt{2}} = x$

14. $\log_5 25 = x$

15. $\log_2 \sqrt{2} = x$

16. $\log_7 \sqrt[3]{7} = x$

17. $\log_x 64 = 2$

Evaluate the following:

18. Evaluate the logarithmic expression by translating it into an exponential equation. Remember to start with a logarithmic equation.

$$\log_7 49$$

19. Evaluate the logarithmic expression by translating it into an exponential equation. Remember to start with a logarithmic equation.

$$\log_3 \sqrt[5]{27}$$

20. Combine into a single logarithm and translate into an exponential equation:

$$\log_2 x + \log_2 (x + 1) = 1$$

HA1-857: Solving Logarithmic Equations

To solve logarithmic equations, you need to look closely at the definition of a logarithm. The definition states:

$$\log_b x = y \text{ if and only if } b^y = x, \text{ for } b > 0 \text{ and } b \neq 1$$

This equation is read, "log base b of x equals y if and only if b to the y equals x." Notice that b is the base of the logarithm, and of the exponent. "Log base b of x" can be translated as "The power of b that will yield x." For example, you could think of $\log_4 16 = 2$ as "The power of 4 that will yield 16 is 2." The equivalent statement, according to the definition, would be $4^2 = 16$, which is true.

Example 1   Solve: $\log_2 x = 5$

$2^5 = x$	**Step 1:** Use the definition to write the equation in exponential form.
$32 = x$	**Step 2:** Simplify using order of operations.
$\log_2 x = 5$	**Step 3:** Check your answer by substitution.
$\log_2 32 = 5$	
$2^5 = 32$	
$\sqrt[5]{2^5} = \sqrt[5]{32}$	
$2 = 2$	

Answer: $x = 32$

Example 2   Solve: $\log_x 81 = 4$.

$x^4 = 81$	**Step 1:** Use the definition to write the equation in exponential form.
$\sqrt[4]{x^4} = \sqrt[4]{81}$	**Step 2:** Take the fourth root of both sides of the equation.
$x = 3$	**Step 3:** Simplify.
$\log_x 81 = 4$	**Step 4:** Check your answer by substitution.
$\log_3 81 = 4$	
$3^4 = 81$	
$81 = 81$	

Answer: $x = 3$

Example 3   Solve: $\log_4\left(\dfrac{1}{64}\right) = x$

$4^x = \left(\dfrac{1}{64}\right)$

Step 1: Use the definition to write the equation in exponential form.

$4^x = 4^{-3}$

Step 2: Rewrite $\dfrac{1}{64}$ as an exponential expression with a base of 4.

$x = -3$

Step 3: Set exponents equal to each other and solve.

Step 4: Check your answer by substitution.

$\log_4\left(\dfrac{1}{64}\right) = x$

$4^x = \dfrac{1}{64}$

$4^{-3} = \dfrac{1}{64}$

$\dfrac{1}{4^3} = \dfrac{1}{64}$

$\dfrac{1}{64} = \dfrac{1}{64}$

Answer: $x = -3$

Example 4   Solve: $\ln(x^2 - 9) = 0$. Remember that **ln** is a logarithm with base e; therefore, if you use the definition, the exponential form will be $e^0 = (x^2 - 9)$.

$e^0 = (x^2 - 9)$

Step 1: Use the definition with the base e.

$1 = x^2 - 9$

$1 + 9 = x^2 - 9 + 9$

$10 = x^2$

$\pm\sqrt{10} = x$

Step 2: Solve the resulting equation. Remember that anything to the zero power is 1.

Step 3: Make sure to get positive and negative roots.

$\ln(x^2 - 9) = 0$

$\ln\left((\pm\sqrt{10})^2 - 9\right) = 0$

$\ln(10 - 9) = 0$

$\ln 1 = 0$

$e^0 = 1$

$1 = 1$

Step 4: Check your answer by substitution.

Answer: $x = \pm\sqrt{10}$

Example 5   Solve: $\log_5 (x+6) - \log_5 x = 2$

$\log_5\left(\dfrac{x+6}{x}\right) = 2$	**Step 1:** Use the property of the difference of two logs to make one log expression on the left side of the equation (you may only use the definition to change the equation to exponential form when there is only one log expression in the equation).
$5^2 = \left(\dfrac{x+6}{x}\right)$	**Step 2:** Use the definition to write the equation in exponential form.
$25 \cdot x = \left(\dfrac{x+6}{x}\right) \cdot x$ $25x = x + 6$ $24x = 6$ $x = \dfrac{1}{4} = 0.25$	**Step 3:** Solve the resulting equation. **Step 4:** $\log_5\left(\dfrac{1}{4} + 6\right) - \log_5 \dfrac{1}{4} = 2$. You only need to check that the base and the argument of the logarithms are non-zero and non-negative. Thus, $\dfrac{1}{4}$ is a solution.

Answer: $x = 0.25$ or $x = \dfrac{1}{4}$

Example 6   Solve: $2\log_7 x = \log_7 12 + \log_7 3$

$2\log_7 x = \log_7 12 + \log_7 3$ $\log_7 x^2 = \log_7 36$	**Step 1:** Use the properties to get one logarithmic expression on both sides of the equation.
$x^2 = 36$ $x = 6$	**Step 2:** Simplify.

Answer: $x = 6$

Problem Set

Solve the following:

1. $\log_9 x = 3$ **2.** $\log_4 x = 5$ **3.** $2 = \log_6 x$ **4.** $2 = \log_7 x$

5. $\log_x 25 = 2$ **6.** $\log_x 49 = 2$ **7.** $\log_x 12 = 2$ **8.** $\log_x 18 = 2$

9. $\log_x 64 = 3$ **10.** $\log_x 81 = 4$ **11.** $\log_x \dfrac{1}{16} = 2$ **12.** $\log_x \dfrac{1}{25} = 2$

13. $\log_x \dfrac{9}{16} = 2$ **14.** $\log_x \dfrac{81}{100} = 2$ **15.** $\log_x \dfrac{1}{216} = 3$ **16.** $\log_x \dfrac{1}{169} = 2$

17. $\ln (x^2 - 7) = 0$ **18.** $\ln (2x^2 - 49) = 0$

19. $2\log x - 2\log (x - 3) = 0$ **20.** $\log_3 (28x - 5) - \log_3 x = 3$

In mathematics, it is important to retain what you have previously learned and apply it to the new information. Recall the following properties:

$a + b = b + a$	The **Commutative Property of Addition** states that changing the order in which numbers are added does not change the sum.
$ab = ba$	The **Commutative Property of Multiplication** states that changing the order in which numbers are multiplied does not change the product.
$y + 0 = y$	The **Identity Property of Addition** states that when zero is added to any real number, the result is that same real number.
$y \cdot 1 = y$	The **Identity Property of Multiplication** states that when a real number is multiplied by one, the result is that same real number.
$y + (-y) = 0$	The **Inverse Property of Addition** states that if a number is added to its opposite, the result is zero.
$y \cdot \dfrac{1}{y} = 1$	The **Inverse Property of Multiplication** states that a real number multiplied by its reciprocal is equal to one.
$(a + b) + c = a + (b + c)$	The **Associative Property of Addition** states that numbers may be grouped in different ways and then added without changing the sum.
$(ab)c = a(bc)$	The **Associative Property of Multiplication** states that numbers may be grouped in different ways and then multiplied without changing the product.
$a(b + c) = ab + ac$	The **Distributive Property** states that a number being multiplied by the sum of two addends will result in the sum of the product of each addend and the number.

All of the properties above work for addition and multiplication, but cannot be used with subtraction and division. Let's look at an example where we are given a statement and must name the property used in the statement.

Example 1 Name the property illustrated in the given statement: $(7 + 3) + 1 = 7 + (3 + 1)$.

The Associative Property of Addition states that $(a + b) + c = a + (b + c)$.	**Step 1:** Using the definitions of the properties, determine which property best matches this statement.

Answer: Associative Property of Addition

Let's look at some additional properties.

$a \cdot (-1) = -a$	The **Property of Negative One for Real Numbers** states that any real number times negative one equals that number's opposite.
$a \cdot 0 = 0$	The **Property of Zero for Multiplication** states that any real number times zero is equal to zero.
$a = a$	The **Reflexive Property** states that a number is equal to itself.
If $a = b$, then $b = a$	The **Symmetric Property** states that two quantities are equal.
If $a = b$, and $b = c$, then $a = c$.	The **Transitive Property** states that if one quantity, a, is equal to another quantity, b, and quantity b is equal to quantity c, then quantities a and c must also be equal.
If $a = b$, and $a + c = d$, then $b + c = d$ as well.	The **Substitution Principle** states that equal quantities may be replaced for one another.
$a + b$ and ab are real numbers	The **Closure Property** states that the sum of a set of real numbers is a unique real number, and the product of a set of real numbers is a unique real number.

The reflexive, transitive, symmetric, and substitution principle properties are considered properties of equality. Let's look at another example.

Example 2   Name the property illustrated in the given statement: $10 \cdot \dfrac{1}{10} = 1$

The Inverse Property of Multiplication states that $y \cdot \dfrac{1}{y} = 1$.

Step 1: Using the definitions of the properties, determine which property best matches this statement.

Answer: Inverse Property of Multiplication

Now that we have reviewed most of the properties, recall the terms postulate and theorem.

Postulate	A statement that we assume, without proof, to be true

Theorem	A statement that must be proven true using definitions, postulates, rules of logic, and other theorems

Postulates and theorems are used to solve problems in algebra. A postulate is assumed to be a true statement, but a theorem must be proven. However, once a theorem is proven it can be used to prove other theorems.

Theorems, along with the properties previously listed, are used in completing a proof. A proof begins with a given statement, called the hypothesis. The hypothesis is followed by steps that are justified using properties and theorems. The final step is the statement that has been proven, called the **conclusion**.

Hypothesis	The given statement in a proof, usually following the "if" statement

Conclusion	The proven statement in a proof, usually following the "then" statement

Let's look at an example where you are asked to determine both the hypothesis and conclusion.

Example 3 Identify the hypothesis and the conclusion in the following statement:
If $7x - 1 = 13$, then $x = 2$.

$7x - 1 = 13$	**Step 1:** Determine the hypothesis, or what is given, in the statement. The hypothesis follows "if" in the statement.
$x = 2$	**Step 2:** Determine the conclusion, or what is to be proven, in the statement. The conclusion follows "then" in the statement.
	Answer: $7x - 1 = 13$ represents the hypothesis and $x = 2$ represents the conclusion.

Now let's look at an example of a proof.

Example 4 Prove for all real numbers, a, b, and c, if $a = b$, then $ac = bc$.

Statements	Reasons

Step 1: Set up a table with a column representing the statements and a column representing the reasons.

Statements	Reasons
$a = b$	Given

Step 2: Place the given statement in the first row.

Statements	Reasons
$a = b$	Given
$ac = ac$	Reflexive Property

Step 3: The second statement, $ac = ac$, is true by the Reflexive Property.

Statements	Reasons
$a = b$	Given
$ac = ac$	Reflexive Property
$ac = bc$	Substitution Principle

Step 4: Since $a = b$, substitute a for b in ac.

Answer:

Statements	Reasons
$a = b$	Given
$ac = ac$	Reflexive Property
$ac = bc$	Substitution Principle

Problem Set

1. Name the property illustrated in the given statement:
$$2(-1) = -2$$

    Associative Property   Distributive Property

    Property of Negative One   Reflexive Property

2. Name the property illustrated in the given statement.
$$6(a - 8) = 6(a) - 6(8)$$

    Reflexive Property   Distributive Property

    Commutative Property   Associative Property

3. Name the property illustrated in the given statement:
$$6 \cdot 0 = 0$$

    Commutative Property   Reflexive Property

    Identity Property   Zero Product Property

4. Complete the following sentence: The statement that we want to verify in a proof is called the _____.

    Theorem   Postulate

    Hypothesis   Conclusion

5. Complete the following sentence: A _____ begins with the hypothesis then, through reasoning, reaches the desired conclusion.

    Conclusion   Direct proof

    Hypothesis   Theorem

6. Name the property of addition illustrated in the given statement:
$$a + b + c = c + b + a$$

    Associative Property   Identity Property

    Commutative Property   Inverse Property

7. Name the property of addition illustrated in the given statement:
$$(a + b) + c = a + (b + c)$$

    Associative Property   Commutative Property

    Identity Property   Inverse Property

8. Name the property of multiplication illustrated in the given statement:
$$ab = ba$$

    Identity Property   Associative Property

    Commutative Property   Inverse Property

9. Name the property of multiplication illustrated in the given statement:

$$5 \cdot \frac{1}{5} = 1$$

Identity Property   Inverse Property

Associative Property   Commutative Property

10. Name the property of multiplication illustrated in the given statement:

$$5 \cdot 1 = 5$$

Commutative Property   Inverse Property

Identity Property   Associative Property

11. Is the given statement true or false?

$$a - b = b - a$$

12. Is the given statement true or false?

$$(a + b) - c = (b + a) - c$$

13. Is the given statement true or false?

$$a - b + c = a - c + b$$

14. Is the given statement true or false?

$$(m - n) - s = m - (n - s)$$

15. Is the given statement true or false?

$$\frac{z}{xy} = \frac{xy}{z}$$

16. Name the property illustrated in the given statement:

If $a = 3 + 6$, and $3 + 6 = 9$, then $a = 9$.

Inverse Property   Symmetric Property

Commutative Property   Transitive Property

17. Name the property illustrated in the given statement:

$$-b + b = 0$$

Reflexive Property   Symmetric Property

Identity Property   Inverse Property

18. Name the property illustrated in the given statement:

$$(a + bc) + df = a + (bc + df)$$

Associative Property   Commutative Property

Inverse Property   Identity Property

19. Name the property illustrated in the given statement:

$$xy \cdot \frac{1}{xy} = 1$$

Commutative Property   Associative Property

Identity Property   Inverse Property

20. Name the property illustrated in the given statement:

$$-3 + 4(8) = -3 + 32$$

Reflexive Property   Distributive Property

Identity Property   Substitution Property

HA1-866: Drawing a Line Using Slope-Intercept Form and Determining if Two Lines are Parallel or Perpendicular

You have previously learned about the slope of a line, how to graph a line, and the different forms for the equation of a line. Recall that the slope of a line is the slant of the line and is defined as the ratio of the change in y-coordinates to the corresponding change in x-coordinates. The formula for determining the slope is

$$m = \frac{y_2 - y_1}{x_2 - x_1} = \frac{\text{rise}}{\text{run}}.$$

The graph below shows a line that passes through the points $(-2, 0)$ and $(2, 2)$.

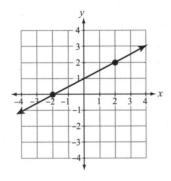

Using the points plotted on the graph, we can determine the slope of the line using the slope formula.

$$m = \frac{y_2 - y_1}{x_2 - x_1} = \frac{2 - 0}{2 - (-2)} = \frac{2}{2 + 2} = \frac{2}{4} = \frac{1}{2}$$

We can also determine the slope of the line by looking at the graph and counting the length of the rise and run.

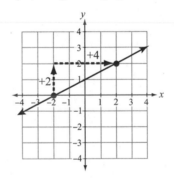

You can see that the rise is positive 2 and the run is positive 4. Therefore, the slope is $\frac{2}{4}$ or $\frac{1}{2}$. This is the same result

we found using the slope formula. When using the rise over run method, the direction in which you count is very important. For example, if you count down instead of up, the rise is negative. If you count to the left instead of to the right, the run is also negative.

Therefore, whenever you have a positive slope, you always count up and to the right, or down and to the left. For a negative slope, you always count down and to the right, or up and to the left.

Now let's review the standard form and slope-intercept form for the equation of a line. Recall that when graphing equations it is easier to have the equation in slope-intercept form in order to easily identify the slope and y-intercept of the line.

Standard Form for the Equation of a Line	$Ax + By = C$, where A, B, and C are real numbers (written in integer form when possible). $A \geq 0$, A and B are not both zero.

Slope-intercept Form for the Equation of a Line	$y = mx + b$, where m is the slope and b is the y-intercept.

Example 1   Identify the slope and y-intercept. $y = 2x + 1$

$y = mx + b$
$y = \underline{2}x + \underline{1}$

Step 1: Recall that the slope-intercept form for the equation of a line is $y = mx + b$, where m is the slope and b is the y-intercept.

Answer: The slope is 2 and the y-intercept is 1.

Example 2   Identify the slope and y-intercept. $2x + 3y = 6$

$2x + 3y = 6$
$\quad 3y = -2x + 6$
$\quad\quad y = -\frac{2}{3}x + 2$

Step 1: Rewrite the equation in slope-intercept form.

$y = mx + b$
$y = -\frac{2}{3}x + 2$

Step 2: Recall that the slope-intercept form for the equation of a line is $y = mx + b$, where m is the slope and b is the y-intercept.

Answer: The slope is $-\frac{2}{3}$ and the y-intercept is 2.

Example 3   Graph the equation $y = x + 3$ using the slope and y-intercept.

$y = mx + b$
$y = x + 3$
$y = \underline{1}x + \underline{3}$
$m = 1, b = 3$

Step 1: Identify the slope and the y-intercept.

Step 2: Plot the point (0, 3) for the *y*-intercept and use the slope, 1, to obtain another point on the graph.

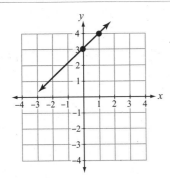

Step 3: Draw the line through the points.

Answer: The graph of $y = x + 3$ is given in step 3.

Example 4   Given the graph, find the equation of the line in slope-intercept form.

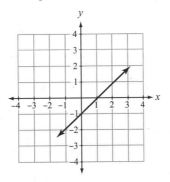

Since the graph intersects the *y*-axis at (0, –1), $b = -1$.   **Step 1:** Determine the *y*-intercept.

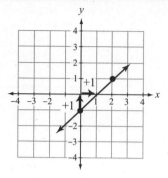

Step 2: Determine the slope.

Since the rise is +1 and the run is +1,

$$m = \frac{1}{1} = 1.$$

$y = mx + b$

$y = 1x - 1$

$y = x - 1$

Step 3: Substitute $m = 1$ and $b = -1$ into the slope-intercept form to find the equation.

Answer: $y = x - 1$

Slopes and the slope-intercept form of an equation are important in determining if two lines are parallel or perpendicular. If two lines have the same slope they are said to be parallel and if the slopes of two lines are opposite reciprocals of each other they are said to be perpendicular.

Parallel Lines	Two lines are parallel if and only if their slopes are equal.

Perpendicular Lines	Two lines are perpendicular if and only if their slopes are opposite reciprocals of each other.

Example 5 Determine whether the two lines are parallel, perpendicular, or neither.

$$4x + y = 1$$

$$y = \frac{1}{4}x + 3$$

$4x + y = 1$

$4x - 4x + y = -4x + 1$

$y = -4x + 1$

Step 1: Rewrite the first equation into the slope-intercept form.

The slope of the first line is –4.

The slope of the second line is $\frac{1}{4}$.

Step 2: Identify the slopes of the two lines.

Since the slopes are opposite reciprocals of each other, they are perpendicular.

Step 3: Compare the slopes of the two equations.

Answer: The two lines are perpendicular.

Problem Set

Identify the slope and the *y*-intercept for the following:

1. $2x + 5y = 1$

2. $2x + y = 4$

3. $3x + y = 6$

4. $-7x + y = 8$

5. $7y = 14x - 21$

6. $-y = 3x + 7$

7. $-y = 12x + 14$

8. $-4x + y = 6$

9. $3y - 9 = 5x$

10. $3x - y = 3$

Graph the following equations using the slope and *y*-intercept:

11. $x - 2y = -4$

12. $12x - 3y = -3$

13. $y = 2x + 3$

14. $y = 3x - 2$

15. $x + 2y = 6$

16. $y - 4x = 1$

17. $3x + y = -3$

Determine if the two lines in the following questions are parallel, perpendicular, or neither:

18. $3y = 2x + 14$
$2x - 3y = 2$

19. $y = -3x + 4$
$6x + 2y = -10$

20. $4y = -12x + 16$
$y = 3x - 5$

HA1-867: Identifying Domain and Range of Relations Given Graphs, Tables, or Sets of Ordered Pairs

You know that relations are very common, both in mathematics and in everyday life. You also know relations can be represented in many ways: tables, graphs, equations, and sets of ordered pairs. In previous lessons, you learned about domain and range as they pertain to relations. In this lesson, you will continue with these two ideas. First, review the following definitions.

Here is a chart that shows the relation between the day of the week and how many miles a traveling salesman drives, on average, for job-related trips.

Day of the Week	Miles Traveled
Sunday	0
Monday	87
Tuesday	132
Wednesday	63
Thursday	150
Friday	25
Saturday	184

The ordered pairs in this relation are {(Sunday, 0), (Monday, 87), (Tuesday, 132), (Wednesday, 63), (Thursday, 150), (Friday, 25), (Saturday, 184)}. The domain for this relation is {Sunday, Monday, Tuesday, Wednesday, Thursday, Friday, Saturday}, and the range is {0, 25, 63, 87, 132, 150, 184}.

Remember, if there had been repeated days of the week in the left column of the table, or repeated numbers in the right column of the table, you would not have written them more than once in the sets that represent the domain and the range. You only list elements of sets once.

Example 1   What are the domain and range for the relation {(0, 1), (1, 1), (2, 3), (5, 1),(2, 2)}?

{0, 1, 2, 5, 2}   **Step 1:** Because the domain is the set of all first elements, list all the first elements in the relation.

{1, 1, 3, 1, 2}   **Step 2:** Because the range is the set of all second elements, list all the second elements in the relation.

domain: {0, 1, 2, 5}   **Step 3:** Now be sure that the elements in each set are listed only once.
range: {1, 3, 2}

Answer: The domain is {0, 1, 2, 5} and the range is {1, 2, 3}.

When a relation is given by a graph, finding the domain and range can be very different; for example, look at the following graph.

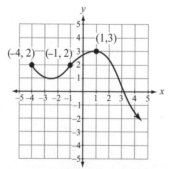

What are the ordered pairs in this relation? You can see that (1, 3) and (–1, 2) are in the relation, but you can also see that there are many other ordered pairs in this relation as well. All of the points along the curve are in the relation, and there are so many of these points that you really can't list them all. So how do you determine a domain and a range?

When you have graphs like this one, use **interval notation** to designate the domain and the range. To determine the domain, you must determine which x-values are included among the points on the graph. Since this graph is continuous from –4 on its left end, all the way to the arrow that appears on its right end, you can conclude that all x-values –4 and greater are part of the domain. The x-values extend to positive infinity, or ∞. Writing this as an interval gives you [–4, ∞) as the interval that denotes the domain. For the range, you want to know which y-values are included on the graph. There is really no lowest point on this graph, since the arrow at the right end points down. The arrow tells you that the graph continues downward forever, and so all negative numbers are included in the range. The highest point on the graph is the point (1, 3), and so no y-values larger than 3 are included. There are no gaps in this graph, so all of the negative y-values, and all numbers up to y-value 3 are part of the range. The y-values extend to negative infinity or $-\infty$. As an interval, this range is $(-\infty, 3]$.

In general, to find the domain for a relation that is given as a graph, you want to look to the left and then to the right. You must look to the left of the graph to determine the smallest x-value that is included in the domain. If there is an arrow on the left end, then the left side of the interval is $-\infty$; otherwise, it is the x-coordinate of the point where the graph ends. Then look to the right to find the largest x-value in the domain. If there is an arrow on the right end, then the right side of the interval is ∞. Otherwise, it is the x-coordinate of the point where the graph ends. To find the range for such a relation, you must be concerned with the y-values, so you must look down and then up. Looking down gives you the smallest y-value (an arrow pointing down means that the left end of the interval is $-\infty$), and looking up gives you the largest y-value (an arrow pointing up means that the right end of the interval is ∞). Remember that with interval notation, you always put the smaller quantity on the left and the larger quantity on the right. You always use parentheses for ∞ and $-\infty$, and brackets for numbers that are not included in the interval, or brackets for numbers that are included in the interval.

Example 2   What are the domain and range for the relation given by this graph?

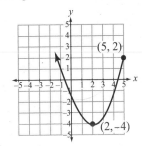

$-\infty$	**Step 1:**	Determine the left side of the interval for the domain by looking to the left end of the graph. On the left end there is an arrow; the left side of the interval will be $-\infty$.
5	**Step 2:**	Determine the right side of the domain interval. The right side of the graph ends at point (5, 2); the right side of the interval is the x-coordinate of this point, 5.
$(-\infty, 5]$	**Step 3:**	Write down the domain. The interval is $(-\infty, 5]$.
–4	**Step 4:**	Determine the left side of the interval for the range. The lowest point is the point (2, –4); the left side of the interval will be the y-coordinate of this point, –4.
∞	**Step 5:**	Determine the right side of the range interval by looking to the top of the graph. There is no highest point on the graph because the arrow at the left end points up; the right side of the interval is ∞.

$[-4, \infty)$ **Step 6:**   Write down the range. The interval is $[-4, \infty)$.

                 Answer: The domain is $(-\infty, 5]$; the range is $[-4, \infty)$.

Remember that when relations are presented by equations, the x-variable is always associated with the domain, and the y-variable is always associated with the range.

Example 3   For the relation $3x - 2y = 9$, if the domain is $\{1, 5, -1\}$, what is the range?

Step 1:   Substitute each element of the given domain for x and solve for y.

$$3(-1) - 2y = 9 \qquad\qquad 3(1) - 2y = 9 \qquad\qquad 3(5) - 2y = 9$$
$$-3 - 2y = 9 \qquad\qquad 3 - 2y = 9 \qquad\qquad 15 - 2y = 9$$
$$-3 + 3 - 2y = 9 + 3 \qquad 3 - 3 - 2y = 9 - 3 \qquad 15 - 15 - 2y = 9 - 15$$
$$\frac{-2y}{-2} = \frac{12}{-2} \qquad\qquad \frac{-2y}{-2} = \frac{6}{-2} \qquad\qquad \frac{-2y}{-2} = \frac{-6}{-2}$$
$$y = -6 \qquad\qquad\qquad y = -3 \qquad\qquad\qquad y = 3$$

Step 2:   The y-values found in Step 1 make up the range.

Answer: The range is $\{-6, -3, 3\}$.

Note that if you had been given a range instead of a domain, you would substitute each element of the range for y and solve for x, and those values would make up the domain.

Problem Set

1. What is the domain of the relation given by the following set?
$$\{(6, 2)(2, 4)(4, 8)(8, 4)(4, 6)(6, 4)\}$$

2. What is the range of the relation given by the following set?
$$\{(6, 2)(2, 4)(4, 8)(8, 4)(4, 6)(6, 4)\}$$

3. What is the domain of the relation given by the following set?
$$\{(1, 2)(2, 3)(3, 4)(4, 5)(5, 6)(6, 7)(7, 8)(8, 9)\}$$

4. What is the range of the relation given by the following set?
$$\{(1, 2)(2, 3)(3, 4)(4, 5)(5, 6)(6, 7)(7, 8)(8, 9)\}$$

5. What is the range of the relation given by the following set?
$$\{(9, 6)(6, 9)(9, 4)(4, 6)(6, 7)(7, 2)(2, 5)\}$$

6. The table shows the number of homework problems assigned from each chapter in Mrs. Jackson's science class. What is the range of the relation given by this table?

Chapter	Problems
1	84
2	120
3	79
4	55
5	83
6	90
7	80

7. The table shows inches of rainfall per month in a certain Midwestern city. What is the domain of the relation given by this table?

Inches of Rainfall Per Month in 1999
in a Certain Midwestern City

Month	Rainfall
January	1.2
February	0.5
March	0.5
April	2.3
May	3.1
June	1.8
July	1.8
August	0.7
September	0.5
October	1.1
November	0.7
December	0.7

8. The table shows inches of rainfall per month in a certain Midwestern city. What is the range of the relation given by this table?

Inches of Rainfall Per Month in 1999
in a Certain Midwestern City

Month	Rainfall
January	1.2
February	0.5
March	0.5
April	2.3
May	3.1
June	1.8
July	1.8
August	0.7
September	0.5
October	1.1
November	0.7
December	0.7

9. What is the domain of the relation given by this table?

Number of Newspapers Sold at the Corner Drug Store Last Week

Day	Monday	Tuesday	Wednesday	Thursday	Friday	Saturday	Sunday
Papers	20	15	10	5	7	7	25

10. What is the range of the relation given by this table?

Number of Newspapers Sold at the Corner Drug Store Last Week

Day	Monday	Tuesday	Wednesday	Thursday	Friday	Saturday	Sunday
Papers	20	15	10	5	7	7	25

11. What is the range of the relation given by this graph?

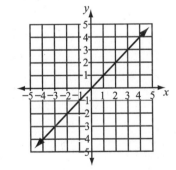

12. What is the domain of the relation given by this graph?

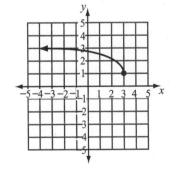

13. What is the range of the relation given by this graph?

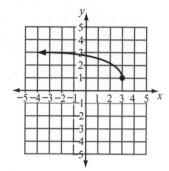

14. What is the domain of the relation given by this graph?

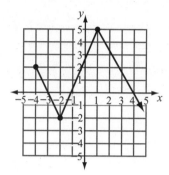

15. What is the range of the relation given by this graph?

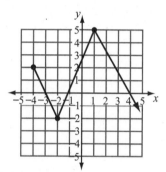

16. What is the domain of the relation given by this graph?

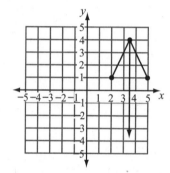

17. What is the range of the relation given by this graph?

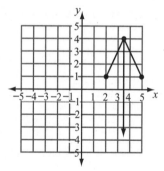

18. For the relation given by the equation $9x - 2y = 7$, if the domain is $\{1, 3, 5\}$, what is the range?

19. For the relation given by the equation $4x - y^2 = 0$, if the domain is $\{1, 4\}$, what is the range?

20. For the relation given by the equation $2x + 4y = -28$, if the range is $\{-2, 0, 2\}$, what is the domain?

Many students believe that application problems encountered in algebra have little to do with real life situations. The truth is that expecting to solve a real life application problem in your first lesson is no more realistic that expecting to play a piano concerto in your first piano lesson. The real objective in this lesson is to practice mathematical technique. Part of the technique is being able to translate a problem given in words into a purely mathematical problem, and then to solve the problem and interpret the solution. A wide variety of real world problems are solved using the same types of problems you will be solving in this lesson.

The problems in this lesson involve finding two unknown quantities. Before attempting a solution, first carefully read the problem and make sure that you understand what you are supposed to do. All of the problems are solved using the following general procedure. It is not possible to give a detailed procedure, because the details vary so much from problem to problem.

Step 1: Define variables. That is, determine the unknown quantities in the problem and state what letters will be used to represent those quantities.

Step 2: Translate the information in the problem into a system of equations or inequalities.

Step 3: Solve the system of equations or inequalities.

Step 4: Interpret the solution found in step 3. The answer should be given in words using no mathematical symbols and must include the correct units. For example, "The length is 3 feet," rather than "The length is 3".

Example 1 A total of 33 students attended the basketball game, some from Lincoln High School and the rest from Washington High School. The number of Washington students was five more than three times the number of Lincoln students. Find the number of students from each school by setting up a system of equations and solving it by graphing.

Let x = number of Lincoln students. Let y = number of Washington students.	**Step 1:** The unknown quantities are the numbers of students from each school.
$x + y = 33$	**Step 2:** From the information in the problem, you can say that the number of Lincoln students plus the number of Washington students is 33. Write an equation.
$y = 3x + 5$	**Step 3:** From the information in the problem, you can also say that the number of Washington students equals 3 times the number of Lincoln students plus 5. Write an equation.

Step 4: Now, the system of equations is $x + y = 33$
$$y = 3x + 5$$
The best way to graph the first equation is by using the intercept method. The T table for $x + y = 33$ is given at left.

x	y
0	33
33	0

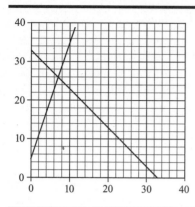

Step 5: The best way to graph the second equation is to use the fact that the y-intercept is 5 and the slope is 3. The solution of the system is given by the point where the lines intersect: (7, 26).

Answer: Recall that x is the number of Lincoln students and that y is the number of Washington students. Therefore, there were 7 students from Lincoln High and 26 students from Washington at the basketball game.

Example 2   Juan, a chemist, would like to obtain 140 ml of a 48% hydrochloric acid solution. Juan has supplies of 40% hydrochloric acid solution and 75% hydrochloric acid solution. What amount of each solution should he mix to produce the desired solution?

Let x = amount of 40% HCl solution
Let y = amount of 75% HCl solution

Step 1: The problem is to find how much of each of the available solutions Juan should mix. Let x be the number of ml of 40% hydrochloric acid solution and y be the number of ml of 75% hydrochloric acid solution.

$$x + y = 140$$

Step 2: Since the amount required is 140 ml, you can say that the amount of 40% hydrochloric acid solution plus the amount of 75% hydrochloric acid solution equals 140 ml. Write an equation.

$$0.40x + 0.75y = 0.48(140)$$

Step 3: Next, look at where the actual amount of acid in the mixture comes from. The amount of acid in the 40% solution plus the acid in the 75% solution must equal the amount of acid in the 48% solution. Write an equation.

$$\begin{aligned} x + y &= 140 \\ x - x + y &= 140 - x \\ y &= 140 - x \end{aligned}$$

Step 4: Now the system of equations is:

$$\begin{cases} 0.40x + 0.75y = 0.48(140) \\ x + y = 140 \end{cases}$$

You can solve the system using any method. It is solved here using substitution, by first solving the second equation for y.

$$0.40x + 0.75(140 - x) = 0.48(140)$$
$$0.40x + 105 - 0.75x = 67.2$$
$$-0.35x + 105 = 67.2$$
$$-0.35x + 105 - 105 = 67.2 - 105$$
$$-0.35x = -37.8$$
$$\frac{-0.35x}{-0.35} = \frac{-37.8}{-0.35}$$
$$x = 108$$

Step 5: Now substitute into the first equation and solve for x.

$$y = 140 - x$$
$$y = 140 - 108$$
$$y = 32$$

Step 6: Now find y.

Answer: Recall that x was defined to be the number of ml of 40% hydrochloric acid solution and y was defined to be the number of ml of 75% hydrochloric acid solution. Therefore, Juan must combine 108 ml of the 40% solution and 32 ml of the 75% solution to obtain 140 ml of 48% hydrochloric acid solution.

The next example is a maximization problem. It is not an application problem, but it is a type of problem that you will be required to solve. The objective is to maximize the value of a linear expression, such as $3x - 9y$, given information about x and y. To maximize the value means to find the highest value of x that satisfies the conditions of the equation or system. In application problems, x and y usually represent quantities whose signs are known. For this reason, problems often specify that (x, y) is a point in some quadrant. For example, if you know for some reason that x is positive and y is negative, then (x, y) would have to be a point in the fourth quadrant.

Example 3 Maximize $3x - 9y$ in quadrant IV, subject to the constraints: $\begin{aligned}2x - y \le 8 \\ x - 2y \le 6\end{aligned}$

Step 1: To solve the problem, graph the solution set of the system of inequalities, following the procedure you previously learned. However, only the shaded part of the solution set that lies in quadrant IV will be considered, because the problem restricts you to points in the fourth quadrant.

x	y
0	-8
4	0

x	y
0	-3
6	0

Step 2: Graph the lines $2x - y = 8$ and $x - 2y = 6$. The T tables are at left.

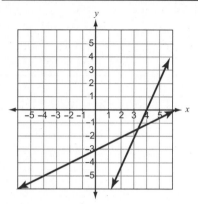

Step 3: Here the lines are graphed using the intercept method.

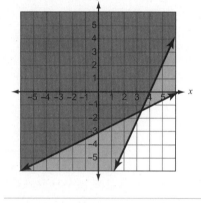

Step 4: By testing each inequality at the origin you will find that you need to shade the side of each line that contains the origin. Recall that only points in quadrant IV must be considered.

Step 5: The maximum value of $3x - 9y$ must occur at one of the corners of the shaded region. The location of the corners on the axes is already known. They are $(0,0)$, $(0, -3)$, and $(4, 0)$. To find the fourth corner you must solve the

system: $\begin{cases} 2x - y = 8 \\ x - 2y = 6 \end{cases}$.

$$2x - y = 8$$
$$\underline{-2x + 4y = -12}$$
$$3y = -4$$
$$\frac{3y}{3} = \frac{-4}{3}$$
$$y = \frac{-4}{3}$$

Step 6: We have already solved these graphically, but the solution is unclear; therefore, it is best to solve the system algebraically. Here, the system is solved by multiplying each side of the second equation by –2, and then using the addition method.

$$2x - \left(\frac{-4}{3}\right) = 8$$

$$2x + \frac{4}{3} - \frac{4}{3} = 8 - \frac{4}{3}$$

$$2x = \frac{24}{3} - \frac{4}{3}$$

$$2x = \frac{20}{3}$$

$$\frac{1}{2}(2x) = \frac{1}{2}\left(\frac{20}{3}\right)$$

$$x = \frac{10}{3}$$

Step 7: Now, substitute y into the first equation to find x.

The lines intersect at $\left(\frac{10}{3}, \frac{-4}{3}\right)$.

$(0, 0) \rightarrow 3(0) - 9(0) = 0$

$(0, 3) \rightarrow 3(0) - 9(-3) = 27$

$(4, 0) \rightarrow 3(4) - 9(0) = 12$

$\left(\frac{10}{3}, -\frac{4}{3}\right) \rightarrow 3\left(\frac{10}{3}\right) - 9\left(-\frac{4}{3}\right) = 22$

Answer: To complete the solution, evaluate $3x - 9y$ at the four corners of the shaded region. From the table at left, the maximum value of $3x - 9y$ is 27.

Example 4   Darla wants to invest her $1,350 Christmas bonus to buy two types of figurines that she collects. Large figurines cost $45 each and take up 12 square inches in her display case. Small ones cost $30 each and take up 4 square inches. Darla has only 240 square inches available in her display case. Large figurines increase in value at a rate of 5% per year, and small ones increase at a rate of 4% per year. Darla has decided that she would like the total value of the figurines to increase as much as possible after one year. How many of each should she buy?

Step 1: The problem requires finding how many of each type of figurine Darla should buy. Let x be the number of large figurines and y be the number of small figurines.

Step 2: The objective in this step is to formulate a maximization problem of the type solved in Example 3. It is helpful to first organize all of the information in a chart.

	Number	Shelf area	Value	Increase in value
Large	x	$12x$	$45x$	$0.05(45x)$
Small	y	$4y$	$30y$	$0.04(30y)$
Total		$12x + 4y$	$45x + 30y$	$0.05(45x) + 0.04(30y)$

The objective is to maximize the total increase in value, $0.05(45x) + 0.04(30y)$.

This simplifies to $2.25x + 1.2y$.

Step 3: Darla is not obliged to fill all of the available shelf space, but she cannot use more than the 240 square inches available. This gives rise to the inequality $12x + 4y \leq 240$. Likewise, the fact that Darla has only $1,350 to spend gives rise to the inequality $45x + 30y \leq 1,350$. Note that x and y, being numbers of figurines, cannot be negative quantities.

Maximize $2.25x + 1.2y$ in quadrant I subject to the following constraints:
$$12x + 4y \leq 240$$
$$45x + 30y \leq 1,350$$

Step 4: To solve the maximization problem, first graph the lines $12x + 4y = 240$ and $45x + 30y = 1,350$. Here they are graphed using the intercept method. The T tables are at left.

x	y
0	60
20	0

x	y
0	45
30	0

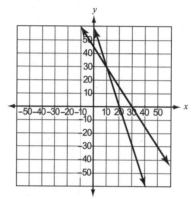

Step 5: By testing each inequality at the origin you will find that you must shade the side of each line that contains the origin. Recall that only points in the darker shaded region of quadrant I are to be considered.

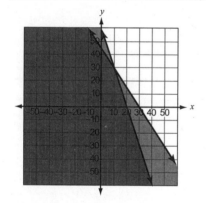

$$\begin{cases} 12x + 4y = 240 \\ 45x + 30y = 1,350 \end{cases}$$

Step 6: The maximum value of $2.25x + 1.2y$ occurs at one of the four corners of the region. Three of the four corners of the region are $(0, 0), (0, 45)$, and $(20, 0)$. To find the fourth corner, solve the system at left.

$$\frac{12x}{4} + \frac{4y}{4} = \frac{240}{4}$$

$$\frac{45x}{15} + \frac{30y}{15} = \frac{1350}{15}$$

$$-1(3x + y = 60)$$

$$\frac{3x + 2y = 90}{y = 30}$$

Step 7: The system can be simplified by dividing each term of the first equation by 4 and each term of the second equation by 15. Then simplify both equations and subtract the sides of the first equation from the sides of the second equation.

$$3x + 30 = 60$$
$$3x + 30 - 30 = 60 - 30$$
$$3x = 30$$
$$\frac{3x}{3} = \frac{30}{3}$$
$$x = 10$$

Step 8: Substitute y in the first equation. Since $x = 10$ and $y = 30$, the solution to the system of equations and the fourth corner of the region is $(10, 30)$.

$(0, 0) \rightarrow 2.25(0) + 1.2(0) = 0$

$(0, 45) \rightarrow 2.25(0) + 1.2(45) = 54$

$(20, 0) \rightarrow 2.25(20) + 1.2(0) = 45$

$(10, 30) \rightarrow 2.25(10) + 1.2(30) = 58.5$

Answer: To complete the solution, evaluate $2.25x + 1.2y$ at the four corners of the quadrant I shaded region. From the table at left, the maximum value of $2.25x + 1.2y$ is 58.5. The ordered pair that gives the expression the greatest value is $(10, 30)$. Recall that x is the number of large figurines and y is the number of small figurines. Therefore, in order to maximize her percent increase in value, Darla should buy 10 of the large figurines and 30 of the small figurines.

You will find in maximization problems that answers often contradict your intuition. For example, in the last example you might expect that Darla would do better to buy as many as possible of the large figurines because they increase in value more than the small figurines. To mathematicians the above problem is a **linear programming** problem. This example should also help you to understand how mathematics can be used to help you make decisions in real-world situations.

Problem Set

1. Peter is 12 years older than his brother David. If four times Peter's age plus two times David's age is 66, how old are Peter and David?

2. A large bag of flour weighs 2 pounds more than 2 small bags of flour. If the combined weight of 3 large bags and 5 small bags is 39 pounds, how much does each bag weigh?

3. A book costs $1 more than 3 magazines. If the cost of four books and two magazines is $46, how much does each book and each magazine cost?

4. A used CD costs $2 less than 2 used cassettes. Find the cost of a used CD and a used cassette if the total cost for two CDs and six cassettes is $46.

5. A dress shirt costs $1 less than three T-shirts. If Nigel bought three dress shirts and one T-shirt for a total cost of $37, how much did Nigel pay for each dress shirt and each T-shirt?

6. Alvin sold 80 tickets for the school play. He gave the treasurer $575. If adult tickets cost $10 each and child tickets cost $5 each, how many of each did he sell?

7. The golf club charges $12 for a round of golf. On Tuesdays, senior citizens play for a discounted price of $5. Last Tuesday, 280 people played golf and $2,100 was collected. How many people paid full price and how many were given the senior discount?

8. Maggie has been saving nickels and dimes. She has saved 30 coins totaling $2.10. How many of each coin has she saved?

9. Gus has three dollars worth of quarters and dimes. If he has a total of 24 coins, how many quarters and dimes does he have?

10. Shannon had $10,000 to invest. He invested part of the money in an account that paid 5% simple interest and the remainder in an account that paid 8% simple interest. If he received $710 in interest for a year, how much money did he invest in each account?

11. A beverage producer wishes to blend two punches to make one that is 11% fruit juice. One of the punches contains 14% fruit juice, while the other contains 9% fruit juice. How much of each punch must be used to produce 10 liters of the desired blend?

12. A chemist has a 22% acid solution and a pure acid solution. How much of each solution must she use to produce 390 ml of a 30% acid solution?

13. A pharmacist has 1% hydrocortisone cream and 4% hydrocortisone cream. How many milliliters of each cream needs to be used to produce 33ml of 3% hydrocortisone cream?

14. To raise money for new uniforms, a school will be selling tickets to the spring play. Adult tickets will cost $8 and child tickets will cost $5. If the auditorium can seat 150 people and the school needs to raise at least $1,000, what is the minimum number of adult tickets that must be sold?

15. A trucking company has been hired to transport sand to a road building project. A small truck can carry 10 tons of sand and a large truck can carry 23 tons of sand. If 15 drivers are available and at least 230 tons of sand must be delivered, what is the minimum number of large trucks that must be used to deliver the sand?

16. A large cup holds 12 ounces of coffee and a small cup holds 7 ounces. Coffee from a 96-ounce pot can be poured into a total of nine cups. What is the maximum number of large cups that will be required? (Note: The cups do not need to be filled.)

17. Johanna's digital camera has 8,000 kilobytes of memory. A medium-resolution picture requires 250 kilobytes of memory and a high-resolution picture requires 570 kilobytes of memory. If Johanna needs to take twenty pictures, what is the maximum number of high-resolution pictures she can take?

18. Assuming that x and y are positive quantities, at what point is $2x + 4y$ maximized subject to the constraints $x + y \leq 6$ and $3x + y \leq 12$?

19. Assuming that x and y are positive quantities, at what point is $4x + y$ maximized subject to the constraints $x + y \leq 4$ and $3x + y \leq 6$?

20. Janet is making birdhouses and bird feeders to sell at a craft store. The store told her to build no more than 12 items. This week, Janet can spend no more than 16 hours working on the project. A birdhouse takes 2 hours to make and sells for $25. A bird feeder takes 1 hour to make and sells for $15. What combination of birdhouses and bird feeders should she make to maximize revenue?

HA1-871: Simplifying Radical Expressions

In this lesson we will simplify radical expressions. We have previously learned that radical expressions have two basic parts: the root (or index) and the base (or radicand).

Root (or index) $\longrightarrow$ $\sqrt[n]{x}$ $\longleftarrow$ Base (or radicand)

The radical expression $\sqrt{x}$ indicates the square root of x. The root or index, 2, is not usually shown since it is understood. The radical expression $\sqrt[3]{x}$ indicates the cube root of x. Before working some examples, let's review some basic rules or properties for exponents.

Rule for Rational Exponents	$\sqrt[n]{x} = x^{\frac{1}{n}}$
Power Rule for Exponents	$\sqrt[n]{x^m} = x^{\frac{m}{n}}$
Rule for Exponents with Signed Numbers	$\pm\sqrt{n^2} = \pm n$
Rule for Negative Squares	$\sqrt{-n^2}$ is not a real number.
Product Property for Exponents	$\sqrt{m \cdot n} = \sqrt{m} \cdot \sqrt{n}$ where $m \geq 0$ and $n \geq 0$.

Example 1   Simplify completely: $\sqrt[2]{54}$

$\sqrt[2]{54} = \sqrt[2]{9 \cdot 6}$

$\quad = \sqrt[2]{9} \cdot \sqrt[2]{6}$

Step 1:   Factor the base.

$\quad = 3\sqrt[2]{6}$

Step 2:   Simplify.

Answer: $3\sqrt[2]{6}$ or $\sqrt{6}$

Example 2   Simplify completely: $\sqrt[3]{432x^5}$

$\sqrt[3]{432x^5} = \sqrt[3]{216 \cdot 2 \cdot x^3 \cdot x^2}$ $= \sqrt[3]{216} \cdot \sqrt[3]{2} \cdot \sqrt[3]{x^3} \cdot \sqrt[3]{x^2}$	**Step 1:** Factor the base
$= 6x\sqrt[3]{2x^2}$	**Step 2:** Simplify.
	Answer: $6x\sqrt[3]{2x^2}$

Example 3   Simplify completely: $\sqrt{49a^9b^6}$

$\sqrt{49a^9b^6} = \sqrt{49 \cdot a^8 \cdot a \cdot b^6}$ $= \sqrt{49} \cdot \sqrt{a^8} \cdot \sqrt{a} \cdot \sqrt{b^6}$	**Step 1:** Factor the base.
$= 7a^4b^3\sqrt{a}$	**Step 2:** Simplify.
	Answer: $7a^4b^3\sqrt{a}$

Example 4   Simplify completely: $(27x^4z^6)^{\frac{1}{3}}$

	Step 1: Apply the rule for rational exponents.
$(27x^4z^6)^{\frac{1}{3}} = \sqrt[3]{27x^4z^6}$	
$= \sqrt[3]{27x^4z^6}$ $= \sqrt[3]{27 \cdot x^3 \cdot x \cdot z^6}$ $= \sqrt[3]{27} \cdot \sqrt[3]{x^3} \cdot \sqrt[3]{x} \cdot \sqrt[3]{z^6}$	**Step 2:** Factor the base.
$= 3xz^2\sqrt[3]{x}$	**Step 3:** Simplify.
	Answer: $3xz^2\sqrt[3]{x}$

Example 5 Simplify completely: $\pm\sqrt[4]{16m^{12}n^5}$

$\pm\sqrt[4]{16m^{12}n^5} = \pm\sqrt[4]{16 \cdot m^{12} \cdot n^5}$ $= \sqrt[4]{16} \cdot \sqrt[4]{m^{12}} \cdot \sqrt[4]{n^4} \cdot \sqrt[4]{n}$	**Step 1:** Factor the base.
$= \pm 2m^3 n \sqrt[4]{n}$	**Step 2:** Simplify.
	Answer: $\pm 2m^3 n \sqrt[4]{n}$

Problem Set

Simplify the following completely:

1. $\sqrt{252}$

2. $\sqrt{224}$

3. $\sqrt{396}$

4. $\sqrt{184}$

5. $\sqrt{72m}$

6. $\sqrt{224c^4}$

7. $\sqrt{148k^3}$

8. $\sqrt{800a}$

9. $\sqrt{76n^{13}}$

10. $\sqrt{54a^{16}}$

11. $\sqrt{64c^9 d^5}$

12. $\sqrt{28a^8 b^3}$

13. $\sqrt{a^{16}b^2}$

14. $\sqrt{20x^7 y^6}$

15. $\sqrt{117m^5 n^2 p^7}$

16. $\sqrt{50r^6 s}$

17. $\sqrt{168m^2 n}$

18. $(32q^5 r^7)^{\frac{1}{5}}$

19. $(-256t^3 u^4)^{\frac{1}{4}}$

20. $(256q^3 z^8)^{\frac{1}{4}}$

In this lesson, we will simplify radicals. When simplifying radicals, we can combine radicals that have like radicands by using addition and subtraction.

Like Radicals	Radicals that have the same root (index) and the same radicand

There are four helpful steps to remember when using addition and subtraction to simplify radicals:

1. Express each radical in simplest form.

2. Determine "like radicands".

3. Use the Distributive Property to add or subtract radicals with like radicands.

4. Keep the roots of the radicals the same.

Let's look at some examples.

$3\sqrt{2} + 4\sqrt{2}$ $= (3+4)\sqrt{2}$ $= 7\sqrt{2}$	$\sqrt[3]{5} + \sqrt[3]{5}$ $= 2\sqrt[3]{5}$ (note: $\sqrt[3]{5} = 1\sqrt[3]{5}$, so $1\sqrt[3]{5} + 1\sqrt[3]{5} = (1+1)\sqrt[3]{5} = 2\sqrt[3]{5}$)	$5\sqrt[4]{3} - \sqrt[4]{3}$ $= (5-1)\sqrt[4]{3}$ $= 4\sqrt[4]{3}$
$3x\sqrt{7} + 2x\sqrt{7}$ $= 5x\sqrt{7}$	$2y\sqrt{3} + 5\sqrt{3}$ can be written as $(2y+5)\sqrt{3}$ to write the expression as a single term.	$5\sqrt[3]{xy} + 2\sqrt[3]{xy}$ $= 7\sqrt[3]{xy}$
$8\sqrt{5} + 3\sqrt{5} - c\sqrt[3]{5}$ $= 11\sqrt{5} - c\sqrt[3]{5}$ This is considered to be in simplest form.	$\sqrt{80} - 3\sqrt{5}$ $= \sqrt{16 \cdot 5} - 3\sqrt{5}$ $= \sqrt{16} \cdot \sqrt{5} - 3\sqrt{5}$ $= 4\sqrt{5} - 3\sqrt{5}$ $= 1\sqrt{5}$ $= \sqrt{5}$	

You may combine like radicals by using the Distributive Property, but you must keep the same roots.

Example 1   Simplify: $2\sqrt[4]{ab} - 2\sqrt[4]{ab} + 3\sqrt{ab} + 3\sqrt[4]{ab}$

$2\sqrt[4]{ab} - 2\sqrt[4]{ab} + 3\sqrt{ab} + 3\sqrt[4]{ab}$

$= 2\sqrt[4]{ab} - 2\sqrt[4]{ab} + 3\sqrt[4]{ab} + 3\sqrt{ab}$

Step 1:   Determine the like radicals (radical having the same root [index] and same radicands).

$= (2 - 2 + 3)\sqrt[4]{ab} + 3\sqrt{ab}$ | **Step 2:** Combine like terms using the Distributive Property.

$= 3\sqrt[4]{ab} + 3\sqrt{ab}$ | **Step 3:** Write the simplified expression.

Answer: $3\sqrt[4]{ab} + 3\sqrt{ab}$

More complicated radical expressions may be combined using the same steps.

Example 2 Simplify: $\sqrt{32x^3} - \sqrt{4x^2} + \sqrt{72x^4y^3} + \sqrt{2y}$

$\sqrt{32x^3} - \sqrt{4x^2} + \sqrt{72x^4y^3} + \sqrt{2y}$
$= \sqrt{16x^2} \cdot \sqrt{2x} - \sqrt{4x^2} + \sqrt{36x^4y^2} \cdot \sqrt{2y} + \sqrt{2y}$ | **Step 1:** Express each radical in simplest form.

$= 4x \cdot \sqrt{2x} - 2x + 6x^2y \cdot \sqrt{2y} + \sqrt{2y}$
$= 4x\sqrt{2x} - 2x + 6x^2y\sqrt{2y} + 2y$ | **Step 2:** Simplify and determine the like radicals.

$= 4x\sqrt{2x} - 2x + (6x^2y + 1)\sqrt{2y}$ | **Step 3:** Combine like terms using the Distributive Property.

$= 4x\sqrt{2x} - 2x + (6x^2y + 1)\sqrt{2y}$ | **Step 4:** Write the simplified expression.

Answer: $4x\sqrt{2x} - 2x + (6x^2y + 1)\sqrt{2y}$

Example 3 Simplify: $4\sqrt{a^3b^2} - \sqrt{64a^2b^3} + 3\sqrt{25a^2b^3} + \sqrt{25a^3b^2}$

$4\sqrt{a^3b^2} - \sqrt{64a^2b^3} + 3\sqrt{25a^2b^3} + \sqrt{25a^3b^2}$
$= 4 \cdot ab\sqrt{a} - 8ab\sqrt{b} + 3 \cdot 5ab\sqrt{b} + 5ab\sqrt{a}$
$= 4ab\sqrt{a} - 8ab\sqrt{b} + 15ab\sqrt{b} + 5ab\sqrt{a}$ | **Step 1:** Express each radical in simplest form.

$= 4ab\sqrt{a} + 5ab\sqrt{a} - 8ab\sqrt{b} + 15ab\sqrt{b}$ | **Step 2:** Determine the like radicals.

$= (4ab + 5ab)\sqrt{a} + (-8ab + 15ab)\sqrt{b}$ | **Step 3:** Combine like terms using the Distributive Property.

$= 9ab\sqrt{a} + 7ab\sqrt{b}$ | **Step 4:** Write the simplified expression.

Answer: $9ab\sqrt{a} + 7ab\sqrt{b}$

Example 4   Simplify: $\sqrt[4]{16x} - \sqrt[3]{27x^4} + 2\sqrt[4]{81x} - \sqrt[3]{64x^4}$

$\sqrt[4]{16x} - \sqrt[3]{27x^4} + 2\sqrt[4]{81x} - \sqrt[3]{64x^4}$ $= \sqrt[4]{16} \cdot \sqrt[4]{x} - \sqrt[3]{27x^3} \cdot \sqrt[3]{x} + 2\sqrt[4]{81} \cdot \sqrt[4]{x} - \sqrt[3]{64x^3} \cdot \sqrt[3]{x}$	**Step 1:** Express each radical in simplest form.
$= 2\sqrt[4]{x} - 3x\sqrt[3]{x} + 2 \cdot 3 \cdot \sqrt[4]{x} - 4x \cdot \sqrt[3]{x}$ $= 2\sqrt[4]{x} - 3x\sqrt[3]{x} + 6\sqrt[4]{x} - 4x\sqrt[3]{x}$	**Step 2:** Simplify and determine the like radicals.
$= (2 + 6)\sqrt[4]{x} + (-3x - 4x)\sqrt[3]{x}$	**Step 3:** Combine like terms using the Distributive Property.
$= 8\sqrt[4]{x} - 7x\sqrt[3]{x}$	**Step 4:** Write the simplified expression.

Answer: $8\sqrt[4]{x} - 7x\sqrt[3]{x}$

Problem Set

Simplify the following:

1. $5\sqrt{x} + 4\sqrt{x}$

2. $10\sqrt{3x} - 5\sqrt{3x}$

3. $7\sqrt{15} + 2\sqrt{15}$

4. $8\sqrt{10} + 5\sqrt{10}$

5. $6\sqrt{3x} + 3\sqrt{3x}$

6. $\sqrt{x} + 5\sqrt{x}$

7. $\sqrt{27} - 2\sqrt{3}$

8. $3\sqrt{24y} + 9\sqrt{54y}$

9. $10\sqrt{8} + 2\sqrt{2}$

10. $\sqrt{9y} + \sqrt{16y}$

11. $6\sqrt{y} - 7\sqrt{y} + 11\sqrt{y}$

12. $5\sqrt{xy} + 8\sqrt{xy} + \sqrt{xy}$

13. $4\sqrt{6} + 9\sqrt{6} - 6\sqrt{6}$

14. $2\sqrt{12y} + \sqrt{27y} - \sqrt{48y}$

15. $10\sqrt{75} - 8\sqrt{27} + 5\sqrt{12}$

16. $6\sqrt{ab} + 8\sqrt{a} - 3\sqrt{ab}$

17. $3\sqrt{5xy} + 2\sqrt{5x} + 3\sqrt{5xy}$

18. $\sqrt[4]{16a^4b^2} - \sqrt[4]{81a^4b^2} + 2\sqrt{9ab^2} - \sqrt{25ab^2}$

19. $\sqrt{98x} - \sqrt[4]{81x^4y} + \sqrt[4]{16x^4y} - \sqrt{162x}$

20. $2\sqrt[6]{64a^6b^3} - 2\sqrt[5]{96ab} + \sqrt[6]{a^6b^3} - \sqrt[5]{3ab}$

In a previous lesson, you learned how to simplify radical expressions. Recall that when simplifying a square root the product property of square roots is applied. The radicand is in simplest form when it has no perfect square factors other than 1. This is similar for simplifying nth roots.

Look at the examples below:

$$\sqrt{8} = \sqrt{4 \cdot 2} \qquad\qquad \sqrt[3]{54} = \sqrt[3]{27 \cdot 2}$$
$$= \sqrt{4} \cdot \sqrt{2} \qquad\qquad\qquad = \sqrt[3]{27} \cdot \sqrt[3]{2}$$
$$= 2\sqrt{2} \qquad\qquad\qquad\quad = 3\sqrt[3]{2}$$

Let's review the Distributive Property and the FOIL Method before working some problems.

Distributive Property	For real numbers a, b, and c, $a(b+c) = ab + ac$.

	A method used to multiply two binomials, in the following order:
	F First Multiply the first terms of each binomial.
FOIL Method	O Outer Multiply the outer terms of each binomial.
	I Inner Multiply the inner terms of each binomial.
	L Last Multiply the second terms of each binomial.

Example 1 Simplify: $\sqrt{14} \cdot \sqrt{7}$

$\sqrt{14} \cdot \sqrt{7} = \sqrt{14 \cdot 7}$ $= \sqrt{98}$	**Step 1:** Multiply the radical expressions.
$= \sqrt{49 \cdot 2}$	**Step 2:** Factor the terms under the square root.
$= 7\sqrt{2}$	**Step 3:** Simplify.
	Answer: $7\sqrt{2}$

Example 2 Simplify: $-2\sqrt{10} \cdot 3\sqrt{5}$

$-2\sqrt{10} \cdot 3\sqrt{5} = -2 \cdot 3 \cdot \sqrt{10 \cdot 5}$	**Step 1:** Multiply the radical expressions.
$= -2 \cdot 3 \cdot \sqrt{2 \cdot 5 \cdot 5}$	**Step 2:** Factor the terms under the square root.

$$= -2 \cdot 3 \cdot 5 \cdot \sqrt{2}$$

$$= -30\sqrt{2}$$

Step 3: Simplify

Answer: $-30\sqrt{2}$

Example 3 Simplify: $4\sqrt{2y} \cdot 4\sqrt{6y}$

$4\sqrt{2y} \cdot 4\sqrt{6y} = 4 \cdot 4 \cdot \sqrt{2y \cdot 6y}$

Step 1: Multiply the radical expressions.

$$= 4 \cdot 4\sqrt{2y \cdot 2y \cdot 3}$$

Step 2: Factor the terms under the square root.

$$= 4 \cdot 4 \cdot 2y \cdot \sqrt{3}$$

$$= 32y\sqrt{3}$$

Step 3: Simplify.

Answer: $32y\sqrt{3}$

Example 4 Simplify: $-\sqrt[3]{6x^2y} \cdot 2\sqrt[3]{18xy}$

$-\sqrt[3]{6x^2y} \cdot 2\sqrt[3]{18xy} = -1 \cdot 2 \cdot \sqrt[3]{6 \cdot 18 \cdot x^2 \cdot x \cdot y \cdot y}$

Step 1: Multiply the radical expressions.

$$= -1 \cdot 2 \cdot \sqrt[3]{2 \cdot 3 \cdot 9 \cdot 2 \cdot x^2 \cdot x \cdot y^2}$$

$$= -1 \cdot 2 \cdot \sqrt[3]{27 \cdot 4 \cdot x^3 \cdot y^2}$$

Step 2: Factor the terms under the cube root.

$$= -1 \cdot 2 \cdot 3 \cdot x \cdot \sqrt[3]{4 \cdot y^2}$$

$$= -6x\sqrt[3]{4y^2}$$

Step 3: Simplify.

Answer: $-6x\sqrt[3]{4y^2}$

Example 5 Simplify: $(3 + 4\sqrt{2})^2$

$(3 + 4\sqrt{2})^2 = (3 + 4\sqrt{2})(3 + 4\sqrt{2})$

Step 1: Rewrite the radical expression as the product of two binomials.

F $3 \cdot 3 = 9$

Step 2: Multiply the first terms of each binomial.

O $3 \cdot 4\sqrt{2} = 12\sqrt{2}$

Step 3: Multiply the outer terms of each binomial.

I $4\sqrt{2} \cdot 3 = 12\sqrt{2}$

Step 4: Multiply the inner terms of each binomial.

| L | $4\sqrt{2} \cdot 4\sqrt{2} = 16 \cdot 2 = 32$ | **Step 5:** | Multiply the last terms of each binomial. |

$$(3 + 4\sqrt{2})(3 + 4\sqrt{2}) = 9 + 12\sqrt{2} + 12\sqrt{2} + 32$$
$$= 41 + 24\sqrt{2}$$

Step 6: Combine all the terms together.

Answer: $73 + 24\sqrt{2}$

Problem Set

Simply the following products:

1. $\sqrt{30} \cdot \sqrt{3}$

2. $\sqrt{32} \cdot \sqrt{12}$

3. $\sqrt{3} \cdot \sqrt{33}$

4. $2\sqrt{5} \cdot \sqrt{5}$

5. $\sqrt{10} \cdot \sqrt{20}$

6. $(\sqrt{4})^2$

7. $(\sqrt{6})^2$

8. $(\sqrt{12})(\sqrt{48})$

9. $(\sqrt{6})(\sqrt{14})$

10. $\sqrt{14} \cdot \sqrt{2}$

11. $\sqrt{20xy} \cdot \sqrt{10x^2y^4}$

12. $\sqrt[3]{6} \cdot \sqrt[3]{36}$

13. $\sqrt[3]{2} \cdot \sqrt[3]{4}$

14. $\sqrt[4]{16} \cdot \sqrt[3]{216}$

15. $\sqrt[3]{5x^2} \cdot \sqrt[3]{25x^4}$

16. $\sqrt[3]{4x^2} \cdot \sqrt[3]{2x^3}$

17. $\sqrt[3]{4x^2} \cdot \sqrt[3]{4x^2}$

18. $\sqrt{5}(\sqrt{2} - \sqrt{3})$

19. $(\sqrt[3]{3} + \sqrt[3]{2})(-\sqrt[3]{243} + 2\sqrt[3]{32})$

20. $(\sqrt[3]{2} + \sqrt[3]{5})(\sqrt[3]{4} - \sqrt[3]{25})$

An important application of radical expressions is found when the distance between two points is needed to solve a problem in algebra or geometry or to investigate a real-world situation.

On the Cartesian Plane, if you know the coordinates of two points you can determine the distance between the two points using the distance formula.

The distance formula states that given two points, (x_1, y_1) and (x_2, y_2), the distance, d, between the points can be written as: $d = \sqrt{(x_2 - x_1)^2 + (y_2 - y_1)^2}$.

For example, given point R(3, –1), and S(6, –5), you can use the distance formula to get:

$$d = \sqrt{(6-3)^2 + ((-5)-(-1))^2}$$
$$= \sqrt{3^2 + ((-5)+1)^2}$$
$$= \sqrt{3^2 + (-4)^2}$$
$$= \sqrt{9 + 16}$$
$$= \sqrt{25}$$
$$= 5$$

Therefore, the length of segment $\overline{RS}$ is 5 units. But where does the distance formula come from and why does it work? To answer these questions, look at coordinate points on a plane. You can see the connection between the points as they are graphed.

Consider the graph with the points (x_1, y_1) and (x_2, y_2) plotted. Using these points, a right triangle can be constructed from the points A, B and C.

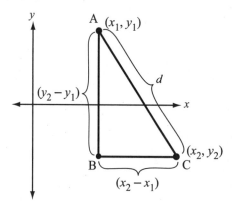

To determine the distance of the side AB, you could find the value of $y_2 - y_1$. This represents the "change in y."

To determine the distance of the side BC, you could find the value of $x_2 - x_1$. This represents the "change in x."

To find the distance of AC (the distance, d), you could use the relationship of the sides of a right triangle that states that the sum of the squares of the legs (AB, BC) of a right triangle is equal to the square of the longest side (AC), the hypotenuse. You may recognize this as the Pythagorean Theorem.

From this theorem, you can state that:

$$AB^2 + BC^2 = AC^2$$

Write the theorem.	$AB^2 + BC^2 = AC^2$
Substitute the values for each and you have:	$(y_2 - y_1)^2 + (x_2 - x_1)^2 = d^2$
Solve the equation for d by eliminating the radical.	$\sqrt{(y_2 - y_1)^2 + (x_2 - x_1)^2} = d$
So the distance between the two points is:	$d = \sqrt{(y_2 - y_1)^2 + (x_2 - x_1)^2}$

You also know the formula for the slope of a segment as $m = \dfrac{y_2 - y_1}{x_2 - x_1}$. You may have learned this as the formula for the slope of a line, but remember that a segment is a part of a line. Therefore, if you find the slope of a line, you have found the slope of any segment on that line. Look at the following example to review how to use the slope formula.

Using the two points given previously for $\overline{RS}$, you can find the slope of $\overline{RS}$ by putting the coordinates into the formula as follows:

$$m = \frac{(-5) - (-1)}{6 - 3}$$

$$= \frac{(-5) + 1}{3}$$

$$= -\frac{4}{3}$$

Therefore, the slope of $\overline{RS}$ is $-\dfrac{4}{3}$.

Example 1   Find the length and slope of $\overline{AB}$ given points $A(-2, 3)$ and $B(4, 0)$.

$d = \sqrt{(4 - (-2))^2 + (0 - 3)^2}$ $= \sqrt{(4 + 2)^2 + (-3)^2}$	**Use the distance formula to find length.** **Step 1:** Put coordinates into the formula.
$= \sqrt{6^2 + (-3)^2}$ $= \sqrt{36 + 9}$	**Step 2:** Simplify using order of operations.
$= \sqrt{45} \approx 6.71$	**Step 3:** Use a calculator to get the decimal approximation for the square root.
$m = \dfrac{0 - 3}{4 - (-2)}$	**Use the slope formula to find the slope of the segment.** **Step 4:** Put coordinates into the formula.

$$= \frac{-3}{4+2}$$

$$= -\frac{3}{6}$$

$$= -\frac{1}{2}$$

Step 5: Simplify using order of operations.

Answer: Length $\overline{AB} \approx 6.71$; Slope $\overline{AB} = -\frac{1}{2}$

Midpoint of a Segment

The midpoint of a segment is what the name implies — the point at the middle of the segment.

Midpoint of a Segment	M is the midpoint of a segment AB if M is between A and B, and if $AM = MB$.

Before you look at the formula for finding the midpoint of a segment on a Cartesian Plane, think about how you would find your average grade in a class if you have two test scores. You would add the two test scores together and then divide by two to find a number that is right in the middle of those two test scores. The concept is the same for finding the midpoint of a segment. You are going to find the average of the x-coordinates of the endpoints to find the x-coordinate of the midpoint, and the average of the y-coordinates of the endpoints to find the y-coordinate of the

midpoint. Thus, the midpoint formula is as follows: $M = \left(\frac{x_1 + x_2}{2}, \frac{y_1 + y_2}{2} \right)$

For example, with the points for $\overline{RS}$ given previously, $R(3, -1)$ and $S(6, -5)$, you would use the midpoint formula to find the midpoint this way:

$$M = \left(\frac{6+3}{2}, \frac{(-5)+(-1)}{2} \right)$$

$$= \left(\frac{9}{2}, \frac{-6}{2} \right)$$

$$= \left(4\frac{1}{2}, -3 \right)$$

Therefore, the midpoint of $\overline{RS}$ is the point $\left(4\frac{1}{2}, -3 \right)$.

Example 2   Find the midpoint of segment PQ if its endpoints are $P(0, -4)$ and $Q(8, 2)$.

$$M = \left(\frac{8+0}{2}, \frac{2+(-4)}{2} \right)$$

Step 1: Put the coordinates of P and Q into the midpoint formula.

$$= \left(\frac{8}{2}, \frac{-2}{2} \right)$$

$$= (4, -1)$$

Answer: $(4, -1)$

Applications of Length, Slope, and Midpoint

Using the ideas of length, slope and midpoint in real life situations requires a few helpful techniques. First, draw a picture of the problem situation and relate the distances as coordinates in the Cartesian Plane. Then assign ordered pairs to the points of reference and use these points to calculate the distance and slope needed to solve the questions asked.

Example 3   A ramp is to be built from one building to another such that produce can be sent out a window to the window of the building next door. The buildings are 400 feet apart and the higher window is 300 feet above the lower window. The lower window is 20 feet from the ground. The ramp will require a support beam to be placed halfway between the two windows to support the weight of the produce being sent. From this information, determine the:

  A) length of the plank needed to reach from one window to the next
  B) slope of the ramp
  C) position and length of the support beam

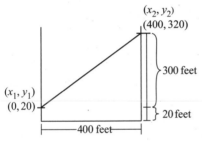

Step 1:   First, draw a diagram of the problem situation. Let the lower window be positioned at the coordinates (0, 20) and the higher window be at the coordinates (400, 320).

$$d = \sqrt{(x_2 - x_1)^2 + (y_2 - y_1)^2}$$

$$= \sqrt{(400 - 0)^2 + (320 - 20)^2}$$

$$= \sqrt{(400)^2 + (300)^2}$$

$$= \sqrt{160,000 + 90,000}$$

$$= \sqrt{250,000}$$

$$= 500$$

Step 2:   To find the length of the plank (distance), use the distance formula. The plank must be 500 feet long.

$$m = \frac{y_2 - y_1}{x_2 - x_1}$$

$$= \frac{320 - 20}{400 - 0}$$

$$= \frac{300}{400}$$

$$= \frac{3}{4}$$

Step 3:   To find the slope of the ramp, use the formula for slope.

$$M = \left(\frac{x_1 + x_2}{2}, \frac{y_1 + y_2}{2}\right)$$

$$= \left(\frac{0 + 400}{2}, \frac{320 + 20}{2}\right)$$

$$= \left(\frac{400}{2}, \frac{340}{2}\right)$$

$$= (200, 170)$$

Step 4: To find the position and length of the support beam, use the formula for midpoint.

Answer: A) length of the plank needed to reach from one window to the next: 500 feet.

B) slope of the ramp: The ramp rises 3 feet for every 4 feet across.

C) position and length of the support beam: The support beam must be placed 200 feet between the buildings and must be 170 feet long.

Problem Set

1. Given points $C(0, 3)$ and $D(-2, 6)$, find the slope of the line segment $\overline{CD}$.

2. Given points $P(3, 4)$ and $Q(1, 0)$, find the slope of the line segment $\overline{PQ}$.

3. Given points $A(-5, -7)$ and $B(-1, -11)$, find the slope of the line segment $\overline{AB}$.

4. Given points $J(10, 8)$ and $K(-4, 3)$, find the slope of the line segment $\overline{JK}$.

5. Given points $B(4, 7)$ and $W(-12, -3)$, find the slope of the line segment $\overline{BW}$.

6. Given points $D(2, -5)$ and $E(-5, 4)$, find the midpoint of the line segment $\overline{DE}$.

7. Given points $S(10, 8)$ and $T(-10, 10)$, find the midpoint of the line segment $\overline{ST}$.

8. Given points $B(-9, 6)$ and $C(0, 3)$, find the midpoint of the line segment $\overline{BC}$.

9. Given points $N(-3, 3)$ and $O(-8, 3)$, find the midpoint of the line segment $\overline{NO}$.

10. Given points $R(3, -1)$ and $F(13, -9)$, find the midpoint of the line segment $\overline{RF}$.

11. Given points $A(2, 5)$ and $B(3, -3)$, find the distance of line segment $\overline{AB}$. Round the answer to the nearest hundredth.

12. Given points $W(-1, 4)$ and $X(3, 7)$, find the distance of line segment $\overline{WX}$. Round the answer to the nearest hundredth.

13. Given points $F(4, -4)$ and $G(5, 1)$, find the distance of line segment $\overline{FG}$. Round the answer to the nearest hundredth.

14. Given points $N(6, -4)$ and $O(-2, 5)$, find the distance of line segment $\overline{NO}$. Round the answer to the nearest hundredth.

15. Given points $R(8, -2)$ and $S(-5, -5)$, find the distance of line segment $\overline{RS}$. Round the answer to the nearest hundredth.

16. Lisa opened a savings account with $500. After four years, she saved $1,750. How much money did Lisa save each year?

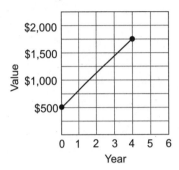

17. Gas is $1.25 per gallon. After five months, gas prices increased to $2.50 per gallon. If gas prices increase evenly each month, by how much money did gas prices increase each month?

18. The segment $\overline{KB}$ has a midpoint $M(6, 15)$ and the endpoint $K(4, 25)$. Find the coordinates of B.

19. The segment $\overline{CB}$ has a midpoint $M(0, 0)$ and the endpoint $C(6, 4)$. Find the coordinates of B.

20. The segment $\overline{DE}$ has a midpoint $M\left(18, -\frac{5}{2}\right)$ and the endpoint $D(-4, -4)$. Find the coordinates of E.

Consider these statements:
- A triangle has three sides.
- Only odd numbers are prime.
- A negative number plus another negative number equals a positive number.

When statements such as these are made in mathematics, you must question whether they are always true, sometimes true, or never true.

For a statement to be "always true," you must not be able to find a counterexample of the statement. A **counterexample** is a sample answer that makes the statement false. For example, examine the statement above that says "A triangle has three sides." If you think about the definition of a triangle, you know that all triangles have three sides. In other words, you cannot draw a shape with less than or more than three sides and call it a triangle. Therefore, the statement "A triangle has three sides" is always true.

For a statement to be "sometimes true," you must be able to find at least one counterexample of the statement. The statement "Only odd numbers are prime" is sometimes true. If you begin to list some prime numbers, you may believe that only odd numbers are prime. For example, 3, 5, 7, 11, 13, and so on. But think again. The number 2 is also prime. This is a counterexample. Therefore, the statement is sometimes true.

Finally, a statement can be "never true" (false). This statement means that you cannot find one example where the statement is true. The statement "A negative number plus another negative number equals a positive number" is never true. When you add two negative numbers, the sum is never positive.

Look at a few more examples.

Example 1 An even number plus another even number is odd. Is this statement always true, sometimes true, or never true?

> **Answer:** There is not a single instance where the sum of two even numbers is odd, therefore the statement is never true.

Example 2 A polygon has 5 sides. Is this statement always true, sometimes true, or never true?

> **Answer:** Some polygons have 5 sides; these figures are called pentagons. There are also polygons with less than and more than 5 sides. The statement is sometimes true.

Example 3 Review this statement: $a + b = b + a$. Is this statement always true, sometimes true, or never true?

> **Answer:** Try substituting whole numbers, integers, and decimals for the variables. You will find that this statement is always true. You can also say that this statement illustrates the Commutative Property of Addition, which is further proof that the statement is always true.

Problem Set

1. Justify the statement with a property of real numbers:
$$4m + 5n - 6p = 4m + 5n - 6p$$

2. Justify the statement with a property of real numbers:
$$(7 + 3a)4 = 28 + 12a$$

3. Justify the statement with a property of real numbers:
$$\text{If } p = 2q, \text{ then } 2q = p$$

4. Justify the statement with a property of real numbers:
$$8(2x - 4y + 3) = 16x - 32y + 24$$

5. Justify the statement with a property of real numbers:
$$9 \cdot (16 \cdot 7) = (9 \cdot 16) \cdot 7$$

6. Justify the statement with a property of real numbers:
$$0 = 0$$

7. Which property is illustrated below?
$$0 + 7 = 7$$

8. Which property is illustrated below?
$$9a + (-9a) = 0$$

9. Which property is illustrated below?
$$\frac{5}{a} \cdot \frac{a}{5} = 1$$

10. Justify the statement with a property of real numbers:
Let $y = 75$. If the measure of $\angle A = y$, then $\angle A = 75°$.

11. Determine whether the statement is always true, sometimes true, or never true:
The difference of two positive integers is positive.

12. Determine whether the statement is always true, sometimes true, or never true:
The reciprocal of a fraction is less than one.

13. Determine whether the statement is always true, sometimes true, or never true:
$$4(11) = 4(6) + 4(5)$$

14. Determine whether the statement is always true, sometimes true, or never true:
Twenty-five hundredths has the same value as one fourth.

15. Determine whether the statement is always true, sometimes true, or never true:
A number and its opposite have the same absolute value.

16. Determine whether the statement is always true, sometimes true, or never true:
Numbers that end in 0 are divisible by 5.

17. Determine whether the statement is always true, sometimes true, or never true:
Multiples of 3 are odd numbers.

18. Name the property that is missing from the problem-solving steps for each expression:

$$4(-3c + 7) + 12c \qquad \text{Given}$$
$$= -12c + 28 + 12c \qquad \text{Distributive Property}$$
$$= -12c + 12c + 28 \qquad \text{Commutative Property of Addition}$$
$$= 0 + 28 \qquad \underline{\hspace{4cm}}$$
$$= 28 \qquad \text{Identity Property of Addition}$$

19. Name the property that is missing from the problem-solving steps for each expression.

$$(a + 7)(3 - 5) \qquad \text{Given}$$
$$= 3a - 5a + 7(3) - 7(5) \qquad \underline{\hspace{4cm}}$$
$$= 3a - 5a + 21 - 35 \qquad \text{Multiplication}$$
$$= -2a - 7 \qquad \text{Subtraction}$$

20. Name the property that is missing from the problem-solving steps for each expression:

$$56 + (25 + 44) \qquad \text{Given}$$
$$= 56 + (44 + 25) \qquad \underline{\hspace{4cm}}$$
$$= (56 + 44) + 25 \qquad \text{Associative Property of Addition}$$
$$= 100 + 25 \qquad \text{Addition}$$
$$= 125 \qquad \text{Addition}$$

In previous lessons, we learned what functions are, and we have seen examples of linear functions and quadratic functions. There are many types of functions, each with special uses in real-world applications. In this lesson, we will examine three types of functions that are useful in particular applications. These functions include: absolute value functions, step functions, and constant functions.

The **absolute value function** $f(x) = |x|$ takes any number as input, and its output is the distance from that number to 0 on a number line. For example, $|5| = 5$ and $|-8| = 8$. This function has a graph that looks like the letter V.

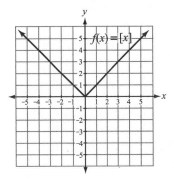

Absolute Value Function	The absolute value function is defined as $f(x) = |x|$, for every real number x.

A **constant function** is a function like $g(x) = 2$ that takes any number as an input, but its output is always the same (in this case, the output is always 2.) For example, $g(-13) = 2$ and $g(6) = 2$. This function has a graph that is a horizontal line

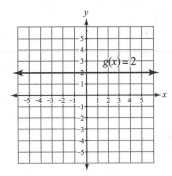

Constant Function	A constant function is any function of the form $g(x) = k$, where k is a real number. The graph of a constant function is a horizontal line with y-intercept $(0, b)$.

A **step function** is any function that has constant values over continuous intervals. There are common examples of step functions: the **floor function** (or **greatest integer function**) and the **ceiling function** (or **smallest integer function**).

Step Function	Any function that has constant values over continuous intervals.

The **floor function**, or **greatest integer function**, is usually denoted by $[x]$, and is defined as the greatest integer less than or equal to x. For example, $[2.7] = 2$ and $[9.95] = 9$ and $\left[\frac{1}{2}\right] = 0$ and $[-3.6] = -4$.

The graph of a floor function is shown here.

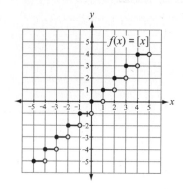

Floor Function or Greatest Integer Function	A step function, $f(x) = [x]$, where $[x]$ represents the greatest integer less than or equal to x.

The **ceiling function,** or **least integer function,** is usually denoted by $\lceil x \rceil$, and it is defined as the least integer greater than or equal to x. For example, $\lceil 3.4 \rceil = 4$ and $\lceil 10.98 \rceil = 11$ and $\lceil -4.5 \rceil = -4$ and $\lceil -7.7 \rceil = -7$.

Ceiling Function or Least Integer Function	A step function, $f(x) = \lceil x \rceil$, where $\lceil x \rceil$ represents the least integer greater than or equal to x.

Example 1   Given the domain $\{-6, -3, 0, 3, 6\}$ find the range of $f(x) = \frac{1}{3}|x - 6|$.

$f(x) = \frac{1}{3}|-6-6| = \frac{1}{3}(12) = 4$

$f(x) = \frac{1}{3}|-3-6| = \frac{1}{3}(9) = 3$

$f(x) = \frac{1}{3}|0-6| = \frac{1}{3}(6) = 2$

$f(x) = \frac{1}{3}|3-6| = \frac{1}{3}(3) = 1$

$f(x) = \frac{1}{3}|6-6| = \frac{1}{3}(0) = 0$

Step 1:   Substitute each number from the domain for x and evaluate.

Range: $\{4, 3, 2, 1, 0\}$

Step 2:   List the values of $f(x)$ obtained.

Answer: The range is $\{4, 3, 2, 1, 0\}$.

Example 2   Find the range of the least integer function, $f(x) = \lceil x \rceil$ given the domain $\{-4.2, -2.7, 3.6, 5.4\}$.

Step 1: Draw a number line and locate each number in the set.

$f(-4.2) = \lceil -4.2 \rceil = -4$

$f(-2.7) = \lceil -2.7 \rceil = -2$

$f(3.6) = \lceil 3.6 \rceil = 4$

$f(5.4) = \lceil 5.4 \rceil = 6$

Step 2: Evaluate each integer function by selecting the integer immediately to the right of the given number.

Range: $\{-4, -2, 4, 6\}$

Step 3: List the values of $f(x)$ obtained.

Answer: The range is $\{-4, -2, 4, 6\}$.

Example 3   Graph $f(x) = \lceil x \rceil$ over the domain of all real numbers from -2 to 2.

If $-2 \le x < -1$, then $\lceil x \rceil = -1$

If $-1 \le x < 0$, then $\lceil x \rceil = 0$

If $0 \le x < 1$, then $\lceil x \rceil = 1$

If $1 \le x < 2$, then $\lceil x \rceil = 2$

Step 1: Determine the intervals over which the function is constant and the value of each interval.

Step 2: Graph these values as a step function.

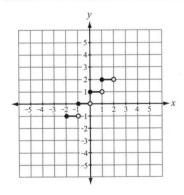

Answer: See the graph in Step 2.

Example 4   Two students, Todd and Janelle, are at 0 on the x-axis. They leave at the same instant and Todd walks to the right while Janelle walks to the left. As they leave, their speed increases at the same rate. Find the function of the graph that represents their speed in feet-per-second versus their distance in feet.

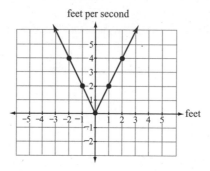

$(0, 0), (1, 2), (-1, 2), (2, 4),$ and $(-2, 4)$	**Step 1:** Locate the points.

$f(x) = 2\lvert x \rvert$	**Step 2:** Find a function that contains these points and check.

Check:

$(0, 0)$	$2\lvert 0 \rvert = 0$
$(1, 2)$	$2\lvert 1 \rvert = 2$
$(-1, 2)$	$2\lvert -1 \rvert = 2$
$(2, 2)$	$2\lvert 2 \rvert = 4$
$(-2, 2)$	$2\lvert -2 \rvert = 4$

Answer: The function that matches the graph
is $f(x) = 2\lvert x \rvert$.

Example 5   A cellular phone company offers two plans. Plan A charges \$60 per month for unlimited minutes. Plan B charges \$20 per month, plus \$0.08 per minute used. Which plan is better if you plan to use 400 minutes?

x = the number of minutes	**Step 1:** Write a function to find the amount charged for each plan.

Plan A: $f(x) = \$60$

Plan B: $g(x) = \$20 + 0.08x$ dollars per minute

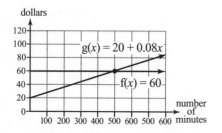

Step 2:   Graph each function on the same set of axes.

Plan B is least expensive plan below 500 minutes.

Step 3: Observe the graph to see which plan is least expensive if you plan to use 400 minutes.

Check: $g(400) = 20 + 0.08(400)$

$\qquad = 20 + 32$

$\qquad = \$52$

$\qquad \$52 < \$60$ True

Step 4: Verify the observation.

Answer: Plan B is the better plan if you plan to use 400 minutes.

Problem Set

1. Given the domain $\{-6, -2, 1, 3\}$, find the range of $f(x) = 3|x|$.

2. Given the domain $\{-2, 0, 2, 3\}$, find the range of $f(x) = |x|$.

3. Given the domain $\{-5, -3, -1, 2\}$, find the range of $f(x) = 2|x|$.

4. Given the domain $\{-3, -2, 2, 3\}$, find the range of $f(x) = 2|x|$.

5. Given the domain $\{-7, -4, 0, 4, 7\}$, find the range of $f(x) = 3|x|$.

6. Given the domain $\{-4, -1, 2, 4\}$, find the range of $f(x) = 4|x|$.

7. Given the domain $\{-8.1, -2.5, 3.5, 6.2\}$, find the range of this smallest integer function $f(x) = \lceil x \rceil$.

8. Given the domain $\{-3.2, -1.95, 0.5, 3.1\}$, find the range of this smallest integer function $f(x) = \lceil x \rceil$.

9. Given the domain $\{-4.01, -0.5, 1.13, 5.04\}$, find the range of this smallest integer function $f(x) = \lceil x \rceil$.

10. Given the domain $\{-5.98, -2.01, -0.3, 0.5, 1.3\}$, find the range of this greatest integer function $f(x) = [x]$.

11. Given the domain $\{-2.01, -0.98, 0.98, 1.35, 2.99\}$, find the range of this greatest integer function $f(x) = [x]$.

12. Given the domain $\{-8.29, -4.13, -1.63, 0.74, 4.35\}$, find the range of this greatest integer function $f(x) = [x]$.

13. Given the domain $\{-6.21, -3.79, -0.44, 1.37, 5.94\}$, find the range of this greatest integer function $f(x) = [x]$.

14. Given the domain $\{-9.5, -5.7, 3.8, 6.2, 8.3\}$, find the range of this greatest integer function $f(x) = [x]$.

15. Given the domain $\{-4.37, -2.91, -0.8, 0.75, 3.83\}$, find the range of this greatest integer function $f(x) = [x]$.

16. Sketch the graph of $f(x) = [x]$ over the domain of $-4 \le x \le 2$.

17. Sketch the graph of $f(x) = [x]$ over the domain of $-3 \leq x < 1$.

18. Sketch the graph of $f(x) = [x]$ over the domain of $-2 \leq x < 4$.

19. Sketch the graph of $f(x) = [x]$ over the domain of $-2 \leq x < 1$.

20. Sketch the graph of $f(x) = [x]$ over the domain of $-1 \leq x < 2$.

21. Sketch the graph of $f(x) = [x]$ over the domain of $-2 \leq x < 3$.

22. Sketch the graph of $f(x) = [x]$ over the domain of $-1 \leq x < 3$.

23. Sketch the graph of $f(x) = \lceil x \rceil$ over the domain of $-2 < x \leq 3$.

24. Sketch the graph of $f(x) = \lceil x \rceil$ over the domain of $-2 < x \leq 2$.

25. Sketch the graph of $f(x) = \lceil x \rceil$ over the domain of $-1 < x \leq 2$.

26. Sketch the graph of $f(x) = \lceil x \rceil$ over the domain of $-3 < x \leq 1$.

27. If the highway commission charges $0.20 per mile, what is the graph of the cost of a trip versus the distance traveled east or west?

28. Two people, Jackie and Bill, are at 0 on the x-axis. They leave at the same instant and Jackie walks to the right while Bill walks to the left. As they leave 0, their speeds increase at the same rate. A graph of their speeds in feet per second versus their distances in feet from (0, 0) on the x-axis is shown below. Find the function that describes this graph.

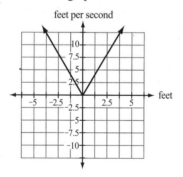

29. Two runners are traveling on a path. They leave from the same point at the same time with one traveling east and the other traveling west. They travel at the same speeds. Their speed depends on their locations from the starting point. A graph of their speed versus their distance east or west from the starting point (0, 0) is provided on the graph. Find a function to describe the graph.

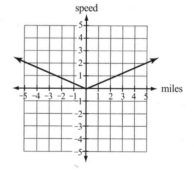

30. If the highway commission charges $0.40 per mile, what is the graph of the cost of a trip versus the distance traveled east or west?

31. Cheyenne is planning a wedding. She has interviewed three wedding planners. Planner A charges a flat fee of $1,750 no matter how many guests. Planner B charges $900 plus $5 per guest, and Planner C charges $750 plus $7.50 per guest. How many guests would Cheyenne need to invite in order for Planner A to be the least expensive?

32. Chloe is planning a wedding. She has interviewed three wedding planners. Planner A charges a flat fee of $1,200 no matter how many guests. Planner B charges $1,000 plus $5 per guest, and planner C charges $800 plus $7 per guest. How many guests would Chloe need to invite in order for Planner A to be the least expensive?

33. Long distance Company A charges a flat rate of $22.00 per month. Company B charges $9.00 per month plus $0.05 per minute used. Use a graph to determine the maximum number of minutes that can be used for Company B to be the least expensive company?

34. A wireless company offers Plan A, which charges $90 per month for any number of minutes used. It offers Plan B which charges $55 per month plus $0.10 per minute used. It also offers Plan C, which charges $70 per month plus $0.05 per minute used. Use a graph to determine how many minutes a person should use for Plan A to be the least expensive.

35. Shin is planning a wedding. She has interviewed three wedding planners. Planner A charges a flat fee of $2,400 no matter how many guests. Planner B charges $1,500 plus $5 per guest, and Planner C charges $1,000 plus $7 per guest. How many guests would Shin need to invite in order for Planner A to be the least expensive one to hire?

36. Santiago inquired about the daily rental fees from three car rental companies. He found that ABC Car Rental Company charges a flat rate of $55 per day with unlimited mileage. XYZ Car Rental Company charges $35 per day plus $0.10 per mile driven, while KLM Car Rental Company charges $25 per day plus $0.25 per mile driven. If Santiago plans to use a rental car for 4 days and drive about 300 miles, which company would be the best choice for him?

37. Alan inquired about the daily rental fees from three car rental companies. He found that ABC Car Rental Company charges a flat rate of $65 per day with unlimited mileage. XYZ Car Rental Company charges $45 per day plus $0.10 per mile driven, while KLM Car Rental Company charges $30 per day plus $0.20 per mile driven. If Alan plans to use a rental car for 5 days and drive about 600 miles, which company would be the best choice for him?

38. Chaundra inquired about the daily rental fees from three car rental companies. She found that ABC Car Rental Company charges a flat rate of $60 per day with unlimited mileage. XYZ Car Rental Company charges $45 per day plus $0.10 per mile driven, while KLM Car Rental Company charges $30 per day plus $0.15 per mile driven. If Chaundra plans to use a rental car for 3 days and drive about 200 miles, which company would be the best choice for her?

39. A ski resort charges a flat rate of $90.00 for ski lessons or charges $30.00 plus $15.00 per hour. Use a graph to determine the number of hours that would make the flat rate the least expensive.

40. A company needs to hire a plumber for a project. Plumber A charges $240 no matter how many hours are worked. Plumber B charges a $60 setup fee and then $30 for each hour worked. Use a graph to determine the number of hours required for Plumber A to charge less than Plumber B.

In this lesson we will use the TI-83 Plus™ graphing calculator to analyze data to determine whether it is a linear, a quadratic, or an exponential function and then find the **regression equation**.

Data is analyzed to make decisions, and sometimes we are asked to model the data with a function that best represents the data. A picture of some data points (*x*-*y* pairs) is given below.

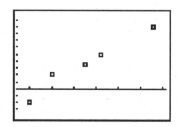

In this case, the data roughly lies along a line. We would therefore model it with a linear equation ($y = mx + b$). We look for the "best" straight line that will approximate the data. See the figure below.

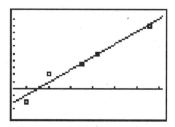

Data could also look like a parabola. When it does, we use a quadratic function to approximate it: ($y = ax^2 + bx + c$).

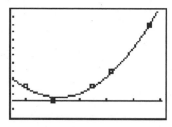

Lastly, we might have data that shows either exponential growth or decay. We would approximate this kind of data ($y = ab^x$) as shown in the diagram below.

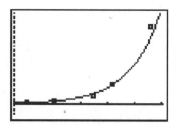

The process used to model a given set of data involves seven steps:

- Step 0: Settings (Initialize graphics and statistics functions for a given problem)
- Step 1: Enter data (we will always use lists L_1 and L_2 on the calculator)
- Step 2: Graph the data
- Step 3: Visually examine the data to determine the model we will use
- Step 4: Find the regression or modeling equation
- Step 5: Graph the regression equation with data
- Step 6: Solve the given question

Note: Before doing any of these examples you should check your calculator's settings to be sure that it will function as described above.

Press the [MODE] key and be sure that your settings appear as shown below.

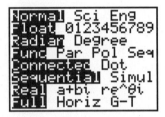

Next press the [2nd][ZOOM] keys and be sure that your settings appear as shown below.

Next press the [ZOOM] key then the [6] key to select the standard window setting.

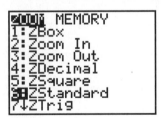

Press the [WINDOW] key to get the following screen.

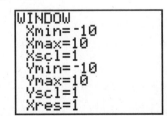

Example 1 Determine whether or not a linear, quadratic, or exponential function exactly matches the given set of data. Then, find the equation of the function.

Days	Height of Plant (cm)
1	1.2
2	2.0
3	2.9
4	3.7
5	5.1

Step 0: (Settings) Be sure you have the default settings as directed above.

Step 1: (Initial setup) First we need to activate the plot and adjust its settings. Press [2nd][Y=] to get to the STAT PLOTS menu. Once there, select [1].

Next, turn the plot on by selecting [ON] and then use the [▼] to select graph type 🌫. Use the [▼] again and make sure that your screen looks like the one shown to the left.

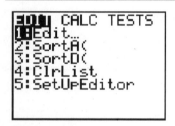

Step 2: (Enter the data) Press the [STAT] key followed by [1]: Edit.

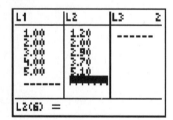

Now enter the data in lists L_1 and L_2 on the calculator. When you are done, your screen should look like the picture to the left.

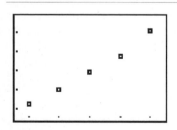

Step 3: (Graph the data) Press [ZOOM][9] (Zoom data) to obtain the graph to the left.

Step 4: (Visual examination of data) The data appears to lie along a straight line, so the function is linear.

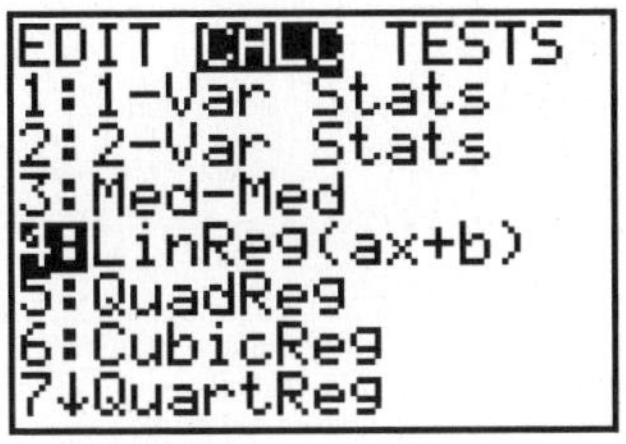

Step 5: (Find the linear regression equation) Begin by pressing the [STAT] key then the [▶] to get to the CALC menu.
Select [4]: LinReg ($ax + b$).

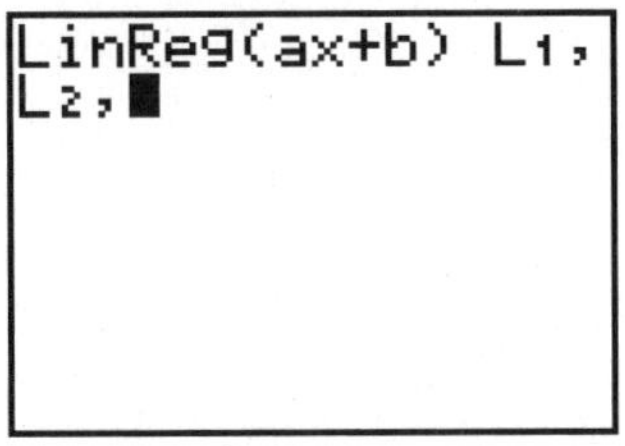

```
EDIT CALC TESTS
1:1-Var Stats
2:2-Var Stats
3:Med-Med
4:LinReg(ax+b)
5:QuadReg
6:CubicReg
7↓QuartReg
```

Next, put in the correct list names, L_1 and L_2, separated by commas as shown to the left. Note that L_1 can be obtained by pressing [2nd][1] and L_2 by pressing [2nd][2].

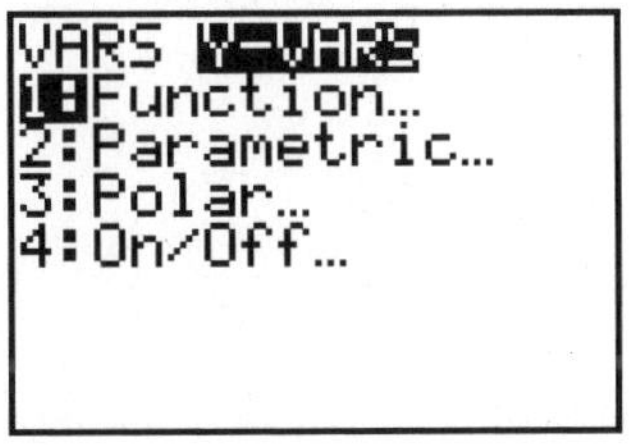

```
LinReg(ax+b) L₁,
L₂,■
```

Press the [VARS] key followed by the [▶] to get to the Y-VARS menu. Select [1]: Function.

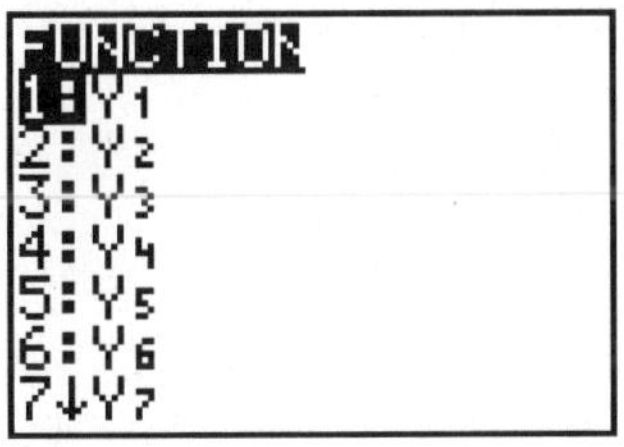

```
VARS Y-VARS
1:Function...
2:Parametric...
3:Polar...
4:On/Off...
```

Now choose [1]: Y_1 to put the regression equation into the Y_1 slot for graphing.

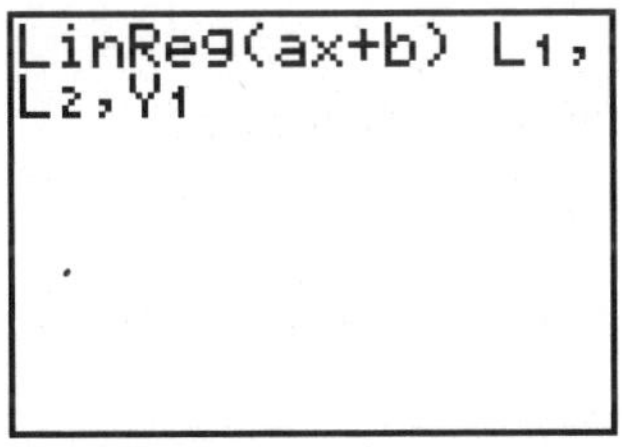

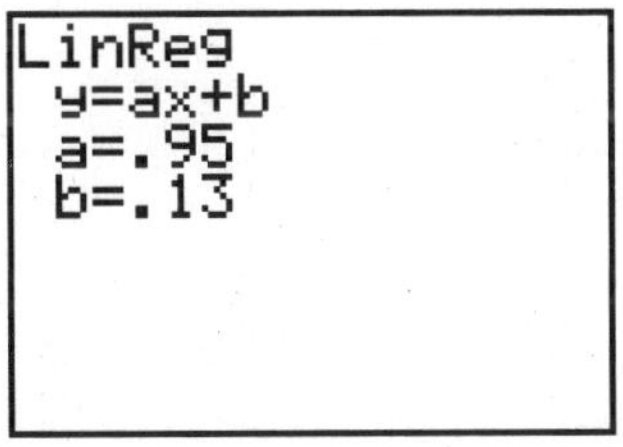

```
FUNCTION
1:Y₁
2:Y₂
3:Y₃
4:Y₄
5:Y₅
6:Y₆
7↓Y₇
```

```
LinReg(ax+b) L₁,
L₂,Y₁
```

Press [ENTER]. You should see a screen similar to the one shown to the left. This shows that our line of best fit has the equation $y = 0.95x + 0.13$.

```
LinReg
 y=ax+b
 a=.95
 b=.13
```

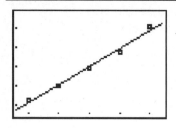

Step 6: (Graph the regression equation with data) Press the GRAPH key to obtain a graph like the one to the left.

Notice that the line passes very close to all of the data points and is therefore a good model for the data.

Answer: The line of best fit is $y = 0.95x + 0.13$.

Example 2   Determine whether or not a linear, quadratic, or exponential function exactly matches the given set of data. Then, find the equation of the function.

Speed(mph)	Gas Mileage (mpg)
40	27.6
45	30.2
50	31.5
55	30.6
60	28.0
65	25.3

Step 0: (Settings) Be sure you have the default settings as described in the beginning of the lesson.

Step 1: (Initial setup) First we need to activate the plot and adjust the settings. Press the 2nd Y= key to get the STAT PLOTS menu. Once there, select 1 as shown to the left.

Next, turn the plot on by selecting ON and then use the ▾ to select graph type ⬚. Use the ▾ again and make sure that your screen looks like the one shown to the left.

Step 2: (Enter the data) Press the STAT key followed by 1: Edit.

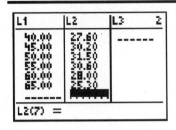

Now enter the data in lists L$_1$ and L$_2$ on the calculator. When you are done, your screen should look like the picture to the left.

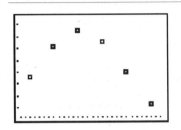

Step 3: (Graph the data) Press $\boxed{\text{ZOOM}}\boxed{9}$ (Zoom data) to obtain a graph like the one shown to the left.

Step 4: (Visual examination of data) The data appear to lie along a parabola, so we will use a quadratic regression model.

Step 5: (Find the quadratic regression equation) Begin by pressing the $\boxed{\text{STAT}}$ key then $\boxed{\blacktriangleright}$ to get to the CALC menu. Select $\boxed{5}$: QuadReg.

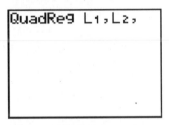

Next, put in the correct list names, L$_1$ and L$_2$, separated by commas as shown to the left. Note that L$_1$ can be obtained by pressing $\boxed{\text{2nd}}\boxed{1}$ and L$_2$ by pressing $\boxed{\text{2nd}}\boxed{2}$.

Press the $\boxed{\text{VARS}}$ key followed by the $\boxed{\blacktriangleright}$ to get to the Y–VARS menu. Select $\boxed{1}$: Function.

Now, choose $\boxed{1}$: Y$_1$ to put the regression equation into the Y$_1$ slot for graphing.

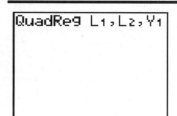

`QuadReg L₁,L₂,Y₁`

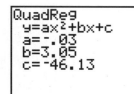

`QuadReg`
`y=ax²+bx+c`
`a=⁻.03`
`b=3.05`
`c=⁻46.13`

Finally, press ENTER. You should see a screen like the one to the left.

This demonstrates that our quadratic function of best fit has the equation $y = -0.03x^2 + 3.05x - 46.13$.

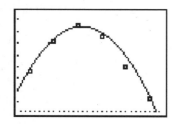

Step 6: (Graph the regression equation with data) Press the GRAPH key to obtain a graph like the one to the left.

Notice that the parabola passes very close to all of the data points, and is therefore a good model for the data.

Answer: The equation that best fits is $y = -0.03x^2 + 3.05x - 46.13$.

Example 3 Determine whether or not a linear, quadratic, or exponential function exactly matches the given set of data. Then, find the equation of the function.

Time (hours)	Cell count (thousands)
4	2.6
6	3.6
8	5.3
10	7.5
12	10.8
14	15.1

Step 0: (Settings) Be sure you have the default settings as described in the beginning of the lesson.

`STAT PLOTS`
`1:Plot1…Off`
`    L1   L2`
`2:Plot2…Off`
`    L1   L3`
`3:Plot3…Off`
`    L2   L3`
`4↓PlotsOff`

Step 1: (Initial setup) First we need to activate the plot and adjust the settings. Press 2nd Y= to get the STAT PLOTS menu. Once there, select 1.

Next, turn the plot on by selecting $\boxed{\text{ON}}$ and then use the $\boxed{\blacktriangledown}$ to select graph type $\underline{}$. Use the $\boxed{\blacktriangledown}$ again and make sure that your screen looks like the one shown to the left.

Step 2: (Enter the data) Press the $\boxed{\text{STAT}}$ key followed by $\boxed{1}$: Edit.

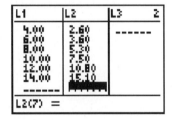

Now enter the data in lists L_1 and L_2 into the calculator. When you are finished, your screen should look like the picture to the left.

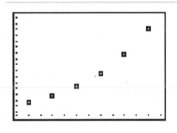

Step 3: (Graph the data) Press $\boxed{\text{ZOOM}}\boxed{9}$ (Zoom data) to obtain a graph like the one shown to the left.

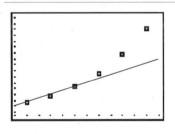

Step 4: (Visual examination of the data) The data values appear to be increasing, and do not lie along a line, as we move from left to right. Therefore, we will use an exponential regression model.

Step 5: (Find the exponential regression equation) Begin by pressing the $\boxed{\text{STAT}}$ key then $\boxed{\blacktriangleright}$ to get to the CALC menu. Select $\boxed{0}$: ExpReg.

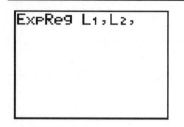

Next, put in the correct list names, L_1 and L_2, separated by commas as shown to the left. Note that L_1 can be obtained by pressing [2nd][1], and L_2 by pressing [2nd][2].

Press the [VARS] key followed by the [▶] to get to the Y–VARS menu. Select [1]: Function.

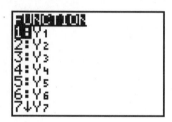

Choose [1]: Y_1 to put the regression equation into the Y_1 slot for graphing.

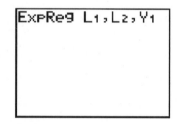

Press [ENTER]. Your screen should look like the picture to the left.

This shows that our quadratic function of best fit has equation $y = 1.27(1.19)^x$.

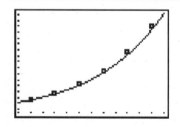

Step 6: (Graph the regression equation with data) Press the [GRAPH] key to obtain a graph similar to the one to the left.

Notice that the exponential function passes very close to all of the data points and is therefore a good model for the data.

Answer: The equation that best fits is $y = 1.27(1.19)^x$.

Problem Set

1. The data in the table represents what type of function?

x	y
0	-6.5
1	-2.5
2	1.5
3	5.5
4	9.5

2. Determine the equation that best represents the data in the table.

x	y
0	3
1	5
2	7
3	9
4	11

3. The data in the table represents what type of function?

x	y
-2	24
-1	3
0	0
1	3
2	24

4. The data in the table represents what type of function?

x	y
-2	4
-1	5
0	4
1	1
2	-4

5. Determine the equation that best represents the data in the table.

x	y
-1	8
0	0
1	-4
2	-4
3	0

6. The data in the table represents what type of function?

u	v
1	0.75
2	1.5
3	3
4	6
5	12

7. Determine the equation that best represents the data in the table.

x	y
1	0.75
2	1.5
3	3
4	6
5	12

8. Determine the equation that best represents the data in the table.

p	q
0	-2
2	14
5	75.5
7	141.5
8	182

9. Determine the equation that best represents the data in the table.

r	s
-5	16
-2	10
0	6
3	0
7	-8

10. Determine the equation that best represents the data in the table.

x	y
2	96
3	24
4	6
5	1.5
6	0.375

HA1-905: Quadratic Equations with Irrational Roots

In this lesson, we will practice solving quadratic equations with irrational roots and writing their solutions in simplified form. Remember from previous lessons that an irrational number is one that neither terminates nor repeats. These can often be best represented by fractions, but in the case of irrational roots, we leave the number in root notation. The simplified form of an irrational root is therefore a square root notation in which the radicand has been simplified as much as possible. You already know how to solve quadratic equations; look at the following examples of quadratic equations with irrational roots.

Example 1   Find the solution set of the quadratic equation $x^2 - 5 = 0$.

$x^2 - 5 = 0$ $x^2 - 5 + 5 = 0 + 5$ $x^2 = 5$	**Step 1:** Add five to both sides.
$x = \pm\sqrt{5}$	**Step 2:** Take the square root of both sides.
	Answer: The solution set is $\{\sqrt{5}, -\sqrt{5}\}$.

Example 2   Find the solution set of the quadratic equation $2x^2 - 1 = 0$.

$2x^2 - 1 = 0$ $2x^2 - 1 + 1 = 0 + 1$ $2x^2 = 1$	**Step 1:** Add one to both sides.
$\dfrac{2x^2}{2} = \dfrac{1}{2}$ $x^2 = \dfrac{1}{2}$	**Step 2:** Divide both sides by two.
$x = \pm\sqrt{\dfrac{1}{2}}$ $x = \pm\dfrac{\sqrt{1}}{\sqrt{2}}$	**Step 3:** Take the square root of both sides.
$x = \pm\dfrac{\sqrt{1}}{\sqrt{2}} \cdot \dfrac{\sqrt{2}}{\sqrt{2}}$ $x = \pm\dfrac{\sqrt{2}}{2}$	**Step 4:** Now we need to eliminate the square root in the denominator. To do this, multiply both the numerator and the denominator by the square root of two.
	Answer: The solution set is $\left\{\dfrac{-\sqrt{2}}{2}, \dfrac{\sqrt{2}}{2}\right\}$.

Example 3   Find the solution set of the quadratic equation $x^2 + 3x - 3 = 0$.

$x^2 + 3x - 3 = 0$ $a = 1, b = 3, c = -3$	**Step 1:** First we must identify the coefficients a, b and c of the quadratic equation.
$x = \dfrac{-3 \pm \sqrt{3^2 - 4(1)(-3)}}{2(1)}$ $= \dfrac{-3 \pm \sqrt{9 + 12}}{2}$ $= \dfrac{-3 \pm \sqrt{21}}{2}$ $x = \dfrac{-3 + \sqrt{21}}{2}$ or $x = \dfrac{-3 - \sqrt{21}}{2}$	**Step 2:** Substitute these coefficients into the quadratic formula and simplify.

Answer: The solution set is $\left\{ \dfrac{-3 - \sqrt{21}}{2}, \dfrac{-3 + \sqrt{21}}{2} \right\}$.

Example 4   Find the solution set of the quadratic equation $5x^2 - 12 = 0$.

$5x^2 - 12 = 0$ $5x^2 - 12 + 12 = 0 + 12$ $5x^2 = 12$	**Step 1:** Add 12 to both sides.
$x^2 = \dfrac{12}{5}$	**Step 2:** Divide both sides by 5.
$x = \pm\sqrt{\dfrac{12}{5}}$ $x = \pm\dfrac{\sqrt{12}}{\sqrt{5}}$	**Step 3:** Take the square root of both sides.

$$x = \pm \frac{\sqrt{4} \cdot \sqrt{3}}{\sqrt{5}}$$

$$= \pm \frac{2\sqrt{3}}{\sqrt{5}}$$

$$= \pm \frac{2\sqrt{3}}{\sqrt{5}} \cdot \frac{\sqrt{5}}{\sqrt{5}}$$

$$= \pm \frac{2\sqrt{15}}{5}$$

$$x = \frac{2\sqrt{15}}{5} \quad \text{or} \quad x = \frac{-2\sqrt{15}}{5}$$

Step 4: Now we need to eliminate the square root in the denominator. To do this, multiply both the numerator and the denominator by the square root of five. Note that the square root of 12 can be simplified.

Answer: The solution set is $\left\{ \dfrac{-2\sqrt{15}}{5}, \dfrac{2\sqrt{15}}{5} \right\}$.

Example 5   Find the solution set of the quadratic equation $2x^2 + 4x - 1 = 0$.

$$2x^2 + 4x - 1 = 0$$

$$a = 2, b = 4, c = -1$$

Step 1: First, we must identify the coefficients a, b and c of the quadratic equation.

$$x = \frac{-4 \pm \sqrt{4^2 - 4(2)(-1)}}{2(2)}$$

$$= \frac{-4 \pm \sqrt{16 + 8}}{4}$$

$$= \frac{-4 \pm \sqrt{24}}{4}$$

$$= \frac{-4 \pm \sqrt{4} \cdot \sqrt{6}}{4}$$

$$= \frac{-4 \pm 2\sqrt{6}}{4}$$

$$= \frac{\overset{1}{\cancel{2}}(-2 \pm \sqrt{6})}{\overset{2}{\cancel{4}}}$$

$$= \frac{-2 \pm \sqrt{6}}{2}$$

$$x = \frac{-2 + \sqrt{6}}{2} \quad \text{or} \quad x = \frac{-2 - \sqrt{6}}{2}$$

Step 2: Substitute these coefficients into the quadratic formula and simplify. Note that the square root of 24 can be simplified. Also note that we can factor out a 2 in the numerator and denominator.

Answer: The solution set is $\left\{ \dfrac{-2 - \sqrt{6}}{2}, \dfrac{-2 + \sqrt{6}}{2} \right\}$.

Problem Set

Find the solution set of the quadratic equation:

1. $x^2 - 6 = 0$

2. $x^2 - 15 = 0$

3. $x^2 - 23 = 0$

4. $x^2 - 29 = 0$

5. $x^2 - 43 = 0$

6. $x^2 - 8 = 0$

7. $x^2 - 12 = 0$

8. $x^2 - 20 = 0$

9. $x^2 - 24 = 0$

10. $x^2 - 54 = 0$

11. $2x^2 - 5 = 0$

12. $2x^2 - 7 = 0$

13. $2x^2 - 11 = 0$

14. $2x^2 - 13 = 0$

15. $2x^2 - 17 = 0$

16. $x^2 + x - 3 = 0$

17. $x^2 + x - 4 = 0$

18. $x^2 + x - 7 = 0$

19. $x^2 + x - 13 = 0$

20. $x^2 + 3x - 2 = 0$

21. $x^2 + 3x - 1 = 0$

22. $x^2 + 3x - 7 = 0$

23. $x^2 + 5x - 4 = 0$

24. $x^2 + 3x + 1 = 0$

25. $x^2 + 5x + 2 = 0$

26. $2x^2 - 9 = 0$

27. $2x^2 - 45 = 0$

28. $3x^2 - 64 = 0$

29. $5x^2 - 24 = 0$

30. $5x^2 - 32 = 0$

31. $6x^2 - 27 = 0$

32. $7x^2 - 20 = 0$

33. $x^2 + 2x - 1 = 0$

34. $x^2 + 4x + 1 = 0$

35. $x^2 + 6x - 1 = 0$

36. $2x^2 + 8x + 4 = 0$

37. $2x^2 + 4x - 5 = 0$

38. $3x^2 + 4x - 2 = 0$

39. $2x^2 + 8x - 1 = 0$

40. $3x^2 + 6x + 1 = 0$

HA1-910: Complex Numbers

In this lesson, we will learn about complex numbers, their properties, and why they are necessary for solving some quadratic equations. In the past, we have said that there are certain kinds of equations with no real solution. For instance, the square root of a negative number has no real solution. The set of real numbers is insufficient as a list of all possible solutions to quadratic equations with real number coefficients.

A sixteenth century mathematician named Rene Descartes reasoned that, while there is no "real" number solution to the square root of negative one, there is a theoretical solution. He chose a symbol, lowercase "*i*," for this theoretical solution and called it the imaginary unit. "*i*" is equal to the square root of negative one. When the imaginary unit "*i*" is squared, the result is negative one. The word *imaginary* is used here to describe the number "*i*." The use of the term imaginary here does not imply that "*i*" does not exist. In fact, "*i*" is no more "imaginary" than any number. All numbers are abstract ideas and exist only in our minds.

Descartes created a new system of numbers, called the complex numbers, that include the new imaginary numbers along with all the real numbers. The inclusion of "*i*" in the number system means that we can now solve equations involving the square root of negative one.

We can write the solution to the $x^2 = -1$ as $x = \pm i$. The solution set of our equation becomes the set whose elements are "*i*" and negative "*i*." An imaginary number is any real number plus any non-zero multiple of "*i*."

Therefore, real numbers can be written in the form "*a*" plus zero times "*i*." **Complex numbers**, which are real numbers together with imaginary numbers, can be written in the form $a + bi$, where "*a*" and "*b*" are any real number, even zero. The standard form of a complex number is "*a*" plus "*b*" "*i*," where the number "*a*" represents the real part of the complex number and "*b*" represents the imaginary part of the complex number. Two complex numbers with the same real part but opposite imaginary parts are called **complex conjugates**. Complex numbers $a + bi$ and $a - bi$ are complex conjugates.

Example 1   Simplify: $\sqrt{-100}$

$\sqrt{-100}$ $= \sqrt{100} \cdot \sqrt{-1}$	**Step 1:** In order to simplify this equation, we must factor -100.
$= \sqrt{10^2} \cdot \sqrt{-1}$ $= 10 \cdot \sqrt{-1}$	**Step 2:** Since we know that one hundred is ten squared, we can write the square root of ten squared times the square root of negative one. This gives us ten times the square root of negative one.
$10i$	**Answer:** We know that the square root of negative one is *i* so the result is $10i$.

Example 2   Simplify: $\sqrt{-54}$

$\sqrt{-54}$ $= \sqrt{54} \cdot \sqrt{-1}$ $= \sqrt{9} \cdot \sqrt{6} \cdot \sqrt{-1}$ $= \sqrt{3^2} \cdot \sqrt{6} \cdot \sqrt{-1}$	**Step 1:** In order to simplify this equation we must factor -54.
$3 \cdot i \cdot \sqrt{6}$	**Step 2:** We know that the square root of negative one is *i* and the square root of three squared is three. Therefore the equation becomes $3 \cdot i \cdot \sqrt{6}$.
$3i\sqrt{6}$	**Answer:** The answer is $3i\sqrt{6}$.

Example 3   Find the real part of the complex number $3 + 4i$.

$3 + 4i$	**Step 1:** Remember, the real part of a complex number in the form $a + bi$ is a.
$a = 3, \quad b = 4$	**Step 2:** Identify a and b.
	Answer: Therefore, the real part of the complex number is 3.

Example 4   Find the imaginary part of the complex number $7 - 2i$.

$7 - 2i$	**Step 1:** Remember that the imaginary part of a complex number in the form $a + bi$ is b. Therefore, we must identify a and b.
$a = 7, b = -2$	**Step 2:** Identify a and b.
	Answer: The imaginary part of the complex number is -2.

Example 5   Find the complex conjugate of the complex number $4 - 11i$.

$4 - 11i$	**Step 1:** The complex conjugate of a complex number has the same real part and the opposite imaginary part of the complex number. To begin this problem, we must identify the real and the imaginary parts of the number.
$4 + 11i$	**Step 2:** In this equation, the real part is four and the imaginary part is negative eleven. Therefore the complex conjugate is $4 + 11i$.
	Answer: $4 + 11i$

Example 6   Find the solution set of the quadratic equation $x^2 + 11 = 0$.

$x^2 + 11 = 0$ $x^2 + 11 - 11 = 0 - 11$ $x^2 = -11$	**Step 1:** First, we subtract eleven from both sides of the equation to get $x^2 = -11$.
$x = \pm\sqrt{-11}$	**Step 2:** Solve for x by taking the square root of both sides of the equation.
$x = \pm\sqrt{11} \cdot \sqrt{-1}$ $= \pm i \cdot \sqrt{11}$ $= \pm i\sqrt{11}$ $x = -i\sqrt{11}$ or $x = i\sqrt{11}$	**Step 3:** Simplify.
	Answer: The solution set is $\{-i\sqrt{11}, i\sqrt{11}\}$.

Problem Set

1. Simplify: $\sqrt{-9}$

2. Simplify: $\sqrt{-16}$

3. Simplify: $\sqrt{-49}$

4. Find the real part of the complex number:
$$3 - 6i$$

5. Find the real part of the complex number:
$$4 - 10i$$

6. Find the imaginary part of the complex number:
$$5 - 7i$$

7. Find the imaginary part of the complex number:
$$2 - 5i$$

8. Find the complex conjugate of $4 - 8i$.

9. Find the complex conjugate of $3 - 7i$.

10. Find the complex conjugate of -13.

11. Find the complex conjugate of $3i$.

12. Find the solution set of the quadratic equation:
$$x^2 + 7 = 0$$

13. Find the solution set of the quadratic equation:
$$x^2 + 4 = 0$$

14. Find the solution set of the quadratic equation:
$$x^2 + 9 = 0$$

15. Find the solution set of the quadratic equation:
$$x^2 + 11 = 0$$

16. Simplify: $\sqrt{-32}$

17. Simplify: $\sqrt{-44}$

18. Simplify: $\sqrt{-45}$

19. Simplify: $\sqrt{-48}$

20. Simplify: $\sqrt{-50}$

21. Simplify: $\sqrt{-52}$

22. Simplify: $\sqrt{-\dfrac{36}{49}}$

23. Simplify: $\sqrt{-\dfrac{1}{9}}$

Find the solution set of the quadratic equations:

24. $x^2 + 20 = 0$

25. $x^2 + 8 = 0$

26. $x^2 + x + 11 = 0$

27. $x^2 + x + 9 = 0$

28. $x^2 + 3x + 11 = 0$

29. $x^2 + 3x + 6 = 0$

30. $x^2 + x + 8 = 0$.

31. $2x^2 + 2x + 6 = 0$

32. $2x^2 + 4x + 5 = 0$

33. $2x^2 + 5x + 11 = 0$

34. $3x^2 - 4x + 5 = 0$

35. $3x^2 + 4x + 5 = 0$

36. $3x^2 + 52 = 0$

37. $2x^2 + 29 = 0$

38. $7x^2 + 45 = 0$

39. $5x^2 + 36 = 0$

40. $3x^2 + 16 = 0$

HA1-915: Algebraic Operations with Complex Numbers

In this lesson, we will learn how to perform algebraic operations, such as addition, subtraction, multiplication, and division, with complex numbers. To add complex numbers, we first add their real parts and then add their imaginary parts. In subtraction, we subtract the real parts and the imaginary parts separately. In subtracting, remember to distribute the negative sign over the complex number. In multiplying, we treat complex numbers just like polynomials and use the FOIL method. Remember that FOIL means First, Outer, Inner, Last. The product of these complex numbers is the sum of the squares of the real part and the square of the imaginary part, and is always a real number.

Example 1   Add: $(6 + 3i) + (5 + i)$

$(6 + 3i) + (5 + i)$ $= 6 + 3i + 5 + i$	**Step 1:** Since everything is being added, remove the parenthesis.
$= 6 + 5 + 3i + i$	**Step 2:** Place like terms together.
$= 11 + 4i$	**Step 3:** Add the similar terms.
	Answer: $11 + 4i$

Example 2   Subtract: $(8 + 2i) - (3 + i)$

$(8 + 2i) - (3 + i)$ $= 8 + 2i - 3 - i$	**Step 1:** Distribute the negative to remove the parenthesis.
$= 8 - 3 + 2i - i$	**Step 2:** Place like terms together.
$= 5 + i$	**Step 3:** Add or subtract the similar terms.
	Answer: $5 + i$

Example 3   Multiply: $4(5 - 4i)$

$4(5 - 4i)$ $= 4(5) - 4(4i)$	**Step 1:** Distribute the four through the parenthesis.
$= 20 - 16i$	**Step 2:** Multiply everything by four.
	Answer: $20 - 16i$

Example 4   Simplify: $7(1 - 2i) + 3(7 + 6i)$

$7(1 - 2i) + 3(7 + 6i)$ $= 7(1) - 7(2i) + 3(7) + 3(6i)$	**Step 1:** Distribute the seven and the three.
$= 7 - 14i + 21 + 18i$	**Step 2:** Multiply.

$= 7 + 21 - 14i + 18i$	**Step 3:**	Place like terms together.
$= 28 + 4i$	**Step 4:**	Add the similar terms.
	Answer:	$28 + 4i$

Example 5 Divide: $9 - 27i$ by 3

$\dfrac{9 - 27i}{3}$	**Step 1:**	Set up the problem.
$= \dfrac{9}{3} \cdot \dfrac{27i}{3}$	**Step 2:**	Create two separate problems
$= 3 - 9i$	**Step 3:**	Reduce the fractions.
	Answer:	$= 3 - 9i$

Example 6 Divide: $9 - 27i$ by $3 + 2i$

$\dfrac{9 - 27i}{3 + 2i}$	**Step 1:**	Set up the problem.
$= \dfrac{(9 - 27i)}{(3 + 2i)} \cdot \dfrac{(3 - 2i)}{(3 - 2i)}$	**Step 2:**	Rationalize the denominator by multiplying by the complex conjugate.
$= \dfrac{27 - 18i - 81i + 54i^2}{9 - 6i + 6i - 4i^2}$	**Step 3:**	Multiply the binomials–use the FOIL method–and simplify.
$= \dfrac{-27 - 99i}{13}$		*Note:* $i^2 = -1$
	Answer:	$\dfrac{-27 - 99i}{13}$

Example 7 Simplify: i^{12}

$i^{12} = \left(i^4\right)^3$	**Step 1:**	Separate the exponent into a more manageable form.
$= (1)^3$	**Step 2:**	Since $i^2 = -1\,i$, then $i\,i^4 = 1$.
$= 1$	**Step 3:**	Take the cube of one.
	Answer:	1

Problem Set

Solve:

1. Add: $(4 + 2i) + (4 - 4i)$

2. Subtract: $(5 + 2i) - (4 - 4i)$

3. Subtract: $(4 + 2i) - (3 + 4i)$

4. Subtract: $(4 + 3i) - (3 - 4i)$

5. Add: $(4 + 2i) + (3 - 4i)$

6. Multiply: $3(4 - 7i)$

7. Multiply: $3(7 - 3i)$

8. Multiply: $3(4 - 7i)$

9. Multiply: $2(7 - 3i)$

10. Multiply: $2(4 - 5i)$

11. Add the complex conjugates: $(-3 + 4i) + (-3 - 4i)$

12. Add the complex conjugates: $(-4 + 4i) + (-4 - 4i)$

13. Add the complex conjugates: $(-8 + 3i) + (-8 - 3i)$

14. Subtract the complex conjugates: $(-8 + 3i) - (-8 - 3i)$

15. Simplify: $3(4 - 4i) + 5(-5 + i)$

16. Simplify: $3(4 - 2i) - 5(-2 + i)$

17. Simplify: $4(4 - 2i) + 3(-2 + i)$

18. Simplify: $3(4 - 2i) - 5(-2 + 2i)$

19. Divide $16 - 8i$ by 4.

20. Divide $4 - 3i$ by $2i$.

21. Divide $36 - 8i$ by 4.

22. Divide $5 - 3i$ by $2i$.

23. Divide $4 - 7i$ by $2i$.

24. Multiply: $(-3 + 2i)^2$

25. Multiply: $(3 + 2i)(3 - 2i)$

26. Multiply: $(3 + 4i)(3 - 4i)$

27. Multiply: $(2i)^7$

28. Multiply: $(1 - i)^3$

29. Multiply: $(3 + i)^3$

30. Multiply: $(1 - 2i)^3$

31. Multiply: $(4 - i)^3$

32. Multiply: $(2 - i)^3$

33. Multiply: $(1 - 3i)^3$

34. Divide $(3 - 6i)$ by $(2 - 5i)$.

35. Divide $(3 + 6i)$ by $(2 + 5i)$.

36. Divide: $\dfrac{(1 - i)^2}{(2 - i)}$

37. Divide $(4 - 6i)$ by $(2 + 5i)$.

38. Divide $(3 - 5i)$ by $(2 - 5i)$.

39. Divide $(1 + 6i)$ by $(2 + 5i)$.

40. Divide $(2 + i)^2$ by $(2 - i)$.

In this lesson, we will learn how to simplify algebraic expressions using the Distributive Property. To use this property, we multiply the term outside the parentheses by each term inside the parentheses. The same procedure can be applied when multiplying a monomial by a polynomial or when multiplying two binomials. Remember, when we multiply two binomials or a binomial and a trinomial, we use the Distributive Property of multiplication repeatedly.

Distributive Property of Multiplication	For real numbers a, b, and c: $$a(b + c) = ab + ac.$$
Product of Two Binomials	$(a + b)(c + d)$ $$= ((a + b)c + (a + b)d)$$ $$= ac + bc + ad + bd$$
Product of a Binomial and a Trinomial	$(a + b)(c + d + e)$ $$= (a + b)c + (a + b)d + (a + b)e$$ $$= ac + bc + ad + bd + ae + be$$

Example 1　Simplify: $4x^2(2x^3 + 3x^2)$

$4x^2(2x^3 + 3x^2)$

$= (4x^2)(2x^3) + (4x^2)(3x^2)$

Step 1: In order to solve this equation, we must multiply the term outside the parentheses by each term inside the parentheses. We will do this by using the Distributive Property of multiplication. Therefore, we get $(4x^2)(2x^3) + (4x^2)(3x^2)$.

$= (4 \cdot 2 \cdot x^2 \cdot x^3) + (4 \cdot 3 \cdot x^2 \cdot x^2)$

$= 8x^5 + 12x^4$

Step 2: Now we must simplify the equation. Remember, when multiplying terms with the same base we need to add the exponents. So $(4)(2) = 8$ and $(x^2)(x^3) = x^5$; $(4)(3) = 12$ and $(x^2)(x^2) = x^4$.

Answer: The result is $8x^5 + 12x^4$.

Example 2　Simplify: $x^2(x - 2x^4)$

$x^2(x - 2x^4) = (x^2)(x) - (x^2)(2x^4)$

Step 1: In order to solve this equation we must multiply the term outside the parentheses by each term inside the parentheses.

$$= (x^2)(x) - (x^2)(2x^4)$$
$$= x^3 - 2x^6$$

Step 2: Now we will simplify the equation by multiplying the terms in parentheses.

Answer: The result is $x^3 - 2x^6$.

Example 3   Simplify: $x^2y^2(2xy + 3x^2y^2 + 4xy^3)$

$x^2y^2(2xy + 3x^2y^2 + 4xy^3)$
$=(x^2y^2)(2xy) + (x^2y^2)(3x^2y^2) + (x^2y^2)(4xy^3)$

Step 1: In order to solve this equation we must multiply the term outside the parentheses by each term inside the parentheses.

$=(x^2y^2)(2xy) + (x^2y^2)(3x^2y^2) + (x^2y^2)(4xy^3)$
$=2x^3y^3 + 3x^4y^4 + 4x^3y^5$

Step 2: We now need to multiply all the terms in parentheses and add their results.

Answer: Since there are no like terms to add, the answer is $2x^3y^3 + 3x^4y^4 + 4x^3y^5$.

Example 4   Simplify: $(2x^3 + x^2)(4x^2 + 3x^2)$

$(2x^3 + x^2)(4x^2 + 3x^2)$
$=(2x^3 + x^2)(4x^2) + (2x^3 + x^2)(3x^2)$

Step 1: We will use the Distributive Property of Multiplication to solve this problem. In this case, we will multiply the expression in the first set of parentheses by each term in the second set of parentheses.

$= (2x^3)(4x^2) + (2x^3)(3x^2) + (x^2)(4x^2) + (x^2)(3x^2)$
$= 8x^5 + 6x^5 + 4x^4 + 3x^4$
$= 14x^5 + 7x^4$

Step 2: We now need to multiply all the terms in parentheses, add their results and combine like terms.

Answer: The answer is $14x^5 + 7x^4$.

Example 5   Simplify: $(3x^3y^2 + 4x^2y)(5x^2y^3 + xy)$

$(3x^3y^2 + 4x^2y)(5x^2y^3 + xy)$
$= (3x^3y^2 + 4x^2y)(5x^2y^3) + (3x^3y^2 + 4x^2y)(xy)$

Step 1: To solve this equation we need to use the Distributive Property to multiply the first expression by each term in the second expression.

$=(3x^3y^2)(5x^2y^3) + (4x^2y)(5x^2y^3) + (3x^3y^2)(xy) + (4x^2y)(xy)$
$= 15x^5y^5 + 20x^4y^4 + 3x^4y^3 + 4x^3y^2$

Step 2: We now need to multiply all the terms in parentheses and add their results. Since there are no like terms the answer is stated here.

Answer: Since there are no like terms the answer is
$$15x^5y^5 + 20x^4y^4 + 3x^4y^3 + 4x^3y^2$$

Example 6   Simplify: $(xy^2)(x^3y^2 + xy^2 + x)$

$(xy^2)(x^3y^2 + xy^2 + x)$

$= (xy^2)(x^3y^2) + (xy^2)(xy^2) + (xy^2)(x)$

Step 1: To solve this equation we need to use the Distributive Property to multiply the first expression by each term in the second expression.

$= (xy^2)(x^3y^2) + (xy^2)(xy^2) + (xy^2)(x)$

$= x^4y^4 + x^2y^4 + x^2y^2$

Step 2: We now need to multiply all the terms in parentheses and add their results.

Answer: The answer is $x^4y^4 + x^2y^4 + x^2y^2$.

Problem Set

Simplify completely:

1. $3x^3(7x^5 - 3x^2)$

2. $2x^2(7x^7 - 3x^4)$

3. $x^3(7x^7 - 3x^4)$

4. $4x^3(7x^7 - 3x^4)$

5. $4x^3(7x^8 - 2x^4)$

6. $x^3y^2(4x^3y - 3xy^2 - 3x^3y)$

7. $x^3y^2(4xy + 3x^2y - 3x^3y)$

8. $x^3y^2(4xy^2 + 3x^2y^2 - 3x^3y)$

9. $x^3y^2(4xy - 3xy + 3x^3y)$

10. $x^3y^2(4xy + 3xy + 8xy)$

11. $(2x^3 + x^2)(3x^2 - 4x)$

12. $(2x^3 - x^2)(3x^2 - 4x)$

13. $(3x^3 + x^2)(3x^2 + 4x)$

14. $(3x^3 + x^2)(x^2 + 4x)$

15. $(5x^3 + x^2)(x^2 + 4x)$

16. $(2x^3y^2 - 3x^2y)(2x^2y^3 + 4xy)$

17. $(2x^3y^2 + 3x^2y)(2x^2y^3 - 4xy)$

18. $(2x^3y^2 + 3x^2z)(2x^2y^3 - 4xz)$

19. $(2x^3y^2 - 3x^2z)(2x^2y^3 - 4xz)$

20. $(2x^3y^2 - 3x^2z)(2x^2y^3 - 5xz)$

21. $(2x^3y^2 - 3x^2y)(2x^2y^3 - 5xy)$

22. $(2x^2 + x)(3x^2 - 4x - 9)$

23. $(2x^2 + x)(3x^2 + 4x + 9)$

24. $(3x^2 - x)(3x^2 + x + 9)$

25. $(3x^2 + x)(3x^2 - 4x + 9)$

26. $(3x^2 - x)(3x^2 + 4x + 9)$

27. $(3x^2 + x)(3x^2 - x + 9)$

28. $(3x^2 + 2)^2$

29. $(3x^2 + 2y)^2$

30. $(3x^2 - 2y)^2$

31. $(3x^2 + 4y)^2$

32. $(4x^2 + 4y)^2$

33. $(4x^2 - 4y)^2$

34. $(3x^2 - 3y)^2$

35. $(4x^2 + 3y)^2$

36. $(2xy^2 + 3x^2y)(3x^3y^2 + 4xy^2 - 6x)$

37. $(2xy^2 + 3x^2y)(3x^3y^2 + 4xy^2 + 6x)$

38. $(2xy^2 - 3x^2y)(3x^3y^2 + 4xy^2 + 6x)$

39. $(2xy^2 + 3x^2y)(-3x^3y^2 + 4xy^2 + 6x)$

40. $(4xy^2 + 3x^2y)(3x^3y^2 - 4xy^2 + 6x)$

We will now learn how to determine what type of solutions a quadratic equation will have without actually having to solve the equation first. This is a useful tool when checking the solutions we've found to a problem; if there is a convenient way to know whether the answer should be real, imaginary, positive, or negative, we can quickly see if our solution is reasonable. We do this by finding a value called the **discriminant** for the equation.

Discriminant	A value, derived from the quadratic equation, which indicates the nature of the solution set $d = b^2 - 4ac$

Discriminant Solutions

If the discriminant has a positive value, then the quadratic equation has two real solutions. When the discriminant has a value of zero, the equation has only one real solution. When the discriminant has a negative value, the quadratic equation has two complex solutions. The quadratic equation has complex solutions if the value of its discriminant is negative. If the value of the discriminant b squared minus 4 a c is a perfect square, then the solutions of the quadratic equation are rational numbers. If the discriminant is not a perfect square, then the solutions of the quadratic equation are irrational numbers.

Discriminant	Solutions to Quadratic Equation
$d > 0$	2 real solutions
$d = 0$	1 real solution that is a double root.
$d < 0$	2 complex solutions

Example 1   Find the discriminant of the quadratic equation $3x^2 - 4x + 3$.

$3x^2 - 4x + 3$

$a = 3, b = -4, c = 3$

Step 1:   Identify the coefficients a, b, and c of the quadratic equation.

$d = b^2 - 4ac$

$d = (-4)^2 - 4(3)(3)$

$\quad = 16 - 36$

$\quad = -20$

Step 2:   Substitute values of a, b, and c into the discriminant.

Answer: The discriminant is equal to -20.

Example 2   Determine the type of solutions when the discriminant of a quadratic equation equals 4.

Answer: When the discriminant of a quadratic equation has a positive value, then the quadratic equation has two real solutions.

Example 3   The roots of a quadratic equation with integer coefficients are $x = 6$ and $x = 2$. Determine the nature of the discriminant.

Answer: Since the roots of this equation are integers, they are rational roots. Therefore, the discriminant must be a perfect square.

Example 4   Determine the type of solutions for the quadratic equation $x^2 - 12x + 36$.

$x^2 - 12x + 36$

$a = 1, b = -12, c = 36$

Step 1: Identify the coefficients a, b, and c of the quadratic equation

$d = b^2 - 4ac$

$= (-12)^2 - 4(1)(36)$

$= 144 - 144$

$= 0$

Step 2: Substitute values of a, b, and c into the discriminant.

Answer: When the discriminant is zero, the quadratic equation has a double real root.

Example 5   Find the value of t such that the equation $tx^2 - 4x + 2$ has a double real root solution.

$tx^2 - 4x + 2 = 0$

$a = t, b = -4, c = 2$

Step 1: Identify the coefficients a, b, and c of the quadratic equation.

$b^2 - 4ac = 0$

$(-4)^2 - 4(t)(2) = 0$

$16 - 8t = 0$

$16 - 8t + 8t = 0 + 8t$

$16 = 8t$

$\dfrac{16}{8} = \dfrac{8t}{8}$

$2 = t$

$t = 2$

Step 2: A quadratic equation with a double real root has a discriminant equal to 0. Therefore, let $d = b^2 - 4ac = 0$.

Answer: The equation has a double real root when $t = 2$.

Example 6   Given $x^2 - 6x + 1 = 0$, determine which of the following statements are true for the roots of the quadratic equation:

    I. The discriminant is positive.
    II. The equation has real roots.
    III. The roots are rational numbers.

$x^2 - 6x + 1 = 0$

$a = 1, b = -6, c = 1$

Step 1: Identify the coefficients a, b, and c of the quadratic equation.

$$d = b^2 - 4ac$$
$$= (-6)^2 - 4(1)(1)$$
$$= 36 - 4$$
$$= 32$$

Step 2: Find the discriminant of the quadratic equation.

Answer: The discriminant is positive and the roots are real. Therefore, conditions I and II are true.

Problem Set

Find the discriminant of each quadratic equation:

1. $3x^2 - 4x + 1 = 0$ **2.** $4x^2 - 4x + 1 = 0$ **3.** $4x^2 - 4x + 4 = 0$ **4.** $2x^2 + 4x + 3 = 0$

5. $3x^2 - 6x + 3 = 0$ **6.** $x^2 - 3x + 4 = 0$ **7.** $x^2 - 7x + 6 = 0$ **8.** $x^2 - 4x - 2 = 0$

Solve:

9. Determine the type of solutions when the discriminant of a quadratic equation equals 0.

One double real root   Conjugate complex roots

Two rational roots   Two irrational roots

10. Determine the type of solutions when the discriminant of a quadratic equation equals 24.

Two irrational roots   Two rational roots

Conjugate complex roots   One double real root

11. Determine the type of solutions when the discriminant of a quadratic equation equals –17.

Two irrational roots   Two rational roots

Conjugate complex roots   One double real root

12. Determine the type of solutions when the discriminant of a quadratic equation equals 25.

Two rational roots   Conjugate complex roots

One double real root   Two irrational roots

13. Determine the type of solutions for the quadratic equation.

$$x^2 + 4x - 5 = 0$$

Two irrational roots   Two rational roots

One double real root   Conjugate complex roots

14. Determine the type of solutions for the quadratic equation.

$$x^2 + 2x - 3 = 0$$

Two rational roots   Two irrational roots

One double real root   Conjugate complex roots

15. Determine the type of solutions for the quadratic equation.

$$-3x^2 + 4x + 5 = 0$$

Conjugate complex roots   Two rational roots

One double real root   Two irrational roots

16. Determine the type of solutions for the quadratic equation.

$$x^2 + 6x + 9 = 0$$

Two irrational roots   One double real root

Two rational roots   Conjugate complex roots

17. Determine the type of solutions for the quadratic equation.

$$2x^2 - 3x + 2 = 0$$

Two irrational roots   Two rational roots

One double real root   Conjugate complex roots

18. Determine the nature of the discriminant given the following: The roots of the quadratic equation with integer coefficients are $x = \dfrac{7}{4}$ and $x = \dfrac{4}{9}$.

Negative   Positive   Zero

19. Determine the nature of the discriminant given the following: The roots of a quadratic equation with integer coefficients

are $x = 3$ and $x = 4$.

        Zero   Negative   Positive

20. Determine the nature of the discriminant given the following: The roots of a quadratic equation with integer coefficients is $x = 5$.

        Positive   Zero   Negative

21. Find the value(s) of t such that the equation $tx^2 - 6x + 3 = 0$ has a double real root.

22. Find the value(s) of t such that the equation $tx^2 - 8x + 2 = 0$ has a double real root.

23. Find the value(s) of t such that the equation $tx^2 - 5x + 3 = 0$ has real and distinct roots.

24. Find the value(s) of t such that the equation $tx^2 - 6x + 5 = 0$ has conjugate complex roots.

25. Find the value(s) of t such that the equation $tx^2 - 2x + 1 = 0$ has conjugate complex roots.

26. Find the value(s) of b such that the equation $-2x^2 + bx - 3 = 0$ has rational roots.

27. Find the value(s) of b such that the equation $x^2 + bx + 6 = 0$ has rational roots.

28. Find the value(s) of b such that the equation $x^2 + bx + 8 = 0$ has rational roots.

29. Find the values of b such that the quadratic equation $2x^2 + bx + b = 0$ has a double real root solution.

30. Find the values of b such that the quadratic equation $x^2 + bx - b = 0$ has a double real root solution.

31. Find the values of b such that the quadratic equation $x^2 + 4bx - b = 0$ has a double real root solution.

32. Find the values of b such that the quadratic equation $3x^2 + bx + b = 0$ has a double real root solution.

33. Find the values of b such that the quadratic equation $5x^2 + bx + b = 0$ has a double real root solution.

34. Find the values of b such that the quadratic equation $-3x^2 + bx + b = 0$ has a double real root solution.

35. Given the quadratic equation $2x^2 - 7x + 2 = 0$, determine which of the following is true.

   I. The discriminant is positive.
   II. The equation has real roots.
   III. The roots are rational numbers.

36. Given the quadratic equation $x^2 - 5x + 2 = 0$, determine which of the following is true.

   I. The discriminant is positive.
   II. The equation has real roots.
   III. The roots are rational numbers.

37. Given the quadratic equation $x^2 - 5x + 8 = 0$, determine which of the following is true.

   I. The discriminant is negative.
   II. The equation has real roots.
   III. The roots are conjugate complex.

38. Given the quadratic equation $3x^2 - 5x + 7 = 0$, determine which of the following is true.

   I. The discriminant is negative.
   II. The equation has real roots.
   III. The roots are conjugate complex.

39. Given the quadratic equation $x^2 - 6x + 8 = 0$, determine which of the following is true.

   I. The discriminant is a perfect square.
   II. The equation has real roots.
   III. The roots are rational.

40. Given the quadratic equation $x^2 - 6x + 2 = 0$, determine which of the following is true.

   I. The discriminant is positive.
   II. The equation has real roots.
   III. The roots are rational numbers.

HA1-927: Graphing $f(x) = ax^2$ Using Dilations

The graph of $y = x^2$ or $f(x) = x^2$ is called a parabola. It is an essential graph to understand, because it will help you learn how to graph all quadratic functions. A parabola looks like the graph below; it is symmetric with respect to the y-axis and passes through the points $(0, 0)$, $(1, 1)$, and $(2, 4)$.

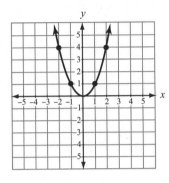

x	–2	–1	0	1	2
x^2	4	1	0	1	4

We will examine the graph of $y = ax^2$, where a is a positive constant. The effect of having a constant in front of the square-term is called a **dilation**. Graphs similar to $f(x) = \frac{1}{2}x^2$, where $0 < a < 1$, will become wider (shrinking) than the graph of $f(x) = x^2$. Graphs similar to $f(x) = 3x^2$, where $a > 1$, will become narrower (stretching) than the graph of $f(x) = x^2$.

Dilation ($a > 0$) - Vertical Stretching and Shrinking

For $a > 1$, the graph of $y = ax^2$ can be found by vertically stretching the graph of the parent function $y = x^2$. **Stretching** causes the graph to become **narrower**; points on the graph are moving away from the x-axis.

For $0 < a < 1$, the graph of $y = ax^2$ can be found by vertically shrinking the graph of the parent function $y = x^2$. **Shrinking** causes the graph to become **wider**; points on the graph are getting closer to the x-axis.

Example 1   Describe, without graphing, how the graph of h can be obtained from the graph of f when $f(x) = x^2$ and $h(x) = 7x^2$.

$f(x) = x^2$	**Step 1:** Notice that $f(x)$ is the basic parabola.
$a = 7$	**Step 2:** Determine the value of a in $h(x)$.
	Step 3: Since $a = 7 > 1$, the graph of $f(x)$ is stretched by a factor of 7.
	Answer: The graph of $h(x)$ can be obtained by stretching the graph of $f(x)$ by 7.

Example 2   If $k(x) = \frac{1}{9}x^2$, find the set of values of $k(x)$ when $x = -3, 0, 9$.

$k(-3) = \frac{1}{9}(-3)^2$

$\qquad = \frac{1}{9}(9)$

$\qquad = 1$

Step 1:   Substitute $x = -3$ into the function $k(x)$ and solve.

$k(0) = \frac{1}{9}(0)^2$

$\qquad = \frac{1}{9}(0)$

$\qquad = 0$

Step 2:   Substitute $x = 0$ into the function $k(x)$ and solve.

$k(9) = \frac{1}{9}(9)^2$

$\qquad = \frac{1}{9}(81)$

$\qquad = 9$

Step 3:   Substitute $x = 9$ into the function $k(x)$ and solve.

$\{1, 0, 9\}$

Step 4:   Create the set of all the values of $k(x)$ for the given set of x-values.

Answer: The set of values for $k(x)$ are $\{1, 0, 9\}$.

Example 3   Which function best matches the graph?

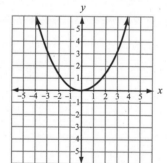

A) $y = \frac{3}{4}x^2$

B) $y = \frac{1}{3}x^2$

C) $y = 4x^2$

D) $y = 3x^2$

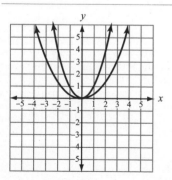

Step 1:   Graph the parent function $y = x^2$ on the same graph and compare the graphs.

Step 2: The graph is wider than the parent function, $y = x^2$.
Therefore, the graph must be in the form $y = ax^2$,
with $0 < a < 1$.

Step 3: Choose a point, such as (3, 3), and substitute it into the
equations with $0 < a < 1$.

$$y = \frac{3}{4}x^2 \qquad y = \frac{1}{3}x^2$$

$$3 \overset{?}{=} \frac{3}{4}(3)^2 \qquad 3 \overset{?}{=} \frac{1}{3}(3)^2$$

$$3 \overset{?}{=} \frac{3}{4}(9) \qquad 3 \overset{?}{=} \frac{1}{3}(9)$$

$$3 \neq 6\frac{3}{4} \qquad 3 = 3$$

Answer: The function that best matches the graph is B) $y = \frac{1}{3}x^2$.

Example 4 Arrange the functions in order from the widest to the narrowest parabola.

$$y = \frac{1}{7}x^2, \quad y = 6x^2, \quad y = x^2, \quad y = \frac{3}{2}x^2$$

Step 1: Determine the a values for the functions.

$$a = \frac{1}{7}, 6, 1, \frac{3}{2}$$

Step 2: Arrange the a values from smallest to largest.
Note: The smaller the "a" value, the wider the parabola.

$$\frac{1}{7} < 1 < \frac{3}{2} < 6$$

Step 3: Order the functions.

$$y = \frac{1}{7}x^2, \quad y = x^2, \quad y = \frac{3}{2}x^2, \quad y = 6x^2$$

Answer: The arrangement of functions from widest to narrowest is:

$$y = \frac{1}{7}x^2, \quad y = x^2, \quad y = \frac{3}{2}x^2, \quad y = 6x^2$$

Example 5 Match each graph to its function.

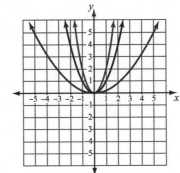

$$f(x) = x^2$$

$$g(x) = 2x^2$$

$$h(x) = \frac{1}{5}x^2$$

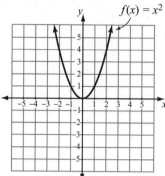

Step 1: The function $f(x)$ is the basic parabola.

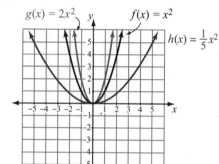

Step 2: The function $g(x)$ can be obtained by stretching $f(x)$ by a factor of 2, since $a = 2$. Similarly, the function $h(x)$ can be obtained by shrinking $f(x)$ by a factor of $\frac{1}{5}$, since $a = \frac{1}{5}$.

Answer: See the graph in Step 2.

Problem Set

1. Describe, without graphing, how the graph of g can be obtained from the graph of f, when $f(x) = x^2$ and $g(x) = \frac{5}{2}x^2$.

2. If $f(x) = -2x^2$, find the set of values of $f(x)$ when $x = -2, -1, 0, 1, 2$.

3. Describe, without graphing, how the graph of g can be obtained from the graph of f, when $f(x) = x^2$ and $g(x) = \frac{1}{3}x^2$.

4. If $f(x) = \frac{1}{3}x^2$, find the set of values of $f(x)$ when $x = -9, -3, 0, 3, 9$.

5. Describe, without graphing, how the graph of g can be obtained from the graph of f, when $f(x) = x^2$ and $g(x) = 4x^2$.

6. If $f(x) = -\frac{1}{2}x^2$, find the set of values of $f(x)$ when $x = -2, -1, 0, 1, 2$.

7. Describe, without graphing, how the graph of g can be obtained from the graph of f, when $f(x) = x^2$ and $g(x) = \frac{3}{4}x^2$.

8. If $f(x) = 8x^2$, find the set of values of $f(x)$ when $x = -\frac{1}{2}, -\frac{1}{4}, 0, \frac{1}{4}, \frac{1}{2}$.

9. Describe, without graphing, how the graph of g can be obtained from the graph of f, when $f(x) = x^2$ and $g(x) = \frac{11}{2}x^2$.

10. If $f(x) = \frac{3}{8}x^2$, find the set of values of $f(x)$ when $x = -2, -1, 0, 1, 4$.

11. Describe, without graphing, how the graph of g can be obtained from the graph of f, when $f(x) = x^2$ and $g(x) = \frac{3}{7}x^2$.

12. If $f(x) = 6x^2$, find the set of values of $f(x)$ when $x = -2, -1, 0, 1, 2$.

13. Describe, without graphing, how the graph of g can be obtained from the graph of f, when $f(x) = x^2$ and $g(x) = \frac{6}{5}x^2$.

14. If $f(x) = 10x^2$, find the set of values of $f(x)$ when $x = -2, -1, 0, 1, 2$.

15. Describe, without graphing, how the graph of g can be obtained from the graph of f, when $f(x) = x^2$ and $g(x) = \frac{1}{16}x^2$.

16. Which function best matches the graph below?

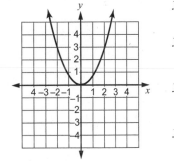

$y = x^2$

$y = \frac{1}{4}x^2$

$y = \frac{3}{4}x^2$

$y = \frac{4}{3}x^2$

17. Arrange the functions in order from the narrowest to the widest parabola.

$y = x^2, \quad y = 3x^2, \quad y = \frac{5}{2}x^2, \quad y = \frac{1}{3}x^2$

18. Which function best matches the graph below?

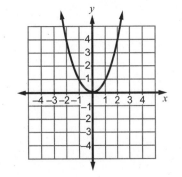

$y = \frac{1}{2}x^2$

$y = x^2$

$y = 2x^2$

$y = 3x^2$

19. Arrange the functions in order from the widest to the narrowest parabola.

$$y = \frac{2}{3}x^2, \quad y = x^2, \quad y = \frac{1}{4}x^2, \quad y = \frac{1}{2}x^2$$

20. Which function best matches the graph below?

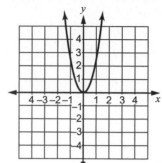

$$y = \frac{1}{2}x^2$$

$$y = \frac{1}{3}x^2$$

$$y = \frac{5}{2}x^2$$

$$y = 5x^2$$

21. Arrange the functions in order from the narrowest to the widest parabola.

$$y = x^2, \quad y = 5x^2, \quad y = \frac{11}{2}x^2, \quad y = 6x^2$$

22. Which function best matches the graph below?

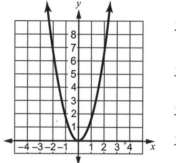

$$y = \frac{5}{4}x^2$$

$$y = \frac{7}{4}x^2$$

$$y = 2x^2$$

$$y = 4x^2$$

23. Arrange the functions in order from the widest to the narrowest parabola.

$$y = x^2, \quad y = 3x^2, \quad y = \frac{5}{7}x^2, \quad y = \frac{7}{2}x^2$$

24. Which function best matches the graph below?

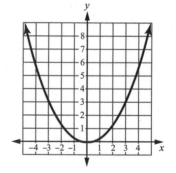

$$y = \frac{1}{2}x^2$$

$$y = \frac{1}{3}x^2$$

$$y = 2x^2$$

$$y = 3x^2$$

25. Which function best matches the graph below?

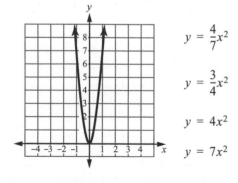

$$y = \frac{4}{7}x^2$$

$$y = \frac{3}{4}x^2$$

$$y = 4x^2$$

$$y = 7x^2$$

26. Arrange the functions in order from the narrowest to the widest parabola.

$$y = \frac{1}{4}x^2, \quad y = x^2, \quad y = \frac{3}{2}x^2, \quad y = \frac{1}{6}x^2$$

27. Arrange the functions in order from the narrowest to the widest parabola.

$$y = 6x^2, \quad y = 8x^2, \quad y = \frac{3}{2}x^2, \quad y = \frac{2}{9}x^2$$

28. Which function best matches the graph below?

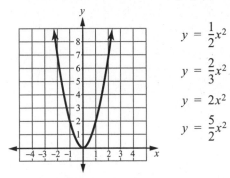

$$y = \frac{1}{2}x^2$$

$$y = \frac{2}{3}x^2$$

$$y = 2x^2$$

$$y = \frac{5}{2}x^2$$

29. Arrange the functions in order from the widest to the narrowest parabola.

$$y = x^2, \quad y = \frac{5}{2}x^2, \quad y = \frac{3}{2}x^2, \quad y = 3x^2$$

30. Which function best matches the graph below?

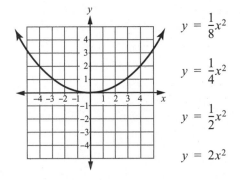

$$y = \frac{1}{8}x^2$$

$$y = \frac{1}{4}x^2$$

$$y = \frac{1}{2}x^2$$

$$y = 2x^2$$

31. Match each function with its graph.

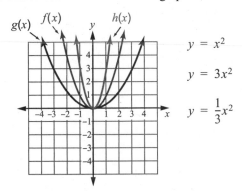

$$y = x^2$$

$$y = 3x^2$$

$$y = \frac{1}{3}x^2$$

32. Match each function with its graph.

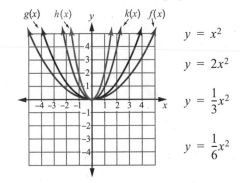

$$y = x^2$$

$$y = 2x^2$$

$$y = \frac{1}{3}x^2$$

$$y = \frac{1}{6}x^2$$

33. Match each function with its graph.

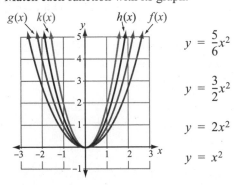

$$y = \frac{5}{6}x^2$$

$$y = \frac{3}{2}x^2$$

$$y = 2x^2$$

$$y = x^2$$

34. Match each function with its graph.

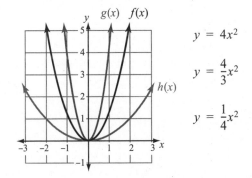

$$y = 4x^2$$

$$y = \frac{4}{3}x^2$$

$$y = \frac{1}{4}x^2$$

35. Match each function with its graph.

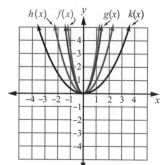

$y = x^2$

$y = \dfrac{5}{2}x^2$

$y = \dfrac{2}{5}x^2$

$y = \dfrac{17}{5}x^2$

36. Match each function with its graph.

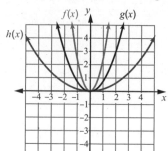

$y = \dfrac{3}{4}x^2$

$y = \dfrac{1}{6}x^2$

$y = \dfrac{7}{3}x^2$

37. Match each function with its graph.

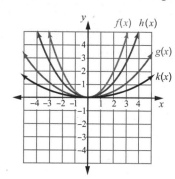

$y = \dfrac{1}{2}x^2$

$y = \dfrac{1}{8}x^2$

$y = \dfrac{1}{16}x^2$

$y = \dfrac{1}{4}x^2$

38. Match each function with its graph.

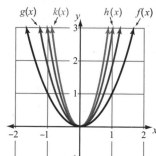

$y = x^2$

$y = 3x^2$

$y = 4x^2$

$y = 2x^2$

39. Match each function with its graph.

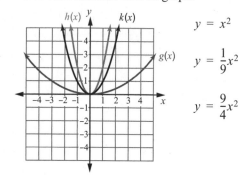

$y = x^2$

$y = \dfrac{1}{9}x^2$

$y = \dfrac{9}{4}x^2$

40. Match each function with its graph.

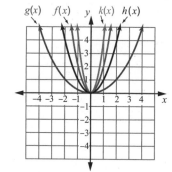

$y = 4x^2$

$y = x^2$

$y = 2x^2$

$y = \dfrac{1}{4}x^2$

HA1-928: Graphing $f(x) = ax^2$ Using Dilations and Reflections

One technique for graphing quadratic functions is known as reflection. First, let's review dilations.

Dilation ($a > 0$) - Vertical Stretching and Shrinking

For $a > 1$,

- the graph of $y = ax^2$ can be found by vertically **stretching** the graph of the parent function $y = x^2$. Stretching causes the graph to become **narrower**; points on the graph are moving away from the x-axis.

For $0 < a < 1$,

- the graph of $y = ax^2$ can be found by vertically **shrinking** the graph of the parent function $y = x^2$. Shrinking causes the graph to become **wider**; points on the graph are getting closer to the x-axis.

Reflection is another technique used to graph quadratic functions. Below are the graphs of $f(x) = x^2$ and $g(x) = -x^2$. When comparing the two graphs, we see that the graph of $g(x)$ is a mirror image of $f(x)$. Therefore, we can say that $g(x)$ is a reflection over the x-axis of the graph of $f(x)$.

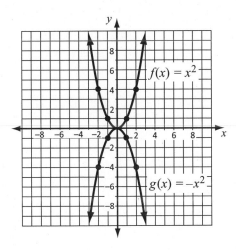

x	-2	-1	0	1	2
$f(x) = x^2$	4	1	0	1	4
$g(x) = -x^2$	-4	-1	0	-1	-4

Reflection across the x-axis

- The graph of $y = -ax^2$ can be obtained by reflecting (mirroring) the graph of the parent function $y = ax^2$ across the x-axis.

- The graphs of $y = -ax^2$ and $y = ax^2$ are "reflections" of each other over the x-axis.

Example 1   Describe, without graphing, how $g(x) = \dfrac{2}{5}x^2$ can be obtained from $f(x) = x^2$.

$f(x) = x^2$

Step 1: Notice that $f(x)$ is the basic parabola.

$a = \dfrac{2}{5}$

Step 2: Determine the value of a in $g(x)$.

Step 3: Since $|a| = \frac{2}{5} < 1$, the graph of $g(x)$ is obtained by shrinking the graph
of $f(x) = x^2$.

Answer: The graph of $g(x)$ can be obtained by shrinking the graph of $f(x)$.

Example 2   Describe which transformation was used to get the graph of $g(x)$ from $f(x)$ in the
figure shown below.

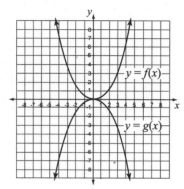

Step 1: Compare the graphs of $y = f(x)$ and $y = g(x)$. The graph $y = g(x)$ is a
mirror image of the graph $y = f(x)$. Therefore, $y = g(x)$ is the reflection
of $y = f(x)$.

Answer: The graph of $g(x)$ can be obtained by reflecting the graph of $f(x)$ across
the x-axis.

Example 3   Describe, without graphing, how $h(x) = -5x^2$ can be obtained from $g(x) = x^2$.

$g(x) = x^2$	**Step 1:** Notice that $g(x)$ is the basic parabola.
$a = -5$	**Step 2:** Determine the value of a in $h(x)$.
	Step 3: Since a is negative for $h(x)$, the graph is obtained by reflecting the graph of the parent function $g(x) = x^2$ across the x-axis.
$|-5| = 5 > 1$	**Step 4:** Determine the absolute value of a.
	Step 5: Since $|a| = 5 > 1$, the graph is obtained by stretching the graph of the parent function $g(x) = x^2$.

Answer: The graph of $h(x) = -5x^2$ can be obtained by reflecting and stretching the
graph of the parent function $g(x) = x^2$.

Example 4   Select the equation that best matches the graph.

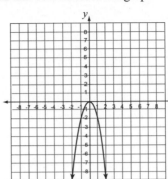

A) $y = 4x^2$

B) $y = \dfrac{1}{3}x^2$

C) $y = -2x^2$

Step 1:   The parabola is reflected over the x-axis so $a < 0$. The only function with a negative coefficient is C.

Answer: The best match is the function c: $y = -2x^2$.

Example 5   In the following example, match the given graphs of functions with the equations.

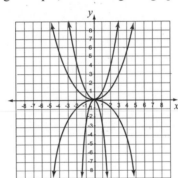

A) $y = -\dfrac{2}{7}x^2$

B) $y = \dfrac{1}{3}x^2$

C) $y = x^2$

D) $y = -3x^2$

Step 1:   Two of the graphs open up, so their corresponding equations have a positive "a" value: B: $y = \dfrac{1}{3}x^2$ and C: $y = x^2$.

Step 2:   The graph of B is wider than the graph of C since $\left|\dfrac{1}{3}\right| = \dfrac{1}{3} < 1$ and $|1| = 1$.

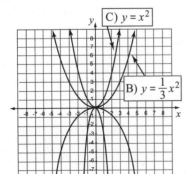

Step 3: The other two graphs open downward, so their corresponding equations have a negative "*a*" value: A: $y = -\frac{2}{7}x^2$ and D: $y = -3x^2$.

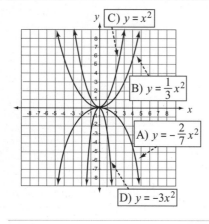

Step 4: The graph of A is wider than the graph of D since $\left|-\frac{2}{7}\right| = \frac{2}{7} < 1$ and $|-3| = 3 > 1$.

Answer: See graph in Step 4.

Problem Set

Solve:

1. Describe which transformation was used to get the graph of *g(x)* from *f(x)*.

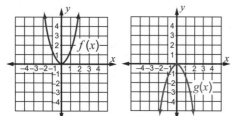

2. Describe which transformation was used to get the graph of *g(x)* from *f(x)*.

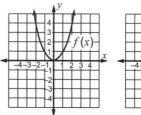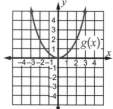

3. Describe, without graphing, how the graph of *h* can be obtained from the graph of *f*, when $f(x) = 3x^2$ and $h(x) = -3x^2$.

4. Describe, without graphing, how the graph of *g* can be obtained from the graph of *f*, when $f(x) = x^2$ and $g(x) = \frac{3}{7}x^2$.

5. Describe which transformation was used to get the graph of $g(x)$ from $f(x)$.

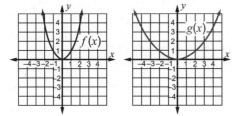

6. Describe, without graphing, how the graph of g can be obtained from the graph of f, when $f(x) = x^2$ and $g(x) = \dfrac{9}{5}x^2$.

7. Describe, without graphing, how the graph of g can be obtained from the graph of f, when $f(x) = 2x^2$ and $g(x) = -2x^2$.

8. Describe which transformation was used to get the graph of $g(x)$ from $f(x)$.

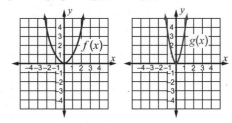

9. Describe, without graphing, how the graph of g can be obtained from the graph of f, when $f(x) = x^2$ and $g(x) = \dfrac{7}{9}x^2$.

10. Describe which transformation was used to get the graph of $g(x)$ from $f(x)$.

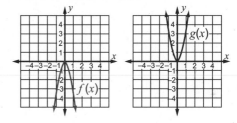

11. Describe, without graphing, how the graph of g can be obtained from the graph of f, when $f(x) = x^2$ and $g(x) = \dfrac{13}{2}x^2$.

12. Describe which transformation was used to get the graph of $g(x)$ from $f(x)$.

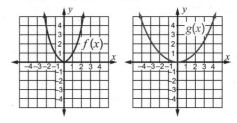

13. Describe, without graphing, how the graph of g can be obtained from the graph of f, when $f(x) = -\frac{5}{2}x^2$ and $g(x) = \frac{5}{2}x^2$.

14. Describe which transformation was used to get the graph of $g(x)$ from $f(x)$.

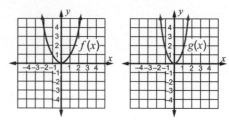

15. Describe, without graphing, how the graph of g can be obtained from the graph of f, when $f(x) = x^2$ and $g(x) = \frac{3}{20}x^2$.

16. Select the equation that best matches the graph.

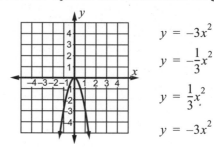

$y = -3x^2$

$y = -\frac{1}{3}x^2$

$y = \frac{1}{3}x^2$

$y = -3x^2$

17. Describe, without graphing, how $k(x) = -\frac{1}{9}x^2$ can be obtained from the graph of $f(x) = x^2$.

18. Select the equation that best matches the graph.

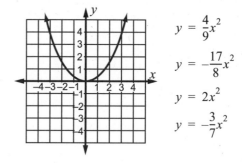

$y = \frac{4}{9}x^2$

$y = -\frac{17}{8}x^2$

$y = 2x^2$

$y = -\frac{3}{7}x^2$

19. Select the equation that best matches the graph.

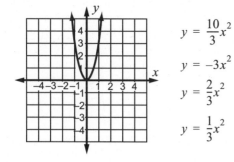

$y = \frac{10}{3}x^2$

$y = -3x^2$

$y = \frac{2}{3}x^2$

$y = \frac{1}{3}x^2$

20. Describe, without graphing, how $g(x) = -\frac{5}{3}x^2$ can be obtained from the graph of $f(x) = x^2$.

21. Select the equation that best matches the graph.

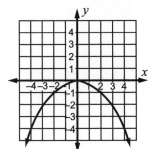

$y = \dfrac{1}{4}x^2$

$y = -\dfrac{5}{4}x^2$

$y = -\dfrac{1}{4}x^2$

$y = 4x^2$

22. Describe, without graphing, how $k(x) = -\dfrac{7}{12}x^2$ can be obtained from the graph of $f(x) = x^2$.

23. Select the equation that best matches the graph.

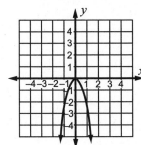

$y = \dfrac{7}{3}x^2$

$y = -\dfrac{3}{7}x^2$

$y = \dfrac{3}{7}x^2$

$y = -\dfrac{7}{3}x^2$

24. Describe, without graphing, how $h(x) = -\dfrac{9}{2}x^2$ can be obtained from the graph of $f(x) = x^2$.

25. Select the equation that best matches the graph.

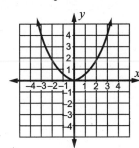

$y = -\dfrac{5}{11}x^2$

$y = -\dfrac{11}{5}x^2$

$y = \dfrac{5}{11}x^2$

$y = \dfrac{11}{5}x^2$

26. Describe, without graphing, how $g(x) = -\dfrac{3}{10}x^2$ can be obtained from the graph of $f(x) = x^2$.

27. Select the equation that best matches the graph.

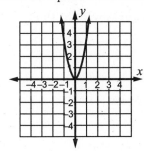

$y = -3x^2$

$y = \dfrac{7}{2}x^2$

$y = -\dfrac{2}{7}x^2$

$y = \dfrac{1}{3}x^2$

28. Describe, without graphing, how $h(x) = -\dfrac{10}{3}x^2$ can be obtained from the graph of $f(x) = x^2$.

29. Select the equation that best matches the graph.

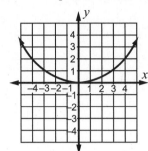

$y = \dfrac{1}{8}x^2$

$y = -\dfrac{1}{8}x^2$

$y = \dfrac{8}{5}x^2$

$y = -8x^2$

30. Describe, without graphing, how $k(x) = -\dfrac{2}{7}x^2$ can be obtained from the graph of $f(x) = x^2$.

31. Match each function with its graph.

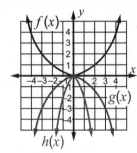

$y = -2x^2$

$y = \dfrac{1}{4}x^2$

$y = -\dfrac{1}{3}x^2$

32. Match each function with its graph.

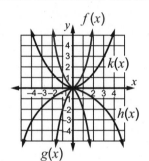

$y = \dfrac{1}{3}x^2$

$y = -\dfrac{1}{5}x^2$

$y = \dfrac{3}{2}x^2$

$y = -2x^2$

33. Match each function with its graph.

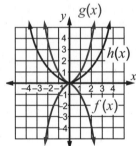

$y = x^2$

$y = -x^2$

$y = \dfrac{1}{3}x^2$

34. Match each function with its graph.

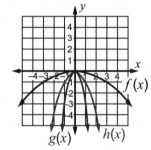

$y = -\dfrac{1}{9}x^2$

$y = -x^2$

$y = -3x^2$

35. Match each function with its graph.

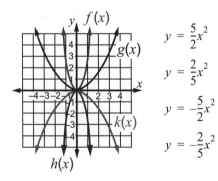

$y = \dfrac{5}{2}x^2$

$y = \dfrac{2}{5}x^2$

$y = -\dfrac{5}{2}x^2$

$y = -\dfrac{2}{5}x^2$

36. Match each function with its graph.

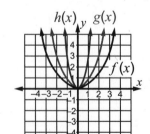

$y = \dfrac{2}{3}x^2$

$y = \dfrac{1}{4}x^2$

$y = \dfrac{7}{2}x^2$

37. Match each function with its graph.

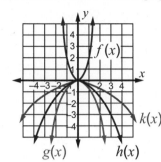

$y = 2x^2$

$y = \dfrac{1}{3}x^2$

$y = -\dfrac{1}{8}x^2$

$y = -\dfrac{3}{4}x^2$

38. Match each function with its graph.

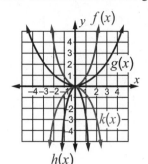

$y = x^2$

$y = -\dfrac{2}{3}x^2$

$y = \dfrac{3}{10}x^2$

$y = -\dfrac{10}{3}x^2$

39. Match each function with its graph.

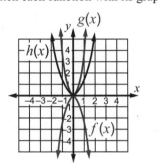

$y = \dfrac{3}{2}x^2$

$y = -\dfrac{5}{2}x^2$

$y = 4x^2$

40. Match each function with its graph.

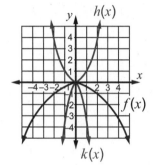

$y = -\dfrac{1}{5}x^2$

$y = x^2$

$y = -\dfrac{9}{2}x^2$

HA1-929: Graphing $f(x) = ax^2 + c$ Using Dilations, Reflections, and Vertical Translations

In addition to dilations and reflections, vertical translations can be used to graph $f(x) = ax^2 + c$. First we will review dilations and reflections.

Dilation ($a > 0$) – Vertical Stretching and Shrinking

- For $0 < a < 1$:

  the graph of $y = ax^2$ can be found by vertically shrinking the graph of the parent function $y = x^2$.
  Shrinking causes the graph to become **wider**; points on the graph are getting closer to the x-axis.

- For $a > 1$:

  the graph of $y = ax^2$ can be found by vertically stretching the graph of the parent function $y = x^2$.
  Stretching causes the graph to become **narrower**; points on the graph are moving away from the x-axis.

Reflection across the x-axis

- The graph of $y = -ax^2$ can be obtained by reflecting (mirroring) the graph of the parent function $y = ax^2$ across the x-axis.

- The graphs of $y = -ax^2$ and $y = ax^2$ are "reflections" of each other over the x-axis.

In general, new functions can be obtained from old functions by shifting or translating them vertically. The first graph pictured below shows the comparison of $y = ax^2$ and $y = ax^2 + c$. Notice that the graph of $y = ax^2 + c$ is shifted up c units from the graph of $y = ax^2$. The second graph shows the graphs of $y = ax^2$ and $y = ax^2 - c$. Notice that the graph of $y = ax^2 - c$ is shifted down c units from $y = ax^2$.

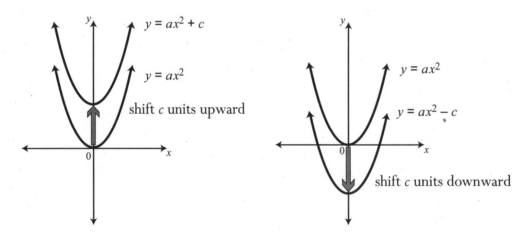

Vertical Shifts

Let $c > 0$,

- The graph of $y = ax^2 + c$ can be obtained by shifting (translating) the graph of the parent function $y = ax^2$ **upward** c units.

- The graph of $y = ax^2 - c$ can be obtained by shifting (translating) the graph of the parent function $y = ax^2$ **downward** c units.

Example 1   Using the function $f(x) = 3x^2 - 5$, find the values of $f(x)$ for $x = -2, -1, 0, 1, 2$.

Step 1:   Substitute each value for x in the function.

$$
\begin{aligned}
f(-2) &= 3(-2)^2 - 5 & f(-1) &= 3(-1)^2 - 5 & f(0) &= 3(0)^2 - 5 & f(1) &= 3(1)^2 - 5 & f(-2) &= 3(2)^2 - 5 \\
&= 3(4) - 5 & &= 3(1) - 5 & &= 3(0) - 5 & &= 3(1) - 5 & &= 3(4) - 5 \\
&= 12 - 5 & &= 3 - 5 & &= 0 - 5 & &= 3 - 5 & &= 12 - 5 \\
&= 7 & &= -2 & &= -5 & &= -2 & &= 7
\end{aligned}
$$

Answer: The $f(x)$ values are 7, –2, –5.

Example 2   Describe how the graph of $h(x) = x^2$ will change if 7 is subtracted from the equation of $h(x)$.

$h(x) = x^2 - 7$

Step 1: Subtract 7 from the given function.

Shift 7 units down.

Step 2: Since 7 is the "c" value in the equation $y = ax^2 + c$, the graph will shift 7 units downward.

Answer: The graph will be shifted 7 units downward.

Example 3   Without graphing, describe how $g(x) = 4x^2 - 9$ can be obtained from the graph of $y = x^2$.

Step 1: Notice that $y = x^2$ is the parent function.

Parent function: $y = x^2$

Vertical stretch: $y = 4x^2$

Step 2: Since the "a" value in $g(x)$ is 4, which is greater than 1, the parabola of $g(x)$ is obtained by stretching $y = x^2$ by a factor of 4.

$y = 4x^2$

Vertical shift down 9: $y = 4x^2 - 9$

Step 3: Since the "c" value in the equation $y = ax^2 + c$ is –9, the parabola of $g(x)$ is obtained by vertically shifting 9 units down.

Answer: The graph of $g(x) = 4x^2 - 9$ can be obtained from $y = x^2$ by stretching and then vertically shifting 9 units down.

Example 4   Given the graph below, choose the equation that best matches the graph.

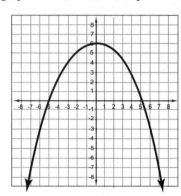

A. $y = 3x^2 - 5$

B. $y = -2x^2 + 4$

C. $y = -\dfrac{1}{4}x^2 + 6$

Step 1:   Since the parabola opens downward, the coefficient of "a" must be negative. This eliminates $y = 3x^2 - 5$ as a possible answer.

Step 2:   We can see when $x = 0$ that the y-value is 6. This is true for $y = -\dfrac{1}{4}x^2 + 6$.

Answer: The equation that most closely resembles this graph is: c) $y = -\dfrac{1}{4}x^2 + 6$

Example 5   Given $f(x) = -3x^2$, find $g(x)$, which is obtained by:
1) reflecting the graph of $f(x)$ across the x-axis, and
2) shifting the obtained graph two units downward.

$f(x) = -3x^2$

Reflection across the x-axis: $y = 3x^2$

Step 1:   Start with the graph of $f(x) = -3x^2$. To reflect this graph across the x-axis, change the sign of the "a" value.

$y = 3x^2$

Shift down two units: $y = 3x^2 - 2$

Step 2:   To shift the graph two units down, subtract 2.

Answer: The function obtained is $g(x) = 3x^2 - 2$.

Problem Set

Solve:

1. Find the values for $f(x) = x^2 - 3$ when x is $-2, -1, 0, 1, 2$.

2. Describe, without graphing, how the graph of g can be obtained from the graph of f, when $f(x) = 3x^2$ and $g(x) = 3x^2 - 4$.

3. Find the values for $f(x) = x^2 - 2$ when x is $-2, -1, 0, 1, 2$.

4. Describe, without graphing, how the graph of g can be obtained from the graph of f, when $f(x) = -2x^2$ and $g(x) = -2x^2 + 3$.

5. Find the values for $f(x) = -x^2 - 2$ when x is $-4, -3, 0, 3, 4$.

6. Describe, without graphing, how the graph of g can be obtained from the graph of f, when $f(x) = \frac{1}{4}x^2$ and $g(x) = \frac{1}{4}x^2 + 2$.

7. Find the values for $f(x) = -4x^2 + 2$ when x is $-2, -1, 0, 1, 2$.

8. Describe, without graphing, how the graph of g can be obtained from the graph of f, when $f(x) = -3x^2$ and $g(x) = -3x^2 - 7$.

9. Find the values for $f(x) = 4x^2 - 3$ when x is $-1, -\frac{1}{2}, 0, \frac{1}{2}, 1$.

10. Describe, without graphing, how the graph of g can be obtained from the graph of f, when $f(x) = -x^2$ and $g(x) = -x^2 + 6$.

11. Find the values for $f(x) = 3x^2 + 1$ when x is $-2, -1, 0, 1, 2$.

12. Describe, without graphing, how the graph of g can be obtained from the graph of f, when $f(x) = 4x^2$ and $g(x) = 4x^2 - 1$.

13. Find the values for $f(x) = -5x^2 + 2$ when x is $-2, -1, 0, 1, 2$.

14. Describe, without graphing, how the graph of g can be obtained from the graph of f, when $f(x) = -4x^2$ and $g(x) = -4x^2 + \frac{1}{2}$.

15. Find the values for $f(x) = x^2 - 4$ when x is $-4, -3, -2, -1, 0$.

16. Describe, without graphing, how $g(x) = 5x^2 + 1$ can be obtained from the graph of $y = x^2$.

17. Given the graph below, choose the equation that best matches the graph.

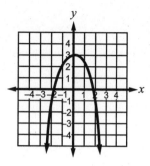

$$y = x^2 + 3 \qquad y = -x^2 + 3$$

$$y = -x^2 - 3 \qquad y = -2x^2 - 3$$

18. Describe, without graphing, how $g(x) = -\dfrac{1}{2}x^2 + 6$ can be obtained from the graph of $y = x^2$.

19. Given the graph below, choose the equation that best matches the graph.

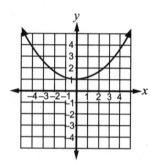

$$y = x^2 + 1 \qquad y = 2x^2 + 1$$

$$y = \dfrac{1}{6}x^2 + 1 \qquad y = -\dfrac{1}{3}x^2 + 1$$

20. Describe, without graphing, how $g(x) = \dfrac{4}{7}x^2 - 5$ can be obtained from the graph of $y = x^2$.

In this lesson, we will learn how the graphs of some quadratic functions are related to the graph of the basic quadratic function, $f(x) = x^2$. In general, the graphs of new functions can be found from old ones by performing translations on the function. To graph the quadratic function defined as $f(x) = x^2 + bx + c$, we first use the method of completing the square to write this function in the convenient form, $f(x) = (x - h)^2 + k$. Then, graph the parent function $y = x^2$. Finally, shift the graph of the parent function horizontally and vertically.

Horizontal Shifts

Let $h > 0$

- The graph of $y = f(x + h)$ can be found by shifting the parent function $y = f(x)$, h units to the left.
- The graph of $y = f(x - h)$ can be found by shifting the parent function, $y = f(x)$, h units to the right.

Vertical Shifts

Let $k > 0$

- The graph of $y = f(x) + k$ can be found by shifting the parent function, $y = f(x)$, k units upward.
- The graph of $y = f(x) - k$ can be found by shifting the parent function, $y = f(x)$, downward k units.

Example 1   The graph of the parabola $f(x) = x^2 - 1$ can be found from the graph of the parent function $f(x) = x^2$ by shifting _____.

A. downward 1 unit   B. right 1 unit

C. left 1 unit   D. upward 1 unit

Step 1:   For quadratic functions of the type $f(x) = x^2 - k$ where $k > 0$, the graph is the same as the graph of $y = x^2$ but shifted downward k units. Therefore, the graph of $f(x) = x^2 - 1$ is the same as that of $f(x) = x^2$ but shifted downward 1 unit.

Answer: A. downward 1 unit.

Example 2   The graph below can be found from the graph of $f(x) = x^2$ by shifting the graph of $f(x) = x^2$:

A. 5 units upward

B. 5 units downward

C. 5 units to the left

D. 5 units to the right

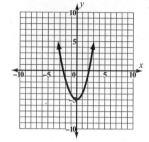

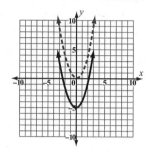

Step 1:   The dashed curve represents the graph of $y = x^2$. The graph obtained from shifting $y = x^2$ is the solid curve. The solid curve is obtained by shifting the dashed curve 5 units downward.

Answer: B. 5 units downward.

Example 3   Which translation of the graph $y = x^2$ produces the graph below?

A) 2 units to the left and 1 unit upward

B) 2 units to the right and 1 unit upward

C) 1 unit to the left and 2 units upward

D) 2 units to the left and 1 unit downward

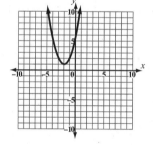

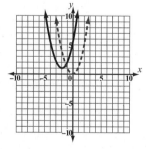

Step 1:   First we locate the point (0, 0) on the graph $y = x^2$. The given graph passes through the point (–2, 1). To get to this point we must move the point (0, 0) 2 units to the left and 1 unit upward.

Answer: A) two units to the left and 1 unit upward.

Example 4   Which of the following graphs best represents the graph of $f(x) = x^2 + 2x - 5$?

A. 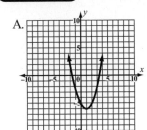   B. 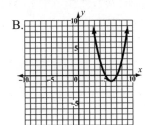   C. 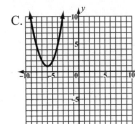   D.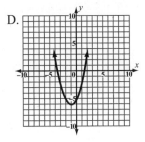

$x^2 + 2x - 5 = 0$	**Step 1:** We must first use the method of completing the square to get the equation in standard form. Set the equation equal to 0.
$x^2 + 2x - 5 + 5 = 0 + 5$ $x^2 + 2x = 5$	**Step 2:** Add five to each side.
$\dfrac{2}{2} = (1)^2 = 1$	**Step 3:** Divide the coefficient of x, which is 2, by two and square the result.
$x^2 + 2x + 1 = 5 + 1$ $x^2 + 2x + 1 = 6$	**Step 4:** Add the result, 1, to each side of the equation.
$(x + 1)^2 = 6$ $(x + 1)^2 - 6 = 0$	**Step 5:** Factor the left hand side of the equation and subtract 6 from both sides to get the equation in standard form.
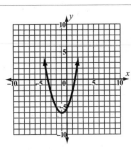	**Step 6:** When the function is written in this form we can see that we have to shift the graph of the basic quadratic function $y = x^2$ to the left 1 unit and 6 units downward.

Answer: Graph D

Problem Set

1. The graph of $y = x^2 - 4$ can be obtained from the graph of the parent function $y = x^2$ by _____.

2. The graph of $y = x^2 + 3$ can be obtained from the graph of the parent function $y = x^2$ by _____.

3. The graph of $y = x^2 + 12$ can be obtained from the graph of the parent function $y = x^2$ by _____.

4. The graph of $y = x^2 - 14$ can be obtained from the graph of the parent function $y = x^2$ by _____.

5. The graph of $y = (x-6)^2$ can be obtained from the graph of the parent function $y = x^2$ by _____.

6. The graph of $y = (x-5)^2$ can be obtained from the graph of the parent function $y = x^2$ by _____.

7. The graph of $y = (x+8)^2$ can be obtained from the graph of the parent function $y = x^2$ by _____.

8. The graph of $y = (x+10)^2$ can be obtained from the graph of the parent function $y = x^2$ by _____.

9. Sketch the graph of the function $f(x) = x^2 + 2$.

10. Sketch the graph of the function $f(x) = x^2 - 3$.

11. Sketch the graph of the function $f(x) = (x+1)^2$.

12. Sketch the graph of the function $f(x) = (x-7)^2$.

13. Sketch the graph of the function $f(x) = (x-2)^2$.

14. Sketch the graph of the function $f(x) = (x+5)^2$.

15. The graph can be obtained from the graph of $y = x^2$ by shifting the graph of $y = x^2$

_____.

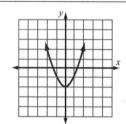

16. The graph can be obtained from the graph of $y = x^2$ by shifting the graph of $y = x^2$

_____.

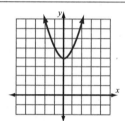

17. The graph can be obtained from the graph of $y = x^2$ by shifting the graph of $y = x^2$

_____.

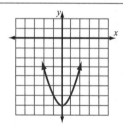

18. The graph can be obtained from the graph of $y = x^2$ by shifting the graph of $y = x^2$

_____.

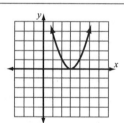

19. The graph can be obtained from the graph of $y = x^2$ by shifting the graph of $y = x^2$

_____.

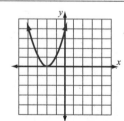

20. The graph can be obtained from the graph of $y = x^2$ by shifting the graph of $y = x^2$

_____.

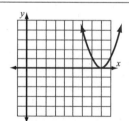

21. This is the graph of $y = x^2 - 1$ Find the translation of the given graph that will produce the graph of $y = (x + 2)^2 - 1$.

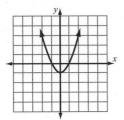

22. Here is the graph of the quadratic function $y = x^2 + 3$. Find the translation of the given graph that will produce the graph of $y = (x + 4)^2 + 3$.

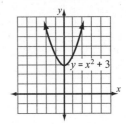

23. Here is the graph of the quadratic function $y = x^2 - 4$. Find the translation of the given graph that will produce the graph of $y = (x - 2)^2 - 4$.

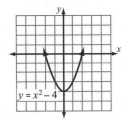

24. Here is the graph of the quadratic function $y = x^2 - 2$. Find the translation of the given graph that will produce the graph of $y = x^2 - 7$.

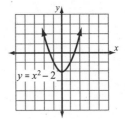

25. Here is the graph of the quadratic function $y = x^2 + 1$. Find the translation of the given graph that will produce the graph of $y = x^2 + 4$.

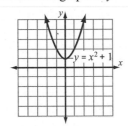

26. If the graph of $y = x^2$ has been translated to obtain the graph of $y = (x - 2)^2 + 4$, what are the translations?

27. If the graph of $y = x^2$ has been translated to obtain the graph of $y = (x - 3)^2 - 6$, what are the translations?

28. If the graph of $y = x^2$ has been translated to obtain the graph of $y = (x - 1)^2 + 3$, what are the translations?

29. If the graph of $y = x^2$ has been translated to obtain the graph of $y = (x - 2)^2 + 3$, what are the translations?

30. If the graph of $y = x^2$ has been translated to obtain the graph of $y = (x + 1)^2 + 2$, what are the translations?

31. The graph of the curve is obtained from the graph of the parent function $y = x^2$ by shifting it

_____.

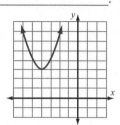

32. The graph of the curve is obtained from the graph of the parent function $y = x^2$ by shifting it

_____.

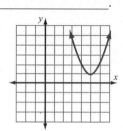

33. The graph of the curve is obtained from the graph of the parent function $y = x^2$ by shifting it

_____.

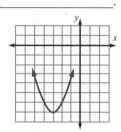

34. Sketch the graph of the following translations:

The graph of $y = x^2$ is translated 3 units to the right and 5 units upward.

35. Sketch the graph of the following translations:

The graph of $y = x^2$ is translated 6 units to the left and 4 units downward.

36. Use transformations to graph the function of $f(x) = (x + 7)^2 + 2$.

37. Use transformations to graph the function of $f(x) = (x - 2)^2 - 3$.

38. Which of the following functions has the same graph as $f(x) = x^2 - 4x - 3$?

$f(x) = (x - 2)^2 + 2$ $f(x) = (x + 2)^2 + 8$

$f(x) = (x - 2)^2 - 7$ $f(x) = (x + 2)^2 + 7$

39. Which of the following functions has the same graph as $f(x) = x^2 + 10x - 8$?

$f(x) = (x + 5)^2 - 17$ $f(x) = (x + 5)^2 - 8$

$f(x) = (x + 5)^2 - 33$ $f(x) = (x + 5)^2 + 2$

40. Which of the following graphs best represents the graph of $f(x) = x^2 + 8x + 18$?

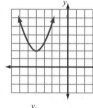 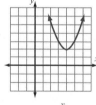

In this lesson, we will learn additional techniques for graphing quadratic functions, such as reflections and dilations. Graphs of negative functions can generally be found by reflecting the corresponding positive function over the x-axis. Dilations can be subdivided into stretches and shrinks. Stretching means that the values of the y- coordinates of the points are increased, while the x-values remain the same. That causes the graph to become narrower than the original function. Likewise, the graph of one-half "x squared" can be found by shrinking the graph of the parent function. Shrinking means the values of the y-coordinates are decreased and the graph becomes wider.

Using reflection together with dilation, we can summarize some properties of the quadratic functions of the form $y = ax^2$. When a is a positive number, the graph opens upward. When a is a negative number, the graph opens downward. When the absolute value of a increases, the graphs become narrower, and when it decreases, they become wider.

Reflection Across the x-axis	The graph of $y = -f(x)$ is obtained by reflecting the graph of the parent function, $y = f(x)$, across the x-axis.
Dilations	• For $k > 1$, the graph of $y = kf(x)$ is obtained by vertically stretching the graph of the parent function, $y = f(x)$. • For $0 < k < 1$, the graph of $y = kf(x)$ is obtained by vertically shrinking the graph of the parent function, $y = f(x)$.
Standard Form of a Quadratic Function	$f(x) = a(x-h)^2 + k$ where $h = -\dfrac{b}{2a}$ and $k = f(h) = c - \dfrac{b^2}{4a}$

Example 1 For the parabola $y = 8x^2$, which of the following statements is true?

The graph is the same as the graph of $y = x^2$, but:
- A) shifted downward 8 units
- B) shifted right 8 units
- C) stretched by a factor of 8
- D) shrunk by a factor of 8

Step 1: For the quadratic function of the type $y = ax^2$ where $a > 1$, the graph is the same as the graph of $y = x^2$ but stretched vertically by a factor of a.

Therefore, the graph of $y = 8x^2$ is the same as the graph of $y = x^2$ but stretched by a factor of 8.

Answer: C) stretched by a factor of 8

Example 2   Which graph best represents the graph of the function $f(x) = -2x^2$?

A)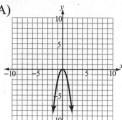

B)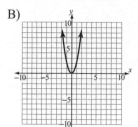

C)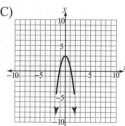

D)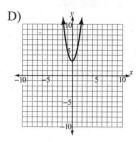

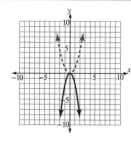

Step 1:   For quadratic functions of the type $y = ax^2$ where $a > 1$, the graph is the same as the graph of $y = x^2$, but stretched vertically by a factor of a. Therefore, the graph of $y = 2x^2$ is the same as the graph of $y = x^2$, but stretched by a factor of 2.

Step 2:   The graph of $y = ax^2$ and the graph of $y = -ax^2$ are reflections of each other over the x-axis. The graph of $y = -2x^2$ can be found by reflecting the graph of $y = 2x^2$ over the x-axis.

Answer: Graph A

Example 3   Which transformations of the given graph $y = x^2$ will produce the graph of $y = 3(x+2)^2$?

   A) Shift 2 units upward and stretch by a factor of 3
   B) Shift 2 units downward and stretch by a factor of 3
   C) Shift 2 units to the left and stretch by a factor of 3
   D) Shift 2 units to the left and shrink by a factor of 3.

Step 1:   The formula $y = x^2$ has been changed by replacing the x with $x + 2$. This shifts the graph two units to the left.

Step 2:   Multiplying the formula by a factor of 3, stretches the graph by a factor of 3.

Answer: C) 2 units to the left and stretch by a factor of 3

Example 4   Which of the following graphs best represents the graph of $f(x) = 2(x + 2)^2 + 1$?

A) 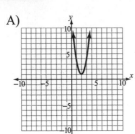 B) 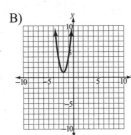 C) 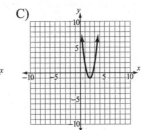 D)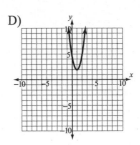

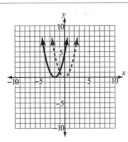

Step 1:   The parent function is $y = x^2$. Replacing x with $x + 2$ shifts the graph 2 units to the left.

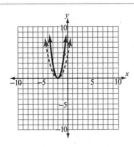

Step 2:   Multiplying the formula by 2 stretches the graph by a factor of 2.

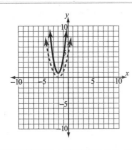

Step 3:   When we add 1, we shift the graph up 1 unit.

Answer: Graph B

Problem Set

1. Describe, without graphing, how the parabola $y = 3x^2$ can be obtained from the the graph of $y = x^2$.

2. Describe, without graphing, how the parabola $y = 6x^2$ can be obtained from the the graph of $y = x^2$.

3. Describe, without graphing, how the parabola $y = \frac{1}{4}x^2$ can be obtained from the graph of $y = x^2$.

4. Describe, without graphing, how the parabola $y = \frac{2}{3}x^2$ can be obtained from the graph of $y = x^2$.

5. Describe, without graphing, how the parabola $y = 14x^2$ can be obtained from the graph of $y = x^2$.

6. The graph of $y = -4x^2$ can be obtained by reflecting the graph of $y = 4x^2$ over the x-axis. Answer True or False.

7. The graph of $y = -6x^2$ can be obtained by reflecting the graph of $y = x^2$ over the x-axis. Answer True or False.

8. The graph of $y = 8x^2$ can be obtained by stretching the graph of $y = x^2$. Answer True or False.

9. The graph of $y = -\frac{1}{3}x^2$ can be obtained by reflecting the graph of $y = \frac{1}{3}x^2$ over the x-axis. Answer True or False.

10. The graph of $y = -20x^2$ can be obtained by shrinking the graph of $y = 20x^2$. Answer True or False.

11. The graph of $y = \frac{1}{2}x^2$ can be obtained by shrinking the graph of $y = x^2$ over the x-axis. Answer True or False.

12. Draw the graph of the function: $f(x) = 4x^2$

13. Draw the graph of the function: $f(x) = \frac{1}{3}x^2$

14. Draw the graph of the function: $f(x) = -3x^2$

15. Draw the graph of the function: $f(x) = -\frac{1}{2}x^2$

16. Which translation of the given graph, $f(x) = 2x^2 - 1$, will produce the graph of $y = 2(x-1)^2 - 1$?

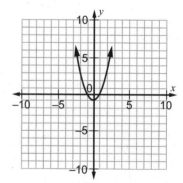

17. Which translation of the given graph, $f(x) = 2x^2 - 1$, will produce the graph of $y = 2(x + 2)^2 - 1$?

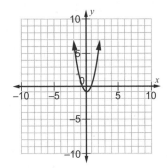

18. Which translation of the given graph, $f(x) = 2x^2 - 2$, will produce the graph of $y = 2x^2 - 5$?

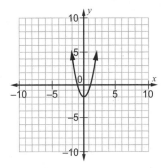

19. Which translation of the given graph, $f(x) = 2x^2 - 1$, will produce the graph of $y = -2(x - 1)^2$?

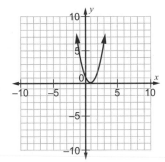

20. Which translation of the given graph, $f(x) = 2(x + 3)^2$, will produce the graph of $y = -2(x + 3)^2$?

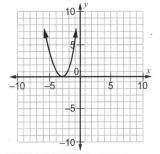

21. Which transformations of the graph $y = x^2$ will produce the graph of $y = 2(x + 1)^2$?

22. Which transformations of the graph $y = x^2$ will produce the graph of $y = 2(x - 2)^2$?

23. Which transformations of the graph $y = x^2$ will produce the graph of $y = 2(x + 4)^2$?

24. Which transformations of the graph $y = x^2$ will produce the graph of $y = 3(x + 2)^2$?

25. Which transformations of the graph $y = x^2$ (dashed curve) will produce the graph of the solid curve?

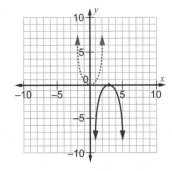

26. Which transformations of the graph $y = x^2$ (dashed curve) will produce the graph of the solid curve?

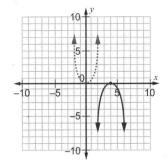

27. Which transformations of the graph $y = x^2$
(dashed curve) will produce the solid curve below?

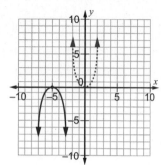

28. Which transformations of the graph $y = x^2$
(dashed curve) will produce the solid curve below?

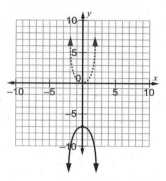

29. Draw the graph of $y = x^2$ reflected over the
x-axis, and then shifted 6 units to the right and
1 unit upward.

30. Draw the graph of $y = x^2$ reflected over the
x-axis, and then shifted 3 units to the left and
4 units downward.

31. Draw the graph of $y = x^2$ reflected over the
x-axis, and then shifted 2 units to the left and
3 units upward.

32. Draw the graph of $y = x^2$ reflected over the
x-axis, and then shifted 3 units to the right and
6 units downward.

33. Draw the graph of the function:
$$y = 4(x + 1)^2 - 1$$

34. Draw the graph of the function:
$$y = 2(x + 4)^2 + 3$$

35. Draw the graph of the function:
$$y = 3(x - 2)^2 + 8$$

36. Find the function that has the same graph as the
following function:
$$f(x) = 2x^2 + 12x + 3$$

37. Find the function that has the same graph as the
following function:
$$f(x) = 3x^2 + 6x + 17$$

38. Find the function that has the same graph as the
following function:
$$f(x) = -2x^2 + 4x - 5$$

39. Graph the function:
$$f(x) = 2x^2 + 4x + 1$$

40. Graph the function:
$$f(x) = 4x^2 - 8x - 3$$

HA1-935: Analyzing Graphs of Quadratic Functions

In this lesson, we will analyze the graphs of quadratic functions. We first should recall that the general form for a quadratic function is: $f(x) = ax^2 + bx + c$, where a, b, and c are real numbers. However, it is easier to draw the graph of a quadratic function by first using the method of completing the square to rewrite the function in standard form: $f(x) = a(x-h)^2 + k$. We should note that the value of h can be determined from the formula: $h = -\dfrac{b}{2a}$.

Furthermore, k can be determined as $f(h)$.

General Form of a Quadratic Function	$f(x) = ax^2 + bx + c$ where a, b, and c are real numbers.

Standard Form of a Quadratic Function	$f(x) = a(x-h)^2 + k$ where $h = -\dfrac{b}{2a}$, and $k = f(h)$

There are some important features of the graph of a quadratic function: vertex, line (or axis) of symmetry, and x- and y-intercepts. Finding the values of these will help in plotting the graph.

Vertex: (h, k) where $h = -\dfrac{b}{2a}$ and $k = f(h) = c - \dfrac{b^2}{4a}$

Line (or axis) of symmetry: $x = h$

x-intercepts: $\left(\dfrac{-b \pm \sqrt{b^2 - 4ac}}{2a}, 0 \right)$

y-intercept: point $(0, c)$

Example 1   Find the vertex of the quadratic function $f(x) = 3x^2 - 12x - 14$.

$a = 3, b = -12$

Step 1: Identify the coefficients a and b of the quadratic equation.

$h = -\dfrac{b}{2a}$

$= \dfrac{-(-12)}{2(3)}$

$= 2$

Step 2: The quadratic function $f(x) = ax^2 + bx + c$ has vertex (h, k). Substitute a and b into the formula for h.

$k = f(2)$

$= (3(2)^2 - 12(2) - 14)$

$= 12 - 24 - 14$

$= -26$

Step 3: To find value for k, substitute the value h into our original equation, $k = f(h)$.

Answer: The vertex of the quadratic equation is $(2, -26)$.

Example 2 Find the axis of symmetry of the quadratic function $f(x) = -x^2 - 12x + 16$.

$a = -1, b = -12$

Step 1: Identify the coefficients a and b of the quadratic equation.

$h = -\dfrac{b}{2a}$

$= -\dfrac{(-12)}{2(-1)}$

$= -6$

Step 2: The quadratic function $f(x) = ax^2 + bx + c$ has an axis of symmetry at $x = h$. Substitute a and b into the formula for h.

Answer: The axis of symmetry is $x = -6$.

Example 3 Find the vertex of the quadratic function whose graph is given below.

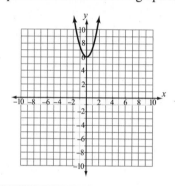

Step 1: The parabola opens upward, so the vertex is at the lowest point.

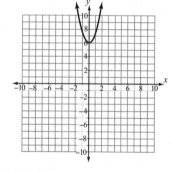

Answer: Therefore, the vertex is $(0, 6)$.

Example 4 The quadratic function has the vertex at the point $(-2, -1)$ and passes through the point $(1, -7)$. Find the equation of the quadratic function.

$h = -2$ and $k = -1$

Step 1: The standard form of the equation $y = a(x - h)^2 + k$ has a vertex at (h, k). Identify h and k.

$y = a(x + 2)^2 - 1$

Step 2: Substitute h and k into the standard form of the equation.

$$y = a(x+2)^2 - 1$$

$$-7 = a(1+2)^2 - 1$$

$$-7 = a(3)^2 - 1$$

$$-7 = 9a - 1$$

$$-7 + 1 = 9a - 1 + 1$$

$$-6 = 9a$$

$$\frac{-6}{9} = \frac{9a}{9}$$

$$-\frac{2}{3} = a$$

Step 3: Substitute the point (1,–7) into the equation found in the previous step.

$$y = -\frac{2}{3}(x+2)^2 - 1$$

Step 4: Substitute a into the equation found in Step 2.

Answer: $y = -\frac{2}{3}(x+2)^2 - 1$

Example 5   The graph of the quadratic function $f(x)$ is shown on the coordinate grid. The graph of the equation has the line of symmetry $x = 4$ and an x-intercept at (8, 0). For which other value of x is $f(x) = 0$?

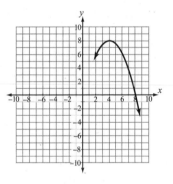

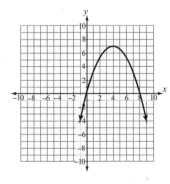

Step 1: On the graph, $f(x) = 0$ for $x = 8$. The point (8, 0) is 4 units to the right of the axis of symmetry $x = 4$. The point that is symmetrical to (8, 0), that is 4 units to the left of the axis of symmetry, is the point (0, 0).

Answer: The other value of x where $f(x) = 0$, is $x = 0$.

Problem Set

1. Find the vertex of the quadratic function.

$$f(x) = x^2 - 6x + 10$$

2. Find the vertex of the quadratic function.

$$f(x) = 2x^2 - 8x - 6$$

3. Find the vertex of the quadratic function.

$$f(x) = x^2 + 2x - 3$$

4. Find the vertex of the quadratic function.

$$f(x) = 2x^2 - 4x + 8$$

5. Find the vertex of the quadratic function whose graph is given below.

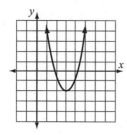

6. Find the vertex of the quadratic function whose graph is given below.

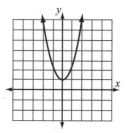

7. Find the vertex of the quadratic function whose graph is given below.

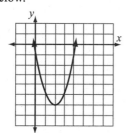

8. Find the vertex of the quadratic function whose graph is given below.

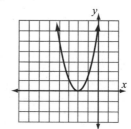

9. Find the axis of symmetry of the quadratic function.

$$f(x) = 2x^2 - 12x + 16$$

10. Find the axis of symmetry of the quadratic function.

$$f(x) = 3x^2 - 12x + 16$$

11. Find the axis of symmetry of the quadratic function.

$$f(x) = -3x^2 - 12x + 8$$

12. Find the axis of symmetry of the quadratic function.

$$f(x) = 6x^2 - 12x + 8$$

13. Find the axis of symmetry of the quadratic function for the graph below.

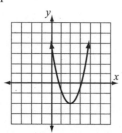

14. Find the axis of symmetry of the quadratic function for the graph below.

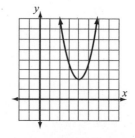

15. Find the axis of symmetry of the quadratic function for the graph below.

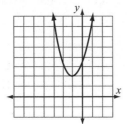

16. Find the axis of symmetry of the quadratic function for the graph below.

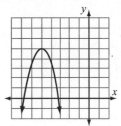

17. Find the y-intercept of the quadratic function for the graph.

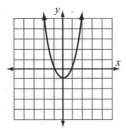

18. Find the y-intercept of the quadratic function for the graph.

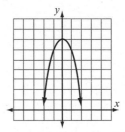

19. Find the y-intercept of the quadratic function for the graph.

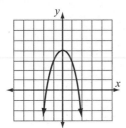

20. Find the y-intercept of the quadratic function for the graph.

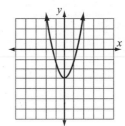

21. Find the equation of the quadratic function that has a vertex at $(-2, -1)$ and passes through the point $(1, 4)$.

22. Find the equation of the quadratic function has a vertex at $(-2, -2)$ and passes through the point $(0, -5)$.

23. Find the equation of the quadratic function that has a vertex at $(-2, -3)$ and passes through the point $(1, -4)$.

24. Find the equation of the quadratic function that has a vertex at $(-2, -1)$ and passes through the point $(0, -5)$.

25. A portion of the graph of the quadratic function f is shown on the coordinate grid. The graph of the equation has the line of symmetry $x = 1$. If $f(x) = 0$ for $x = 4$, for which other value of x is $f(x) = 0$?

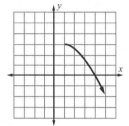

26. A portion of the graph of the quadratic function f is shown on the coordinate grid. The graph of the equation has the line of symmetry $x = 0$. If $f(x) = 0$ for $x = 3$, for which other value of x is $f(x) = 0$?

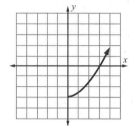

27. A portion of the graph of the quadratic function f is shown on the coordinate grid. The graph of the equation has the line of symmetry $x = -1$. If $f(x) = 0$ for $x = 2$, for which other value of x is $f(x) = 0$?

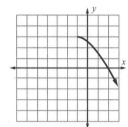

28. A portion of the graph of the quadratic function f is shown on the coordinate grid. The graph of the equation has the line of symmetry $x = -5$. If $f(x) = 0$ for $x = -7$, for which other value of x is $f(x) = 0$?

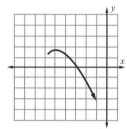

29. Which set of ordered pairs satisfies the equation $y = -4x^2 + 5x - 6$?

x	−1	0	1
y	−15	−6	−15

x	−1	0	1
y	−7	−6	−5

x	−1	0	1
y	−1	0	1

x	−1	0	1
y	−15	−6	−5

30. Which set of ordered pairs satisfies the equation $y = -4x^2 + 5x + 6$?

x	−1	0	1
y	−1	0	1

x	−1	0	1
y	−7	−6	7

x	−1	0	1
y	−3	6	7

x	−1	0	1
y	−3	−6	−15

31. Which set of ordered pairs satisfies the equation $y = -2x^2 + 5x + 6$?

x	−1	0	1
y	−3	−6	−3

x	−1	0	1
y	−1	6	9

x	−1	0	1
y	−9	−6	7

x	−1	0	1
y	−1	0	1

32. Which set of ordered pairs satisfies the equation $y = 2x^2 + 5x - 6$?

x	−1	0	1
y	−9	−6	1

x	−1	0	1
y	−13	−6	−5

x	−1	0	1
y	−3	−6	−13

x	−1	0	1
y	−1	0	1

33. A portion of the graph of the quadratic function f is shown on the coordinate grid. The graph of the equation has the axis of symmetry $x = 1$. Between which two integers will the graph again cross the x-axis?

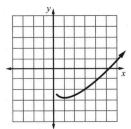

34. A portion of the graph of the quadratic function f is shown on the coordinate grid. The graph of the equation has the axis of symmetry $x = 4$. Between which two integers will the graph again cross the x-axis?

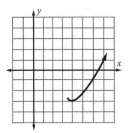

35. The graph of a quadratic function opens downward and its discriminant is negative. Which of the following curves represents a possible graph of the function?

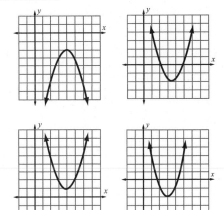

36. The graph of a quadratic function opens downward and its discriminant is positive. Which of the following curves represents a possible graph of the function?

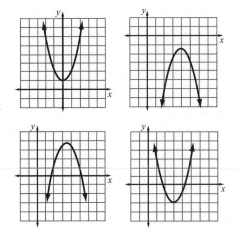

37. The quadratic function $f(x)$ is evaluated for different values of x, as shown in the table.

x	-3	-1	1
y	12	0	-4

The graph has an axis of symmetry $x = 1$. For which other value of x does $f(x) = 0$?

38. The quadratic function $f(x)$ is evaluated for different values of x, as shown in the table.

x	-3	-2	1
y	12	0	-4

The graph has an axis of symmetry $x = 2$. For which other value of x does $f(x) = 0$?

39. Between which two integers will the graph of $y = -\frac{1}{2}(x+2)^2 + 4$ cross the x-axis?

x	0	1	2	3	4
y	2	-0.5	-4	-8.5	-14

40. Between which two integers will the graph of $y = -\frac{1}{2}(x+1)^2 + 3$ cross the x-axis?

x	0	1	2	3	4
y	2.5	1	-1.5	-5	-9.5

HA1-940: Applications of Quadratic Equations

In this lesson, we will apply quadratic equations to solve problems in geometry and word problems. Quadratic equations appear frequently in real-world situations, and it is important to recognize when to use quadratic functions to solve a problem. Remember that when we solve word problems, we must always check that our solution is reasonable; we know that the length must be a positive number, so we eliminate the negative solutions.

Example 1   The area of a square is described by the equation $x^2 = 9$, where x is the length of a side of the square, in feet. What is the length of the side of the square?

x = length of a side of a square Area $= x^2$	**Step 1:** The length of each side is x. The area of the square is equal to x^2.
$x^2 = 9$ $\sqrt{x^2} = \sqrt{9}$ $x = \pm 3$	**Step 2:** We solve the given equation, $x^2 = 9$, by taking the square root of both sides. Notice that we have two solutions: $x = 3$ and $x = -3$.
$x = 3$ or $x = -3$	**Step 3:** Since the length of the square must be a positive number, we eliminate $x = -3$.
	Answer: The length of a side of the square is 3 feet.

Example 2   The length of a rectangle is $2x + 3$ and its width is $x + 1$. Find the expression that represents the area of the rectangle in simplest form.

length: $l = 2x + 3$ width: $w = x + 1$ Area $= l \cdot w$	**Step 1:** The length, l, of each side is $2x + 3$ and the width, w, is $x + 1$. The area of the rectangle is $l \cdot w$.
Area $= (2x + 3)(x + 1)$	**Step 2:** To find the area of the rectangle, multiply the length, $2x + 3$, by the width, $x + 1$.
F $\quad (2x + 3)(x + 1) = 2x^2$	**Step 3:** To find the product, we apply the FOIL method. Multiply the first terms, $2x$ and x, to get $2x^2$.
O $\quad (2x + 3)(x + 1) = 2x^2 + 2x$	**Step 4:** Multiply the outer terms, $2x$ and 1, to get $2x$.
I $\quad (2x + 3)(x + 1) = 2x^2 + 2x + 3x$	**Step 5:** Multiply the inner terms, 3 and x, to get $3x$.
L $\quad (2x + 3)(x + 1) = 2x^2 + 2x + 3x + 3$	**Step 6:** Multiply the last terms, 3 and 1, to get 3.
$(2x + 3)(x + 1) = 2x^2 + 5x + 3$	**Step 7:** Simplify by adding the outer and inner terms.
	Answer: $2x^2 + 5x + 3$

Example 3　The length of a rectangle is $x - 2$, its width is $8 - 2x$, and its area is $-2x^2 + 4x - 16$. Find all possible values for the variable x.

$l = x - 2 > 0$ $w = 8 - 2x > 0$ and $8 - 2x < x - 2$	**Step 1:** Since length and width must be positive, set each greater than 0. Also, the width should be less than the length.
$x - 2 > 0$ $x > 2$	**Step 2:** Solve the length for x.
$8 - 2x > 0$ $8 > 2x$ $4 > x$ or $x < 4$	**Step 3:** Solve the width for x.
$8 - 2x < x - 2$ $8 < 3x - 2$ $10 < 3x$ $\dfrac{10}{3} < x$	**Step 4:** Solve the third inequality for x.
	Answer: To satisfy all three inequalities, $\dfrac{10}{3} < x < 4$.

Example 4　The area of a rectangle is given by $x^2 + x - 2$. For which of the following values: 0, 1, 2, is the variable x valid?

When $x = 0$, $A = (0)^2 + (0) - 2$ $A = -2$	**Step 1:** Substitute 0 into the equation.
When $x = 1$, $A = (1)^2 + (1) - 2$ $A = 0$	**Step 2:** Substitute 1 into the equation.
When $x = 2$, $A = (2)^2 + (2) - 2$ $A = 4$	**Step 3:** Substitute 2 into the equation.
	Answer: Since the area of the rectangle must be a positive value, $x = 2$ is the only valid value.

Example 5 The height of a triangle is 2 inches longer than its base. The area of the triangle is 4 square feet. Write the equation that can be used to find b, the base of the triangle.

Area $= \dfrac{1}{2}b \cdot h$ Let b = base of the triangle. Then the height of the triangle is $h = b + 2$	**Step 1:** The area of a triangle is equal to $\dfrac{1}{2}b \cdot h$. Let b denote the base of the triangle.
$4 = \dfrac{1}{2}b(b + 2)$	**Step 2:** Substitute the values for the variables in the equation.
$4 = \dfrac{1}{2}(b^2 + 2b)$ $8 = b^2 + 2b$ $0 = b^2 + 2b - 8$ or $b^2 + 2b - 8 = 0$	**Step 3:** Simplify the equation.

Answer: $b^2 + 2b - 8 = 0$

Example 6 The length of a rectangle is 3 feet longer than its width. If the area of the rectangle is 28 square feet, find its width.

Let w = width of the rectangle. Then the length of the rectangle is $l = w + 3$. Area $= l \cdot w$	**Step 1:** A rectangle is a quadrilateral in which opposite sides are equal and all angles are right angles. In our problem, the length of each side, l, is the longer side and the width, w, is the shorter side. The area of the rectangle is $l \cdot w$.
$28 = (w + 3)w$	**Step 2:** Substitute the values for the variables in the equation.
$28 = w^2 + 3w$ $0 = w^2 + 3w - 28$ or $w^2 + 3w - 28 = 0$	**Step 3:** Simplify the equation.
$w^2 + 3w - 28 = 0$ $(w - 4)(w + 7) = 0$ $w - 4 = 0$ or $w + 7 = 0$ $w = 4$ or $w = -7$	**Step 4:** Factor the equation and set each factor equal to 0. Solve for w.
	Step 5: Width must be a positive value, so we eliminate $w = -7$.
	Answer: The width of the rectangle is 4 feet.

Problem Set

Solve:

1. The area of a square is described by the equation $x^2 = 4$, where x is the length of a side of the square, in feet. What is the length of the side of the square?

2. The area of a square is described by the equation $x^2 = 25$, where x is the length of a side of the square, in feet. What is the length of the side of the square?

3. The area of a square is described by the equation $x^2 = 169$, where x is the length of a side of the square, in feet. What is the length of the side of the square?

4. The area of the rectangle is given by the equation $x(x + 2) = 15$, where x represents the width of the rectangle. What is the width of the rectangle?

5. The area of the rectangle is given by the equation $x(x - 2) = 15$, where x represents the length of the rectangle. What is the length of the rectangle?

6. Find the expression that best represents the area of the right triangle with legs $4xy$ and $3xy$?

7. Find the expression that best represents the area of the right triangle with legs $2x^2y$ and $2xy^2$?

8. Find the expression that best represents the area of the right triangle with legs $7xy^3$ and $4x^3y$?

9. The length of a rectangle is $2x + 5$ and its width is $x + 2$. Find the expression that represents the area of the rectangle in simplest form.

10. The length of a rectangle is $2x + 5$ and its width is $x - 2$. Find the expression that represents the area of the rectangle in simplest form.

11. The area of a rectangle is given by $x^2 - x - 6$. Find the valid value of x, given the following values: 2, 3, 4.

12. The area of a rectangle is given by $x^2 + 2x - 4$. Find the valid value of x, given the following values: 0, 1, 2.

13. The length of a rectangle is $x - 3$, its width is $10 - 2x$, and its area is $-2x^2 + 16x - 30.$. Find all possible values for the variable x.

14. The length of a rectangle is $x - 2$, its width is $18 - 3x$, and its area is $-3x^2 + 24x - 36.$. Find all possible values for the variable x.

15. The height of a triangle is 5 inches longer than its base. The area of the triangle is 20 square inches. Write the quadratic equation that can be used to find the base, b, of the triangle.

16. The height of a triangle is 3 inches longer than its base. The area of the triangle is 16 square inches. Write the quadratic equation that can be used to find the base, b, of the triangle.

17. The length of a rectangle is 4 inches more than its width. The area of the rectangle is 12 square inches. Write the quadratic equation that can be used to find the width, w, of the rectangle.

18. The length of a rectangle is 2 inches more than its width. The area of the rectangle is 35 square inches. Write the quadratic equation that can be used to find the width, w, of the rectangle.

19. What is the area of the shaded region of the rectangle, in simplest terms?

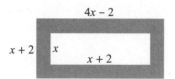

20. What is the area of the shaded region of the rectangle, in simplest terms?

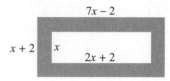

21. The length of a rectangle is $x - 1$. Its width is $9 - 3x$, and its area is $-3x^2 + 12x + 9$. Find all possible values for the variable x.

22. The length of a rectangle is $x - 4$. Its width is $14 - 2x$, and its area is $-2x^2 + 22x - 56$. Find all possible values for the variable x.

23. The length of a rectangle is $x - 5$. Its width is $20 - 2x$, and its area is $-2x^2 + 10x - 80$. Find all possible values for the variable x.

24. The length of a rectangle is $x - 3$. Its width is $24 - 3x$, and its area is $-3x^2 + 3x - 72$. Find all possible values for the variable x.

25. The height of a triangle is 15 inches longer than its base. The area of the triangle is 50 square inches. Write the quadratic equation that can be used to find the base, b, of the triangle.

26. The height of a triangle is 14 inches longer than its base. The area of the triangle is 60 square inches. Write the quadratic equation that can be used to find the base, b, of the triangle.

27. The height of a triangle is 10 inches longer than its base. The area of the triangle is 100 square inches. Write the quadratic equation that can be used to the base, b, of the triangle.

28. The length of a rectangle is 3 inches more than its width. The area of the rectangle is 28 square inches. Write the quadratic equation that can be used to find the width, w, of the rectangle.

29. The length of a rectangle is 4 inches more than its width. The area of the rectangle is 32 square inches. Write the quadratic equation that can be used to find the width, w, of the rectangle.

30. The length of a rectangle |is 2 inches more than its width. The area of the rectangle is 63 square inches. Write the quadratic equation that can be used to find the width, w, of the rectangle.

31. What is the area of the shaded region of the rectangle, in simplest terms?

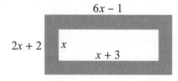

32. What is the area of the shaded region of the rectangle, in simplest terms?

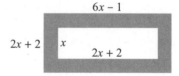

33. A company uses a rectangular figure as its logo in many different sizes throughout its operations. The length of the rectangle equals twice the width, x. The table of values describes the shaded area of the rectangle in square units, y, as a function of the width.

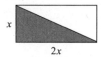

x	1	3	4	5	7
y	1	9	16	25	49

Which equation best describes this functional relationship?

$y = x$ $y = 2x^2$

$y = x^2$ $y = \frac{1}{2}x^2$

34. A company uses a rectangular figure as its logo in many different sizes throughout its operations. The length of the rectangle is six times the width, x. The table of values describes the shaded area of the rectangle in square units, y, as a function of the width.

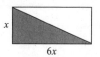

x	1	2	3	4
y	3	12	27	48

Which equation best describes this functional relationship?

$y = 6x$ $y = 3x^2$

$y = 6x^2$ $y = \frac{1}{2}x^2$

35. A company uses a square figure as its logo in many different sizes throughout its operations. The table of values describes the shaded area of the square in square units, y, as a function of the length of side x.

x	1	2	5	6	8
y	0.5	2	12.5	18	32

Which equation best describes this functional relationship?

$y = x^2 - \frac{1}{2}$ $y = x^2$

$y = \frac{1}{2}x^2$ $y = 2x^2$

36. The length of a rectangular rug is 6 feet longer than its width. If the area of the rug is 40 square feet, find its width.

37. The length of a rectangular rug is 10 feet longer than its width. If the area of the rug is 200 square feet, find its width.

38. The length of a rectangular rug is 2 feet longer than its width. If the area of the rug is 24 square feet, find its width.

39. The length of a rectangular rug is 6 feet longer than its width. If the area of the rug is 27 square feet, find its width.

40. The length of a rectangular rug is 6 feet longer than its width. If the area of the rug is 72 square feet, find its width.

HA1-945: Real-World Applications of Quadratic Functions

Applications of quadratic functions appear not only in geometrical, physical problems, but also in science and business scenarios. With these word problems involving science and business, use your knowledge of the discriminant, the vertex, line of symmetry, and the intercepts to help you.

Vertex	(h, k) where $h = -\dfrac{b}{2a}$ and $k = f(h) = c - \dfrac{b^2}{4a}$

Line of Symmetry	$x = h$

Example 1   A ball was thrown upward with an initial velocity of 80 feet per second. The height of the ball in feet, h, is a function of t, the time in seconds since the ball left the ground. The graph of the function h is a parabola and is given below. How many seconds will it take the ball to return to the ground?

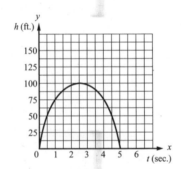

Step 1:   The ball is on the ground when the height, h, is equal to zero. We see from the graph that the height, $h = 0$, when the time, $t = 0$, and also when $t = 5$.

Answer: The answer is $t = 5$ seconds.

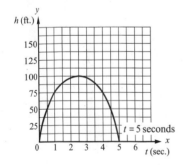

Example 2

A rocket was shot upward with an initial velocity of 160 feet per second. The height of the rocket in feet, h, is a function of t, the time in seconds since the rocket left the ground. The graph of the function h is a parabola, and is given below. Estimate how high the rocket will be after 2.5 seconds.

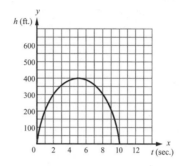

Step 1: From the graph, it follows that the value of h when $t = 2.5$ seconds is approximately 350 feet.

Answer: Therefore, the answer is 350 ft.

Example 3

The cost, C (in dollars), of producing telephones depends on the number of items produced. The graph of C is the parabola, given below. Approximately how many items should be produced to yield the minimum cost?

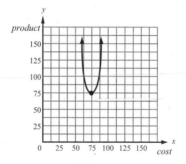

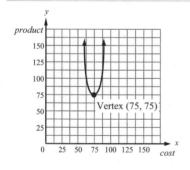

Step 1: From the graph, we can see that the parabola has a lowest point at the vertex (75, 75). This means that seventy-five items should be produced to yield the minimum cost.

Answer: The answer is 75.

Example 4   A ball was thrown upward with an initial velocity of 48 feet per second. The height of the ball in feet, h, is a function of t, the time in seconds since the ball left the ground. The graph of the function h is a parabola, given below. What is the reasonable domain of the function h that describes the height of the ball? What is the reasonable range that describes the height of the ball?

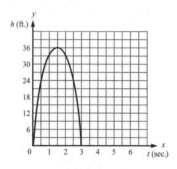

Step 1:   The ball will be in the air from the moment it is shot, $t = 0$, until it reaches the ground, $t = 3$ seconds. The function h describes the height of the ball in that interval. Therefore, the domain is $0 \le t \le 3$.

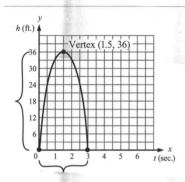

Step 2:   The parabola also has its highest point at the vertex. We can see from the graph that the vertex is approximately $(1.5, 36)$. The maximum height of the ball is 36 feet and the minimum is 0.

Answer: The domain is $0 \le t \le 3$ and the range is $0 \le h \le 36$.

Example 5   A rocket was shot upward with an initial velocity of 304 feet per second. The height of the rocket in feet, h, is a function of t, the time in seconds since the rocket left the ground, and can be expressed by the equation $h(t) = 304t - 16t^2$. How many seconds will it take the rocket to return to the ground?

$h(t) = 304t - 16t^2$

$304t - 16t^2 = 0$

$16t(19 - t) = 0$

$16t = 0$ or $19 - t = 0$

$t = 0$ or $t = 19$

Step 1:   To find the time when the rocket will hit the ground, find the time when the height is zero. To do this we need to solve the equation $h(t) = 0$.

Step 2:   The value $t = 0$ corresponds to the time when the rocket was shot upward, and $t = 19$ corresponds to the time the rocket landed.

Answer: Thus, the answer is $t = 19$ seconds.

Example 6

The leap of a rabbit can be represented in a graph. The graph below represents the curve of the leap (where the *x*-axis represents the distance in feet and the *y*-axis represents the height in feet). Write the equation of the parabola.

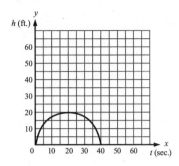

$$y = a(x-h)^2 + k$$

$$a(x-h)^2 + k = 0$$

$$a(x-20)^2 + 20 = 0$$

$$a(0-20)^2 + 20 = 0$$

$$a(-20)^2 + 20 = 0$$

$$400a + 20 = 0$$

$$400a = -20$$

$$a = -\frac{1}{20}$$

Step 1: From that graph, we see that the vertex of the parabola is at (20, 20). So, *h* = 20 and *k* = 20. We also know that the formula for a parabola in general form is $a(x-h)^2 + k = 0$. We will use (0, 0) for (*x*, *y*) and insert the values for *h* and *k* in this equation and solve for *a*.

$$y = a(x-h)^2 + k \text{ where}$$

$$a = -\frac{1}{20}, h = 20, k = 20$$

$$y = -\frac{1}{20}(x-20)^2 + 20$$

Step 2: Insert the given values into the formula to find the equation of the parabola.

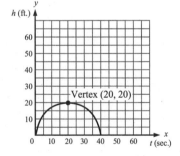

Answer: $y = -\frac{1}{20}(x-20)^2 + 20$

Problem Set

1. The height, in feet, of a ball thrown upward from the ground as a function of time, in seconds, is shown on the graph. How many seconds will it take the ball to return to the ground?

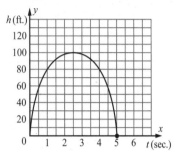

2. The height, in feet, of a rocket shot upward from the ground as a function of time, in seconds, is shown on the graph. How many seconds will it take the rocket to return to the ground?

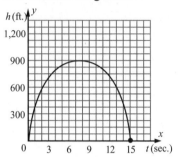

3. The height, in feet, of a ball thrown upward from the ground as a function of time, in seconds, is shown on the graph. How many seconds will it take the ball to return to the ground?

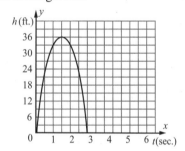

4. The height, in feet, of a rocket shot upward from the ground as a function of time, in seconds, is shown on the graph. How high will the rocket be after 5 seconds?

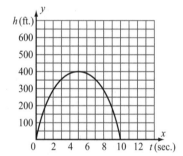

5. The height, in feet, of a ball thrown upward from the ground as a function of time, in seconds, is shown on the graph. When will the ball reach its maximum height?

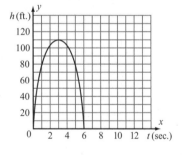

6. The height, in feet, of a ball thrown upward from the ground as a function of time, in seconds, is shown on the graph. How many seconds will it take the ball to return to the ground?

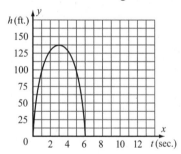

7. The height, in feet, of a ball thrown upward from the ground as a function of time, in seconds, is shown on the graph. When will the ball reach its maximum height?

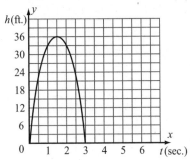

8. The height, in feet, of a rocket shot upward from the ground as a function of time, in seconds, is shown on the graph. How high will the rocket be after 9.5 seconds?

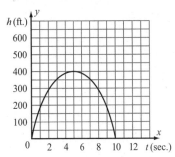

9. The height, in feet, of a rocket shot upward from the ground as a function of time, in seconds, is shown on the graph. What is a reasonable estimate for the maximum height of the rocket?

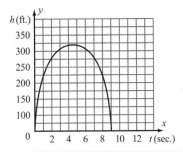

10. The cost, C (in dollars), of producing shirts depends on the number of items produced. The graph of C is a parabola. Approximately how many items should be produced to yield the minimum cost?

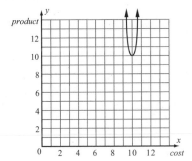

11. The cost, C (in dollars), of producing video recorders depends on the number of items produced. The graph of C is a parabola. Approximately how many items should be produced to yield the minimum cost?

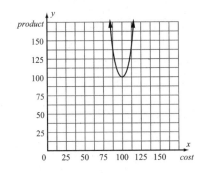

12. The height, in feet, of a rocket shot upward from the ground as a function of time, in seconds, is shown on the graph. What is a reasonable domain of h, the function that describes the height of the rocket?

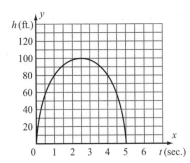

13. The height, in feet, of a ball thrown upward from the ground as a function of time, in seconds, is shown on the graph. What is a reasonable domain of h, the function that describes the height of the ball?

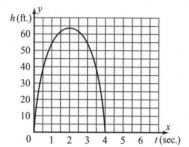

14. The height of the rocket in feet, h, is a function of t, the time in seconds since the rocket left the ground. The graph of the function h is a parabola and is given below. What is the reasonable range of h, the function that describes the height of the rocket?

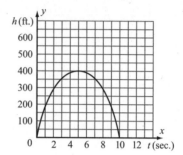

15. The height, in feet, of a ball thrown upward from the ground as a function of time, in seconds, is shown on the graph. What is the reasonable range of h, the function that describes the height of the ball?

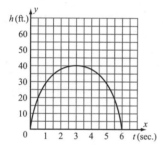

16. A ball was thrown upward with an initial velocity of 16 feet per second. The height of the ball in feet, h, is a function of t, the time in seconds since the ball was thrown from the ground, and can be expressed by the equation $h(t) = 16t - 16t^2$. How many seconds will it take the ball to return to the ground?

17. A ball was thrown upward with an initial velocity of 32 feet per second. The height of the ball in feet, h, is a function of t, the time in seconds since the ball was thrown from the ground, and can be expressed by the equation $h(t) = 32t - 16t^2$. How many seconds will it take the ball to return to the ground?

18. An arrow was shot upward with an initial velocity of 80 feet per second. The height of the arrow in feet h, is a function of t, the time in seconds since the arrow was shot from the ground, and can be expressed by the equation $h(t) = 80t - 16t^2$. How many seconds will it take the arrow to return to the ground?

19. A tennis ball was thrust upward with an initial velocity of 48 feet per second. The height of the ball in feet, h, is a function of t, the time in seconds since the ball was thrown from the ground, and can be expressed by the equation $h(t) = 48t - 16t^2$. How many seconds will it take the ball to return to the ground?

20. A rocket was shot upward with an initial velocity of 112 feet per second. The height of the rocket in feet, h, is a function of t, the time in seconds since the rocket left the ground, and can be expressed by the equation $h(t) = 112t - 16t^2$. How many seconds will it take the rocket to return to the ground?

21. The height in feet of a ball thrown upward from the ground, as a function of time, in seconds is shown on the graph below. Which is the best conclusion about the object's action?

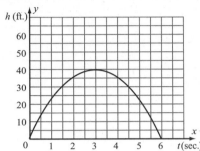

The ball fell on the ground after approximately three seconds.

The ball reached the maximum height after approximately three seconds.

The ball traveled less than three seconds before falling to the ground.

The ball reached the maximum height of approximately one hundred feet.

22. The height in feet of a ball thrown upward from the ground, as a function of time, in seconds is shown on the graph below. Which is the best conclusion about the object's action?

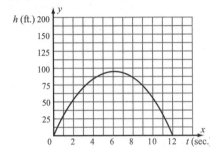

The ball traveled less than four seconds before falling to the ground.

The ball reached the maximum height of approximately one hundred feet.

The ball reached the maximum height after approximately six seconds.

The ball fell on the ground after approximately six seconds.

23. The height in feet of a ball thrown upward from the ground, as a function of time, in seconds is shown on the graph below. Which is the best conclusion about the object's action?

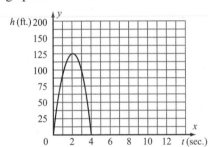

The ball reached the maximum height of about two hundred feet.

The ball reached the maximum height after about one second.

The ball traveled less than two seconds before falling to the ground.

The ball fell on the ground after about four seconds.

24. A ball was thrown upward with an initial velocity of thirty-two feet per second. The height of the ball in feet, h, is a function of t, the time in seconds since the ball was thrown from the ground, and can be expressed by the equation $h(t) = 32t - 16t^2$. What is the maximum height of the ball?

25. A ball was thrown upward with an initial velocity of sixty-four feet per second. The height of the ball in feet, h, is a function of t, the time in seconds since the ball was thrown from the ground, and can be expressed by the equation $h(t) = 64t - 16t^2$. What is the maximum height of the ball?

26. A ball was thrown upward with an initial velocity of ninety-six feet per second. The height of the ball in feet, h, is a function of t, the time in seconds since the ball was thrown from the ground, and can be expressed by the equation $h(t) = 96t - 16t^2$. What is the maximum height of the ball?

27. A rocket was shot upward with an initial velocity of one hundred twenty-eight feet per second. The height of the rocket in feet, h, is a function of t, the time in seconds since the rocket left the ground, and can be expressed by the equation $h(t) = 128t - 16t^2$. What is the maximum height of the rocket?

28. A rocket was shot upward with an initial velocity of one hundred sixty feet per second. The height of the rocket in feet, h, is a function of t, the time in seconds since the rocket left the ground, and can be expressed by the equation $h(t) = 160t - 16t^2$. What is the maximum height of the rocket?

29. A rocket was shot upward with an initial velocity of one hundred ninety-two feet per second. The height of the rocket in feet, h, is a function of t, the time in seconds since the rocket left the ground, and can be expressed by the equation $h(t) = 192t - 16t^2$. What is the maximum height of the rocket?

30. A feather was tossed upward with an initial velocity of sixteen feet per second. The height of the feather in feet, h, is a function of t, the time in seconds since the feather left the ground, and can be expressed by the equation $h(t) = 16t - 16t^2$. What is the maximum height of the feather?

31. A feather was tossed upward with an initial velocity of eight feet per second. The height of the feather in feet, h, is a function of t, the time in seconds since the feather left the ground, and can be expressed by the equation $h(t) = 8t - 16t^2$. What is the maximum height of the feather?

32. A feather was tossed upward with an initial velocity of four feet per second. The height of the feather in feet, h, is a function of t, the time in seconds since the feather was tossed from the ground and can be expressed by the equation $h(t) = 4t - 16t^2$. What is the maximum height of the feather?

33. The GHI company manufactures televisions and the profit, P, in dollars, for selling televisions is described with the equation $P(x) = x(10 - 0.008x)$ where x denotes the cost of each television sold. The graph of the profit function is given below. Which is the best conclusion about the company's profit?

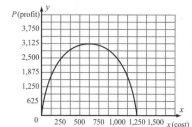

If the cost of each television increases to $1,000, then the profit increases.

The profit, based on a cost of $1,000 per television, is greater than if the television costs $750.

The maximum profit is made when the company sells each television for $625.

The profit increases if the cost of the televisions increases.

34. The DEF company manufactures shoes, and the profit, P, in dollars, for selling shoes is described with the equation $P(x) = x(10 - 0.1x)$ where x denotes the cost of each pair of shoes sold. The graph of the profit function is given below. Which is the best conclusion about the company's profit?

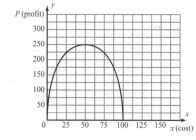

The profit, based on a cost of $75 per pair of shoes, is greater than if the shoes cost $50.

The maximum profit is made when each pair of shoes is sold for $50.

If the cost of shoes increases to $75, then the profit increases.

The profit increases if the cost of shoes increases.

35. The company GHI manufactures watches, and the profit, P, in dollars, for selling watches is described with the equation $P(x) = x(10 - 0.01x)$ where x denotes the cost of each watch sold. The graph of the profit function is given below. Which is the best conclusion about the company's profit?

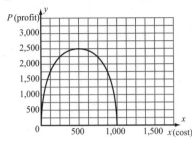

The profit increases if the cost of the watch increases.

If the cost of the watches increases to $1,000, then the profit increases.

The maximum profit is made when each watch is sold for $500.

The profit, based on a cost of $500 per watch, is greater than if the watch costs $1,000.

36. The company ABC manufactures cars, and the profit P, in dollars, for selling cars is described with the equation $P(x) = x(10 - 0.001x)$ where x denotes the cost of each car sold. The graph of the profit function is given below. Which is the best conclusion about the company's profit?

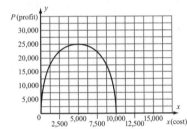

If the cost of each car increases to $10,000, then the profit increases.

The maximum profit is made when each car is sold for $5,000.

The profit increases if the cost of each car increases.

The profit, based on a cost of $10,000, is greater than if each car cost $2,500.

37. An engineering company is building a bridge to cross a 350 ft. canyon. The graph represents the arch of the bridge (where the x-axis represents the distance in feet and the y-axis represents the height in feet). Write the equation of the parabola.

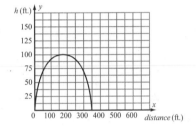

38. An engineering company is designing the loop of a roller coaster. The graph represents the curve of the loop (where the x-axis represents the distance in feet and the y-axis represents the height in feet). Write the equation of the parabola.

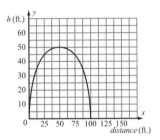

39. The leap of a frog can be represented in a graph. The graph represents the curve of the leap (where the x-axis represents the distance in feet, and the y-axis represents the height in feet). Write the equation of the parabola.

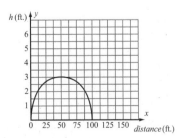

Graphing absolute value equations is not unlike graphing linear functions. We have discussed the absolute value of a number as the distance on the number line between the number and zero. Since distance cannot be negative, the absolute value of a number is always positive or zero. The absolute value of the number x is the same number x if x is positive or zero. If x is negative, then its absolute value is the opposite of that number. The graph of an absolute value function, when unaltered by translations or transformations, always has a positive y-value.

Absolute Value	$|x|; \quad |x| = \begin{cases} x & \text{if } x \geq 0 \\ -x & \text{if } x < 0 \end{cases}$

Example 1 Simplify: $|-8 - 4|$

$|-8 - 4| = |-12| = 12$

Step 1: To simplify an absolute value expression, we first simplify inside the absolute value signs.

Answer: The absolute value of -12 is 12.

Example 2 The graph of $y = |x| - 2$ is given below:

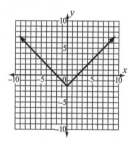

Which graph best represents the graph of the function that has been translated 2 units left?

A) 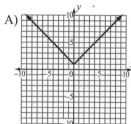 B) 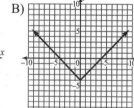 C) 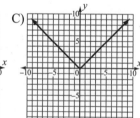 D)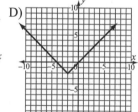

Answer: Graph D.

Example 3   For $x < -1$, which of the following is the graph of the function $y = 2|x - 2|$?

A) 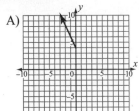   B) 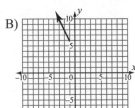   C) 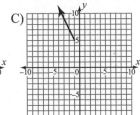   D)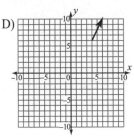

When $x < 0$, then $\|x - 2\| = -(x - 2) = -x + 2$.	**Step 1:** Find the absolute value of $x - 2$, when $x < 0$.
So if $y = 2\|x - 2\|$, then $y = 2(-x + 2)$ $y = -2x + 4$	**Step 2:** Replace $\|x - 2\|$ with $-x + 2$ in the equation.

Answer: The graph of the function $y = -2x + 4$ where $x < -1$ is shown in graph B.

Example 4   Below is the graph of the quadratic function $y = f(x)$ that is obtained by translating the graph of $y = |x|$. Write the equation for the function f.

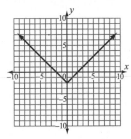

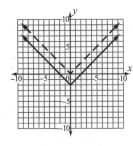

Step 1: The dotted line represents the graph of the parent function $y = |x|$. It passes through the origin. When the graph of $y = |x|$ is translated downward, the origin moves 2 units downward.

Answer: The equation can be obtained by subtracting 2, that is
$$y = |x| - 2.$$

Example 5   Which of the following graphs is the graph of the function $f(x) = 2|x + 3| + 2$?

A) 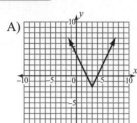   B) 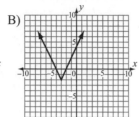   C) 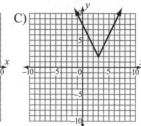   D)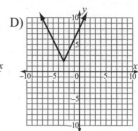

If we can use $x = 0$, then
$f(x) = 2|0 + 3| + 2$
$= 2|3| + 2$
$= 6 + 2$
$= 8$

Step 1: Use test point $x = 0$ to find a point on the graph of the function $f(x) = 2|x + 3| + 2$.

$f(x) = 2|1 + 3| + 2$
$= 2|4| + 2$
$= 8 + 2$
$= 10$

Step 2: When we look at the graphs, only graphs C and D satisfy this point $(0, 8)$. Now use the test point $x = 1$.

Step 3: When we look at graphs C and D, only graph D satisfies the point $(1, 10)$.

Answer: The graph of the function is graph D.

Example 6   For $x < 0$, find the linear equation of the function $y = 2|x| + 1$.

Since $x < 0$, $x = -x$.
Then $y = 2|x| + 1$
$= 2(-x) + 1$
$= -2x + 1$

Step 1: We know that the absolute value of $x = x$ if $x \geq 0$. We also know that absolute value of $x = -x$ if $x < 0$.

Answer: $y = -2x + 1$

Problem Set

Simplify the following:

1. $|-16 + 7|$ **2.** $|-15 - 9|$ **3.** $|-15 - 10|$ **4.** $|-18 + 7|$

5. $|-16 + 10|$ **6.** $|16 - 7|$ **7.** $|15 - 7|$ **8.** $|13 + 7|$

9. $|22 + 7|$ **10.** $|10 - 14|$

Solve:

11. The graph of $y = |x| - 1$ is given below.

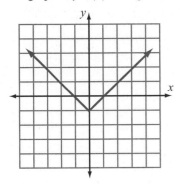

Draw the graph that represents the graph of the function that has been translated 3 units upward.

12. The graph of $y = |x| - 1$ is given below.

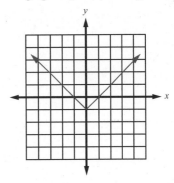

Draw the graph that represents the graph of the function that has been translated 3 units left.

13. The graph of $y = |x| - 1$ is given below.

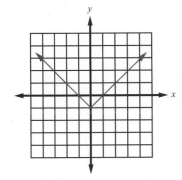

Draw the graph that represents the graph of the function that has been translated 3 units to the right.

14. The graph of $y = |x| - 2$ is given below.

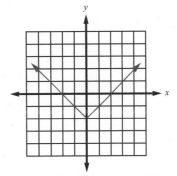

Draw the graph that represents the graph of the function that has been translated 2 units upward.

15. The graph of $y = |x| - 3$ is given below.

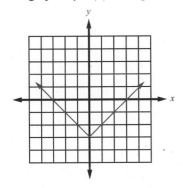

Draw the graph that represents the graph of the function that has been translated 1 unit downward.

16. Complete the following to make a true statement.

For the function $y = |x - 3|$, the graph is the same as the graph of $y = |x|$ but _____.

  shifted downward 3 units

  shifted left 3 units

  shrunk by a factor of 3

  shifted right 3 units

17. Complete the following to make a true statement. For the function $y = |x + 4|$, the graph is the same as the graph of $y = |x|$ but _____.

    shifted upward 4 units

    shifted left 4 units

    shifted downward 4 units

    shifted right 4 units

18. Complete the following to make a true statement. For the function $y = |x| - 5$, the graph is the same as the graph of $y = |x|$ but _____.

    shifted downward 5 units

    shrunk by a factor of 5

    shifted upward 5 units

    shifted right 5 units

19. Complete the following to make a true statement. For the function $y = 6|x|$, the graph is the same as the graph of $y = |x|$ but _____.

    shrunk by a factor of 6

    stretched by a factor of 6

    shifted right 6 units

    shifted upward 6 units

20. Complete the following to make a true statement. For the function $y = \frac{2}{3}|x|$, the graph is the same as the graph of $y = |x|$ but _____.

    shifted upward $\frac{2}{3}$ units

    shrunk by a factor of $\frac{2}{3}$

    stretched by a factor of $\frac{2}{3}$

    shifted right $\frac{2}{3}$ units

The given graphs are translations of the graph $y = |x|$. Find the function that represents each translated graph:

21.

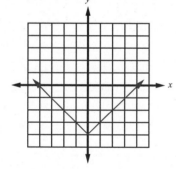

22.

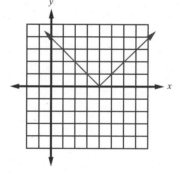

The given graphs are translations of the graph $y = -|x|$. Find the function that represents each translated graph:

23.

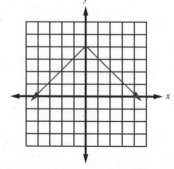

24.

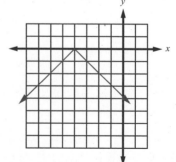

The given graphs are translations of the graph $y = 2|x|$. Find the function that represents each translated graph:

25.

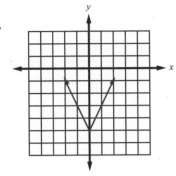

26.

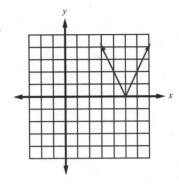

The given graphs are translations of the graph $y = -2|x|$. Find the function that represents each translated graph:

27.

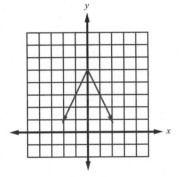

28.

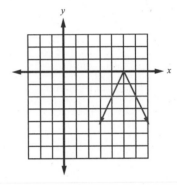

29. Graph the function: $f(x) = 2|x - 2| - 3$

30. Graph the function: $f(x) = -2|x + 2| + 3$

31. Graph the function: $f(x) = 2|x + 3| - 2$

32. Graph the function: $f(x) = 2|x - 3| + 2$

33. For $x < 0$, the function $y = 2|x| + 1$ is the same as what linear equation?

34. For $x < 0$, the function $y = 3|x| - 1$ is the same as what linear equation?

35. For $x < 0$, the function $y = 2|x| + 2$ is the same as what linear equation?

36. For $x < 0$, the function $y = 3|x| - 2$ is the same as what linear equation?

37. For $x < 0$, the function $y = 3|x| + 2$ is the same as what linear equation?

38. For $x < 0$, the function $y = -3|x| + 2$ is the same as what linear equation?

39. For $x < 0$, the function $y = -2|x| + 7$ is the same as what linear equation?

40. For $x < 0$, the function $y = -6|x| - 3$ is the same as what linear equation?

HA1-955: Analyzing Linear Functions

In this lesson, we will analyze linear equations and functions. Determining whether a set of data represent a linear function and finding the linear equation of a given function will help us gain a familiarity with linear functions. There are also two special cases of straight line graphs that we must consider: horizontal lines and vertical lines.

The slope of a horizontal line is 0 and the slope of a vertical line is undefined. We know that the slope of a horizontal line is zero because we can calculate the slope using the change of y divided by the change of x. The change of y is zero in the numerator, so our quotient is zero. Parallel lines have the same slope. Perpendicular lines have slopes that are negative reciprocals of each other.

Example 1   Find the equation of the line that passes through the point (2, 1) and has the slope 3.

$y - y_1 = m(x - x_1)$	**Step 1:** We must use the point-slope form of the equation to solve this problem.
$y - y_1 = m(x - x_1)$ $y - 1 = 3(x - 2)$	**Step 2:** We know that the slope, m, equals three and we will use the point (2, 1).
$y - 1 = 3x - 6$ $y = 3x - 5$	**Step 3:** We will now solve the equation.

Answer: $y = 3x - 5$

Example 2   Find the slope of the line $5x - 3y = 15$.

$5x - 3y = 15$ $-3y = -5x + 15$	**Step 1:** To find the slope of the line, we must rewrite the equation in slope-intercept form by solving for y.
$-3y = -5x + 15$ $y = \dfrac{5}{3}x - 5$ $m = \dfrac{5}{3}$	**Step 2:** Now we need to simplify and divide both sides of the equation by negative three.

Answer: $\dfrac{5}{3}$

Example 3   Which equation describes the graph below?

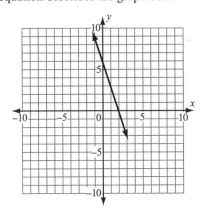

A) $y = 4x + 5$

B) $y = -2x + 3$

C) $y = -3x + 6$

D) $y = -x + 3$

$(0, 6)$ and $(1, 3)$

$m = \dfrac{y_2 - y_1}{x_2 - x_1}$

$= \dfrac{6 - 3}{0 - 1}$

$= \dfrac{3}{-1}$

$= -3$

Step 1: To find the slope we need two points. We already have the y-intercept, so we need to choose another point on the graph. We will select the point $(1, 3)$ to find the slope.

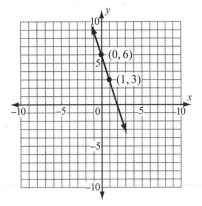

$y = mx + b$

$b = 6$

$m = -3$

$y = -3x + 6$

Step 2: We can now find the equation of the line. We must use the slope-intercept form of the equation to solve this problem. We know that $b = 6$ and the slope, m, is -3.

Answer: The result is $y = -3x + 6$.

Example 4   Find the equation that passes through the points $(3, 2)$ and $(2, 8)$.

$m = \dfrac{y_2 - y_1}{x_2 - x_1}$

$= \dfrac{8 - 2}{2 - 3}$

$= \dfrac{6}{-1}$

$m = -6$

Step 1: We will use the point-slope form of the equation to solve this problem, but first we must find the slope.

$$y - y_1 = m(x - x_1)$$
$$y - 8 = -6(x - 2)$$
$$y - 8 = -6x + 12$$
$$y = -6x + 20$$

Step 2: We can now use the point-slope form to solve the equation.

Answer: $y = -6x + 20$

Example 5 If $(4, y)$ is a point on the line $y = 2x + 3$, what is the value of y?

$$y = 2x + 3$$
$$= 2(4) + 3$$
$$= 8 + 3$$
$$y = 11$$

Step 1: We must solve this equation by first substituting $(4, y)$ into $y = 2x + 3$.

Answer: $y = 11$

Example 6 What equation describes the data in the table?

x	-2	-1	0	1	2
y	3	4	5	6	7

$$m = \frac{y_2 - y_1}{x_2 - x_1}$$
$$= \frac{6 - 3}{1 - (-2)}$$
$$= \frac{6 - 3}{1 + 2}$$
$$= \frac{3}{3}$$
$$m = 1$$

Step 1: In order to solve this equation, we must first find the slope. To do this we will pick the points $(-2, 3)$ and $(1, 6)$.

$$y - y_1 = m(x - x_1)$$
$$y - 3 = 1(x - (-2))$$
$$y - 3 = x + 2$$
$$y = x + 5$$

Step 2: Now that we have found the slope, we can use the point-slope form of the equation to solve.

Answer: $y = x + 5$

Problem Set

1. Find an equation of the line that passes through the point $(1, 0)$ and has the slope 2. Write the equation in slope-intercept form.

2. Find an equation of the line that passes through the point $(0, 0)$ and has the slope 3. Write the equation in slope-intercept form.

3. Find an equation of the line that passes through the point $(2, -1)$ and has the slope 4. Write the equation in slope-intercept form.

4. Find an equation of the line that passes through the point $(0, 0)$ and has the slope 4. Write the equation in slope-intercept form.

5. Find the slope of the line $10x - y = 70$.

6. If $\left(\dfrac{1}{2}, y\right)$ is a point on the line $4x - 5y = -28$, what is the value of y?

7. Find the slope of the line $10x - 5y = 50$.

8. If $(2, y)$ is a point on the line $4x - 5y = -17$, what is the value of y?

9. Determine whether the following lines are parallel, perpendicular, intersecting and non-perpendicular, or identical:
$$y = 4x - 5 \text{ and } 3x - y = 8$$

10. Determine whether the following lines are parallel, perpendicular, intersecting and non-perpendicular, or identical:
$$y = 4x - 5 \text{ and } 8x - 2y = 10$$

11. Determine whether the following lines are parallel, perpendicular, intersecting and non-perpendicular, or identical:
$$y = 2x - 5 \text{ and } 2x - y = 8$$

12. Find an equation of the line that describes the data given in the table. Write the equation in slope-intercept form.

x	-5	-1	3	7	11
y	-2	2	6	10	14

13. Find an equation of the line that describes the data given in the table. Write the equation in slope-intercept form.

x	-5	-1	3	7	11
y	2	-2	-6	-10	-14

14. Find an equation of the line that describes the data given in the table. Write the equation in slope-intercept form.

x	-5	-1	3	7	11
y	-16	-8	0	8	16

15. Find an equation of the line that describes the data given in the table. Write the equation in slope-intercept form.

x	-5	-1	3	7	11
y	-1	-5	-9	-13	-17

16. Find an equation of the line graphed. Write the equation in slope-intercept form.

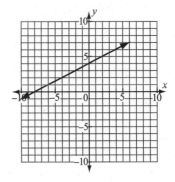

17. Find an equation of the line graphed. Write the equation in slope-intercept form.

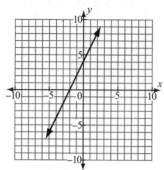

18. Find an equation of the line graphed. Write the equation in slope-intercept form.

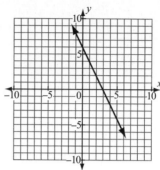

19. Find an equation that passes through the points (–3, 2) and (2, –8). Write the equation in slope-intercept form.

20. Find an equation that passes through the points (5, 3) and (0, –7). Write the equation in slope-intercept form.

21. Which of the following lines is perpendicular to the graph?

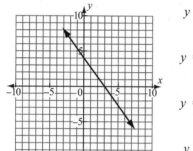

$y = \dfrac{4}{3}x + 3$

$y = -\dfrac{3}{4}x + 3$

$y = -\dfrac{4}{3}x + 4$

$y = \dfrac{3}{4}x + 4$

22. Which of the following lines is parallel to the graph?

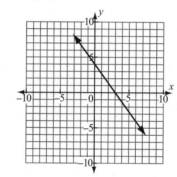

$y = -\dfrac{4}{3}x$

$y = \dfrac{3}{4}x + 3$

$y = \dfrac{4}{3}x + 3$

$y = -\dfrac{3}{4}x + 4$

23. Which of the following lines is parallel to the graph?

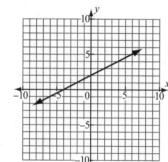

$y = -\dfrac{1}{2}x + 4$

$y = -2x + 3$

$y = \dfrac{1}{2}x + 3$

$y = 2x + 3$

24. Which of the following lines is perpendicular to the graph?

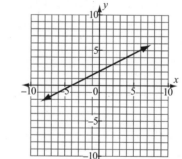

$y = -\dfrac{1}{2} + 4$

$y = 2x + 3$

$y = \dfrac{1}{2}x + 3$

$y = -2x + 3$

25. Is the line $y = \frac{1}{2}x + 3$ parallel to the graph?

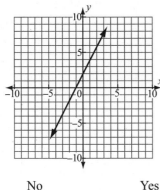

No   Yes

26. Find an equation of the line that is parallel to the line $3x + 6y = 4$ and passes through the point $(4, 0)$. Write the equation in slope-intercept form.

27. Find an equation of the line that is parallel to the line $6x - 3y = 4$ and passes through the point $(-4, -2)$. Write the equation in slope-intercept form.

28. Find an equation of the line that is parallel to the line $3x - 6y = 4$ and passes through the point $(0, -5)$. Write the equation in slope-intercept form.

29. Find an equation of the line that is parallel to the line $3x - 6y = 4$ and passes through the point $(1, 6)$. Write the equation in slope-intercept form.

30. Is $y = -2x + 6$ an equation of the line that is parallel to the line $3x - 6y = 4$ and passes through the point $(1, 6)$?

31. Is $y = -2x - 2$ the equation of the line that is parallel to the line $3x - 6y = 4$ and that passes through the point $(1, 6)$?

32. Is $y = \frac{1}{3}x + 1$ the equation of the line that is parallel to the line $2x - 6y = 4$, and that passes through the point $(-6, -1)$?

33. Find the equation of the line that is perpendicular to the line $-6x + 3y = 4$ and passes through the point $(7, -1)$. Write the equation in slope-intercept form.

34. Find the equation of the line that is perpendicular to the line $6x + 3y = 4$ and passes through the point $(-5, 1)$. Write the equation in slope-intercept form.

35. Find the equation of the line that is perpendicular to the line $8x + 4y = 12$ and passes through the point $(-8, 1)$. Write the equation in slope-intercept form.

36. Find the equation of the line that is perpendicular to the line $8x + 4y = 12$ and passes through the point $(8, 1)$. Write the equation in slope-intercept form.

37. Is the equation of the line $y = -2x + 5$ perpendicular to the line $-4x + 8y = 12$ at the point $(5, -3)$?

38. Is the equation of the line $y = -2x + 5$ perpendicular to the line $-4x + 8y = 12$ at the point $(4, -3)$?

39. Is the equation of the line $y = -5x + 2$ perpendicular to the line $-4x + 8y = 12$ at the point $(5, 3)$?

40. Is the equation of the line $y = 5x + 2$ perpendicular to the line $8x + 4y = 12$ at the point $(-5, -5)$?

HA1-960: Real-World Applications of Linear Functions

In this lesson, we will learn various applications of linear functions.

Example 1   Cynthia likes to walk. The graph below represents the distance Cynthia walked as a function of time. How many miles did Cynthia walk in 4 hours?

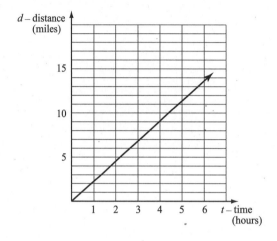

Step 1:   From the graph we need to find the distance when the time, $t = 4$.

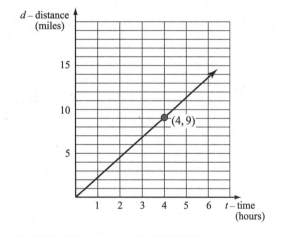

Step 2:   The distance, d, is 9 when $t = 4$.

Answer: In 4 hours she traveled 9 miles.

Example 2　　Angela likes to ride her bike. The graph below represents the distance Angela rides as a function of time. Find the rate of change of the distance with respect to time.

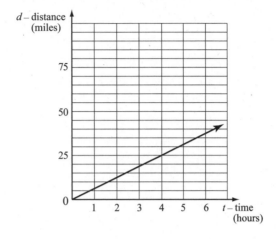

Step 1: The rate of change of a linear function is the slope.

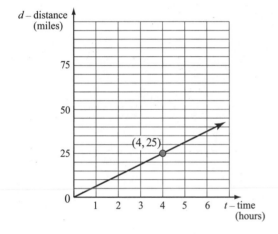

Step 2: To find the slope of a line we need two points. Let's use the origin (0, 0) and point (4, 25).

Step 3: The slope is $m = \dfrac{y_2 - y_1}{x_2 - x_1} = \dfrac{25 - 0}{4 - 0} = \dfrac{25}{4} = 6.25$,

so the rate of change is 6.25 mph.

Answer: 6.25 miles per hour

Example 3　　The table below gives the price P of a medium pizza as a function of the number of toppings, T. Find the equation that describes the price as a function of the number of toppings.

T - number of toppings	0	1	2	3	4	5
P - price [$]	8.00	8.50	9.00	10.00	11.00	13.00

Step 1: To find an equation of a linear function we need the slope and the y-intercept.

Step 2: The y-intercept is (0, 8.00).

Step 3: To find the slope we need two point; let's use the y-intercept (0, 8.00)
and point (1, 8.50). The slope is

$$m = \frac{\text{Change in } P}{\text{Change in } T} = \frac{8.50 - 8.00}{1 - 0} = \frac{0.50}{1} = 0.50$$

Answer: P = 0.50T + 8.00

Example 4 The company XYZ manufactures textbooks and it is found that the monthly cost of producing 100 textbooks is \$57,000 and the monthly cost of producing 1,000 textbooks is \$120,000. Find the cost per textbook produced if the monthly cost is a linear function of the number of textbooks produced.

Step 1: The rate of change equals the change in cost (C) divided by the change in the number of textbooks (N). The slope is

$$m = \frac{\text{Change in } C}{\text{Change in } N} = \frac{120,000 - 57,000}{1000 - 100} = \frac{63,000}{900} = 70$$

Answer: \$70 per textbook

Example 5 The total number of square feet of lawn that can be seeded is a linear function of the number of bags of grass seed used. The following table represents some collected data about the lawn area in square feet as a function of the number of bags of grass seed. Find the rate of change of the lawn area in square feet with respect to the number of bags of grass seed used.

Square feet of lawn	0	25	50	75	100	125
Bags of grass seed	0	5	10	15	20	25

Step 1: The rate of change is

$$m = \frac{\text{Change in } F}{\text{Change in } B} = \frac{50 - 0}{10 - 0} = \frac{50}{10} = 5$$

Step 2: The rate of change of the lawn area in square feet with respect to the number of bags of grass seed used is 5.

Answer: 5 square feet per bag

Problem Set

1. Brian likes to walk. The graph below represents the distance Brian walked as a function of time. How many miles did Brian walk in 1 hour?

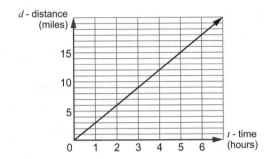

2. The XYZ company plans to produce and sell graphing calculators. The company did a study about the consumer demand — the number of calculators that people are willing to buy at various prices. The function is represented on the graph below. If the price of a calculator is $150, how many calculators has the company sold?

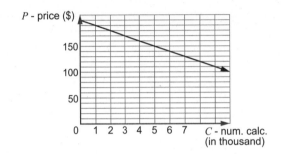

3. The XYZ company plans to produce and sell graphing calculators. The company did a study of consumer demand — the number of calculators that people are willing to buy at various prices. The function is represented on the graph below. If the price of a calculator is $140, how many calculators has the company sold?

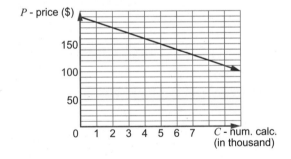

4. The XYZ company plans to produce and sell graphing calculators. The company did a study of consumer demand — the number of calculators that people are willing to buy at various prices. The function is represented on the graph below. If the price of a calculator is $120, how many calculators has the company sold?

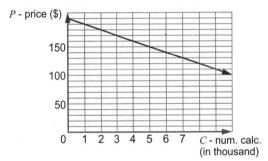

5. The XYZ company plans to produce and sell graphing calculators. The company did a study of consumer demand — the number of calculators that people are willing to buy at various prices. The function is represented on the graph below. If the price of a calculator is $100, how many calculators has the company sold?

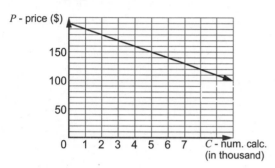

6. Cali likes to walk. The graph below represents the distance Cali walked as a function of time. How many miles did Cali walk in 3 hours?

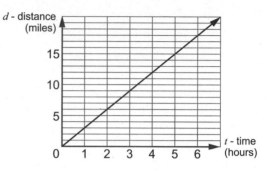

7. Kim likes to bike. The graph below represents the distance Kim rides as a function of time. Find the rate of change of the distance with respect to time.

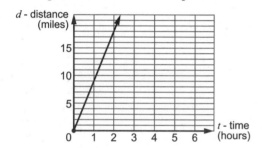

8. Jill likes to bike. The graph below represents the distance Jill rides as a function of time. Find the rate of change of the distance with respect to time.

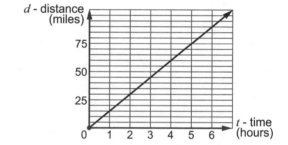

9. Sharon likes to swim. The graph below represents the distance Sharon swims as a function of time. Find the rate of change of the distance with respect to time.

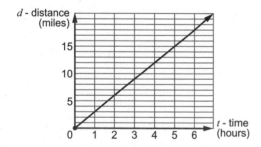

10. The XYZ company plans to produce and sell graphing calculators. The company did a study of consumer demand — the number of calculators that people are willing to buy at various prices. The function is represented on the graph below. Find the rate of change of the price with respect to the number of calculators.

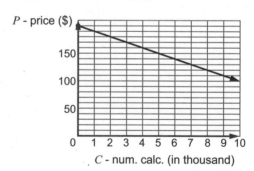

11. The XYZ company plans to produce and sell graphing calculators. The company did a study of consumer demand — the number of calculators that people are willing to buy at various prices. The function is represented on the graph below. Find the rate of change of the price with respect to the number of calculators.

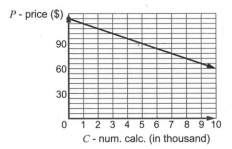

C - num. calc. (in thousand)

12. The XYZ company plans to produce and sell graphing calculators. The company did a study of consumer demand — the number of calculators that people are willing to buy at various prices. The function is represented on the graph below. Find the rate of change of the price with respect to the number of calculators.

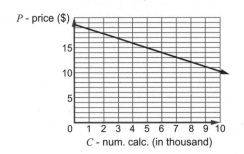

C - num. calc. (in thousand)

13. Nike likes to bike. The graph below represents the distance Nike rides as a function of time. Express the distance, d, as a function of time, t.

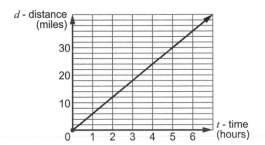

14. Lan likes to bike. The graph below represents the distance Lan rides as a function of time. Express the distance, d, as a function of time, t.

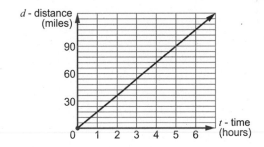

15. The XYZ company plans to produce and sell graphing calculators. The company did a study of consumer demand — the number of calculators that people are willing to buy at various prices. The function is represented on the graph below. Express the change of the price, P, as a function of the number of calculators.

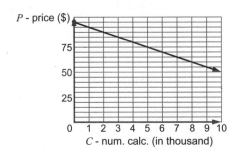

C - num. calc. (in thousand)

16. The XYZ company plans to produce and sell graphing calculators. The company did a study about the consumer demand — the number of calculators that people are willing to buy at various prices. The function is represented on the graph below.
Express the change of the price, p, as a function of the number of calculators.

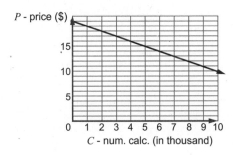

C - num. calc. (in thousand)

17. The table below gives the price, P, of a medium pizza as a function of the number of toppings, T. Find the equation that describes the price as a function of number of toppings.

T - number of toppings	0	1	2	3	4	5
P - price ($)	5.25	6.05	6.85	7.65	8.45	9.25

18. The table below gives the price, P, of a small pizza as a function of the number of toppings, T. Find the equation that describes the price as a function of number of toppings.

T - number of toppings	0	1	2	3	4	5
P - price ($)	3.25	3.75	4.25	4.75	5.25	5.75

19. The table below gives the price, P, of a large pizza as a function of the number of toppings, T. Find the equation that describes the price as a function of number of toppings.

T - number of toppings	0	1	2	3	4	5
P - price ($)	7.25	8.35	9.45	10.55	11.65	12.75

20. The table below gives the price, P, of a large pizza as a function of the number of toppings, T. Find the equation that describes the price as a function of number of toppings.

T - number of toppings	0	1	2	3	4	5
P - price ($)	7.25	8.40	9.55	10.70	11.85	13.00

21. The total number of square feet of wall that can be painted is a linear function of the amount of paint used. The following table represents some collected data about the painted area in square feet as a function of paint used in quarts. Does the given graph represent the total number of square feet of wall that can be painted, based on the information given in the table? Answer yes or no.

P - Amount of paint	0	1	2
F - Number of square feet	0	100	200

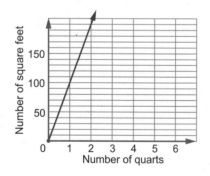

22. The total number of square feet of lawn that can be seeded is a linear function of the number of bags of grass seed used. The following table represents some collected data about the lawn area in square feet as a function of the number of bags of grass seed. Does the given graph represent the total number of square feet of lawn that can be seeded, based on the information given in the table? Answer yes or no.

B - Bags of grass seed	0	1	2
F - Number of square feet	0	32	64

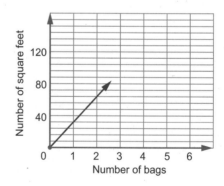

23. The total number of square feet of attic space that can be insulated is a linear function of the number of rolls of insulation used. The following table represents some collected data about the attic area, in square feet, as a function of the number of rolls of insulation. Does the given graph represent the total number of square feet of attic space that can be covered, based on the information given in the table? Answer yes or no.

R - Rolls of insulation used	0	1	2
F - Number of square feet	0	100	200

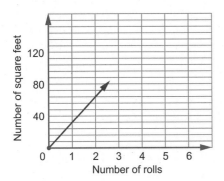

24. The total number of square feet of attic space that can be insulated is a linear function of the number of rolls of insulation used. The following table represents some collected data about the attic area, in square feet, as a function of the number of rolls of insulation. Does the given graph represent the total number of square feet of attic space that can be covered, based on the information given in the table? Answer yes or no.

R - Rolls of insulation used	0	1	2
F - Number of square feet	0	20	40

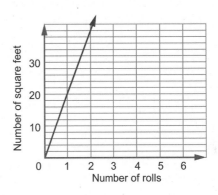

25. The total number of square feet of attic space that can be insulated is a linear function of the number of rolls of insulation used. The following table represents some collected data about the attic area, in square feet, as a function of the number of rolls of insulation. Does the given graph represent the total number of square feet of attic space that can be covered, based on the information given in the table? Answer yes or no.

R - Rolls of insulation used	0	1	2
F - Number of square feet	0	120	140

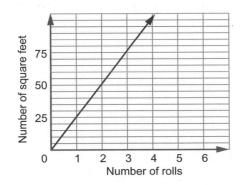

26. The XYZ company plans to produce and sell graphing calculators. The company did a study of consumer demand — the number of calculators that people are willing to buy at various prices. The data is given in the table below. Find the rate of change of the number of calculators with respect to the price.

C - number of calculators	0	250	500	750
P - price ($)	210	190	170	150

27. The total number of square feet of attic space that can be insulated is a linear function of the number of rolls of insulation used. The following table represents some collected data about the attic area in square feet as a function of the number of rolls of insulation. Find the rate of change of the number of square feet with respect to the rolls of insulation used

R - Rolls of insulation used	0	1	2
F - Number of square feet	0	20	40

28. The total number of square feet of lawn that can be seeded is a linear function of the number of bags of grass seed used. The following table represents some collected data about the lawn area in square feet as a function of the number of bags of grass seed. Find the rate of change of the lawn area in square feet with respect to the number of bags of grass seed used.

B - Bags of grass seed	0	1	2
F - Number of square feet	0	20	40

29. The table below gives the price, P, of a large pizza as a function of the number of toppings, T. Find the rate of change of the price of a large pizza, with respect to the number of toppings.

T - number of toppings	0	1	2	3	4	5
P - price ($)	7.25	8.35	9.45	10.55	11.65	12.75

30. The XYZ company manufactures calculators. It costs the company $5,800 to produce 100 calculators per month, and $13,000 to produce 1,000 calculators per month. Find the cost per calculator produced if the monthly cost is a linear function of the number of calculators produced.

31. The XYZ company manufactures calculators. It costs the company $4,000 to produce 100 calculators per month, and $13,000 to produce 1,000 calculators per month. Find the cost per calculator produced if the monthly cost is a linear function of the number of calculators produced.

32. The XYZ company manufactures calculators. It costs the company $50,000 to produce 100 calculators per month, and $122,000 to produce 1,000 calculators per month. Find the cost per calculator produced if the monthly cost is a linear function of the number of calculators produced.

33. The XYZ company manufactures televisions. It costs the company $12,000 to produce 100 televisions per month, and $120,000 to produce 1,000 televisions per month. Find the cost per television produced if the monthly cost is a linear function of the number of televisions produced.

34. The XYZ company manufactures televisions. It costs the company $12,000 to produce 100 televisions per month, and $192,000 to produce 1,000 televisions per month. Find the cost per television produced if the monthly cost is a linear function of the number of televisions produced.

35. The XYZ company manufactures sofas. It costs the company $120,000 to produce 100 sofas per month, and $660,000 to produce 1,000 sofas per month. Find the cost per sofa produced, if the monthly cost is a linear function of the number of sofas produced.

36. The XYZ company plans to produce and sell calculators. The company did a study of consumer demand — the number of calculators that the people are willing to buy at various prices. The function is represented on the graph below. How many calculators will be sold if the price per calculator is $190?

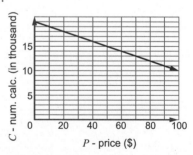

37. The XYZ company plans to produce and sell calculators. The company did a study of consumer demand — the number of calculators that the people are willing to buy at various prices. The function is represented on the graph below. How many calculators will be sold if the price per calculator is $180?

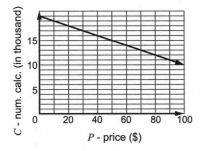

38. The XYZ company plans to produce and sell stereos. The company did a study of consumer demand — the number of stereos that the people are willing to buy at various prices. The function is represented on the graph below. How many stereos will be sold if the price per stereo is $600?

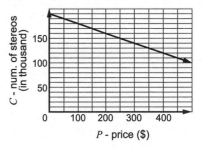

39. The XYZ company plans to produce and sell stereos. The company did a study of consumer demand — the number of stereos that the people are willing to buy at various prices. The function is represented on the graph below. How many stereos will be sold if the price per stereo is $800?

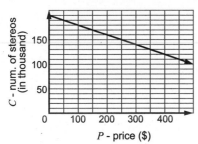

40. The XYZ company plans to produce and sell stereos. The company did a study of consumer demand — the number of stereos that the people are willing to buy at various prices. The function is represented on the graph below. How many stereos will be sold if the price per stereo is $900?

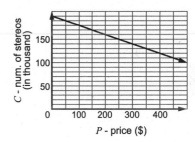

HA1-965: Determining the Best-Fitting Line

In this lesson, we will learn how to determine if a set of data can be represented by a linear function or a nonlinear function. We will also learn how to find the best-fitting line for data represented by a linear function.

To determine if the set of data represents a linear function, we will evaluate the slope between two consecutive points. To do this, we subtract the *x* value in the first point from the *x* value in the second point. Similarly, we find the change in *y* between two consecutive *y* values.

Next, evaluate the slope as the ratio of the change in *y* over the corresponding change in *x*. This means we must divide our change in *y* values by our change in *x* values. Now we have learned that the best-fitting line or "line of best fit" is the line which lies closest to all the points of the data when they are plotted on a graph. In addition to the phrase "line of best fit," there is another word we need to learn to use when describing a table of data. This new word is "correlation."

Correlation is a number, which is very complicated to compute, but that essentially measures exactly how close the points in a table of data are to the line of best fit. Correlation is related to the slope of the line of best fit.

The rule that we need to remember is that for approximately linear data, the sign of the correlation number, is the same as the sign of the slope for the line of best fit. Therefore, we can say that the correlation between variables in a given data set is positive if the slope of the best-fitting line is positive. The correlation is negative if the slope of the best-fitting line is negative, and the correlation is zero if the slope of the best-fitting line is zero. For data that is not approximately linear, and for which a line of best fit is not appropriate, we say that there is no correlation between the values in the data.

Example 1   Does the scatter plot represent a data set with a linear function?

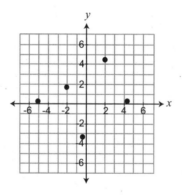

Step 1:   Find the best-fitting line.

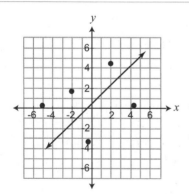

Answer: The line does not fit the data, Therefore, the scatter plot does not represent a data set with a linear function.

Example 2   The table below shows a set of values for x and y. Determine the correlation that this set of data represents.

x	−4	−3	0	1	2	5
y	10	8	6	4	0	−2

Step 1: As the values for x increase, that is, takes values −4, −3, 0, 1, 2, and 5, the corresponding values for y decrease and take values 10, 8, 6, 4, 0 and −2.

Answer: Therefore, since the values of y decrease, the correlation is negative.

Example 3   Determine the type of correlation in the data set represented by the following scatter plot.

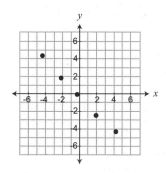

Step 1: Since the points are decreasing, the best-fitting line will have a negative slope.

Answer: Therefore, the scatter plot represents data with a negative correlation.

Example 4   The total sales for calculators were recorded during a period of days and the data is represented on the scatter-plot below. Does the following linear graph best fit the data?

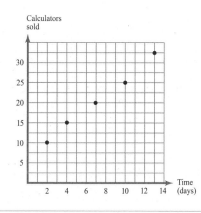 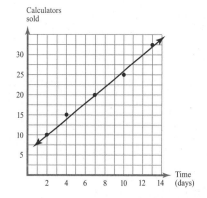

Step 1: The correlation between total sales for calculators and time must be positive because total sales for calculators increase with time. The line is increasing. The given points are on both sides of the line and are as close to the line as possible.

Answer: Therefore, the graph best fits the data.

Example 5 Given the data set below, draw the scatter plot and best-fitting line.

x	-5	-3	-1	1	5
y	4	3	2	1	-1

Which of the following best describes the value of y when x is 3?

A) 4   B) –1   C) 0   D) 6

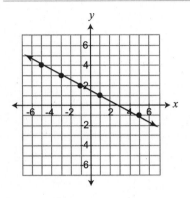

Step 1: The graph gives the scatter plot of data and the best-fitting line.

Step 2: From the graph we see that the point (3, 0) lies closest to the line and it is a reasonable estimate that the value of y = 0 when x = 3.

Answer: c) 0

Problem Set

1. Does the following data set represent a linear function?

x	1	2	3
y	4	6	8

Yes   No

2. Does the following data set represent a non-linear function?

x	1	2	3
y	4	4	4

Yes   No

3. Does the following data set represent a linear function?

x	1	2	3
y	4	9	14

Yes   No

4. Does the following data set represent a linear function?

x	1	2	3
y	7	9	11

Yes   No

5. Does the following data set represent a non-linear function?

x	1	2	3
y	4	0	−7

Yes   No

6. Does the following scatter plot represent a non-linear function?

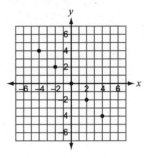

Yes   No

7. Does the following scatter plot represent a linear function?

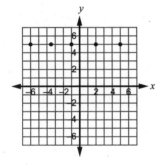

Yes   No

8. Does the following scatter plot represent a linear function?

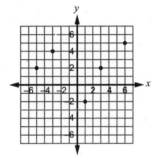

Yes   No

9. Does the following scatter plot represent a non-linear function?

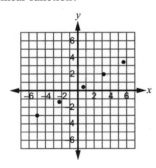

Yes   No

10. Does the following scatter plot represent a non-linear function?

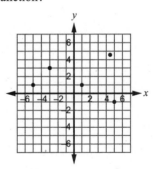

Yes   No

11. The graph below represents the best-fitting line for a given data set. What is the best value of x when $y = 0$?

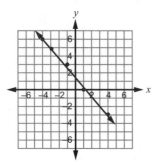

12. The graph below represents the best-fitting line for a given data set. What is the best value of y when $x = 1$?

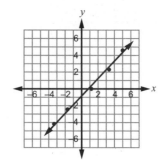

13. The table below shows a set of values for x and y. Determine whether the correlation is positive, negative, or zero.

x	−3	−1	0	2	4	5
y	13	9	6	4	1	−2

14. The table below shows a set of values for x and y. Determine whether the correlation is positive, negative, or zero.

x	−3	−1	0	2	4	5
y	−3	−3	−3	−3	−3	−3

15. The table below shows a set of values for x and y. Determine whether the correlation is positive, negative, or zero.

x	−3	−1	0	2	4	5
y	−3	0	3	6	9	12

16. Does the following scatter plot represent a data set with a positive, negative, or zero correlation?

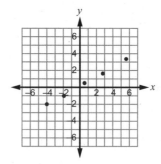

17. Does the following scatter plot represent a data set with a positive, negative, or zero correlation?

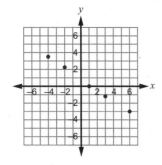

18. Does the following scatter plot represent a data set with a positive, negative, or zero correlation?

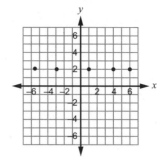

19. Does the following scatter plot represent a data set with a positive, negative, or zero correlation?

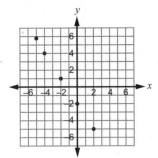

20. Does the following scatter plot represent a data set with a positive, negative, or zero correlation?

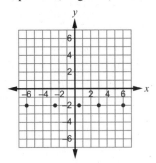

21. The distance traveled by a plane was recorded during a trip, and the data is represented on the scatter plot below.

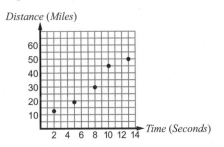

Does the following linear graph best fit the data?

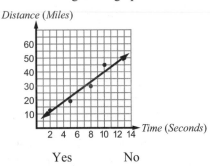

Yes   No

22. The distance traveled by a train was recorded during a trip, and the data is represented on the scatter plot below.

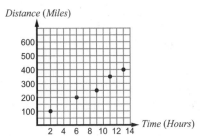

Does the following linear graph best fit the data?

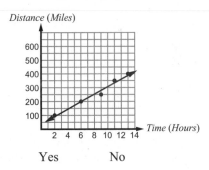

Yes   No

23. The distance traveled by a bus was recorded during a trip and the data is represented on the scatter plot below.

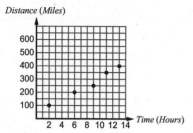

Does the following linear graph best fit the data?

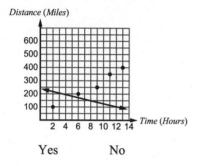

Yes   No

24. The temperature was recorded during a period of sunny days and the data is represented on the scatter plot below.

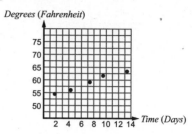

Does the following linear graph best fit the data?

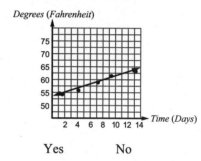

Yes   No

25. The temperature was recorded during a period of sunny days, and the data is represented on the scatter plot below.

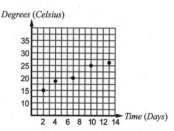

Does the following linear graph best fit the data?

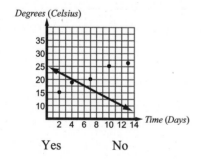

Yes   No

26. The total sales for televisions were recorded during a period of days, and the data is represented on the scatter plot below.

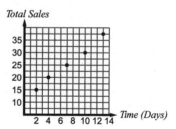

Does the following linear graph best fit the data?

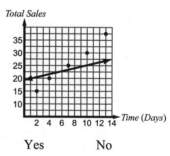

Yes   No

27. The total sales for refrigerators were recorded during a period of days, and the data is represented on the scatter plot below.

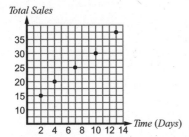

Does the following linear graph best fit the data?

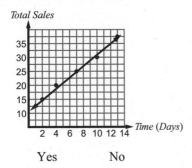

Yes   No

28. The total sales for sofas were recorded during a period of days, and the data is represented on the scatter plot below.

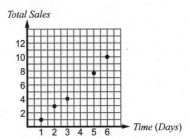

Does the following linear graph best fit the data?

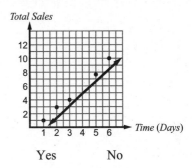

Yes   No

29. Which of the following best describes the value of y when $x = 3$?

x	–3	–1	0	2	4	6	7
y	7	3	2	–1	–4	–8	–9

2   –1

6   –3

30. Which of the following best describes the value of y when $x = 1$?

x	–3	–1	0	2	4	6	7
y	7	3	2	–1	–4	–8	–9

2   –3

0   6

31. Which of the following best describes the value of x when $y = -6$?

x	–3	–1	0	2	4	6	7
y	7	3	2	–1	–4	–8	–9

5   –3

2   0

32. Which of the following best describes the value of y when $x = -4$?

x	–3	–1	0	2	4	6	7
y	7	3	2	–1	–4	–8	–9

–3   5

8   4

33. Which of the following best describes the value of y when $x = -2$?

x	-3	-1	0	2	4	6	7
y	7	3	2	-1	-4	-8	-9

    -3   8

    4   5

34. Chip's Computer Chips, Inc. plans to produce and sell computer chips. The company did a study of consumer demand to determine the number of chips that people will buy at various prices. Using the data in the table, predict the best price estimate if customers are willing to buy 4,000,000 computer chips.

P - price ($)	100	90	75	60
C - number of chips (in millions)	0	1	3	5

35. Chip's Computer Chips, Inc. plans to produce and sell computer chips. The company did a study of consumer demand to determine the number of chips that people will buy at various prices. Using the data in the table, predict the best price estimate if customers are willing to buy 2,000,000 computer chips.

P - price ($)	100	90	75	60
C - number of chips (in millions)	0	1	3	5

36. Chip's Computer Chips, Inc. plans to produce and sell computer chips. The company did a study of consumer demand to determine the number of chips that people will buy at various prices. Using the data in the table, predict the best price estimate if customers are willing to buy 7,000,000 computer chips.

P - price ($)	100	90	75	60
C - number of chips (in millions)	0	1	3	5

37. Cool Calculators, Inc. plans to produce and sell calculators. The company did a study of consumer demand to determine the number of calculators that people will buy at various prices. Using the data in the table, predict the best price estimate if customers are willing to buy 1,000 calculators.

P - price ($)	100	85	70	50
C - number of calculators (in thousands)	0	2	4	7

38. Cool Calculators, Inc. plans to produce and sell calculators. The company did a study of consumer demand to determine the number of calculators that people will buy at various prices. Using the data in the table, predict the best price estimate if customers are willing to buy 3,000 calculators.

P - price ($)	100	85	70	50
C - number of calculators (in thousands)	0	2	4	7

39. Cool Calculators, Inc. plans to produce and sell calculators. The company did a study of consumer demand to determine the number of calculators that people will buy at various prices. Using the data in the table, predict the best price estimate if customers are willing to buy 6,000 calculators.

P - price ($)	100	85	70	50
C - number of calculators (in thousands)	0	2	4	7

40. Cool Calculators, Inc. plans to produce and sell calculators. The company did a study of consumer demand to determine the number of calculators that people will buy at various prices. Using the data in the table, predict the best price estimate if customers are willing to buy 9,000 calculators.

P - price ($)	100	85	70	50
C - number of calculators (in thousands)	0	2	4	7

In this lesson, we will learn how to find the inverses of functions and relations.

Inverse of a Function or Relation	The inverse of a function or relation is the set of ordered pairs obtained by reversing the coordinates of each ordered pair in the given function or relation.

If the relation or function is given as a graph, the inverse can be found by reflecting the given graph over the line $y = x$, sometimes called the identity function.

Identity Function	The function $f(x) = x$, sometimes stated as $y = x$

If the given relation or function is given as an equation, the inverse can be found using the following steps.

1. If the function has a name such as $f(x)$ or $g(x)$, change it to y.

2. Interchange x and y.

3. Solve for y when possible. If asked to find the inverse of a quadratic function, remember to take both square roots when solving for y.

After the inverse of a given function is found, it might be necessary to determine if the inverse is a function. It will be a function if for each x-coordinate there is exactly one y-coordinate. If the inverse is graphed, it must pass the Vertical Line Test.

Vertical Line Test	If a vertical line never intersects a graph in two or more points, then the graph is a function.

It is also possible to tell from a given graph whether or not the inverse will be a function. The given graph must pass the Horizontal Line Test in order for its inverse to be a function.

Horizontal Line Test	If a horizontal line intersects a graph in two or more points, then the graph of the inverse cannot be a function.

If a function with a name such as $f(x)$ is found, and its inverse is a function, the inverse can be denoted $f^{-1}(x)$.

Listed below are some properties of inverse functions. You can use the second property listed to show that two functions are inverses of each other.

Properties of Inverse Functions	If $g(a) = b$, then $g^{-1}(b) = a$.
	If $f(g(x)) = x$ and $g(f(x)) = x$ for any x for which the functions are defined, then functions f and g are inverse functions.

Example 1   Find the inverse of the function whose graph is given and determine whether or not the inverse is a function.

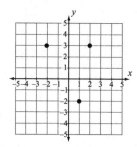

The function is {(–2, 3), (1, –2), (2, 3)}.	**Step 1:** Name the coordinates of the points that lie on the graph.
The inverse is {(3, –2), (–2, 1), (3, 2)}.	**Step 2:** Interchange the *x*- and *y*-coordinates of the ordered pairs in the given function to get the inverse.
The *x*-coordinate 3 is paired with more than one *y*-coordinate.	**Step 3:** Check to see if each *x*-coordinate has exactly one *y*-coordinate.
	Answer: The inverse is {(3, –2), (–2, 1), (3, 2)} and the inverse is not a function.

Example 2   Find the inverse of the function whose graph is given.

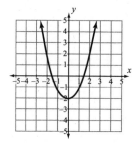

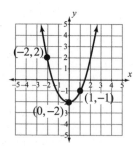

Step 1: Locate and plot a few points on the given graph: (–2, 2), (0, –2), and (1, –1).

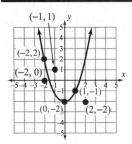

Step 2: Interchange the x- and y-coordinates to find a few points that lie on the graph of the inverse: (2, –2), (–2, 0), and (–1, 1).

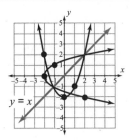

Step 3: Draw the line $y = x$ and reflect the given graph over the line $y = x$. Use the points found in Step 2 to help draw the reflection.

Answer:

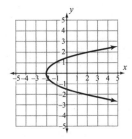

Example 3   Find the inverse of $f(x) = 2x - 6$.

$y = 2x - 6$	**Step 1:** Replace $f(x)$ with y.

$x = 2y - 6$	**Step 2:** Interchange the x and y variables.

$x + 6 = 2y - 6 + 6$	**Step 3:** Solve for y.

$x + 6 = 2y$

$\dfrac{x + 6}{2} = \dfrac{2y}{2}$

$\dfrac{1}{2}x + 3 = y$

$y = \dfrac{1}{2}x + 3$

$f^{-1}(x) = \dfrac{1}{2}x + 3$ **Step 4:** Replace y with $f^{-1}(x)$ since the inverse is a function.

Answer: $f^{-1}(x) = \dfrac{1}{2}x + 3$

Example 4 Find the inverse of $g(x) = \frac{1}{2}x^2 - 4$.

$y = \frac{1}{2}x^2 - 4$	**Step 1:** Replace $g(x)$ with y.
$x = \frac{1}{2}y^2 - 4$	**Step 2:** Interchange the x and y variables.
$x + 4 = \frac{1}{2}y^2 - 4 + 4$ $x + 4 = \frac{1}{2}y^2$ $2(x+4) = 2 \cdot \frac{1}{2}y^2$ $2x + 8 = y^2$ $\pm\sqrt{2x+8} = y$ $y = \pm\sqrt{2x+8}$	**Step 3:** Solve for y. Remember to take both square roots if y is squared.
$y = \pm\sqrt{2x+8}$	**Step 4:** We cannot replace y with $g^{-1}(x)$ since the inverse is not a function. For example, let $x = 4$. Then $y = \pm\sqrt{16} = \pm 4$. A function must have exactly one y value for each x value.
	Answer: $y = \pm\sqrt{2x+8}$

Example 5 Determine whether f and g are inverse functions if $f(x) = 6x - 4$ and $g(x) = \frac{1}{6}x + \frac{2}{3}$.

$f(g(x)) = f\left(\frac{1}{6}x + \frac{2}{3}\right)$ $= 6\left(\frac{1}{6}x + \frac{2}{3}\right) - 4$ $= x + 4 - 4$ $= x$	**Step 1:** Find $f(g(x))$ and check to see if the result is x.
$g(f(x)) = g(6x - 4)$ $= \frac{1}{6}(6x - 4) + \frac{2}{3}$ $= x - \frac{2}{3} + \frac{2}{3}$ $= x$	**Step 2:** Find $g(f(x))$ and check to see if the result is x.
f and g are inverse functions.	**Step 3:** If both results are x, then f and g are inverse functions.
	Answer: f and g are inverse functions.

Problem Set

Solve:

1. Find the inverse of the relation {(0, 1), (2, 3), (4,5)} and determine whether or not the inverse is a function.

2. Find the inverse of the relation {(6, 12), (4, 8), (2, 6)} and determine whether or not the inverse is a function.

3. Find the inverse of the relation {(−5, 8), (9, 12), (−5, 10)} and determine whether or not the inverse is a function.

4. Find the inverse of the relation {(−9, 4), (−6, 4), (12, 5)} and determine whether or not the inverse is a function.

5. Find the inverse of the relation {(−2,−3), (−3,−5), (−4,−7)} and determine whether or not the inverse is a function.

6. Find the inverse of the relation {(0, 2), (1, 5), (2, 8)} and determine whether or not the inverse is a function.

7. Find the inverse of the relation {(0,−8), (2,−8), (4, 0)} and determine whether or not the inverse is a function.

8. Find the inverse of the relation {(−3, 9), (0, 0), (3, 9)} and determine whether or not the inverse is a function.

9. Find the inverse of the function whose graph is shown.

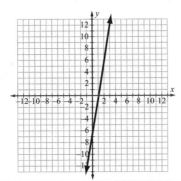

10. Find the inverse of the function whose graph is shown.

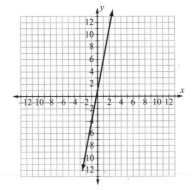

11. Find the inverse of the function whose graph is shown.

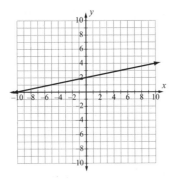

12. Find the inverse of the function whose graph is shown.

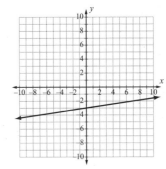

13. Find the inverse of the function whose graph is shown.

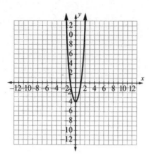

14. Find the inverse of the function whose graph is shown.

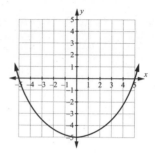

15. Find the inverse of the function whose graph is shown.

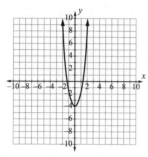

16. Find the inverse of $f(x) = 4x$.

17. Find the inverse of $f(x) = -6x$.

18. Find the inverse of $f(x) = \frac{1}{3}x$.

19. Find the inverse of $f(x) = \frac{-2}{7}x$.

20. Find the inverse of $f(x) = \frac{1}{10}x - 5$.

21. Find the inverse of $f(x) = -2x - 7$.

22. Find the inverse of $f(x) = 9x + 1$.

23. Find the inverse of $f(x) = \frac{-1}{8}x + 6$.

24. Find the inverse of $g(x) = (x + 4)^2$.

25. Find the inverse of $g(x) = (x - 9)^2$.

26. Find the inverse of $g(x) = (x + 10)^2$.

27. Find the inverse of $g(x) = (x - 12)^2$.

28. Find the inverse of $g(x) = 10x^2$.

29. Find the inverse of $g(x) = 8x^2$.

30. Find the inverse of $g(x) = 11x^2$.

31. Determine which pair of functions are not inverses of each other.

$f(x) = (x + 3)^2$ and $g(x) = \pm\sqrt{x} - 3$

$f(x) = 3x^2 + 3$ and $g(x) = (x - 3)^2$

$f(x) = x + 3$ and $g(x) = x - 3$

$f(x) = 3x + 1$ and $g(x) = \frac{1}{3}x - \frac{1}{3}$

32. Determine which pair of functions are not inverses of each other.

$f(x) = 5x + 1$ and $g(x) = \frac{1}{5}x - \frac{1}{5}$

$f(x) = x + 5$ and $g(x) = x - 5$

$f(x) = 5x^2 + 5$ and $g(x) = (x - 5)^2$

$f(x) = (x + 5)^2$ and $g(x) = \pm\sqrt{x} - 5$

33. Determine which pair of functions are not inverses of each other.

$f(x) = (x-12)^2$ and $g(x) = \pm\sqrt{x} + 12$

$f(x) = x + 15$ and $g(x) = x - 15$

$f(x) = x^2 + 18$ and $g(x) = (x-18)^2$

$f(x) = 14x - 1$ and $g(x) = \frac{1}{14}x + \frac{1}{14}$

34. Determine which pair of functions are not inverses of each other.

$f(x) = x - 10$ and $g(x) = \frac{1}{10}x + 1$

$f(x) = (x+10)^2$ and $g(x) = \pm\sqrt{x} - 10$

$f(x) = x + 10$ and $g(x) = x - 10$

$f(x) = (x-10)^2$ and $g(x) = \pm\sqrt{x} + 10$

35. Determine which pair of functions are not inverses of each other.

$f(x) = x + 4$ and $g(x) = x - 4$

$f(x) = (x+4)^2$ and $g(x) = \pm\sqrt{x} - 4$

$f(x) = (x-4)^2$ and $g(x) = \pm\sqrt{x} + 4$

$f(x) = 4x$ and $g(x) = x - 4$

36. Determine which pair of functions are inverses of each other.

$f(x) = (x+6)^2$ and $g(x) = \pm\sqrt{x} + 6$

$f(x) = \pm\sqrt{x} - 6$ and $g(x) = (x+6)^2$

$f(x) = 6x + 6$ and $g(x) = \frac{1}{6}x - \frac{1}{6}$

$f(x) = x + 6$ and $g(x) = 6 - x$

37. Determine which pair of functions are inverses of each other.

$f(x) = 9x + 9$ and $g(x) = \frac{1}{9}x - \frac{1}{9}$

$f(x) = \pm\sqrt{x} + 9$ and $g(x) = (x-9)^2$

$f(x) = x + 9$ and $g(x) = 9 - x$

$f(x) = (x+9)^2$ and $g(x) = \pm\sqrt{x} + 9$

38. Determine which pair of functions are inverses of each other.

$f(x) = (x+5)^2$ and $g(x) = \pm\sqrt{x} + 5$

$f(x) = 5x - 10$ and $g(x) = \frac{1}{5}x + 2$

$f(x) = (5x+10)^2$ and $g(x) = \pm\sqrt{5x} - 10$

$f(x) = 5x + 10$ and $g(x) = \frac{1}{5}x - \frac{1}{2}$

39. Determine which pair of functions are inverses of each other.

$f(x) = (5x+1)^2$ and $g(x) = \pm\sqrt{5x} - 1$

$f(x) = 5x + 1$ and $g(x) = \frac{1}{5}x - 5$

$f(x) = (5x+1)^2$ and $g(x) = \pm\sqrt{5x} + 1$

$f(x) = 5x + 1$ and $g(x) = \frac{1}{5}x - \frac{1}{5}$

40. Determine which pair of functions are inverses of each other.

$f(x) = -10x$ and $g(x) = -\frac{1}{10}x$

$f(x) = (x+10)^2$ and $g(x) = \pm\sqrt{x} + 10$

$f(x) = (10x)^2$ and $g(x) = \pm\sqrt{x} - 10$

$f(x) = 10x$ and $g(x) = -\frac{1}{10}x$

Recall previous definitions of relation, domain, range, and function.

Domain	The set of all x-values of a relation

Range	The set of all y-values of a relation

Algebraic operations can be used to find the sum, difference, product, or quotient of any two functions for all real numbers.

Addition of Functions	For any two functions $f(x)$ and $g(x)$, $(f+g)(x) = f(x) + g(x)$ for all real numbers x.

Subtraction of Functions	For any two functions $f(x)$ and $g(x)$, $(f-g)(x) = f(x) - g(x)$ for all real numbers x.

Multiplication of Functions	For any two functions $f(x)$ and $g(x)$, $(f \cdot g)(x) = f(x) \cdot g(x)$ for all real numbers x.

Division of Functions	For any two functions $f(x)$ and $g(x)$, $\left(\dfrac{f}{g}\right)(x) = \dfrac{f(x)}{g(x)}, g(x) \neq 0$ for all real numbers x.

Remember to evaluate a function for a specific value of x, substitute the given value of x into the function, and calculate the output. This can be done for combination functions as well.

Example 1   Given $f(x) = 11x + 4$ and $g(x) = 3x^2 - 6x$, find $(f-g)(x)$.

$(f-g)(x) = f(x) - g(x)$	**Step 1:** Determine which operation should be used to solve the problem. In this case, use Subtraction of Functions.
$= (11x + 4) - (3x^2 - 6x)$	**Step 2:** Substitute $f(x)$ and $g(x)$.

$= -3x^2 + 17x + 4$	**Step 3:** Simplify.
	Answer: $(f-g)(x) = -3x^2 + 17x + 4$

Example 2   Given $f(x) = 2x^2 + 3x$ and $g(x) = 5x - 6$, find $(f+g)(-2)$.

$(f+g)(x) = f(x) + g(x)$	**Step 1:** Determine which operation should be used to solve the problem. In this case, use Addition of Functions.
$= (2x^2 + 3x) + (5x - 6)$	**Step 2:** Substitute $f(x)$ and $g(x)$.
$= 2x^2 + 8x - 6$	**Step 3:** Combine like terms.
$(f+g)(-2) = 2(-2^2) + 8(-2) - 6$	**Step 4:** Substitute -2 for x to determine $(f+g)(-2)$.
$= -14$	**Step 5:** Simplify.
	Answer: $(f+g)(-2) = -14$

Example 3   Given $f(x) = 5x + 4$ and $g(x) = 9x - 16$, find $\left(\dfrac{f}{g}\right)(x)$.

$\left(\dfrac{f}{g}\right)(x) = \dfrac{f(x)}{g(x)}, g(x) \neq 0$	**Step 1:** Determine which operation should be used to solve the problem. In this case, use Division of Functions
$= \dfrac{5x + 4}{9x - 16}, g(x) \neq 0$	**Step 2:** Substitute $f(x)$ and $g(x)$.
$9x - 16 = 0$	**Step 3:** Set denominator equal to zero.
$x = \dfrac{16}{9}$	**Step 4:** Solve for x.
	Answer: $\left(\dfrac{f}{g}\right)(x) = \dfrac{5x + 4}{9x - 16}, x \neq \dfrac{16}{9}$

Example 4   Given $f(x) = 3x - 6$ and $g(x) = x + 5$, find $(f \cdot g)(-4)$

$(f \cdot g)(x) = f(x) \cdot g(x)$	**Step 1:** Determine which operation should be used to solve the problem. In this case, use Multiplication of Functions.
$= (3x - 6) \cdot (x + 5)$	**Step 2:** Substitute $f(x)$ and $g(x)$.
$= 3x^2 + 9x - 30$	**Step 3:** Use FOIL to multiply the binomials and combine like terms.
$(f \cdot g)(-4) = 3(-4)^2 + 9(-4) - 30$	**Step 4:** Substitute -4 for x to determine $(f \cdot g)(-4)$.
$= -18$	**Step 5:** Simplify.
	Answer: $(f \cdot g)(-4) = -18$

Example 5 Alex wants to take some of his cousins to a concert and spend the night in a nearby hotel. Tickets are $45 each with a $15 processing fee. He knows that the function for the total cost of the tickets is represented by $f(x) = 45x + 15$. Alex found a hotel room that costs $69 plus an additional charge of $12 for each additional person. He knows that the function for the total cost of the hotel room is represented by $g(x) = 69 + 12(x - 1)$. Alex wants to write a function that would give him the average cost per person for the night out. Express the average cost per person for the night out in terms of the number of people, x.

Total Cost = $f(x) + g(x)$, where x is the number of people Average Cost $= \dfrac{f(x) + g(x)}{x}$	**Step 1:** Write a function for the average cost in terms of $f(x)$ and $g(x)$.
$= \dfrac{(45x + 15) + [69 + 12(x - 1)]}{x}$	**Step 2:** Substitute $f(x)$ and $g(x)$.
$= \dfrac{57x + 72}{x}$	**Step 3:** Simplify.

Answer: Average Cost $\dfrac{57x + 72}{x}$, x = number of people

Problem Set

Solve:

1. Let $f(x) = 36x + 12$ and $g(x) = 6x - 9$.
Find $(f - g)(x)$.

2. Let $f(x) = 5x^2 - 6x + 2$ and $g(x) = 2x - 7$.
Find $(f - g)(x)$.

3. Let $f(x) = -14x - 6$ and $g(x) = -7x^2 - x$.
Find $(f - g)(x)$.

4. Let $f(x) = -31x + 13$ and $g(x) = 14x - 4$.
Find $(f + g)(x)$.

5. Let $f(x) = 14x - 13$ and $g(x) = 6x - 7$.
Find $(f + g)(x)$.

6. Let $f(x) = -x^2 + 9x - 6$ and
$g(x) = 3x^2 - 2x - 4$. Find $(f + g)(x)$.

7. Let $f(x) = -x^2 + 3x - 7$ and $g(x) = 3x - 8$.
Find $(f + g)(x)$.

8. Let $h(x) = x^2 - 4$ and $g(x) = 3x^2 + 2x + 1$.
Find $(h + g)(10)$.

9. Let $h(x) = 3x + 2$ and $g(x) = x^2 + 2x + 3$.
Find $(h + g)(-8)$.

10. Let $h(x) = 9x - 1$ and $g(x) = 2x^2 + 3x - 4$.
Find $(h + g)(-3)$.

11. Let $h(x) = 14x^2 - 3x + 2$ and
$g(x) = x^2 + 3x + 1$. Find $(h + g)(5)$.

12. Let $h(x) = x^2 - 4$ and $g(x) = 3x^2 + 2x$.
Find $(h - g)(10)$.

13. Let $h(x) = 4x^2 - 2x + 1$ and $g(x) = x - 1$.
Find $(h - g)(-1)$.

14. Let $h(x) = -5x^2 + 7$ and $g(x) = 5x^2 + 7$.
Find $(h - g)(-12)$.

15. Let $h(x) = 2x^2 - 4x + 5$ and
$g(x) = 2x^2 - 3x + 1$. Find $(h - g)(15)$.

16. Let $f(x) = 20x^2 + 2x - 6$ and $g(x) = -x^2 + 10x$.
Find $\left(\dfrac{f}{g}\right)(x)$.

17. Let $f(x) = 5x^2 + 3x - 8$ and $g(x) = 12x + 2$.
Find $\left(\dfrac{f}{g}\right)(x)$.

18. Let $f(x) = -6x^2 + 7$ and $g(x) = 3x^2 - 4x - 5$.
Find $\left(\dfrac{f}{g}\right)(x)$.

19. Let $f(x) = 7x - 5$ and $g(x) = 3x - 2$.
Find $(f \cdot g)(x)$.

20. Let $f(x) = -x + 4$ and $g(x) = -x - 6$.
Find $(f \cdot g)(x)$.

21. Let $f(x) = -3x + 1$ and $g(x) = 3x - 1$.
Find $(f \cdot g)(x)$.

22. Let $f(x) = -8x - 4$ and $g(x) = 2x + 10$.
Find $(f \cdot g)(x)$.

23. Let $f(x) = -x - 6$ and $g(x) = x + 6$.
Find $(f \cdot g)(2)$.

24. Let $f(x) = 3x + 1$ and $g(x) = -4x - 2$.
Find $(f \cdot g)(5)$.

25. Let $f(x) = -2x + 1$ and $g(x) = 4x + 8$.
Find $(f \cdot g)(-4)$.

26. Let $f(x) = x + 1$ and $g(x) = 6x + 9$.
Find $(f \cdot g)(-3)$.

27. Let $f(x) = -x^2 - 3$ and $g(x) = 3x^2 + 4x$.
Find $\left(\dfrac{f}{g}\right)(-2)$.

28. Let $f(x) = 2x - 5$ and $g(x) = x^2 - 6$.
Find $\left(\dfrac{f}{g}\right)(-3)$.

29. Let $f(x) = -3x^2 + 7x + 1$ and $g(x) = 5x - 5$.
Find $\left(\dfrac{f}{g}\right)(10)$.

30. Let $f(x) = 6x^2 - 2x - 1$ and
$g(x) = 3x^2 + 8x + 1$. Find $\left(\dfrac{f}{g}\right)(9)$.

31. Hot Rods builds and sells motorcycles. The cost of building x motorcycles is given by the function
$C(x) = 2,500 + 1,500x - 0.002x^2$. The price for a single motorcycle is $15,000. The revenue, R, is defined as the product of the number of motorcycles sold and the price of a single motorcycle. The profit, P, is the difference between the revenue and the cost. Express the profit in terms of the number of motorcycles.

32. The physics class is going on a field trip to an amusement park. The tickets cost $5 each and there is a $100 fee for exclusive use of the park. The function for the total cost of the tickets is $T(x) = 5x + 100$. The bus ride costs $100 plus an additional charge of $2 for each person. The function for the total cost of the bus is represented by $B(x) = 100 + 2x$. The class wants to write a function that would give them the average cost per person for the field trip. Express the average cost per person for the field trip in terms of the number of people, x.

33. John and Tom took a taxi to a Christmas party in the city. On the way to the party, Taxi A cost them $3 for the first mile and $1.50 for each additional mile. John knows that the function for the total cost of Taxi A is $A(x) = 3 + 1.5(x - 1)$. On the way home from the party, Taxi B cost them $4.50 for the first mile and $1.25 for each additional mile. Tom knows that the function for the total cost of Taxi B is $B(x) = 4.5 + 1.25(x - 1)$. Express the average cost per mile for the rides in terms of the number of miles, x.

34. Joy and Jerry are building a garden with a walkway around it as shown. The garden is going to measure 15 feet long by 7 feet wide. The walkway will have the same width, x, all the way around it. The length of the entire space is defined by the function $L(x) = 15 + 2x$. The width of the entire space is defined by the function $W(x) = 7 + 2x$. Express the area of the entire space including the garden and the walkway in terms of x.

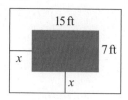

35. House's Incorporated is building a house with a wrap-around porch as shown. The house is going to measure 60 feet long by 55 feet wide. The wrap-around porch will have the same width, x, around the entire porch. The length of the entire space is defined by the function $L(x) = 60 + 2x$. The width of the entire space is defined by the function $W(x) = 55 + 2x$. Express the perimeter of the entire space including the house and porch in terms of x.

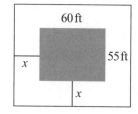

36. Bonnie is trying to decide whether or not to join a movie club. The discount movie store charges $11 per movie. She knows that the function for the total cost of movies she buys at the store is $C(x) = 11x$. The movie club will give her eight free movies to join and charges $14 per movie after that. She knows that the function for the total cost of movies she buys from the movie club is $D(x) = 14(x - 8)$. Find the difference in price between the club and the store in terms of the number of movies purchased, x.

37. Shaw analyzed his last twelve paychecks and discovered that taxes were deducted at a rate of 9.15% of his earnings. The function for the total tax deductions is $T(x) = 0.0915x$. He also discovered that his medical insurance premiums were deducted at a rate of 2% of his earnings. The function for the total medical insurance deductions is $M(x) = 0.02x$. Find a function for the total deductions in terms of Shaw's earnings, x.

38. A radio station has a daytime charge of $5,000 for the first five seconds of a commercial and $500 for each additional second. The function for the daytime charge is $D(x) = 5,000 + 500(x - 5)$. The nighttime charge for commercials is $10,000 for the first five seconds and $750 for each additional second. The function for the nighttime charge is $N(x) = 10,000 + 750(x - 5)$. Find a function for the difference between the nighttime charge and daytime charge of airing a commercial in terms of the number of seconds, x.

39. Bonnie and George each opened a savings account with money from their own paychecks. Bonnie opened her account with $1,000 the first month and she plans to add $400 each additional month. The function for Bonnie's savings is $B(x) = 1,000 + 400(x - 1)$. George opened his account with $800 and he plans to add $350 each additional month. The function for George's savings is $G(x) = 800 + 350(x - 1)$. Find a function for their total savings after x months.

40. Mark is getting cable television and he has two cable companies to choose from. Company A charges $185 for the hookup and equipment and $65 per month for service. The function for the cost of Company A is $A(x) = 185 + 65x$. Company B charges $250 for hookup and equipment and $55 per month for service. The function for the cost of Company B is $B(x) = 250 + 55x$. Find a function for the average cost of cable service between the two companies in terms of the number of months, x.

HA1-200: Combined Inequalities

1. ![number line from -5 to 5, shaded left with open circles at 3 and 4]

3. ![number line with open circles]

5. ![number line with open circle at 0, shaded left]

7. ![number line with closed dots at -4 and 1]

9. ![number line fully shaded]

11. $-1 \leq x \leq 4$

13. $-2 < x < 1$

15. $-3 \leq x \leq 2$

17. $x < -4$ or $x > -2$

19. ![number line with open circles at -4 and -1]

HA1-205: Solving Combined Inequalities

1. $x > 4$ or $x < 1$ **3.** $x < 2$ or $x > 3$ **5.** $-9 < x < 2$ **7.** $x > 4$ or $x < 10$ **9.** $-3 \leq x \leq 1$

11. $x < 10$ or $x > 5$

13. $x > -6$ or $x < -1$

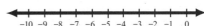

15. $x > -2$

17. $x < -7$

19. $-1 < x < 6$![number line with open circles at -1 and 6]

HA1-210: Solving Equations Involving Absolute Value

1. $\{-2,2\}$ **3.** $\varnothing$ **5.** $\{12, -20\}$ **7.** $\{24, -8\}$ **9.** $\{15, -15\}$

11. $\{17, -20\}$ **13.** $\left\{11, -\dfrac{55}{3}\right\}$ **15.** $\{-1\}$ **17.** $\{3, -7\}$ **19.** $\left\{3, -\dfrac{25}{3}\right\}$

HA1-215: Solving Absolute Value Inequalities

1. ![number line with closed dots at -5 and 5, shaded between]

3. $x > 8$ or $x < -4$

5. $x < 3$ and $x > -23$

7. ![number line from -10 to 10 fully shaded]

9. ![number line from -10 to 10 fully shaded]

11. $\{n : -4 \leq n \leq 11\}$

13. $x < 6$ and $x > -7$

15.

$$\begin{array}{ccccccc} -3 & -2 & -1 & 0 & 1 & 2 & 3 \end{array}$$

17. All real numbers

19. $\{x : -8 \le x \le 3\}$

HA1-276: Factoring Sums and Differences of Cubes

1. $(y - z)(y^2 + yz + z^2)$

3. $(m + p)(m^2 - mp + p^2)$

5. $(k - m)(k^2 + km + m^2)$

7. $(s + v)(s^2 - sv + v^2)$

9. $(c + 11)(c^2 - 11c + 121)$

11. $(5 + n)(25 - 5n + n^2)$

13. $(w - 1)(w^2 + w + 1)$

15. $(r - 13)(r^2 + 13r + 169)$

17. $(e + 7)(e^2 - 7e + 49)$

19. $(h + 8)(h^2 - 8h + 64)$

21. $(n - 10)(n^2 + 10n + 100)$

23. $(s - 12)(s^2 + 12s + 144)$

25. $(9 - 2x)(81 + 18x + 4x^2)$

27. $(11x + 8)(121x^2 - 88x + 64)$

29. $(3f - 10)(9f^2 + 30f + 100)$

31. $(d + 2e)(d - 2e)(d^2 - 2de + 4e^2)(d^2 + 2de + 4e^2)$

33. $(b + 4m)(b - 4m)(b^2 - 4bm + 16m^2)(b^2 + 4bm + 16m^2)$

35. $(d + 7h)(d - 7h)(d^2 - 7dh + 49h^2)(d^2 + 7dh + 49h^2)$

37. $(4y + 9x)(4y - 9x)(16y^2 - 36xy + 81x^2)(16y^2 + 36xy + 81x^2)$

39. $(10s + 8r)(10s - 8r)(100s^2 - 80rs + 64r^2)(100s^2 + 80rs + 64r^2)$

HA1-290: Factoring $ax^2 + bx + c$

1. $3x + 1$

3. $2x - 3$

5. $3x - 2$

7. $4y + 1$

9. $(2x + 5)(x + 1)$

11. $(3x - 1)(3x + 2)$

13. $(2x - 1)(x - 4)$

15. $(3x + 4)(2x - 1)$

17. $(4x + y)(2x - y)$

19. $(3x + 5y)(5x + 3y)$

HA1-295: Factoring by Removing a Common Factor and Grouping

1. $(2x + 4)(y + 2)$

3. $(4y - 3)(x + 2)$

5. $(5a - 1)(b + 5)$

7. $(3x + 2)(y - 4)$

9. $(y + 3)(4x - 1)$

11. $(5y + 7)(x - 2)$

13. $3x + 2y$

15. $x - 5$

17. $a - 3b$

19. $(x - 3 - 2y)(x - 3 + 2y)$

HA1-300: Factoring a Polynomial Completely

1. $5(x - 1)(x - 1)$

3. $a(1 + 6ab - b)$

5. $5(x + 6)(x - 2)$

7. $9x(x + 5)$

9. $8a(b - 8)$

11. $b^2(b + 3)(b - 3)$

13. $-4x(x + 4)^2$

15. $8a(x + 2)(x - 2)$

17. $(x^2 - 5)(x - 1)$

19. $9x(3x - 5)(x + 1)$

HA1-305: Solving Polynomial Equations by Factoring

1. $\{3, -3\}$ **3.** $\{13, -13\}$ **5.** $\{-3, -9\}$ **7.** $\{6, -9\}$ **9.** $\{0, -2\}$

11. $\{-8\}$ **13.** $\{2, -12\}$ **15.** $\{6, -6\}$ **17.** $\{5, -2\}$ **19.** $\{-1\}$

HA1-310: The Practical Use of Polynomial Equations

1. 2 and 3 **3.** 11 and 12 **5.** 16 and 18 **7.** 12 and 14 **9.** 4 sides

11. 7 feet **13.** 4 feet **15.** 6 feet **17.** 4 feet **19.** 5 and 6

HA1-315: Defining Rational Expressions and Determining the Restricted Values

1. 2 **3.** -7 **5.** -21 **7.** 0

9. -4 **11.** -2 **13.** $-\dfrac{1}{2}$ **15.** $x = -5$ or $x = 3$

17. $m = -8$ or $m = 8$ **19.** $x = -\dfrac{4}{9}$ or $x = 4$

HA1-320: Simplifying Rational Expressions

1. $2m^4$ **3.** $\dfrac{11x^4}{12y^3}$ **5.** $\dfrac{16y}{9x}$ **7.** $\dfrac{2x-3}{3}$ **9.** $\dfrac{1}{x-5}$

11. $\dfrac{5}{6}$ **13.** $\dfrac{a}{8}$ **15.** $-\dfrac{1}{2}$ **17.** $12ab$ **19.** $\dfrac{b+5}{b-2}$

HA1-325: Multiplying Rational Expressions

1. $\dfrac{4}{15}$ **3.** $\dfrac{1}{x^4 y^4}$ **5.** $\dfrac{2z^2}{y^2}$ **7.** $\dfrac{(a-8)}{3(a-4)}$ **9.** $\dfrac{6b}{5}$

11. $2(x-10)$ **13.** $2(y-5)$ **15.** $\dfrac{2}{5}$ **17.** $\dfrac{x+4}{4}$ **19.** $\dfrac{b-5}{b-7}$

HA1-330: Dividing Rational Expressions

1. $\dfrac{6}{7}$ **3.** $\dfrac{20}{x}$ **5.** 1 **7.** $\dfrac{18x^2}{125}$ **9.** 14

11. $\dfrac{3}{20(x-4)}$ **13.** $\dfrac{3}{2}$ **15.** 6 **17.** $\dfrac{x-4}{2}$ **19.** $\dfrac{(x+2)(x-3)}{x-2}$

HA1-335: Finding the LCD of Rational Expressions and Changing Fractions to Equivalent Fractions

1. $30ac$ **3.** $80bc$ **5.** $10abc$ **7.** $4b$ **9.** $4c$

11. $30b^2c^2$ **13.** $63b^3c^3$ **15.** $\dfrac{6a^2b}{16abc^2}$ **17.** $\dfrac{21b^2}{27a^3b}$ **19.** $(b+8)^2(b+1)$

HA1-340: Adding and Subtracting Rational Expressions

1. $\dfrac{4d-5}{8}$ **3.** $\dfrac{10}{y-1}$ **5.** $\dfrac{(x+3)}{x}$ **7.** 2

9. $\dfrac{8x^2}{x+4}$ **11.** $\dfrac{5n+8}{4n^2}$ **13.** $\dfrac{2n+28}{3(n-6)(n+4)}$ **15.** $\dfrac{x^2-2x+14}{3(x-2)(x+5)}$

17. $\dfrac{3c+48}{5(c-2)(c+4)}$ **19.** $\dfrac{-18x-21}{x(x-3)(x+3)}$

HA1-345: Adding and Subtracting Polynomials and Rational Expressions

1. $\dfrac{y+59}{8}$ **3.** $\dfrac{5+4x}{x}$ **5.** $\dfrac{10m-4}{m}$ **7.** $\dfrac{3+25y}{5y}$ **9.** $\dfrac{3-28y}{7y}$

11. $\dfrac{n^2-4n+14}{n-2}$ **13.** $\dfrac{39a-4}{5}$ **15.** $\dfrac{-3d+10}{5}$ **17.** $\dfrac{-10b+2}{3}$ **19.** $\dfrac{-8c^2+29c+32}{2c-8}$

HA1-350: Simplifying Complex Fractions

1. $\dfrac{7}{4}$ **3.** $\dfrac{3r^2}{4}$ **5.** $\dfrac{7}{4}$ **7.** $\dfrac{n^2}{3}$ **9.** $\dfrac{2}{3b}$

11. $\dfrac{4m+3}{m^3}$ **13.** $\dfrac{4a}{3b^2}$ **15.** $\dfrac{3x}{(x+3)(x-1)}$ **17.** $\dfrac{2-st^2}{2t^2}$ **19.** $\dfrac{7}{3y^2}$

HA1-360: Expressing Ratios in Simplest Form and Solving Equations Involving Proportions

1. $\dfrac{1}{3}$ **3.** $\dfrac{1}{5}$ **5.** $\dfrac{5}{4}$ **7.** 9 to 10 **9.** $33:20$

11. $\dfrac{49}{3}$ **13.** $-\dfrac{7}{6}$ **15.** $\dfrac{15}{4}$ **17.** $\dfrac{26}{3}$ **19.** -2

HA1-365: Solving Rational Equations

1. $\{20\}$ **3.** $\{10\}$ **5.** $\{3\}$ **7.** $\left\{-\dfrac{2}{3}\right\}$ **9.** $\{20\}$

11. $\left\{\dfrac{32}{9}\right\}$ **13.** $\{-7\}$ **15.** $\{-3\}$ **17.** $\varnothing$ **19.** $\{-3\}$

HA1- 370: Graphing Ordered Pairs on a Coordinate Plane

1. On the x-axis   **3.** Quadrant IV   **5.** Quadrant III   **7.** Quadrant IV

9. 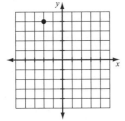   **11.**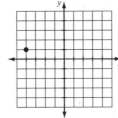

13. Point B

15. Point C

17. $(-3, -2)$

19. $(3, -3)$

HA1-375: Identifying Solutions of Equations in Two Variables

1. Not a solution   **3.** Solution   **5.** Not a solution   **7.** Solution   **9.** Not a solution

11. $(-4, 7)$ **13.** $(3, -2)$ **15.** $(1, 0)$ **17.** $(-1, 2)$ **19.** No

HA1-380: Graphing Linear Equations

1. 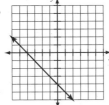   **3.**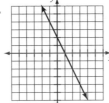

5. x-intercept is -3
     y-intercept is -6

7. x-intercept is -4
     y-intercept is -8

9. 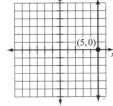   **11.** 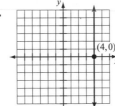   **13.**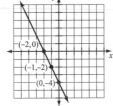

15. 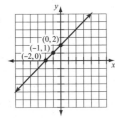   **17.** 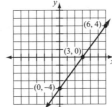   **19.**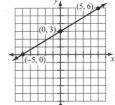

HA1-382: Solving Linear Equations Using the Graphing Calculator

1. 2   **3.** 11   **5.** 114   **7.** $-\dfrac{2}{9}$ **9.** $\dfrac{1}{2}$

HA1-385: Finding the Slope of a Line from its Graph or from the Coordinates of Two Points

1. 1   **3.** 2   **5.** 5   **7.** 0   **9.** 6

11. $-\dfrac{1}{3}$ **13.** $-\dfrac{1}{5}$ **15.** -1 **17.** $\dfrac{2}{3}$ **19.** No slope

HA1-394: Interchanging Linear Equations between Standard Form and Slope-Intercept Form

1. $y = -2x + \dfrac{7}{3}$ **3.** $y = -4x + 8$ **5.** $y = -5x + 7$ **7.** $y = 3x - 8$ **9.** $12x + y = 7$

11. $7x + y = -8$ **13.** $10x - y = 8$ **15.** $9x - y = 1$ **17.** $y = \dfrac{7}{3}x - 4$ **19.** $y = -\dfrac{5}{4}x + 4$

21. $y = -\dfrac{3}{4}x + 4$ **23.** $3x + 5y = -40$ **25.** $5x + 6y = -24$ **27.** $8x + 3y = 48$ **29.** $4x + 7y = 63$

31. $5x - 15y = -3$ **33.** $2x - 9y = -3$ **35.** $9x - 24y = -4$ **37.** $72x - 45y = -20$ **39.** $4x - 6y = -1$

HA1-395: Finding the Equation of a Line Parallel or Perpendicular to a Given Line

1. $y = 8x + 5$ **3.** $y = \dfrac{1}{2}x - 10$ **5.** $y = -\dfrac{3}{7}x - 9$ **7.** $y = -\dfrac{9}{2}x + 2$

9. 4   **11.** $\dfrac{1}{2}$ **13.** $\dfrac{5}{4}$ **15.** 1

17. Neither   **19.** Parallel   **21.** Perpendicular   **23.** Parallel

25. $y = \dfrac{3}{4}x + 7$ **27.** $y = -\dfrac{1}{4}x - 3$ **29.** $y = 2x + 20$ **31.** $y = -\dfrac{1}{3}x + 7$

33. $y = -x + 3$ **35.** $y = 5x + 40$ **37.** $y = -\dfrac{3}{2}x + 14$ **39.** $y = \dfrac{1}{2}x - 7$

HA1-398: Graphing Linear Equations Using Slope and y-intercept or Slope and a Point

1. 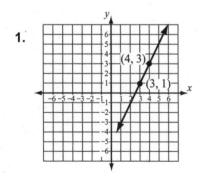   **3.** 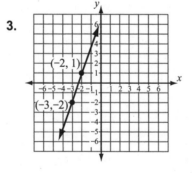   **5.**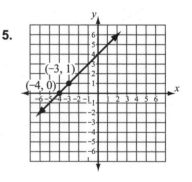

7.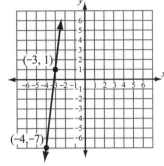

9.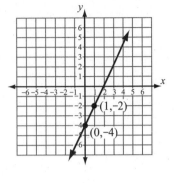

11.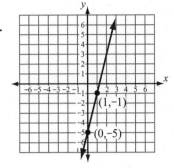

13.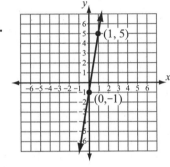

15.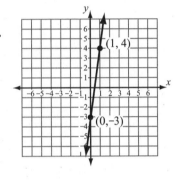

17.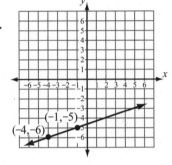

19.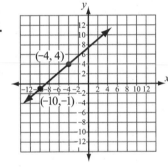

21.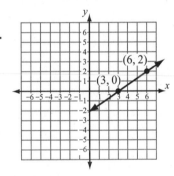

23.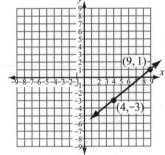

25.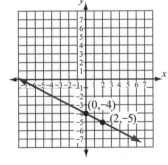

27.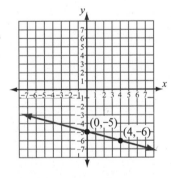

29.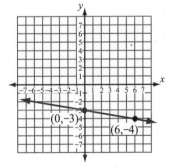

31.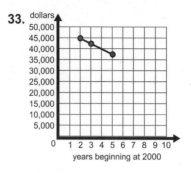
dollars
20,000
18,000
16,000
14,000
12,000
10,000
8,000
6,000
4,000
2,000
0 1 2 3 4 5 6 7 8 9 10
years beginning at 2000

33.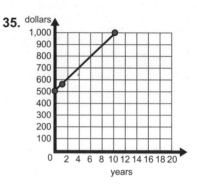
dollars
50,000
45,000
40,000
35,000
30,000
25,000
20,000
15,000
10,000
5,000
0 1 2 3 4 5 6 7 8 9 10
years beginning at 2000

35.
dollars
1,000
900
800
700
600
500
400
300
200
100
0 2 4 6 8 10 12 14 16 18 20
years

37.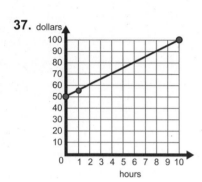
dollars
100
90
80
70
60
50
40
30
20
10
0 1 2 3 4 5 6 7 8 9 10
hours

39.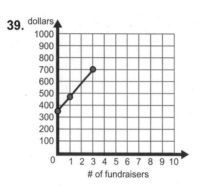
dollars
1000
900
800
700
600
500
400
300
200
100
0 1 2 3 4 5 6 7 8 9 10
# of fundraisers

HA1-401: How Variations of "m" and "b" Affect the Graph of $y = mx + b$

1. $y = 10x$

3. $y = -8x$

5. $y = \frac{3}{7}x$

7. $y = -7x$

9. $y = x$

11. $y = -\frac{2}{7}x$

13. $y = 9x$

15. $y = 0$

17. The angle is less than $45°$.

19. The angle is equal to $45°$.

21. The angle is greater than $45°$.

23. The angle is greater than $45°$.

25. The angle is equal to $45°$.

27. The angle is less than $45°$.

29. The angle is greater than $45°$.

31. $m_A > m_B > 0$
$b_A > b_B$

33. $|m_A| > |m_B|$ $m_B < 0$
$m_A < 0$ $b_A = b_B = 3$

35. $m_A > 0 > m_B$ $b_A = b_B = 2$
$|m_A| > |m_B|$

37. $|m_B| > |m_A|$ $m_B < 0$
$m_A < 0$ $b_B > b_A$

39. $m_A < 0$ $|m_A| > |m_B|$
$m_B < 0$ $b_A > b_B$

HA1-402: Translating Among Multiple Representations of Functions

1.

x	y
0	0
1	5
2	10
3	15
4	20
5	25

3.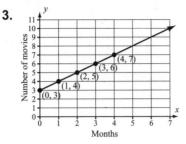

5.

Blackberries (cups)	Sugar (cups)
5	2
10	4
15	6

7.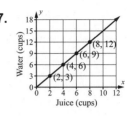

9. $y = 5.5x$

11. $y = x + 6$

13. $y = \frac{4}{5}x$

15. $y = \frac{1}{4}x$

17. $y = \frac{4}{5}x + 5$

19. Angie saves $2 out of every $3 she is given for doing extra housework. She had $11 from her birthday money.

21. $2x + 4$

23. $y = 3x + 10$

25.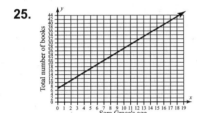

27.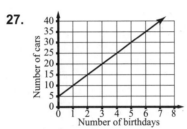

29.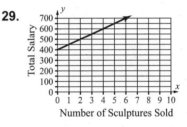

31. J.J. started with 9 CDs and buys 3 every two weeks.

33. The operation costs $1,275 and the semi-private room costs $350 per day.

35. Keri paid $6 to park in the lot and $1.50 for each hour.

37. Darwin will have the $220 in 8 months if he saves $20 each month.

39. Bob gets $100 a day for meals and lodging, and $0.50 per mile traveled.

HA1-405: Determining an Equation of a Line Given the Slope and Coordinates of One Point

1. $y = -2x - 6$

3. $y = 6x - 26$

5. $y = 2x + 2$

7. $y = -3x + 13$

9. $y = -\frac{1}{4}x + \frac{7}{4}$

11. $2x - y = 9$

13. $3x - y = 1$

15. $4x + y = 0$

17. $x + 2y = 8$

19. $y = 5x + 10$

HA1-410: Determining the Equation of a Line Given the Coordinates of Two Points

1. $y = 2x + 3$

3. $y = -x + 1$

5. $y = 2x - 2$

7. $y = \frac{1}{2}x$

9. $y = \frac{1}{6}x + \frac{8}{3}$

11. $2x - 3y = -17$

13. $5x - 2y = 11$

15. $3x + y = 16$

17. $3x - y = 12$

19. $y = 0.1x$

HA1-415: Graphing Linear Inequalities with Two Variables

1. 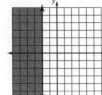 **3.** 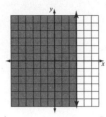 **5.** 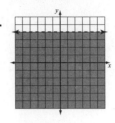 **7.**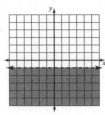

9. 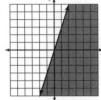 **11.** 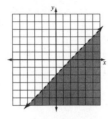 **13.** 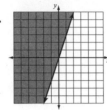 **15.**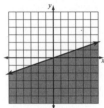

17. 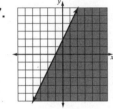 **19.**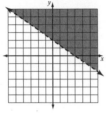

HA1-416: Graphing Linear Inequalities with Two Variables Using the Graphing Calculator

1. (6, 3) **3.** (2, 5) **5.** (3, 7) **7.** (3, 2) **9.**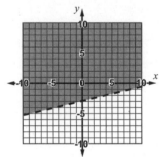

HA1-436: Identifying Relations

1. D = {10, −1, −2, −10}
R = {6, −2, 3}

3. D = {14, 11, −2, 1}
R = {−4, 1, −3}

5. D = {0, −2, −4}
R = {2, 0, −2}

7. D = {−3, −4, 0, 3}
R = {2, 1, −2}

9. D = {−2, 0, 2}
R = {4, −1, −2}

11. D = {−1, 3, 4, 7}
R = {0}

13. D = {−3, 1, −4}
R = {−9, 0, −1, 3}

15. D = {−5, −4, 0, 5}
R = {4, 0, 6}

17. Both points satisfy the relation.

19. Neither point satisfies the relation.

21. (3, −2) satisfies the relation, but (−2, 1) does not.

23. (1, 9) satisfies the relation, but (−2, 6) does not.

25. Neither point satisfies the relation.

27. Both points satisfy the relation.

29. $(-2, -9)$ satisfies the relation, but $(2, 5)$ does not.

31.

x	2	3	6
y	0	3	12

33.

x	0	-2	20
y	5	6	-5

35.

x	0	1	2
y	14	7	0

37.

x	0	8	4
y	3	-1	1

39.

x	-12	-8	-4
y	-3	0	3

HA1-437: Identifying Relations as Functions

1. $\{(-2, 6), (0, -2), (-1, 3), (7, 3)\}$

3. $\{(4, -4), (10, 1), (-2, -4), (1, -3)\}$

5. $\{(-3, -4), (0, -3), (4, -2)\}$

7. $\{(-3, 2), (-2, -1), (0, -2), (4, -3)\}$

9. $\{(-4, 3), (-2, 2), (0, 1), (2, 0)\}$

11. $\{(-1, 0), (1, 0), (3, 0), (5, 0)\}$

13. $\{(3, -9), (1, 0), (-4, -1)\}$

15. $\{(-5, 4), (-4, 0), (0, 6), (5, 4)\}$

17. $\{-2, 1, -1, 8\}$ **19.** $\{2, -2, 0, 1\}$ **21.** $\{2, -5, 6, -8\}$ **23.** $\{-4, -3, -2, 1\}$

25. $\{-1, 5, -2, 6\}$ **27.** $\{-6, 0, 5\}$ **29.** $\{-5, 2, 0.5\}$ **31.** No

33. No   **35.** Yes   **37.** Yes   **39.** $\{(-1, 4), (2, 0), (-3, 4)\}$

HA1-438: Finding the Domain and Range of Functions

1. $\{29, 2, 14\}$ **3.** $\{2, -10\}$ **5.** $\{6, 7, 3\}$ **7.** $\{-2, 0, -8\}$ **9.** $\{1, 2, 3\}$

11. $\{-2, -4, -5\}$ **13.** $\{17, 8, 3\}$ **15.** $\{7, 5, 1\}$ **17.** $3x - 2y = 6$ **19.** $u + 2v = 6$

21. $y = 9 - 2x^2$ **23.** $v = 4 + 3(u^2 - 1)$ **25.** $4u - v = 7$ **27.** $3x - 2y = 10$

29. $v = -4u + 3$ **31.** $-5 < x < 4$ **33.** $-4 \leq x < -1.$ **35.** $x \geq -4.$

37. $x \geq 0.$ **39.** $0 \leq y \leq 3.$

HA1-439: Using Function Notation

1. 8   **3.** 3   **5.** 5   **7.** -6   **9.** 0

11. 2   **13.** 5   **15.** 1   **17.** 3, 6, 9, or 12   **19.** 2 or 5

21. 3, 6, or 12   **23.** 3 or -3   **25.** -4   **27.** 3   **29.** 0

31. x does not exist   **33.** 1   **35.** -2   **37.** 6   **39.** 3

HA1-441: Applications of Functions and Relations Involving Distance, Rate, and Time

1. 18 mph   **3.** 360 mph   **5.** 5 mph   **7.** 54 mph   **9.** 4 mph

11. 40 mph   **13.** 200 mph   **15.** 45 mph

17. Jonathan arrived at his friend's house at 11:00 a.m. and left at 3:00 p.m.

19. From 9:30 a.m. to 10:15 a.m.

21. From 10:00 a.m. to 10:30 a.m.

23. Jacques' second stop began at 10:00 a.m. and ended at 10:30 a.m.

25. 270 miles   **27.** 0 miles   **29.** 16 miles   **31.** $2.5 \leq t \leq 3$

33. $4.5 \le t \le 5$ **35.** 55 mph   **37.** 1.5 hours   **39.** 1.5 hours

HA1-445: Evaluating Composite Functions

1. 1   **3.** 32   **5.** 9   **7.** 0   **9.** 0

HA1-447: Identifying Number Patterns

1. Arithmetic   **3.** Arithmetic   **5.** Geometric   **7.** Quadratic

9. 31   **11.** 9   **13.** –10   **15.** –33

17. The number of triangles is two times the stage number.

19. The pattern of the number of dots is quadratic.

21. The same number of dots is added to each step.

23. The same number of squares is added to each step.

25. 64   **27.** 37   **29.** 1,536   **31.** 16 and 24

33. 160 and 65   **35.** 38 and 48   **37.** 95 and 60   **39.** 54 and 35

HA1-448: Finding the nth Term of a Pattern

1. $4n + 2$ **3.** $8n - 20$ **5.** $9 \cdot \left(\frac{1}{3}\right)^{n-1}$ **7.** $3 \cdot (5)^{n-1}$ **9.** $3n + 9$

11. $-3n + 24$ **13.** $4 \cdot 3^{n-1}$ **15.** $-6 \cdot \left(\frac{1}{2}\right)^{n-1}$ **17.** $n^2 - 2n + 1$ **19.** $\frac{5n^2 - 5n + 2}{2}$

21. $n(n + 1)$ **23.** $\frac{n^2 - n}{2}$ **25.** $2n - 1$ **27.** $n + 1$ **29.** $3n - 1$

31. 157   **33.** 8,192   **35.** 102   **37.** 222   **39.** 885,735

HA1-450: Solving Problems Involving Direct Variation

1. Yes   **3.** Yes   **5.** No   **7.** 1   **9.** 4

11. 3.6   **13.** 6   **15.** 2   **17.** –25.2   **19.** 70 m

HA1-453: Solving Problems Involving Inverse Variation

1. Yes   **3.** Yes   **5.** Yes   **7.** $y = 4$ **9.** $y = 9$

11. No   **13.** Yes   **15.** No   **17.** $y = -1$ **19.** 360 cm

HA1-455: Solving Systems of Linear Equations by Graphing

1. The ordered pair (1, 3) is not a solution because it does not satisfy the second equation.

3. The ordered pair (4, –1) is not a solution because it does not satisfy either equation.

5. The ordered pair (0, –2) is not a solution because it does not satisfy the second equation.

7. The ordered pair (–3, 3) is not a solution because it does not satisfy either equation.

9.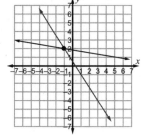

11.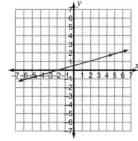

13.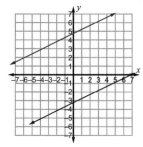

15.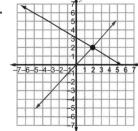

17. Inconsistent

19. Consistent and independent

21. Consistent and dependent

23. Inconsistent

25. $(-1, 1)$

27. No solution

29. No solution

31. $(-4, 2)$

33. $(1, 2)$

35. No solution

37. No solution

39. Infinite number of solutions

HA1-460: Solving Systems of Linear Equations by the Substitution Method

1. $x = 2y + 20$

3. $x = 2y - 9$

5. $x = -y + 3$

7. No

9. No

11. $(2, -1)$

13. $(5, 2)$

15. $(3, 2)$

17. $(8, 5)$

19. $(-2, 3)$

HA1-465: Solving Systems of Linear Equations by the Addition/Subtraction Method

1. Add or subtract the given equations to eliminate one of the variables.

3. $(0, -3)$

5. $\left(-5, -\frac{1}{3}\right)$

7. $(8, -4)$

9. $(2, 1)$

HA1-470: Solving Systems of Linear Equations by the Multiply/Add/Subtract Method

1. Rewrite the equation $m = 2n - 4$ in standard form.

3. Rewrite each equation in standard form.

5. Multiply the second equation by –5.

7. 8

9. –4

11. $\left(\frac{1}{2}, -7\right)$

13. No solution

15. Infinitely many solutions

17. $(1, -1)$

19. $(9, 16)$

HA1-475: Graphing the Solution Set of a System of Linear Inequalities

1.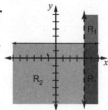

The ordered pairs in the R_3 region.

3.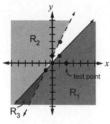

The ordered pairs in the R_3 region.

5. Solution

7. $(-4, -5)$

9.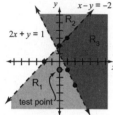

The ordered pairs in the R_3 region.

11.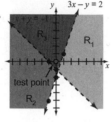

The ordered pairs in the R_3 region.

13.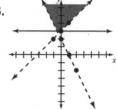

15.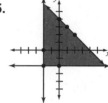

17.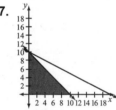

19.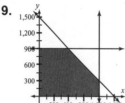

HA1-480: Finding the Square Roots of Rational Numbers

1. -1

3. 22

5. -10

7. not a real number

9. ± 11

11. $\dfrac{1}{3}$

13. $\dfrac{3}{4}$

15. $\pm \dfrac{5}{7}$

17. $\dfrac{5}{12}$

19. 0.7

HA1-485: Writing Rational Numbers as Decimals or Fractions

1. $0.\overline{27}$

3. $0.\overline{18}$

5. 2.4

7. 0.3125

9. $1.1\overline{6}$

11. $\dfrac{29}{9}$

13. $\dfrac{49}{9}$

15. $\dfrac{2}{9}$

17. $\dfrac{68}{9}$

19. $\dfrac{23}{33}$

HA1-490: Simplifying Square Roots

1. $2\sqrt{15}$

3. $3\sqrt{14}$

5. n^9

7. $4\sqrt{6}$

9. c^8

11. $6n^4\sqrt{2n}$

13. $3a^8\sqrt{11a}$

15. $9k^2\sqrt{2k}$

17. $10\sqrt{34}$

19. $7xy^2\sqrt{7xy}$

HA1-492: Simplifying Square and Cube Roots

1. -8 **3.** -10 **5.** 14 **7.** 8 **9.** a^{12}

11. z^{10} **13.** y^8 **15.** c^9 **17.** $9x^4y^7$ **19.** $5p^8q^7r^4$

21. $3a^6b^2$ **23.** $6x^7y^8z^6$ **25.** $\dfrac{6a^8}{11b^6}$ **27.** $\dfrac{12x^3y^2}{13z^8}$ **29.** $\dfrac{2a^7b^5}{5c^9}$

31. $4x^5$ **33.** $3p^{10}q^6$ **35.** $9x^{15}$ **37.** $11c^9$ **39.** $6x^4y^5z^6$

HA1-495: Simplifying Sums and Differences of Radicals

1. $12\sqrt{6}$ **3.** $4\sqrt{10}$ **5.** $13\sqrt{3}$ **7.** $19\sqrt{5}$ **9.** $7\sqrt{5}$

11. $12\sqrt{2}$ **13.** $20\sqrt{5}$ **15.** $9\sqrt{5}$ **17.** $12\sqrt{3}$ **19.** $11\sqrt{2}+6\sqrt{3}$

HA1-500: Simplifying Products of Radicals

1. $\sqrt{35}$ **3.** 9 **5.** 4 **7.** 2 **9.** 8

11. $2\sqrt{6}$ **13.** $192\sqrt{3}$ **15.** $48\sqrt{3}$ **17.** $4\sqrt{3}+10$ **19.** $60x$

HA1-505: Simplifying Quotients of Radicals

1. $\dfrac{2\sqrt{6x}}{x}$ **3.** $\dfrac{\sqrt{10}}{5}$ **5.** $\dfrac{\sqrt{2}}{2}$ **7.** $\dfrac{\sqrt{3}}{2}$ **9.** $6\sqrt{3}$

11. $\dfrac{6\sqrt{5}}{5}$ **13.** $\dfrac{4\sqrt{6}}{3}$ **15.** $\dfrac{7\sqrt{10}}{15}$ **17.** $\dfrac{3\sqrt{2}}{2}$ **19.** $\dfrac{21+8\sqrt{5}}{-11}$

HA1-510: Solving Radical Equations

1. 36 **3.** 324 **5.** 1 **7.** 0 **9.** $2,500$

11. 86 **13.** 4 **15.** 12 **17.** 14 **19.** $3n=4$

HA1-515: Using the Pythagorean Theorem

1. Right triangle **3.** Not a right triangle **5.** 12 **7.** 7 **9.** 15

11. $\sqrt{19}$ **13.** $\sqrt{3}$ **15.** $\sqrt{5}$ **17.** 20 **19.** $3\sqrt{2}$

HA1-516: Applications of the Pythagorean Theorem

1. 13 miles **3.** 5 feet **5.** 127.28 feet **7.** 10.95 inches **9.** 20 feet

11. 24 feet **13.** 69 feet **15.** 21 feet **17.** 43.03 inches **19.** 90 inches

21. 84 meters **23.** 6 decimeters **25.** No **27.** 1.76 feet **29.** No

31. 3 miles **33.** 14 miles **35.** 10 feet **37.** 14.64 meters **39.** 3.4 miles

HA1-520: Finding the Distance Between Two Points on a Coordinate Plane

1. $2\sqrt{2}$ **3.** $2\sqrt{10}$ **5.** $\sqrt{13}$ **7.** $\sqrt{74}$ **9.** $2\sqrt{13}$

11. $3\sqrt{5}$ **13.** $\sqrt{65}$ **15.** $3\sqrt{5}$ **17.** $6\sqrt{2}$ **19.** 56.64 miles

HA1-525: Solving Quadratic Equations Involving Perfect Square Expressions

1. ± 9 **3.** ± 6 **5.** ± 3 **7.** ± 5 **9.** ± 2

11. $\{-4, 20\}$ **13.** $\{-11, 19\}$ **15.** $\{-2, 14\}$ **17.** $\{-7, 1\}$ **19.** $\{7, 9\}$

HA1-530: Solving Quadratic Equations by Completing the Square

1. $\dfrac{9}{4}$ **3.** 81 **5.** $\dfrac{25}{4}$ **7.** $\{2, -8\}$

9. $-3 \pm \sqrt{2}$ **11.** 3 **13.** 2

HA1-535: Developing the Quadratic Formula and Using it to Solve Quadratic Equations

1. $x^2 - 3x + 5 = 0$
where $a = 1$, $b = -3$, and $c = 5$.

3. $2x^2 - 3x + 6 = 0$
where $a = 2$, $b = -3$, and $c = 6$.

5. $x = \dfrac{-(-9) \pm \sqrt{(-9)^2 - 4(5)(-2)}}{2(5)}$

7. $x = \dfrac{-(-4) \pm \sqrt{(-4)^2 - 4(1)(3)}}{2(1)}$

9. $\left\{\dfrac{3}{4}, -1\right\}$

11. $\left\{\dfrac{11 + \sqrt{61}}{6}, \dfrac{11 - \sqrt{61}}{6}\right\}$

13. $\left\{\dfrac{-2 + \sqrt{10}}{2}, \dfrac{-2 - \sqrt{10}}{2}\right\}$

15. $\{1.2, -1.7\}$

17. 0.6 second

19. 2.2 seconds

HA1-536: Solving Quadratic Equations Using the Graphing Calculator

1. $x = -4$ and $x = -2$ **3.** $x = 2$ and $x = 10$ **5.** $m = -6$ and $m = 9$

7. $a = -17$ and $a = 11$ **9.** $x = -\dfrac{4}{3}$ and $x = \dfrac{3}{4}$

HA1-537: Solving Systems of Linear and Nonlinear Equations

1. Yes **3.** No **5.** Yes **7.** $(12, -5)$ **9.** $(4, -5)$ **11.** $(-2, -7)$ **13.** No

15. 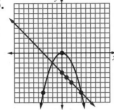 **17.** 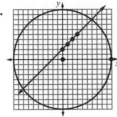 **19.** 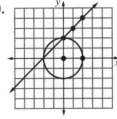 **21.**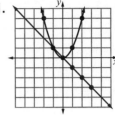

23. $(-3, -6)$ and $(6, 3)$ **25.** $(-5, -4)$ and $(4, 5)$ **27.** $(0, -6)$ and $(6, 0)$ **29.** Yes

31. $\begin{cases} x^2 + y^2 = 169 \\ y = \dfrac{7}{17}x + \dfrac{169}{17} \end{cases}$ **33.** $\begin{cases} x^2 + y^2 = 226 \\ y = 15x \end{cases}$ **35.** Yes

HA1-605: Interpreting the Correlation Coefficient of a Linear Fit

1. positive linear correlation   **3.** no correlation   **5.** 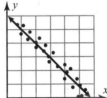   **7.**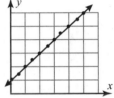

9. $r = 0.89$ **11.** strong positive correlation

13. $r = -0.869702$ **15.** $y = 2x$ **17.** $y = \dfrac{1}{3}x + \dfrac{11}{3}$

19. $y = 0.5x + 3$ **21.** $y = -0.25x + 9$ **23.** no correlation

25. moderate positive correlation   **27.** strong negative correlation   **29.** 331.235 parts per million

31. $9,096.00   **33.** $13,957.75   **35.** prediction is inappropriate

HA1-802: Factoring

1. $(x + 2)(x + 2)$ **3.** $(x + 2)(x + 9)$ **5.** $(x + 4)(x + 8)$ **7.** $(x + 5)(x + 8)$ **9.** $(x + 2)(x + 10)$

11. $(x - 2)(x - 4)$ **13.** $(y - 4)(y - 7)$ **15.** $(a - 3)(a - 6)$ **17.** $(z - 5)(z - 7)$ **19.** $(x + 8)(x - 12)$

HA1-805: Applying Algebra Concepts

1. 10 feet   **3.** 22.63 inches   **5.** 11.83 meters   **7.** 7.6 feet

9. 35 adult tickets and 45 child tickets

HA1- 806: Solving Systems of Linear Equations Using the Graphing Calculator

1. $(-2, 1)$ **3.** $\left(\dfrac{7}{4}, \dfrac{1}{4}\right)$ **5.** $(11.5, -13.5)$ **7.** System has infinitely many solutions   **9.** $\left(\dfrac{37}{3}, 26\right)$

HA1-820: Graphing Exponential Functions

1. 0.25

3. 3

5. $y = \left(\frac{1}{3}\right)^x$

7. $y = 3^x$

9.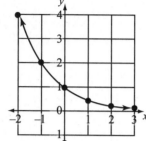

11.

13. The domain is the set of all real numbers. The range is the set of all negative numbers.

15. The domain is the set of all real numbers. The range is the set of all real number greater than 2.

17. The range is the set of all negative numbers.

19. The graph of the function increases from left to right.

HA1-825: Exponential Growth and Decay

1. $y = 0.36(20)^x$

3. $y = 1,000(0.5)^x$

5. decay factor = 0.70
decay rate = 0.30

7. growth factor = 1.25
growth rate = 0.25

9. $y = 48,500(1 - 0.08)^t$

11. $y = 63,000(1 + 0.15)^t$

13. $y = 150(1 + 0.12)^t$
466 bees

15. $y = 26,800(1 - 0.15)$
$16,459

17. $21,002.87

19. $3,923.97

HA1-840: Introduction to Matrices

1. 4×5

3. 5×4

5. 2×4

7. 4×4

9. row 2, column 2

11. row 2, column 4

13. row 4, column 2

15. row 1, column 3

17.

	Rochelle	Myra
A	2	2
B	2	1
C	1	2

19.

	Daryl	Phoebe
Heritage	3	2
Breast cancer	1	1
American flag	1	2

21.

	Kelly	Michelle
SUV	2	1
truck	2	2
car	1	2

23.

	Computer A	Computer B
On	2	4
Off	3	1

25.

	Republican	Democrat
for	2	4
against	4	2

27.

	Batch A	Batch B
Good	3	2
Bad	3	4

29.

	Customer A	Customer B	Customer C
approved	4	2	3
denied	1	3	2

31. Leslie bought 71 stocks and Michelle bought 76 stocks.

33. Keisha earned $373 in week 1 and $402 in week 2.

35. Judy saved $39.55 and Jasmine saved $46.95.

37. 19 wins and 11 losses

39. The average high temperature is 84° and the average low temperature is 66°.

HA1-845: Operations with Matrices

1. $\begin{bmatrix} 6 & 13 \\ 13 & 13 \end{bmatrix}$

3. $\begin{bmatrix} 8 & 7 \\ 11 & 12 \end{bmatrix}$

5. $\begin{bmatrix} 3 & 3 & 3 & 3 \\ 3 & 3 & 3 & 3 \\ 3 & 3 & 3 & 3 \\ 3 & 3 & 3 & 3 \end{bmatrix}$

7. $\begin{bmatrix} 4 & 4 & 4 \\ 5 & 7 & 9 \\ 9 & 12 & 11 \end{bmatrix}$

9. $\begin{bmatrix} 9 & 9 \\ 3 & 3 \\ 3 & 9 \\ 12 & 3 \\ 9 & 9 \\ 3 & 6 \end{bmatrix}$

11. $\begin{bmatrix} 8 & 2 \\ 6 & 4 \\ 8 & 2 \\ 4 & 10 \end{bmatrix}$

13. $\begin{bmatrix} 12 & 36 & 0 \\ 28 & 20 & 8 \\ 0 & 24 & 16 \end{bmatrix}$

15. $\begin{bmatrix} 15 & 12 \\ 9 & 6 \end{bmatrix}$

17. $\begin{bmatrix} 14 & 14 & 12 \\ 26 & 8 & 12 \\ 28 & 16 & 10 \end{bmatrix}$

19. $\begin{bmatrix} -11 & -6 \\ 14 & -13 \end{bmatrix}$

21. $\begin{bmatrix} 8 & 14 & 6 \\ 16 & 8 & 0 \\ 20 & 6 & 10 \end{bmatrix}$

23. $\begin{bmatrix} -15 & 14 & 10 \\ 12 & -3 & 17 \end{bmatrix}$

25. $\begin{bmatrix} -3 & -2 \\ -6 & -5 \end{bmatrix}$

27. $\begin{bmatrix} 13 & 19 \\ 18 & 21 \end{bmatrix}$

29. $\begin{bmatrix} 13 & 7 & 1 \\ 2 & 0 & 2 \\ 16 & 3 & 0 \end{bmatrix}$

31. $\begin{bmatrix} 266 & 245 \\ 175 & 210 \end{bmatrix}$

33. $\begin{bmatrix} 432 & 585 \\ 558 & 441 \end{bmatrix}$

35. $\begin{bmatrix} 424 & 496 & 232 \\ 424 & 508 & 244 \\ 420 & 504 & 252 \\ 432 & 504 & 260 \\ 436 & 536 & 264 \end{bmatrix}$

37. $\begin{bmatrix} 588 & 432 \\ 930 & 762 \\ 408 & 492 \end{bmatrix}$

39. $\begin{bmatrix} 110 & 130 \\ 182 & 142 \end{bmatrix}$

HA1-850: Identifying Matrices and Dimensions of a Matrix

1. $\begin{bmatrix} 6 & 3 & -3 \\ 9 & 0 & 5 \\ 15 & -4 & -1 \end{bmatrix}$

3. 4×2

5. $a_{22} = 12$

7. $a_{13} = 4$

9. $3, 2$

11. $\begin{bmatrix} 0 & 0 & 0 & 0 & 0 \end{bmatrix}$

13. $\begin{bmatrix} 11 & 0 \\ 0 & 11 \end{bmatrix}$

15. $\begin{bmatrix} 0 & 0 & 0 & 0 \\ 0 & 0 & 0 & 0 \end{bmatrix}$

17. $\begin{bmatrix} 0 & 0 \end{bmatrix}$

19. One home run scored by Mark

HA1-851: Performing Row Operations on Matrices

1. $\begin{bmatrix} 2 & 0 & 0 \\ 9 & 1 & 6 \\ 3 & 5 & 7 \end{bmatrix}$

3. $\begin{bmatrix} 6 & 2 & 5 & 8 \\ 0 & 1 & 7 & 8 \\ 3 & 5 & 2 & 4 \\ 0 & 5 & 7 & 2 \end{bmatrix}$

5. $\begin{bmatrix} 9 & 2 & 7 \\ 8 & -4 & 2 \\ 13 & -1 & 14 \end{bmatrix}$

7. $\begin{bmatrix} -6 & 4 & -4 \\ -5 & 3 & 2 \\ 7 & 0 & 1 \end{bmatrix}$

9. $\begin{bmatrix} 4 & 7 & -1 & 0 \\ -18 & 15 & 9 & 6 \\ 7 & 5 & 6 & 7 \\ 3 & 2 & 3 & 5 \end{bmatrix}$

11. $B = \begin{bmatrix} -1 & 3 & -6 \\ -12 & 3 & 2 \\ -7 & 4 & -3 \end{bmatrix}$

13. $B = \begin{bmatrix} -1 & 3 & -6 \\ -12 & 3 & 2 \\ -7 & 4 & -3 \end{bmatrix}$

15. $\begin{bmatrix} 7 & 1 & 3 \\ 5 & 6 & -2 \\ 0 & 1 & 11 \end{bmatrix}$

17. $\begin{bmatrix} 3 & 9 & 6 & 18 \\ 2 & 20 & 11 & 1 \\ 2 & 4 & 6 & 8 \\ 6 & 12 & 18 & 24 \end{bmatrix}$

19. $\begin{bmatrix} 0 & 0 & 0 \\ -9 & 6 & 3 \\ 2 & 2 & 1 \end{bmatrix}$

HA1-852: Solving Systems of Linear Equations in Three Variables Using the Gauss-Jordan Method

1. $\left[\begin{array}{ccc|c} 5 & 3 & -6 & 1 \\ 1 & -2 & 2 & 0 \\ 2 & -7 & 8 & 5 \end{array}\right]$

3. $\left[\begin{array}{ccc|c} 1 & 1 & 3 & 4 \\ 1 & 2 & 5 & 6 \\ 1 & 2 & 6 & 8 \end{array}\right]$

5. $\left[\begin{array}{ccc|c} 3 & 2 & -1 & 3 \\ -2 & 6 & -2 & -4 \\ -8 & -2 & -4 & 5 \end{array}\right]$

7. $\begin{aligned} x + 5z &= -8 \\ 2y - 7z &= -3 \\ z &= 1 \end{aligned}$

9. $\begin{aligned} x + 2y - 3z &= -2 \\ x - 2y + 5z &= 10 \\ 5x - 2y + 9z &= 16 \end{aligned}$

11. $\left(\dfrac{12}{5}, -\dfrac{17}{25}, \dfrac{17}{25} \right)$

13. $(0, 2, 4)$

15. $(-8, -5, -6)$

17. Infinitely many solutions

19. $\left(\dfrac{13}{6}, \dfrac{17}{6}, \dfrac{22}{3} \right)$

HA1-853: Applying the Laws of Logarithms

1. 0

3. 1

5. $\log x + \log y + \log z$

7. $\log y^{12} = 12 \log y$

9. 4

11. -0.406

13. $3 + 2 \ln x$

15. $\ln 2 - \ln x - \ln y$

17. $2 \ln x + 3 \ln y$

19. 1.735

HA1-854: Determining the Value of Common and Natural Logarithms and Irrational Exponents

1. 1.301

3. 0.434

5. 3.045

7. 15.673

9. 0.149

11. 0.356

13. 0.005

15. -6.644

17. 3.415

19. 5.907

HA1-855: Solving Exponential Equations

1. -3

3. -3

5. 2

7. -6

9. 3

11. 1.904

13. 7.565

15. 0.861

17. 23.899

19. 9 minutes

HA1-856: Translating Exponential and Logarithmic Equations

1. $2^4 = 16$

3. $2^{10} = 1,024$

5. $5^{-1} = \dfrac{1}{5}$

7. $5^{-2} = \dfrac{1}{25}$

9. $(\sqrt{2})^8 = 16$

11. 2

13. $\sqrt{2}$

15. $\dfrac{1}{2}$

17. 8

19. $\dfrac{3}{5}$

HA1-857: Solving Logarithmic Equations

1. 729

3. 36

5. 5

7. $2\sqrt{3}$

9. 4

11. $\dfrac{1}{4}$

13. $\dfrac{3}{4}$

15. $\dfrac{1}{6}$

17. $\pm 2\sqrt{2}$

19. no solution

HA1-859: Using the Algebraic System

1. Property of Negative One

3. Zero Product Property

5. Direct proof

7. Associative Property

9. Inverse Property

11. False

13. False

15. False

17. Inverse Property

19. Inverse Property

HA1-866: Drawing a Line Using Slope-Intercept Form and Determining if Two Lines are Parallel or Perpendicular

1. $m = -\dfrac{2}{5}$ and $b = \dfrac{1}{5}$

3. $m = -3$ and $b = 6$

5. $m = 2$ and $b = -3$

7. $m = -12$ and $b = -14$ **9.** $m = \dfrac{5}{3}$ and $b = 3$

11. 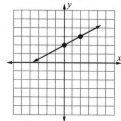   **13.** 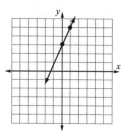   **15.** 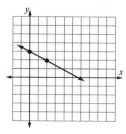   **17.**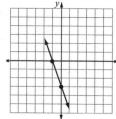

19. Parallel

HA1-867: Identifying Domain and Range of Relations Given Graphs, Tables, or Sets of Ordered Pairs

1. $\{6, 2, 4, 8\}$ **3.** $\{1, 2, 3, 4, 5, 6, 7, 8\}$ **5.** $\{6, 9, 4, 7, 2, 5\}$

7. $\{$January, February, March, April, May, June, July, August, September, October, November, December$\}$

9. $\{$Monday, Tuesday, Wednesday, Thursday, Friday, Saturday, Sunday$\}$ **11.** $(-\infty, \infty)$ **13.** $[1, 3]$

15. $(-\infty, 5]$ **17.** $(-\infty, 4]$ **19.** $\{-4, -2, 2, 4\}$

HA1-870: Solving Problems with Systems of Linear Equations and Inequalities

1. Peter is 15 years old and David is 3 years old.

3. One book costs $10 and one magazine costs $3.

5. A dress shirt costs $11 and a T-shirt costs $4.

7. 100 golfers paid full price and 180 paid the discounted price.

9. Gus has 4 quarters and 20 dimes.

11. The beverage producer should mix 4 L of the 14% fruit juice punch, and 6 L of the 9% fruit juice punch.

13. The pharmacist should mix 11 ml of 1% hydrocortisone cream and 22 ml of 4% hydrocortisone cream.

15. 7

17. 9

19. $(2, 0)$

HA1-871: Simplifying Radical Expressions

1. $6\sqrt{7}$ **3.** $6\sqrt{11}$ **5.** $6\sqrt{2m}$ **7.** $2k\sqrt{37k}$ **9.** $2n^6\sqrt{19n}$

11. $8c^4d^2\sqrt{cd}$ **13.** a^8b **15.** $3m^2np^3\sqrt{13mp}$ **17.** $2m\sqrt{42n}$ **19.** No solution

HA1-872: Simplifying Sums and Differences of Radicals

1. $9\sqrt{x}$ **3.** $9\sqrt{15}$ **5.** $9\sqrt{3x}$ **7.** $\sqrt{3}$ **9.** $22\sqrt{2}$

11. $10\sqrt{y}$ **13.** $7\sqrt{6}$ **15.** $36\sqrt{3}$ **17.** $6\sqrt{5xy} + 2\sqrt{5x}$ **19.** $-2\sqrt{2x} - x\sqrt[4]{y}$

HA1-873: Simplifying Products of Radicals

1. $3\sqrt{10}$ **3.** $3\sqrt{11}$ **5.** $10\sqrt{2}$ **7.** 6   **9.** $2\sqrt{21}$

11. $10xy^2\sqrt{2xy}$ **13.** 2   **15.** $5x^2$ **17.** $2x\sqrt[3]{2x}$ **19.** $4\sqrt[3]{12} - 3\sqrt[3]{18} - 1$

HA1-876: Applying Length, Midpoint and Slope of a Segment on a Cartesian Plane

1. $-\dfrac{3}{2}$ **3.** -1 **5.** $\dfrac{5}{8}$ **7.** $(0, 9)$ **9.** $\left(-\dfrac{11}{2}, 3\right)$

11. 8.06   **13.** 5.10   **15.** 13.34   **17.** $0.25   **19.** $(-6, -4)$

HA1-881: Completing and Validating Algebraic Proofs

1. Reflexive Property of Equality   **3.** Symmetric Property of Equality

5. Associative Property of Multiplication   **7.** Identity Property of Addition

9. Inverse Property of Multiplication   **11.** Sometimes true

13. Always true   **15.** Always true   **17.** Sometimes true   **19.** Distributive Property

HA1-887: Applications of Absolute Value, Step, and Constant Functions

1. $\{3, 6, 9, 18\}$ **3.** $\{2, 4, 6, 10\}$ **5.** $\{0, 12, 21\}$ **7.** $\{-8, -2, 4, 7\}$

9. $\{-4, 0, 2, 6\}$ **11.** $\{-3, -1, 0, 1, 2\}$ **13.** $\{-7, -4, -1, 1, 5\}$ **15.** $\{-5, -3, -1, 0, 3\}$

17. 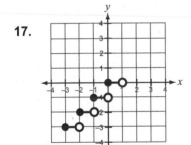   **19.** 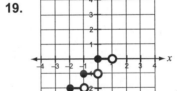   **21.**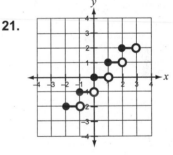

23. 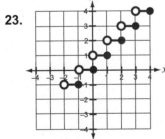   **25.**   **27.**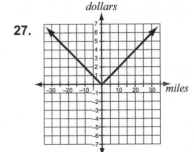

29. $f(x) = 0.4|x|$ **31.** 171 guests   **33.** Less than 260

35. 201 guests   **37.** KLM Car Rental Company   **39.** Greater than 4 hours

HA1-892: Data Analysis Using the Graphing Calculator

1. Linear   **3.** Quadratic   **5.** $y = 2x^2 - 6x$ **7.** $y = 0.375 \cdot 2^x$ **9.** $s = -2r + 6$

HA1-905: Quadratic Equations with Irrational Roots

1. $\{\sqrt{6}, -\sqrt{6}\}$ **3.** $\{\sqrt{23}, -\sqrt{23}\}$ **5.** $\{\sqrt{43}, -\sqrt{43}\}$

7. $\{2\sqrt{3}, -2\sqrt{3}\}$ **9.** $\{2\sqrt{6}, -2\sqrt{6}\}$ **11.** $\left\{\dfrac{\sqrt{10}}{2}, -\dfrac{\sqrt{10}}{2}\right\}$

13. $\left\{\dfrac{\sqrt{22}}{2}, -\dfrac{\sqrt{22}}{2}\right\}$ **15.** $\left\{\dfrac{\sqrt{34}}{2}, -\dfrac{\sqrt{34}}{2}\right\}$ **17.** $\left\{\dfrac{-1+\sqrt{17}}{2}, \dfrac{-1-\sqrt{17}}{2}\right\}$

19. $\left\{\dfrac{-1+\sqrt{53}}{2}, \dfrac{-1-\sqrt{53}}{2}\right\}$ **21.** $\left\{\dfrac{-3+\sqrt{13}}{2}, \dfrac{-3-\sqrt{13}}{2}\right\}$ **23.** $\left\{\dfrac{-5+\sqrt{41}}{2}, \dfrac{-5-\sqrt{41}}{2}\right\}$

25. $\left\{\dfrac{-5+\sqrt{17}}{2}, \dfrac{-5-\sqrt{17}}{2}\right\}$ **27.** $\left\{\dfrac{3\sqrt{10}}{2}, -\dfrac{3\sqrt{10}}{2}\right\}$ **29.** $\left\{\dfrac{2\sqrt{30}}{5}, -\dfrac{2\sqrt{30}}{5}\right\}$

31. $\left\{\dfrac{3\sqrt{2}}{2}, -\dfrac{3\sqrt{2}}{2}\right\}$ **33.** $\{-1+\sqrt{2}, -1-\sqrt{2}\}$ **35.** $\{-3+\sqrt{10}, -3-\sqrt{10}\}$

37. $\left\{\dfrac{-2+\sqrt{14}}{2}, \dfrac{-2-\sqrt{14}}{2}\right\}$ **39.** $\left\{\dfrac{-4+3\sqrt{2}}{2}, \dfrac{-4-3\sqrt{2}}{2}\right\}$

HA1-910: Complex Numbers

1. $3i$ **3.** $7i$ **5.** 4 **7.** -5

9. $3 + 7i$ **11.** $-3i$ **13.** $\{2i, -2i\}$ **15.** $\{i\sqrt{11}, -i\sqrt{11}\}$

17. $2i\sqrt{11}$ **19.** $4i\sqrt{3}$ **21.** $2i\sqrt{13}$

23. $\dfrac{1}{3}i$ **25.** $\{2i\sqrt{2}, -2i\sqrt{2}\}$ **27.** $\left\{-\dfrac{1}{2}+\dfrac{i\sqrt{35}}{2}, -\dfrac{1}{2}-\dfrac{i\sqrt{35}}{2}\right\}$

29. $\left\{-\dfrac{3}{2}+\dfrac{i\sqrt{15}}{2}, -\dfrac{3}{2}-\dfrac{i\sqrt{15}}{2}\right\}$ **31.** $\left\{\dfrac{-1+i\sqrt{11}}{2}, \dfrac{-1-i\sqrt{11}}{2}\right\}$ **33.** $\left\{\dfrac{-5+3i\sqrt{7}}{4}, \dfrac{-5-3i\sqrt{7}}{4}\right\}$

35. $\left\{\dfrac{-2+i\sqrt{11}}{3}, \dfrac{-2-i\sqrt{11}}{3}\right\}$ **37.** $\left\{\dfrac{i\sqrt{58}}{2}, -\dfrac{i\sqrt{58}}{2}\right\}$ **39.** $\left\{\dfrac{6i\sqrt{5}}{5}, -\dfrac{6i\sqrt{5}}{5}\right\}$

HA1-915: Algebraic Operations with Complex Numbers

1. $8 - 2i$ **3.** $1 - 2i$ **5.** $7 - 2i$ **7.** $21 - 9i$ **9.** $14 - 6i$

11. -6 **13.** -16 **15.** $-13 - 7i$ **17.** $10 - 5i$ **19.** $4 - 2i$

21. $9 - 2i$ **23.** $-\dfrac{7}{2} - 2i$ **25.** 13 **27.** $-128i$ **29.** $18 + 26i$

31. $52 - 47i$ **33.** $-26 + 18i$ **35.** $\dfrac{36}{29} - \dfrac{3i}{29}$ **37.** $-\dfrac{22}{29} - \dfrac{32i}{29}$ **39.** $\dfrac{32}{29} + \dfrac{7i}{29}$

HA1-920: Simplifying Algebraic Expressions Using the Distributive Property

1. $21x^8 - 9x^5$ **3.** $7x^{10} - 3x^7$ **5.** $28x^{11} - 8x^7$

7. $4x^4y^3 + 3x^5y^3 - 3x^6y^3$ **9.** $x^4y^3 + 3x^6y^3$ **11.** $6x^5 - 5x^4 - 4x^3$

13. $9x^5 + 15x^4 + 4x^3$ **15.** $5x^5 + 21x^4 + 4x^3$ **17.** $4x^5y^5 + 6x^4y^4 - 8x^4y^3 - 12x^3y^2$

19. $4x^5y^5 - 6x^4y^3z - 8x^4y^2z + 12x^3z^2$ **21.** $4x^5y^5 - 6x^4y^4 - 10x^4y^3 + 15x^3y^2$

23. $6x^4 + 11x^3 + 22x^2 + 9x$ **25.** $9x^4 - 9x^3 + 23x^2 + 9x$

27. $9x^4 + 26x^2 + 9x$ **29.** $9x^4 + 12x^2y + 4y^2$

31. $9x^4 + 24x^2y + 16y^2$ **33.** $16x^4 - 32x^2y + 16y^2$

35. $16x^4 + 24x^2y + 9y^2$ **37.** $6x^4y^4 + 9x^5y^3 + 8x^2y^4 + 12x^3y^3 + 12x^2y^2 + 18x^3y$

39. $-6x^4y^4 - 9x^5y^3 + 8x^2y^4 + 12x^3y^3 + 12x^2y^2 + 18x^3y$

HA1-925: Using the Discriminant to Analyze the Solution of a Quadratic Equation

1. 4 **3.** -48 **5.** 0 **7.** 25

9. One double real root   **11.** Conjugate complex roots   **13.** Two rational roots   **15.** Two irrational roots

17. Conjugate complex roots   **19.** Positive   **21.** $t = 3$ **23.** $t < \dfrac{25}{12}$

25. $t > 1$ **27.** $b = 5$ **29.** $b = 0$ or $b = 8$ **31.** $b = 0$ or $b = -\dfrac{1}{4}$

33. $b = 0$ or $b = 20$ **35.** I and II   **37.** I and III   **39.** I, II, and III

HA1-927: Graphing $f(x) = ax^2$ Using Dilations

1. Stretch f vertically by a factor of $\dfrac{5}{2}$.   **3.** Shrink f vertically by a factor of $\dfrac{1}{3}$.

5. Stretch f vertically by a factor of 4.

7. Shrink f vertically by a factor of $\frac{3}{4}$.

9. Stretch f vertically by a factor of $\frac{11}{2}$.

11. Shrink f vertically by a factor of $\frac{3}{7}$.

13. Stretch f vertically by a factor of $\frac{6}{5}$.

15. Shrink f vertically by a factor of $\frac{1}{16}$.

17. $y = 3x^2, \ y = \frac{5}{2}x^2, \ y = x^2, \ y = \frac{1}{3}x^2$

19. $y = \frac{1}{4}x^2, \ y = \frac{1}{2}x^2, \ y = \frac{2}{3}x^2, \ y = x^2$

21. $y = 6x^2, \ y = \frac{11}{2}x^2, \ y = 5x^2, \ y = x^2$

23. $y = \frac{5}{7}x^2, \ y = x^2, \ y = 3x^2, \ y = \frac{7}{2}x^2$

25. $y = 7x^2$

27. $y = 8x^2, \ y = 6x^2, \ y = \frac{3}{2}x^2, \ y = \frac{2}{9}x^2$

29. $y = x^2, \ y = \frac{3}{2}x^2, \ y = \frac{5}{2}x^2, \ y = 3x^2$

31. $g(x) = \frac{1}{3}x^2, \ h(x) = x^2, \ f(x) = 3x^2$

33. $f(x) = \frac{5}{6}x^2, \ g(x) = x^2, \ h(x) = \frac{3}{2}x^2,$

$k(x) = 2x^2$

35. $k(x) = \frac{2}{5}x^2, \ h(x) = x^2, \ g(x) = \frac{5}{2}x^2,$

$f(x) = \frac{17}{5}x^2$

37. $k(x) = \frac{1}{16}x^2, \ g(x) = \frac{1}{8}x^2, \ h(x) = \frac{1}{4}x^2, \ f(x) = \frac{1}{2}x^2$

39. $g(x) = \frac{1}{9}x^2, \ k(x) = x^2, \ h(x) = \frac{9}{4}x^2$

HA1-928: Graphing $f(x) = ax^2$ Using Dilations and Reflections

1. A reflection across the x-axis

3. Reflect the graph of f across the x-axis

5. A vertical shrink

7. Reflect the graph of f across the x-axis

9. Shrink f vertically

11. Stretch f vertically

13. Reflect the graph of f across the x-axis

15. Shrink f vertically

17. Reflecting over the x-axis and shrinking vertically

19. $y = \frac{10}{3}x^2$

21. $y = -\frac{1}{4}x^2$

23. $y = -\frac{7}{3}x^2$

25. $y = \frac{5}{11}x^2$

27. $y = \frac{7}{2}x^2$

29. $y = \frac{1}{8}x^2$

31. $g(x) = -\frac{1}{3}x^2, \ h(x) = -2x^2, \ f(x) = \frac{1}{4}x^2$

33. $h(x) = \frac{1}{3}x^2, \ g(x) = x^2, \ f(x) = -x^2$

35. $g(x) = \frac{2}{5}x^2, \ f(x) = \frac{5}{2}x^2, \ k(x) = -\frac{2}{5}x^2, \ h(x) = -\frac{5}{2}x^2$

37. $k(x) = -\frac{1}{8}x^2, \ h(x) = -\frac{1}{3}x^2, \ g(x) = -\frac{3}{4}x^2, \ f(x) = 2x^2$

39. $h(x) = \frac{3}{2}x^2, \ g(x) = 4x^2, \ f(x) = -\frac{5}{2}x^2$

HA1-929: Graphing $f(x) = ax^2 + c$ Using Dilations, Reflections, and Vertical Translations

1. $1, -2, -3, -2, 1$ **3.** $2, -1, -2, -1, 2$ **5.** $-18, -11, -2, -11, -18$ **7.** $-14, -2, 2, -2, -14$

9. $1, -2, -3, -2, 1$ **11.** $13, 4, 1, 4, 13$ **13.** $-18, -3, 2, -3, -18$ **15.** $12, 5, 0, -3, -4$

17. $y = -x^2 + 3$ **19.** $y = \frac{1}{6}x^2 + 1$ **21.** $y = \frac{1}{4}x^2 - 4$ **23.** $y = -\frac{2}{5}x^2 + 4$

25. $y = -4x^2 + 2$ **27.** $y = -2x^2$ **29.** $y = 2x^2 + 3$ **31.** $g(x) = -5x^2 + 3$

33. $g(x) = -\frac{1}{3}x^2$ **35.** $g(x) = 2x^2 + 4$ **37.** $g(x) = -\frac{5}{7}x^2 + \frac{1}{3}$ **39.** $g(x) = 3x^2 - 5$

HA1-930: Graphing Quadratic Functions with Horizontal and Vertical Shifting

1. shifting 4 units downward   **3.** shifting 12 units upward

5. shifting 6 units to the right   **7.** shifting 8 units to the left

9. 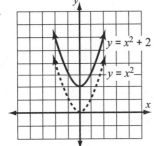   **11.** 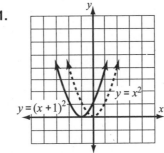   **13.**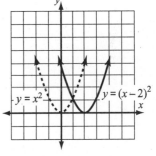

15. 2 units downward   **17.** 7 units downward   **19.** 2 units to the left

21. 2 units to the left   **23.** 2 units to the right   **25.** 3 units upward

27. 3 units to the right and 6 units downward   **29.** 2 units to the right and 3 units upward   **31.** 4 units to the left and 3 units upward

33. 3 units to the left and 7 units downward   **35.** 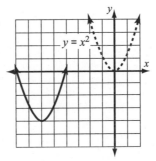   **37.**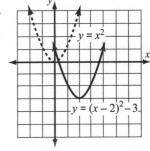

39. $f(x) = (x + 5)^2 - 33$

HA1-931: Graphing Quadratic Functions with Dilations, Reflections, and Transformations

1. Stretched by a factor of 3   **3.** Shrunk by a factor of $\frac{1}{4}$ **5.** Stretched by a factor of 14

7. False   **9.** True   **11.** True

13.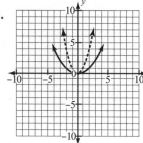

15.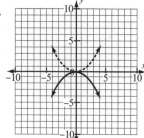

17. 2 units to the left

19. reflection over the x-axis

21. Shift 1 unit to the left and stretch by a factor of 2

23. Shift 4 units to the left and stretch by a factor of 2

25. Shift 3 units to the right and reflect over the x-axis

27. shift 5 units to the left and reflect over the x-axis

29.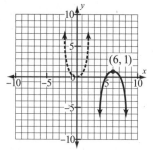

31.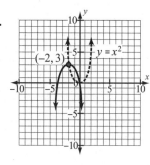

33.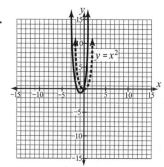

35.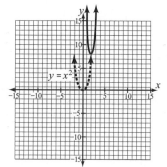

37. $f(x) = 3(x + 1)^2 + 14$

39.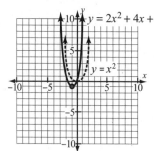

HA1-935: Analyzing Graphs of Quadratic Functions

1. (3, 1) **3.** (−1, −4) **5.** (3, −2) **7.** (2, −6) **9.** $x = 3$

11. $x = -2$ **13.** $x = 2$ **15.** $x = -1$ **17.** (0, −1) **19.** (0, 4)

21. $y = \dfrac{5}{9}(x + 2)^2 - 1$ **23.** $y = -\dfrac{1}{9}(x + 2)^2 - 3$ **25.** $x = -2$

27. $x = -4$ **29.**

x	-1	0	1
y	-15	-6	-5

31.

x	-1	0	1
y	-1	6	9

33. Between -4 and -3 **35.** 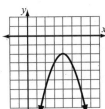   **37.** $x = 3$

39. Between 0 and 1

HA1-940: Applications of Quadratic Equations

1. 2 feet   **3.** 13 feet   **5.** 5   **7.** $2x^3y^3$

9. $2x^2 + 9x + 10$ **11.** $x = 4$ **13.** $3 < x < 5$ **15.** $b^2 + 5b - 40 = 0$

17. $w^2 + 4w - 12 = 0$ **19.** $3x^2 + 4x - 4$ **21.** $1 < x < 3$ **23.** $5 < x < 10$

25. $b^2 + 15b - 100 = 0$ **27.** $b^2 + 10b - 200 = 0$ **29.** $w^2 + 4w - 32 = 0$ **31.** $11x^2 + 7x - 2$

33. $y = x^2$ **35.** $y = \dfrac{1}{2}x^2$ **37.** 10 feet   **39.** 3 feet

HA1-945: Real-World Applications of Quadratic Functions

1. 5 seconds   **3.** 3 seconds   **5.** 3 seconds   **7.** 1.5 seconds   **9.** 324 feet

11. 100   **13.** $0 \le t \le 4$ **15.** $0 \le h \le 40$ **17.** 2 seconds   **19.** 3 seconds

21. The ball reached the maximum height after about three seconds.   **23.** The ball fell on the ground after about four seconds.

25. 64 feet   **27.** 256 feet   **29.** 576 feet   **31.** 1 foot

33. The maximum profit is made when the company sells each television for $625.   **35.** The maximum profit is made when each watch is sold for $500.

37. $y = -\dfrac{4}{1,225}(x - 175)^2 + 100$ **39.** $y = -\dfrac{3}{2,500}(x - 50)^2 + 3$

HA1-950: Graphing Absolute Value Functions

1. 9   **3.** 25   **5.** 6   **7.** 8   **9.** 29

11.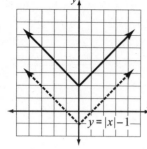

13.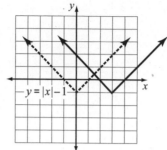

15.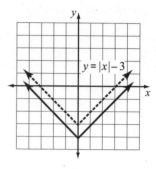

17. Shifted left 4 units

19. Stretched by a factor of 6

21. $y = |x| - 4$

23. $y = -|x| + 4$

25. $y = 2|x| - 5$

27. $y = -2|x| + 5$

29.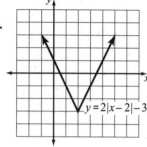

31.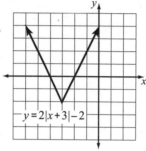

33. $y = -2x + 1$

35. $y = -2x + 2$

37. $y = -3x + 2$

39. $y = 2x + 7$

HA1-955: Analyzing Linear Functions

1. $y = 2x - 2$

3. $y = 4x - 9$

5. 10

7. 2

9. Intersecting, non-perpendicular

11. Parallel

13. $y = -x - 3$

15. $y = -x - 6$

17. $y = 2x + 4$

19. $y = -2x - 4$

21. $y = \frac{3}{4}x + 4$

23. $y = \frac{1}{2}x + 3$

25. No

27. $y = 2x + 6$

29. $y = \frac{1}{2}x + \frac{11}{2}$

31. No

33. $y = -\frac{1}{2}x + \frac{5}{2}$

35. $y = \frac{1}{2}x + 5$

37. No

39. No

HA1-960: Real-World Applications of Linear Functions

1. 3 miles

3. 6,000 calculators

5. 10,000 calculators

7. 9 miles per hour

9. 3 miles per hour

11. –0.006

13. $d = 6t$

15. $p = -0.005C + 100$

17. $P = 0.80T + 5.25$

19. $P = 1.10T + 7.25$

21. Yes

23. No

25. No

27. 20

29. 1.10

31. $10 per calculator

33. $120 per television

35. $600 per sofa

37. 2,000 calculators

39. 40,000 stereos

HA1-965: Determining the Best-Fitting Line

1. Yes   **3.** Yes   **5.** Yes   **7.** Yes   **9.** No

11. 1   **13.** Negative   **15.** Positive   **17.** Negative   **19.** Negative

21. Yes   **23.** No   **25.** No   **27.** Yes   **29.** –3

31. 5   **33.** 5   **35.** $80   **37.** $95   **39.** $55

HA2-443: Finding the Inverses of Linear and Quadratic Functions

1. $\{(1, 0), (3, 2), (5, 4)\}$
Yes, this relation is a function.

3. $\{(8, -5), (12, 9), (10, -5)\}$
Yes, this relation is a function.

5. $\{(-3, -2), (-5, -3), (-7, -4)\}$
Yes, this relation is a function.

7. $\{(-8, 0), (-8, 2), (0, 4)\}$
No, this relation is not a function.

9.
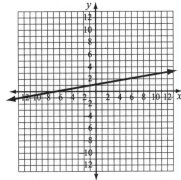

This is the graph of the inverse of the
function whose graph is given.

11.
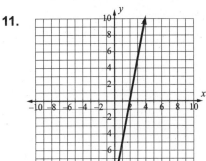

This is the graph of the inverse of the
function whose graph is given.

13.
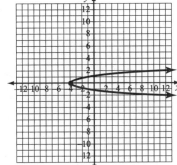

This is the graph of the inverse of the
function whose graph is given.

15.

This is the graph of the inverse of the
function whose graph is given.

17. $f^{-1}(x) = \dfrac{-1}{6}x$

19. $f^{-1}(x) = \dfrac{-7}{2}x$

21. $f^{-1}(x) = \dfrac{-1}{2}x + \dfrac{-7}{2}$

23. $f^{-1}(x) = -8x + 48$

25. $y = \pm\sqrt{x} + 9$

27. $y = \pm\sqrt{x} + 12$

29. $y = \dfrac{\pm 2\sqrt{2x}}{8}$

31. $f(x) = 3x^2 + 3$ and
$g(x) = (x-3)^2$

33. $f(x) = x^2 + 18$ and
$g(x) = (x-18)^2$

35. $f(x) = 4x$ and
$g(x) = x-4$

37. $f(x) = \pm\sqrt{x} + 9$ and
$g(x) = (x-9)^2$

39. $f(x) = 5x + 1$ and
$g(x) = \dfrac{1}{5}x - \dfrac{1}{5}$

HA2-446: Performing Operations with Functions

1. $30x + 21$

3. $7x^2 - 13x - 6$

5. $20x - 20$

7. $-x^2 + 6x - 15$

9. 29

11. 378

13. 9

15. -11

17. $\dfrac{5x^2 + 3x - 8}{12x + 2}$

19. $21x^2 - 29x + 10$

21. $-9x^2 + 6x - 1$

23. -64

25. -72

27. $\dfrac{-7}{4}$

29. $-\dfrac{229}{45}$

31. $0.002x^2 + 13,500x - 2,500$

33. $\dfrac{4.75 + 2.75x}{2x}$

35. $230 + 8x$

37. $0.1115x$

39. $1,050 + 750x$

Index

A

Absolute value
defined 552
equations, solving 7–9
used to solve inequalities 10–13
Absolute value function
applications of 461–465
defined 461
graphing 552–554
Absolute value inequalities
solving 10–13
steps for solving 11
Addition
of functions 590
of matrices 372
with complex numbers 487
Arithmetic sequence
defined 192
finding the nth term of 201
Associative Property
of addition 420
of multiplication 420
Augmented matrix 391–396
Average Speed 178
$Ax + By + C$ **85**
$ax^2 + bx + c$ **17–18**
Axis of symmetry
of a quadratic function 529

B

Base
change of, formula 406
in exponential, linear, or quadratic functions 348
of a logarithm 398–402, 417
of a radical expression 443
Binomial
and a trinomial, product of 488
two, product of 488
Boundary line 138

C

Cartesian plane
creating a graph of a relation 146
length, midpoint, and slope of a segment
on 452–456
Ceiling function (or least integer) 462
Change of Base Formula 406
Closure Property 421
Coefficient matrix 391

Column in a matrix 360
Combined inequalities
defined 2
graphing and solving 1–6
Common factor, defined 20
Commutative Property
of addition 420
of multiplication 420
Completing the square 294–298
Complex conjugates 482
Complex fraction
defined 48
simplifying 48–50
Complex numbers
about 482–483
algebraic operations with 485–486
Composite functions
evaluating 190–191
Conclusion 422
Conjugates
complex 482
defined 269
Conjunction
compact 5
defined 1
Consistent
and dependent systems of linear equations 219
and independent systems of linear equations 217
Constant
difference in an arithmetic sequence 192
effect of in dilations 495
function 461
in a quadratic equation 291
matrix 391
of variation 209
ratio in a geometric sequence 192
scalar multiplication of a matrix 372
Coordinate plane
defined 56
distance between two points 288
distance on 288–289
graphing linear inequalities on 138–141
graphing ordered pairs on 56–58
Coordinate system 56
Coordinates
finding the slope of a line from 78–83
first and second 146, 163
of a point 65
of an ordered pair 146

Correlation
coefficient, of a linear fit 321–326
defined 321
positive and negative 321–326
relation to the slope of the line of best fit 574
Correlation coefficient
linear, defined 322
Counterexample 458
Cube root
definition and properties of 257
radical expression 443
simplifying 256–260
Cubes, sum and difference of 14

D

Decimal
repeating 250
terminating 250
Denominator
least common 39–40
rationalizing 268
Dependent variable
defined 164
of a function 115
Difference of cubes 14
Difference of squares 14–16
Dilations
defined 495, 512, 523
graphing 503–506, 512–514, 523–525
Dimensions of a matrix 361
Direct variation 209–211
Discriminant
used to analyze solutions of quadratic
equations 491–493
Disjunction 1
Distance
absolute value 552
between two points on a coordinate plane 288–289,
452–456
formula 452
functions and relations involving 178–182
Distributive Property
of multiplication 420, 449, 488
used to simplify algebraic expressions 488–490
Division
of functions 590
of rational expressions 36–38
with complex numbers 487
Domain
defined 146, 590
of functions, finding 163–166
of relations, identifying 430–432

E

Elements of a matrix 360, 381
Equation of a line
determined by coordinates of two points 133,
135–136
determined by slope and a point 132–133
finding for parallel or perpendicular lines 88–92
slope-intercept form 88, 426
standard form 88, 426
Equations
in two variables, identifying solutions of 62–63
linear 24
logarithmic 417–419
polynomial, solving by factoring 24–26
quadratic 24
rational, solving 51–55
solving using absolute value 7–9
Exponential equations
solving 409–412
Exponential function
defined 348
graphing 348–352
translating to logarithmic 413–415
Exponential Growth and Decay
compound interest 357
functions and models 354–357
Exponential sequence
see Geometric sequence 192
Exponents
and logarithms, cancelling effect 403
laws of 400, 407
power rule for 443
rational, rule for 443
with signed numbers, rule for 443
Expressions
algebraic, simplified using the Distributive
Property 488–490
perfect squares, in quadratic equations 291–292
radical, simplifying 443–445
rational, adding and subtracting 42–44
rational, adding and subtracting with
polynomials 45–47
rational, defined 30
rational, dividing 36–38
rational, multiplying 34–35
rational, simplifying 32–33
simplifying using properties of real numbers 458
Extrapolation, defined 322

F

Factoring
binomial factors of trinomials 17–18
by grouping 20–21

Input of a function 115
Interest
    compound 357
Interpolation
    defined 322
    using the line of best fit 321–326
Intersection, of graphs 1
Interval notation 431
Inverse
    functions, properties 583
    of a function or relation 583
    of a linear or quadratic function 583–586
    Properties, of addition and multiplication 420
    variation 213–214

L
Laws
    of exponents 400
    of logarithms 400
LCD
    See least common denominator
Least common denominator
    of rational expressions 39–40
Least integer function (or ceiling function) 462
Least-squares Criterion 321
Length
    of the hypotenuse, finding 279
    on a Cartesian plane 452–456
Like Radicals, defined 262
Line of best fit 321
Line of symmetry
    of a quadratic function 529, 542
Linear Correlation Coefficient 322
Linear equations
    defined 24, 65
    graphing 65–69
    graphing using slope and y-intercept or slope
        and a point 97–102
    how variations of m and b affect the graph 104–107
    solving by the Gauss-Jordan method 391–396
    solving problems including systems 435–441
    solving systems 233–235
    solving systems by addition/subtraction
        method 229–231
    solving systems by graphing 216–220
    solving systems by substitution 225–228
Linear inequalities
    defined 138
    graphing 138–141
    graphing systems of 237–246
    graphing using a graphing calculator 142–144
    solving problems including systems of 435–441
Linear programming 441

Logarithms
    and exponents, cancelling effect 403
    applying laws of 398–404
    change of base formula 406
    defined 398
    determining using a calculator 405–408
    laws of 400
    natural 401
    properties of 398
    solving 417–419
    translating to exponential functions 413–415

M
Matrix (matrices)
    addition or subtraction 372
    augmented 391
    coefficient 391
    constant 391
    defined 360, 381
    dimensions 361, 381–383
    element of 381
    elements 360
    identifying 381–383
    introduction 360–365
    operations with 372–376
    row echelon form 391
    row operation 386–389
    transpose of 383
    variable 391
Maximization 437
Midpoint
    of a segment 454
    on a Cartesian plane 452–456
Multiplication
    of functions 590
    of rational expressions 34
    with complex numbers 487

N
Natural logarithms 401
Negative correlation 321–326
Negative one
    Property of, for real numbers 421
    square root of 482
Negative squares, rule for 443
Nonlinear system of equations, defined 311
n^{th} **Term 201**
Number Patterns 192–197

O
Operations
    defined 372
    with functions 590–592

Ordered pairs
    as part of a relation 146, 154, 163, 430
    graphing 56–58
    in a residual plot 322
    in a scatterplot 321
    used in solving real-world problems 455
Origin, on a coordinate system 56
Output of a function 115

P

Parabola
    graph of $y = x^2$ 495
Parallel lines
    defined 88
    determining by slope 428
    properties of 220
Parent function 495
Pearson product moment correlation coefficient 322
Perpendicular lines
    defined 88
    determining by slope 428
Polynomial equations
    practical use 27–29
    solving by factoring 24–25
Polynomials
    adding and subtracting 45–47
    factoring completely 22–23
Positive correlation 321–326
Postulate 421
Power rule for exponents 443
Predicted (and Predictor) Variable 321
Product
    of a binomial and a trinomial, defined 488
    of two binomials, defined 488
Product Property
    for exponents 443
    of square roots, defined 248, 265
Proofs, completing and validating 458
Properties
    of cube roots 257
    of logarithms 398
    of square roots 256
    tables of various properties 420–421
Property of negative one for real numbers 421
Property of zero for multiplication 421
Pythagorean theorem
    applications of 276–277, 279–282
    converse of 279
    defined 276, 279

Q

Quadratic equations
    applications of 536–538
    defined 24, 291, 311

    involving perfect squares 291–292
    solved by completing the square 294–298
    solved using the graphing calculator 305–310
    solved using the quadratic formula 299–303
    standard form 299
    using discriminants to analyze solutions 491–493
    with irrational roots 478–480
Quadratic formula
    defined 300
    used to solve equations 299–303
Quadratic function
    general form 529
    graph of 529
    graphing with horizontal and vertical
        shifting 517–519
    standard form 523, 529
Quadratic sequence, defined 192
Quadratic-linear system of equations, defined 311
Quotient Property of square roots, defined 248

R

Radicals
    like radicals, defined 262, 446
    simplifying 248–249
    simplifying products of 265–267, 449–451
    simplifying quotients of 268–270
    simplifying radical expressions 443–445
    solving radical equations 272–274
    sums and differences of 446–448
    unlike radicals, defined 262
Range
    defined 146, 590
    of functions, finding 163–166
    of relations, identifying 430–432
Rate
    functions and relations involving 178–182
    of change in x- and y-coordinates, or slope 78
    of growth and decay 365
    of interest 357
Ratio
    between consecutive terms in a geometric
        sequence 192
    of change in y-coordinates to the corresponding
        change in x-coordinates 425
Rational equations
    solving 51–55
Rational exponents, rule for 443
Rational expressions
    adding and subtracting 42–47
    defined 30
    dividing 36–38
    finding the LCD 39–40
    multiplying 34–35
    simplifying 32–33